OUTLINES

OF

CLASSIFICATION AND SPECIAL MORPHOLOGY

GOEBEL

London

HENRY FROWDE

OXFORD UNIVERSITY PRESS WAREHOUSE

AMEN CORNER, E.C.

OUTLINES

OF

CLASSIFICATION AND SPECIAL MORPHOLOGY

OF PLANTS

BY

DR. K. GOEBEL

PROFESSOR IN THE UNIVERSITY OF ROSTOCK

A NEW EDITION OF

Sachs' Text-Book of Botany, Book II

AUTHORISED ENGLISH TRANSLATION BY

HENRY E. F. GARNSEY, M.A.

Fellow of Magdalen College, Oxford

REVISED BY

ISAAC BAYLEY BALFOUR, M.A., M.D., F.R.S.

*Fellow of Magdalen College
and Sherardian Professor of Botany in the University of Oxford*

WITH 407 WOODCUTS

𝔒𝔵𝔣𝔬𝔯𝔡

AT THE CLARENDON PRESS

1887

PREFACE TO THE ENGLISH EDITION.

THIS translation of Professor Goebel's book is a natural sequel to those of previous editions of Professor Sachs' standard Text-book which have issued from the Clarendon Press.

The attempt to make use of a consistent terminology based upon homology, which is a prominent feature in the book, adds considerably to its value from an educational standpoint, and to obviate as much as possible any difficulties that may arise from the modification of the terminology adopted in previous editions an 'Explanation of Terms' is given at the end of the volume. It must be borne in mind that the definitions there offered are not exhaustive but have reference to the terms as used in the text. The abandonment of the use of the term 'spore' in the limited sense introduced by Professor Sachs is of sufficient importance to be noted here.

Some of the results of work, supplementing or modifying the statements in the text and published since the appearance of the German Edition, are referred to in foot-notes, and there have also been added citations of some of the more important literature of the past two or three years. There is, however, no pretension to completeness in either respect. No reference is made to Sachs' Vorlesungen über Pflanzenphysiologie—a translation of which is in the press—or to Van Tieghem's Traité de Botanique, as these are books which should be in the hands of every botanical student.

In deciding upon innovations which will be found in some of the English equivalents for German technical terms, I have to acknowledge the benefit of the counsel of several friends, amongst whom I may mention, Professor F. Orpen Bower, Professor Alexander Dickson, Mr. W. T. Thiselton Dyer, Dr. S. H. Vines and Professor H. Marshall Ward.

I. B. B.

BOTANIC GARDEN, OXFORD :
September, 1885.

AUTHORS' PREFACE.

THE present volume, as appears from the title, is a new edition of the second book of Sachs' Text-book of Botany (from page 235 to page 634 of the 4th Edition), and has been undertaken by me at the desire of Professor Sachs. In fulfilling this task I have considered it my business to make those changes only, which seemed to me to be required by the literature which has appeared since the year 1873 and by the results of my own investigations. That these changes are sometimes not inconsiderable will surprise no one who has followed the almost superabundant labours of the last few years in this particular portion of botanical study. But in presence of these changes I desire specially to remind my readers of the large amount of original research which was first communicated to the world in Professor Sachs' Text-book, especially in connection with the Vascular Cryptogams. The present Edition is also indebted to him for the majority of all such additional illustrations as are not copies from other authors, or, like figures 17, 18, 95, 101, 112, 153, 208, 223, 239, 240, 241, 259, 297, have been supplied by myself.

The task of explaining the connection between the several groups has been rendered difficult by the present state of the terminology, which is one of transition. We may hope however that the terminology will soon be greatly simplified and cleared up by applying the acknowledged homologies, and that we shall no longer call the same object in one place a 'placenta,' in another a 'receptacle' or a 'columella,' or use the term 'frons' for the thallus of a Marchantia or a Pellia, or apply the term pro-embryo alike to the protonema of the Mosses, the prothallium of Ferns, and the suspensor of Spermaphytes. I have entirely avoided such antiquated expressions as 'corpusculum' for the archegonium of Gymnosperms, and unmeaning terms like 'Rhizocarps' to designate the Heterosporous Filices, and in connection with the sporangia (including pollen-sacs and ovules) I have endeavoured to carry out the terminology proposed by myself and resting on the homology as established in the development of these organs. Accordingly I use the term archesporium in all cases, even in that of the sporogonia of the Muscineae, to designate the cell, cell-row or cell-layer in which the spore-producing tissue originates, and unlike other writers I apply the same term also to the 'mother-cell of the embryo-sac.' I use the expression 'tapetal cells,' as will be seen in the text, in a narrower sense than that adopted by some authors.

The manuscript was completed in January of the present year, and I have therefore been unable to make use of several interesting publications which have appeared since that date.

K. GOEBEL.

ROSTOCK, *August*, 1882.

TABLE OF CONTENTS.

ERRATA.

Page   7, line 8, *for* Saprolegniae *read* Saprolegnieae.

  „   26, note 3, line 4, *for* 1883 *read* 1883).

  „   86, line 16, *for* Tubercinia *read* Tuburcinia.

  „   87, line 13, *for* abjuncted *read* abjointed.

  „   87, lines 24, 27, *for* Tubercinia *read* Tuburcinia.

  „   102, line 15, *for* sclerotiorum *read* Sclerotiorum.

  „   127, line 3, *for* germinating filament *read* germ-filament.

  „   132, line 20, *for* vitis idaea *read* Vitis Idaea.

  „   158, line 19, *for* R. crystallina *read* Riccia crystallina.

  „   190, line 22, *for* two neck-cells *read* two neck-canal-cells.

  „   190, line 2 from bottom, *for* SEXUAL *read* ASEXUAL.

  „   196, line 23, *for* notrue *read* no true.

  „   232, lines 6, 7 from bottom and in Figs. 183, 186, 190, 193, *for* Marsilia
          Salvatrix *read* Marsilia salvatrix.

  „   274, note 2, line 1, *for* Thuringer *read* Thüringer.

  „   276, line 15, *for* alvifolium *read* aloifolium.

  „   295, line 1, *for* Duriaei *read* Durieui.

  „   327, explanation of Fig., *for* Microcrachys *read* Microcachrys.

  „   449, Fig. 379, *for* Quercus robur *read* Quercus Robur.

INTRODUCTION.

THE vegetable kingdom may be divided into five groups more or less closely related to one another: Thallophytes, Muscineae (Bryophytes), Vascular Cryptogams (Pteridophytes), Gymnosperms, and Angiosperms. The examination of these groups in the following pages will show that the names here given to them by no means happily express their characteristic and distinctive features. This is especially true of the Thallophytes and Vascular Cryptogams; the vegetative body in the Thallophytes is not always a thallus, and true vessels are found, so far as we know at present, only in two forms among the Vascular Cryptogams. These five subdivisions have been grouped together to form higher divisions in different ways at different times. They have been distributed for instance into Thallophytes, that is, plants whose vegetative body is described as a thallus, because it commonly shows no differentiation into stem, leaf and root, such as we observe in the higher plants, and into Cormophytes, or plants with stems and lateral members; but this division rests on purely external and by no means constant marks, and is therefore of no systematic value. The division again into Cryptogams including Thallophytes, Muscineae and Vascular Cryptogams, and Phanerogams comprising Gymnosperms and Angiosperms, is out of date now that we know the relations of the Gymnosperms and Angiosperms to the Vascular Cryptogams. Nevertheless the Gymnosperms and Angiosperms will be considered in the present work as forming one division under the name of seed-plants (Spermaphytes) whose characteristic mark is that they form seeds. It would perhaps be more in accordance with modern views to class the Gymnosperms with the Vascular Cryptogams, for these two groups agree in all essential characters except in the forming of seeds and in the mode of fertilisation, which is by pollen-tubes in the Gymnosperms, by spermatozoids in the Vascular Cryptogams; the method of sexual reproduction especially is the same in both. But it will be found to conduce to clearness and simplicity of statement if we consider Gymnosperms in connection with Angiosperms. The mode of formation of the female sexual organs is the same in the Muscineae, the Vascular Cryptogams and the Gymnosperms; these organs are here termed archegonia, and accordingly these three divisions will be included under the term Archegoniatae. It would be thoroughly in accordance with our present knowledge to divide the forms of the Vegetable Kingdom into Thallophytes, Archegoniatae and Angiosperms. The mutual connection however of the several divisions must be discussed later when we are considering

[2]   B

each group in detail; the tabular arrangement moreover is only a question of convenience; we have not to deal with a directly ascending series of organic forms which advance from the lower and simpler to the higher and more complex, but we must rather conceive of the Vegetable Kingdom—to use a frequent illustration—as a copiously branching tree, whose boughs have their origin in a common stem, but stand in no direct communication with each other. We may then divide the Vegetable Kingdom into the four following groups :—

First group : Thallophytes.
Second group : Bryophytes (Muscineae).
Third group : Vascular Cryptogams (Pteridophytes).
Fourth group: Seed-plants (Spermaphytes).

FIRST GROUP.

THE THALLOPHYTES.

UNDER this name are included the Algae, Fungi and Lichens, whose vegetative body usually consists of a *thallus*, and shows no differentiation into stem, leaf and root, or such differentiation is only rudimentary; at the same time if we set out from the simplest forms which show no outward distinction of parts, we find in different divisions of the Thallophytes indications of advance towards a higher differentiation; and in the most highly developed representatives of the separate divisions the outward distinction of parts goes so far, that the conceptions of stem and leaf are as applicable in their case as in that of higher plants; a true root, such as that of vascular plants, is however always wanting in the Thallophytes, though certain organs are usually present which in a physiological and functional sense we may designate as roots; but they are always distinguished from the roots of vascular plants by the absence of a root-cap and by their branching not being endogenous.

The internal differentiation of the Thallophytes starts like the external from stages of the utmost conceivable simplicity, and ascends through numberless transitions to more and more complex forms of cell and tissue; still in the most highly developed forms we nowhere meet with that differentiation into sharply separated systems of tissue, which we are able to discriminate in the higher plants as dermal, fundamental[1] and fascicular; the homogeneity of the tissue is a striking fact even where the thallus consists of extensive masses of tissue, as in large Fungi. A noteworthy peculiarity of some large Algae (Laminarieae) is that their stems, like those of Gymnosperms and Angiosperms, are capable of a secondary growth in thickness due to the presence of a peripheral zone of meristem.

The Thallophytes, notwithstanding the comparative simplicity of their organisation, afford a great variety of examples of the manner in which the process of development starting from the simplest organic forms passes by very different ways to forms which are more and more highly differentiated and more and more perfect internally and externally. The whole vegetative body in its simplest stage consists of a single small cell with a thin, smooth cell-wall, and cell-contents in which protoplasm, chlorophyll,

---

[1] Sachs in his Lehrbuch, 4th ed., p. 121, gives the name of fundamental tissue to the masses of tissue in the higher plants, which remain over after the first formation and further development of the dermal tissue and the vascular bundles.

cell-sap and other constituents are only imperfectly distinguishable. From this initial stage the process of development may advance, yet still within the limits of a single cell; and while the cell increases in size, often reaching dimensions without parallel in the vegetable kingdom, either the differentiation of the cell-contents, or that of the external form as shown by the branching, may make most rapid progress. In other cases the growth of the cells is accompanied by cell-division, the thallus becoming multicellular, and the single cell producing, according to the nature of the plant, a cell-row or a cellular filament, a cell-surface or simple tissue-layer, or lastly a cell-mass increasing in size in every direction.

Each of these processes is subject to a number of variations. We find for instance cell-rows, in which the connection of the individual cells is but superficial; they consist in fact of unicellular Thallophytes which are merely strung together, and the cells may readily part from one another and commence a separate existence. Other cell-rows again show a differentiation into base and apex; in this case the cells which form the base are usually developed as organs of attachment, *rhizoids* (roots). Again, larger or smaller circumscribed masses of tissue may be formed by the union of cell-rows that were originally free; in some cases, as in many Fungi, massive bodies arise from the simple interweaving of cell-rows. On the other hand, the vegetative body of the Myxomycetes consists of membraneless naked masses of protoplasm endowed with the power of independent motion.

There are simple Thallophytes also, which show a tendency to pass a longer or shorter portion of their existence in the condition of freely motile membraneless primordial cells (swarm-spores for example); in this form they are more or less like the simpler Infusoria, and were till quite recently confounded with them. Cases also occur in which cells that have already clothed themselves with cellulose, and even assemblages of many such cells, swim freely about in water and for a considerable time. But the motile condition is in all cases interrupted by longer stationary periods, during which growth and increase in volume usually take place. In the case of some of the more highly developed Thallophytes the motile condition is confined to the spermatozoids, the male elements in fertilisation, and in many even this form of independent motion is wanting, as for example in the Florideae.

The variety in the modes of reproduction in the Thallophytes is as great as that of the structure of the vegetative body. We find at first the very simplest forms, and we arrive at last at modes of reproduction almost as perfect and as complex as are to be found even in the highest plants. In the simpler forms the unicellular or pluricellular thallus exhibits two modes of increase; it breaks up after a period of growth into separate pieces, each of which continues to live and grow independently, as happens with the Schizomycetes and Cyanophyceae; or separate cells of the thallus persist after the decay of the others and become resting cells, being endowed with more than usual power of withstanding influences from without, especially the effect of desiccation. But both asexual and sexual reproduction are found in the majority of Thallophytes, and phenomena occur in the higher forms which are comparable with the alternation of generations in the Vascular Cryptogams. The organ of reproduction which separates from the mother-plant is almost always a single cell, but the origin, significance and power of development of this cell may vary much.

I. **SEXUAL REPRODUCTION.** In all cases that have been fully examined we find sexual reproduction initiated by a process of fertilisation. This consists in the coalescence of two cells, masses of protoplasm, a male and a female, which may be of different form and size; in the simplest cases they are not distinguishable in outward appearance from one another; the two extremes are however connected by intermediate forms. The two masses of protoplasm which thus coalesce are called *gametes*, and may either possess the power of independent motion ('*planogametes*' or *zoogametes*), or be destitute of it. The chief forms of sexual reproduction are the following [1]:—

1. **Conjugation and Formation of Zygospores.** Two cells of similar if not always the same constitution coalesce and produce a reproductive cell, termed a *zygospore*, which lies dormant for a considerable time and then germinates, and either produces directly a plant of the same kind as that on which the conjugation took place, or gives rise first of all to a number of *brood-cells*.

The process in the formation of zygospores wears a different aspect according to the nature of the conjugating cells. The simplest case is that of the conjugation of swarm-cells (planogametes) discovered by Pringsheim (Fig. 1 *A*); pairs of these bodies as they swim about come in contact with one another at their hyaline anterior ends, and gradually coalesce into a spherical primordial cell, which becomes invested with a cell-wall and increases in size; after a time it breaks up into motile cells, from which proceed plants of the original kind.—The process of conjugation in *Spirogyra* is more complicated; it will be found represented in Fig. 25. There the conjugating cells have firm cell-walls, and put out processes

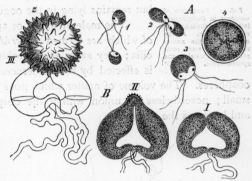

FIG. 1. Different modes of conjugation and formation of zygospores. *A* pairing of the swarm-cells of *Pandorina*. *B* formation of zygospores of *Piptocephalis*. The successive stages in the development are shown in *A* by Arabic, in *B* by Latin numerals. After Pringsheim and Brefeld.

towards one another; these unite and form a canal through which the living contents of the one cell pass over into the other and there coalesce with its contents; the protoplasmic body formed by this coalescence becomes invested with a cell-wall and is a zygospore, which by direct germination produces a spirogyra-filament.—The formation of the zygospore of a Zygomycete is explained by Fig. 1 *B*; in this case two cells, entirely alike and motionless, coalesce by a normal process of growth, and a portion only of the united contents, cut off by transverse walls, produces the thick-coated zygospore, which germinates after a lengthened period of repose.

---

[1] More detailed information with regard to the facts here stated will be found further on in the special description of the Algae and Fungi. For the knowledge of the facts here adduced we are indebted to the labours of De Bary, Pringsheim, Thuret and Bornet, Nägeli, Brefeld, and others.

2. The transition from the formation of zygospores to the second mode of fertilisation, **the Formation of Oospores**, is quite gradual, and it is complete both in forms with motile and in those with non-motile gametes. We find intermediate stages in the former case in different cycles of affinity. For instance, the gametes of *Ectocarpus siliculosus* are perfectly alike externally, but their behaviour is different; one swarm-cell settles down and loses its cilia, and is thus transformed into an *oosphere* with which, as we learn from Berthold, male swarm-cells coalesce. —

FIG. 2. Formation of oospores in *Oedogonium* (after Pringsheim). — *og* the oogonium, *o* the oosphere, *a* the antheridium, *m* a small male plant (dwarf male), *s* the spermatozoid.

In *Cutleria*, which belongs to the same group, the two motile sexual cells differ much in size; the male planogamete, the *spermatozoid*, is much smaller than the female which soon comes to rest, and becomes an oosphere.—In *Fucus* the difference is still greater; the female gamete, the oosphere, is here non-motile, while the male, the spermatozoid, is still a motile cell; but here too the act of fertilisation takes place outside the organ in which the female gamete was formed, and which is known as the *oogonium*.—In the green Algae, on the contrary (the Chlorophyceae), the female gamete or oosphere is not only non-motile, but remains lying in the oogonium (Fig. 2).

The male elements or spermatozoids (Fig. 2), the mother-cells of which are termed *antheridia*, are very small and move by aid of cilia; they swim about seeking for the oospheres, and fertilisation is effected by the coalescence of their substance with that of the oospheres. The volume of matter which goes to form the spermatozoid is extremely small; nevertheless by union with it the oosphere is excited to form a cell-wall and becomes the *oospore*.

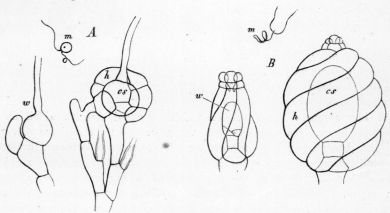

FIG. 3. Examples of the formation of oogonia, the oospore being surrounded with envelope-tubes before or after fertilisation. *A Coleochaete, B Chara, m* spermatozoid, *w* oogonium (in *Coleochaete* with a long beak), *h* envelope, which forms round the oogonium or oospore in *Coleochaete* after, in *Chara* before fertilisation, *cs* oospore.

The oospore may germinate immediately after its formation, and produce a plant like its own mother-plant, as in *Fucus*, or like the zygospores it first passes through a period of rest and then germinates, and this is the usual case. Here too the germinating oospore may at once produce a plant like the mother-plant, as in

Vaucheria and many Saprolegnieae, or it developes from its cell-contents a few or many swarm-cells, each of which ultimately gives rise to a plant like the mother-plant, as in *Sphaeroplea*, *Oedogonium*, and *Cystopus*.

A transition from the formation of zygospores to that of oospores is also to be found in the conjugation of non-motile gametes; indications of it occur in the Conjugatae, a section of Algae; but distinct formation of oospores in this manner has hitherto been certainly ascertained only in some Fungi, the Peronosporeae (as regards the Saprolegniae *vid. infra*). One or more oospheres are formed in a cell which dilates and becomes globular, the oogonium. Close to it grows another branch of the thallus, at the extremity of which a cell is divided off by a septum to form an antheridium. This cell thrusts a tube, the fertilisation-tube, through the wall of the oogonium

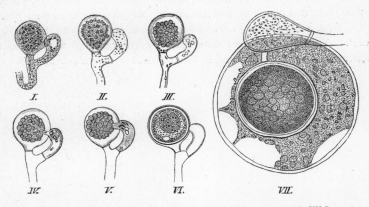

FIG. 4. Formation of oospores in two species of Peronosporeae (*I—VI Pythium gracile, VII Peronospora. arborescens*); in both cases the oogonium swollen into a spherical shape contains only a single oosphere, which is fertilised in *VI* and *VII* and forms the oospore invested with a cell-wall. After De Bary.

as far as the oosphere, and from the opened tube protoplasmic matter issues, which mingles with the substance of the oosphere. Here there are no spermatozoids; the process is closely allied to that of the formation of zygospores by union of non-motile gametes.

3. **Formation of Fructifications producing Spores ('sporocarps') from** procarps and archicarps (carpogonia).

a. FERTILISATION OF PROCARPS IN THE FLORIDEAE. The male elements are small cells without active motion, and are known as *spermatia*. The female organ, the *procarp*, consists before fertilisation of two parts: an apparatus for the reception and transmission of the male fertilising substance, which apparatus disappears after fertilisation has been accomplished, and a part which is excited by fertilisation to a process of growth which results in the fructification which produces the spores. This second portion of the procarp is called the *carpogone*; the cells which compose it, and which are not unfrequently separated by barren cells, are the *carpogenous* cells. The receptive apparatus is called the *trichogyne*.

The simplest form of fertilisation of procarps, apart from the non-motile condition of the spermatia, resembles the processes in the fertilisation of the oogonia of *Oedogonium, Coleochaete*, and their allies. It is exemplified in the Bangieae, where the procarp is a simple cell, and a small protuberance from it forms the trichogyne. The spermatium coalesces with the procarp, whereupon the carpogenous cell, that is the larger part of the procarp-cell, divides into eight cells which become spores, *carpospores,* just as the oosphere of *Oedogonium* divides into a number of (motile) spores; the only difference is that the oospore first passes through a period of rest; but oospores too may dispense with this condition, as we learn from *Fucus.*

In many other Florideae also the procarp is unicellular, and the elongated neck-like upper part serves as the trichogyne, the lower somewhat dilated part as the carpogenous cell, the carpogone. This is the case with the Nemalieae (Fig. 5). But in them the carpogenous cell produces after fertilisation a number of branches, which break up into single cells, each of which is a carpospore. The spore-producing fructifications formed by the sprouting of the carpogone are called *sporocarps.* The sporocarp is often completed by the addition of an investment formed by branches which spring from cells adjoining the carpogone; these closely invest the carpogone and its products. A similar envelope occurs in some zygospores and oospores, as in *Mortierella* among the Zygomycetes, and in the oospores of *Coleochaete* and *Chara* among

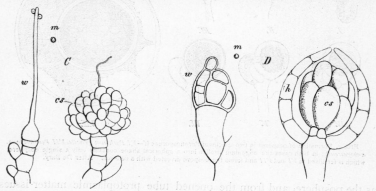

FIG. 5. Formation of procarp and carpospores in two Florideae. *C Nemalion, D Lejolisia, w* procarp, unicellular with a long trichogyne in *Nemalion,* pluricellular with a short trichogyne in *Lejolisia, m* spermatia, *cs* carpospores, *h* envelope of the sporocarp.

the Chlorophyceae (Fig. 3).—In other Florideae (Fig. 5 *D*) the procarp is pluricellular before fertilisation; examples of this will be given in discussing the Florideae.

b. FORMATION OF ARCHICARPS IN THE ASCOMYCETES. Whilst the fertilisation of procarps in the simple forms of the Florideae has some analogy with the formation of oospores by the union of planogametes, the formation of archicarps in the simpler forms of the Ascomycetes is directly related to the formation of the oospores of the Peronosporeae, which results from the union of non-motile gametes. But here a true operation of sexual organs, that is an actual fertilisation, has in no case been proved, and indeed is not probable. The sporocarps of the Ascomycetes are often bodies of considerable size, the most essential elements of which are one or more tube-like cells, placed singly or in groups, and named *asci,* in which the spores are formed.

One of the simplest modes of the formation of sporocarps is seen in *Podosphaera* (Fig. 6 *E*). Two branches arise from the mycelium, one of which is swollen into the shape of a barrel and forms the archicarp; the other, which is a thinner and antheridial branch, becomes closely applied to the archicarp, and a small antheridial cell is parted off from its upper extremity. The archicarp answers therefore to the oogonium of the Peronosporeae, and yet is not an oogonium, for its protoplasm does not contract to form an oosphere but the asci grow out from it, or, as in this which is the simplest case, the archicarp-cell itself becomes the ascus (Fig. 6, *E, cs*), which is borne on a short cell forming the stalk. Branches arise from beneath the stalk and form the envelope of the sporocarp *h.*

The processes are somewhat more complicated in the case of *Ascobolus*, another of the Ascomycetes. In Fig. 6, *F*, which shows a diagrammatic section of the sporocarp, *w* is the archicarp consisting of several cells, *m* a tubular branching antheridial twig closely applied to the archicarp. Numerous filaments then arise from a central cell of the carpogone, which form asci at the upper end of their branches and a number of spores in the asci. The envelope of the sporocarp, which is in this case of considerable thickness, consists of filaments which spring from beneath the archicarp, and form ultimately a compact false parenchyma enclosing the archicarp with the ascogenous filaments which have sprung from it and the asci themselves. The mycelium which produces the archicarps in the two organisms which we have been

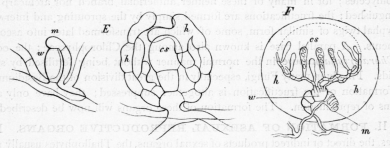

FIG. 6. Formation of a sporocarp in two Ascomycetes diagrammatically represented. *E Podosphaera, F Ascobolus* (after De Bary and Janczewski), *w* archicarp, *m* antheridial branch, *cs* asci, *h* envelope of sporocarp.

describing, is insignificant in comparison with the large sporocarp which is produced from the archicarp, and which continues to grow for a considerable time, in many cases even when separated from the mycelium.

The resemblance between the fertilisation of archicarps and of procarps is shown also by the fact that there are Ascomycetes (see under Lichens) which like the Florideae have a procarp with a carpogone and trichogyne, and in which spermatia form a sexual union with the trichogyne, exactly as in the Florideae.

To sum up briefly what has now been said with respect to the sexual process, it may be stated that its result is always the formation of one or more spores, and that the spores are either an immediate product of fertilisation, as the zygospores of the Conjugatae, or they are the result of a vegetative process set up by the fertilisation, as in the Ascomycetes, Florideae, &c. In extreme cases the product of fertilisation is a definite mass of tissue which produces spores and in many Ascomycetes, for example, is self-supporting, and thus appears as a special spore-producing generation in contradistinction to the thallus, the sexual generation which bears the sexual organs,—a relation the meaning and value of which must be examined more closely when we are considering the sharply defined alternation of generations in the Muscineae and Vascular Cryptogams.

APOGAMY IN THE THALLOPHYTES. It was stated above, that in the formation of the fruit in the Ascomycetes organs make their appearance, which are obviously analogous with the male and female organs of other Thallophytes, but which have no longer any sexual function. This loss of the procreative faculty is termed by De Bary *apogamy*, and is by no means uncommon among the Thallophytes. Thus it occasionally happens with several of the Zygomycetes (*Syzygites*) that the conjugating branches do not unite, but nevertheless they each form at their free extremity a cell which has the properties of a zygospore. The apogamy is still more striking in the case of the Saprolegnieae, and is constant throughout their entire cycle of affinity. The form of the sexual organs agrees with that of the Peronosporeae (Fig. 4). The antheridia in many cases put out their fertilisation-tubes, but these remain closed and emit no fertilising substance. Nevertheless the oospores mature in the usual manner. Other individuals have antheridia, but these put out no tubes; others again have neither antheridial branches nor antheridia, and yet the oospores are developed. In the two last cases we have not only apogamy but a suppression of the sexual organs, which goes still further in the Ascomycetes; for in many of these neither antheridial branch nor archicarp can be distinguished; the fructifications are formed simply by the sprouting and interweaving of hyphal twigs of similar form, some of which are transformed later into ascogenous filaments. A parallel case is known also among the Chlorophyceae: the oospores of *Chara crinita* mature in the normal manner without being fertilised by spermatozoids. Finally in many Fungi, especially in the great division of the Basidiomycetes, the formation of the fructification is altogether suppressed; they have only asexual organs of reproduction. The formation of these organs will now be described.

II. **FORMATION OF ASEXUAL REPRODUCTIVE ORGANS.** Besides spores, the direct or indirect products of sexual organs, the Thallophytes usually possess an extremely fruitful source of propagation in their brood-cells, which are not the product directly or indirectly of sexual organs. Only a few Thallophytes, such as the Conjugatae, *Sphaeroplea*, and the Fucaceae, have no brood-cells, but sexually produced spores alone.

Brood-cells or *gonidia*[1] are formed on the thallus often without preliminary preparation, the whole contents of certain cells of the thallus renewing themselves, or dividing also at the same time, and so producing one or more reproductive cells which separate from the parent-plant. In other cases special stalks or receptacles are formed on the thallus, whose exclusive function it is to produce gonidia, either by abstriction of the extremities of special branches (*stilogonidia* in *Piptocephalis*, *Penicillium* and others), or by free cell-formation inside large cells (*endogonidia* in Saprolegnieae, *Vaucheria*, Mucorineae). In many cases, especially in many Fungi, reproduction is effected almost exclusively by such brood-cells, the normal completion

---

[1] All the reproductive cells of the Thallophytes were formerly termed 'spores' without reference to their mode of origin. To remove the confusion thus caused, Sachs proposed that only the reproductive cells, which were the direct or indirect result of a sexual act, zygospores, oospores, carpospores, ascospores, &c, should be termed spores, and that the asexual organs of reproduction should be called gonidia or conidia, a term common among the Fungi from κονία, dust. But it would appear that the old nomenclature is not to be set aside, being supported by a number of related terms, such as sporangia and others.

of the development by sexual organs and formation of true fructification being attained only under unusually favourable circumstances. In other Fungi, as has been already stated, there is usually no formation of fructification.

Naked, that is, membraneless brood-cells which have the power of free movement, occur frequently among the Algae, and also in some Fungi that live in water or on moist substances. They swim about in the water for some minutes or even hours after they are set free from the parent plant, and combine a rotation on their own axis with a forward movement. The anterior extremity is hyaline, and free from granules and colouring matter, and in many Algae a small red corpuscle lies behind the hyaline portion; the movement is due to the vibrations of very delicate threads (cilia). There are usually two such cilia on the anterior extremity, or near it on the side; sometimes there is only one; or the hyaline anterior extremity is surrounded by a circle of numerous cilia, or finally the whole surface of the swarm-cell is beset with short cilia. A wall of cellulose begins to be secreted during the time of swarming; then the swarm-cell, coming to rest, attaches itself by the anterior extremity to some body, the cilia disappear and germination begins, the posterior end during the period of movement becoming the free growing point, and consequently the anterior extremity of the young plant. It has been already stated that conjugation takes place between swarming cells; such cells must obviously not be regarded as brood-cells, but as sexual cells (gametes), which bear a deceptive resemblance to motile brood-cells; there is moreover reason for thinking that the swarm-cells of many Algae, which have been hitherto taken for gonidia, are capable of conjugation and are therefore gametes. Motile cells of the kind described may appear at very different stages in the course of the development of the plant; it not unfrequently happens that the cell-contents of an oospore, in *Coleochaete* for example, break up into swarm-cells, which then proceed to germinate; even brood-cells may convert their contents into swarm-cells, as happens in the so-called gonidia of the Peronosporeae; in a different class of cases swarm-cells are formed in special branches of the thallus, and any ordinary vegetative cell of the thallus may not unfrequently discharge its contents in the form of swarm-cells. Hitherto all such cells have been called swarm-spores or zoospores; it would be convenient and in accordance with what has been said on page 10, upon the idea of a spore, to employ only the terms swarm-cells or *zoogonidia*, and to call the receptacles, which sometimes contain a vast quantity of swarm-cells, not zoosporangia but *zoogonidia-receptacles*. It is obviously a matter of minor importance, whether the brood-cells simply fall off from the parent plant, as is the case in most Fungi, where they are then usually termed gonidia, and also in many Algae, or whether they appear as swarm-cells; this evidently depends on the mode of life of the plants; the free movement or its absence is physiologically not morphologically important; just as in the seeds and fruits of Phanerogams, some have a special apparatus for flying and are capable of movement, others simply fall from the plant to the ground. Moreover we find in the genus *Vaucheria* all stages of transition from free-moving swarm-cells to gonidia that simply drop from the plant; and still more striking is the state of the case in the Fungi known as the Peronosporeae, where the forms which live in water or on a moist substratum produce motile gonidia, those that are parasitic on land-plants have non-motile gonidia.

CLASSIFICATION OF THE THALLOPHYTES. The systematic division of the Thallophytes was once founded entirely on characters derived from the habit of the plants, and three classes were distinguished, Algae, Fungi, Lichens. It is now established that the Lichens do not form a special class distinct from Algae and Fungi, but must be ranked with Fungi, the much larger number of them with the Ascomycetes, two genera only belonging to the Basidiomycetes. There are therefore only two classes to be distinguished, Algae and Fungi. If we desire to retain these two classes in their traditional form, we can separate them from one another only by regarding all Thallophytes which contain chlorophyll as Algae, all those that have no chlorophyll as Fungi. But this does not supply a satisfactory principle of classification.

The first point to note is that the presence or absence of chlorophyll can be no sufficient reason for separating plants which are nearly related to one another morphologically, and which agree in their structure and in their sexual organs, where these are present. In Phanerogams the principle is thoroughly admitted. If all flowering-plants which do not contain chlorophyll were formed into one class in contradistinction to those which do contain it, the Rafflesiaceae, Balanophoreae, *Corallorhiza, Cuscuta, Orobanche, Monotropa,* &c., would have, in spite of the differences in their organic structure, to be combined into one class, and removed from their true relationship. No one however disputes that *Cuscuta* belongs to the Convolvulaceae, *Orobanche* to the Labiatiflorae, *Monotropa* to the Pyrolaceae, and *Corallorhiza* to the Orchideae. These affinities are inferred among Phanerogams chiefly from the structure of the flowers and the embryo, and no one attaches the least importance to the fact that the want of chlorophyll and the peculiar mode of life of these plants gives them so different an appearance from that of their nearest allies. It is one of the most beautiful results of a truly scientific morphology and classification that, among Phanerogams, the remarkable habit of parasites and saprophytes is regarded as an altogether secondary matter. But the same principle should also be applied in determining the systematic relationships of Thallophytes; habit and mode of life, the presence or absence of chlorophyll should also be treated as characters of altogether subordinate importance, as it is a matter of subordinate importance in the division of humankind into natural races, whether some support themselves by their own industry, and others live by war and plunder. All Thallophytes which are destitute of chlorophyll, i.e. all those which have hitherto been termed Fungi, must necessarily agree with one another more or less in their habit and mode of life, because they are all adapted to take up organised food-material containing carbon from the substances on which they live. If they obtain this from living bodies, we have parasitism developed in very various forms; if they can make use of dead organic remains, the habit and mode of life of the plant must vary accordingly. Algae, in the sense in which the term has hitherto been used, are able to produce carbonaceous food-materials out of carbon dioxide by assimilation; they are not therefore usually either parasites or saprophytes, but can maintain a more free and independent life; they are however compelled by the peculiarities of their organisation to live in water or in damp places: their dependence on assimilation requires that they should inhabit localities where there is free access of light, while Fungi are not absolutely dependent on light for their supply of food.

But all these facts are of altogether secondary importance in determining degrees of affinity in the construction of a natural system of classification of Thallophytes. This object can be attained only by a comparison of such morphological characteristics as are presented in the entire course of development[1]. Before this was ascertained in all the Algae which are now more accurately known, it might have been thought that the form of the sexual organs and the results of the sexual act would offer the simplest means of dividing Thallophytes, without consideration of the presence or absence of chlorophyll, into groups which would give a clear insight into their course of development. There can be no doubt that such groups, in which Fungi and Algae stand side by side, must be adopted. Such a group are the Schizophytes, the simplest of the Thallophytes, including the algal group of Cyanophyceae and one group of Fungi the Schizomycetes. Other algal and fungal groups are more isolated and their connection with the rest is still doubtful: such groups are the Myxomycetes and the Diatoms. The rest of the Thallophytes form two series composed of different but connected groups, one containing Algae only, the other only Fungi. These two series may therefore be termed Algae and Fungi in a narrower sense of the words, since they do not include all Thallophytes usually comprehended under these designations. The form and mode of operation of the sexual organs and the results of the sexual act are different within each of these two large groups, and in members of their subdivisions. Among nearly allied species some form zygospores, some oospores, and it was mentioned above that the development of sporocarps in Fungi and Algae has proceeded in different directions.

The Thallophytes will accordingly be described in the following order, but this order does not coincide with their separation into equivalent groups :—

    I. Myxomycetes (Slime-Fungi).

    II. Diatomaceae (Bacillarieae).

    III. Schizophytes.
        (*a.*) Forms containing chlorophyll (and Phycocyan): Cyanophyceae.
        (*b.*) Forms not containing chlorophyll: Schizomycetes (Fission-Fungi).

    IV. Algae (in the narrower sense).
        (*a.*) Chlorophyceae.
        (*b.*) Phaeophyceae.
        (*c.*) Rhodophyceae (Florideae).

    V. Fungi.
        (*a.*) Chytridieae.
        (*b.*) Ustilagineae.
        (*c.*) Phycomycetes.
        (*d.*) Ascomycetes.
        (*e.*) Aecidiomycetes (Uredineae).
        (*f.*) Basidiomycetes.

---

[1] De Bary, Zur Systematik d. Thallophyten (Bot. Zeit. 1881, No. 1).

I. MYXOMYCETES[1].

The Myxomycetes are so unlike the rest of the Thallophytes in outward appearance, especially as regards their vegetative body, that they have been entirely separated from the vegetable kingdom by many authors. Their mode of life is that of the Fungi; they are chiefly saprophytes, that is, they live on dead organic sub-

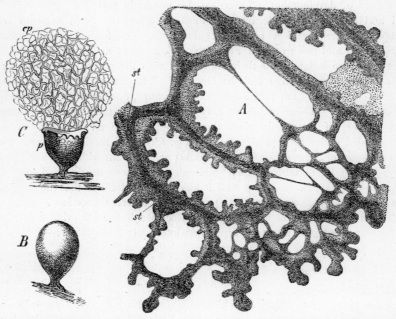

FIG. 7. *A* plasmodium of *Didymium leucopus*, magn. 350 times. *B* fructification of *Arcyria incarnata* still closed, *C* the same after rupture of the wall *p* and expansion of the capillitium *cp* (after De Bary) magn. 20 times. After Cienkowski.

stances; some, like *Plasmodiophora Brassicae*, the cause of the Club-root in Cabbage plants, are parasites; a few only (*Physarum album*) live in water, the greater part

[1] De Bary, Die Mycetozoen, Leipzig 1864, [also Vergl. Morph. u. Biol. d. Pilze Mycetozoen u. Bacterien, Leipzig 1884].—Cienkowski in Jahrb. f. wiss. Bot. III. pp. 325 u. 400.—Brefeld, Ueber *Dictyostelium mucoroides* (Abhandl. d. Senkenb. Ges. zu Frankfurt-à-M. 1869, VII. Bd.).—Rostafinski, Vers. eines Systems d. Mycetozoen, Strasburg 1873.—Woronin, *Plasmodiophora Brassicae* (Pringsheim's Jahrb. f. Wiss. Bot. XI)—Regarding the nuclei, see Schmitz in Sitzungsber. der niederrh. Ges. 4 August 1879, p. 21 des Sept.-Abdr.—Strasburger, Zellbildung u. Zelltheilung, 3rd Ed. p. 79. [Zopf in his Monograph, Die Pilzethiere oder Schleimpilze in Vol. III. Part 2 of Schenk's Handbuch der Botanik, extends considerably the domain of this group. His work and De Bary's volumes quoted above supply a full account of recent views regarding it and give the literature. The following may also be consulted with advantage :—Klebs, Ueber die organisation einiger Flagellatengruppen und ihre Beziehungen zur Algen und Infusorien (Untersuch. aus d. bot. Inst. zu Tübingen, Bd. I. Heft 2, 1883; see also a notice of this work in Biolog. Centralbl. IV. Feb. 1885).—Brefeld, Untersuch. aus d. Gesammtgeb. d. Mykologie, VI (1884).—Goebel, Tetramyxa parasitica (Flora, 1884).—Gobi, Ueber die Gruppe der Amoeboideae (Arb. d. St. Petersb. Naturf. Ges. 1884, extr. in Bot. Centralbl. XXI. 1884).—Ray Lankester, article Protozoa in 9th ed. Encyc. Britan.]

of them in the cavities of moist substrata, where they creep about in the form of naked amoeboid masses of protoplasm (*plasmodia*), which according to modern investigations contain numerous cell-nuclei.

The Myxomycetes are usually first perceived when they come out of their porous substrata and form their relatively large fructifications. The largest of these are the flat sulphur-yellow cakes, which appear in summer on tan and are known as 'flowers of tan' (*Aethalium septicum*); the fructifications of *Lycogala*, which issue from the stumps of trees, are of the size and shape of hazel-nuts; in most other Myxomycetes the fructifications are small stalked capsules; all contain a countless number of small, roundish spores with thick cell-walls. Other structures make their appearance in many cases when the capsules burst; these are known as the *capillitium*,—capillary tubes or threads often combined together into a net or lattice-work, the origin of which will be explained further on. In *Dictyostelium mucoroides*, a species discovered by Brefeld, there is no capillitium and no outer wall to the fructification, which consists simply of a stalk composed of parenchymatous cells, and a small head formed of a roundish mass of spores. These spores develope on a microscopic slide in a watery decoction of rabbits' dung, and produce ripe fructification in a few days. In germination the whole of the protoplasm of a spore escapes from the ruptured wall, and creeps about with amoeboid movement, and feeds and grows. In other Myxomycetes (Fig. 8) a swarm-cell passes out from the spore provided with a cilium, a nucleus and a contractile vacuole, and dances and hops about by vigorous motion of its cilium accompanied by change of shape, and has also a creeping movement over the substratum on which it lies and puts out processes on every side. Eventually the cilium is drawn in, and the cell passes definitively into the amoeboid condition (Fig. 8), which the product of germination in *Dictyostelium* assumes from the first. After a few days, when the amoeboid bodies have increased considerably in size, they multiply by repeated division. Later on their movement grows

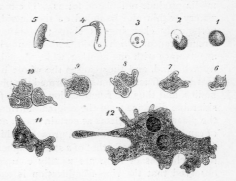

FIG. 8. *Physarum album.* 1 spore; 2 contents issuing from a spore; 3 the contents when set at liberty; 4, 5 the same as a swarm-cell with one cilium; 6, 7 after loss of the cilium; 8, 9, 10, 11 coalescence of amoeboid bodies; 12 a small plasmodium. After Cienkowski.

more sluggish, the amoeboid bodies collect in groups, cling closely to one another, and finally unite together to form larger masses; when one such mass is formed the rest creep towards it from all sides as to a centre and unite with it, and thus increase the size of the protoplasmic body, which eventually rounds itself off more and more. Though some of the details of this proceeding require further observation, yet it can scarcely be disputed that we have here not a real coalescence of the constituents of the protoplasmic body[1], of nucleus with nucleus, protoplasm with protoplasm, as in a sexual act in the Conjugatae or Mucorineae, but only a more superficial union of masses of naked protoplasm. A similar proceeding may be observed in other cases, as in the mycelia of many Basidiomycetes, where the cells come into close union with one another over considerable areas without suggesting the idea of a sexual act. The arranging of the motile cells of *Hydrodictyon* into a net (p. 40) may be quoted as an analogous proceeding, and it is to be observed that there too the amoeboid bodies have no cell-wall. The plasmodium of *Dictyostelium* continues but a short time in the

---

[1] In *Guttulina rosea*, a very simple Myxomycete, the amoeboid bodies according to Cienkowski (Bot. Jahresber. 1873, p. 61) are only heaped together, and do not coalesce.

vegetative stage before proceeding to the formation of its fructification, which takes place in the following manner. A number of cells arise by free cell-formation in the middle of the roundish plasmodium; these cells become invested with cellulose and unite to form a column or stalk of parenchymatous tissue in the interior of the plasmodium at right angles to the substratum. While this column increases constantly in height, the surrounding protoplasm creeps up it and collects at its summit into a round mass, the whole substance of which now breaks up into numerous spores. Here we have the course of development of a Myxomycete in its simplest form. In most other cases the development is more extended and more complex, though the mode of its commencement is essentially the same in all the Myxomycetes. The spores produce from one to eight swarm-cells, which eventually become amoeboid bodies, grow and multiply by repeated division, and finally unite together in large numbers and form plasmodia. But the plasmodia of other Myxomycetes do not proceed at once to the formation of fructifications, but maintain an independent life for a longer period, creeping into the moist cavities in their substrata, like the yellow plasmodia which come at last to the surface, and there run together into large flat cakes known as 'flowers of tan.' Other plasmodia creep about for some time in rotting wood or among decaying leaves, and at length come to the surface, where they usually form a number of fructifications all at once. Fig. 7 *A* will give some idea of the way in which the movements of the plasmodia produce reticulated forms. The mass of the plasmodium, which is granular and watery within and bounded on the outside by a skin of homogeneous protoplasm, is perpetually changing its shape; protuberances are formed at various spots in its circumference, which glide and creep with a forward movement, and ramify and anastomose with one another, while the substance of the plasmodium moves after them from behind, and thus causes the whole body to advance slowly in a given direction. Just before fructifications are formed the plasmodia show a tendency to creep up upright bodies, and thus the fructification is often found on plants, stems and leaves at a considerable distance from the original nutrient substratum. With a view to fructification the plasmodium collects at certain spots, and forms either a broad cake, as in 'flowers of tan,' or weak ascending outgrowths, which gradually assume the form of the typical fructifications, usually that of a stalked spherical or club-shaped body or a winding tube [1]; these changes of form are usually completed in a few hours. It has already been observed that the ripe fructification is usually invested with a firm membrane, and that a so-called capillitium is often formed inside it with numerous spores lying in its interstices. Neither the wall of the fructification, nor its stalk which is usually hollow, nor the capillitium are formed of cellulose; we must suppose that the substance of the plasmodium, after it has assumed the outline of the fructification, becomes differentiated into two substances, one of which is hardened into membranes, tubes and solid threads, and so forms the stalk, the wall of the fructification and the capillitium, while the rest of the protoplasm retaining the power of further development breaks up into small rounded portions, which invest themselves with cell-walls and thus form the spores.

The protoplasm, in becoming differentiated into spores and parts incapable of further development (wall of fructification and capillitium), also gets rid of other portions of its contents which are of no use in reproduction, and especially of the lime, which is eliminated in large quantities in the form of a finely granular carbonate, and of the yellow substance which covers the fructifications of 'flowers of tan' with loose flakes.

The Myxomycetes can pass from all the states of movement to states of rest, in which they are able to bear unharmed the effects of desiccation. The motile cells become rounded and encysted, that is they clothe themselves with a membrane which they abandon when they recover their power of movement under the proper conditions of moisture and warmth. Small plasmodia also become encysted. Larger plasmodia

---

[1] Rostafinski gives the name of '*Aethalium*' to large fructifications which are produced by the coalescence of several simple ones, and which are therefore syncarps, as in 'flowers of tan.'

pass into the resting state in a peculiar manner; they form multicellular bodies, the so-called *sclerotia*, while the plasmodium retracts its branches and becomes sluggish; the plasmodium of 'flowers of tan' forms small tuberous bodies. An important change of structure is connected with this change of form; the plasmodium separates simultaneously into a large number of polyhedral cells, which are divided from one another by walls of cellulose. A section through the sclerotium shows the latter as fine meshes. When a plasmodium which has thus passed into the resting state comes under the conditions necessary for active life, the cellulose in the walls is dissolved, and the whole body is again changed into a motile plasmodium. It appears then from the above description that the plasmodium proper is an organism, to which the laws of cellular structure do not apply, in other words is a non-cellular body[1]; at the same time it has the power under definite conditions of assuming a cellular structure. Apart from their negative geotropism at the time when the fructification is maturing, the plasmodia in their motile condition show sensitiveness to moisture and light[2]. If the tan, in which the plasmodium of the 'flowers of tan' is cultivated, is only moderately moist, the plasmodia make their appearance at once and in large numbers on the surface; if it is more moist, they show themselves gradually and in the drier spots. If the spot where a plasmodium has appeared is sprinkled with water, the plasmodium disappears, and some time elapses before it reappears. A plasmodium moves away from illuminated spots; if a stronger light is thrown directly upon these spots, a number of plasmodia collect in them. All these phenomena of motion depend very much on the exact stage in which the plasmodium happens to be, and especially on its being near to or further from the time of formation of fructification.

II. DIATOMACEAE[3].

The Diatomaceae (Bacillariaceae, Brittleworts), form a very distinctly marked group among the Thallophytes, the Desmidieae, a group of the Chlorophyceae, being the only forms with which they show any points of connection, and these somewhat superficial. They are unicellular plants of microscopic size[4], and are specially distinguished by the peculiar structure of their membranes. These are strongly silicified and composed of two halves, one of which overlaps the other like the lid of a box. The overlapping edges of the two halves are called the *girdles*, the two halves themselves the *valves*. Among the cell-contents are chlorophyll-plates, but the green colour is masked by the presence of a brown colouring matter (*diatomin*) which is closely allied to the brown colouring matter mixed with the chlorophyll of the Phaeophyceae, and gives the brown or yellow appearance to the coloured portions of the contents of the cells (*endochrome-plates*)

---

[1] Sachs, Phys.-med. Ges. Würzburg, 23 Nov. 1878.

[2] Baranetzky, Influence de la lumière sur les plasmodia des Myxomycètes (Mém. de la soc. des sc. nat. de Cherbourg, T. XIX).

[3] Pfitzer, Ueber Bau und Entwicklung der Bacillariaceen (Hanstein, Botan. Abhandl., I. Bd. 2 Heft, [also his monograph in Vol. II. of Schenck's Handb. d. Bot.].—Schmitz, Ueber die Auxosporenbildung der Bacillariaceen (Sitzungsber. der Naturf. Ges. zu Halle, June 9, 1877).—[O. Müller, Gesetz d. Zelltheilungsfolge von *Melosira* (*Orthosira*) *arenaria*, Moore (Mitth. d. Deutsch. bot. Ges. I. 1883), see also Pringsh. Jahrb. XIV. 2, 1883; Id., Die Chromatophoren mar. Bacillariaceen (Deutsch. bot. Ges. 1883).—Deby and Kitton, Bibliography of Diatomaceae, London 1882.—Schmitz, Fr., Beitr. z. K. d. Chromatophoren (Pringsh. Jahrb. XV. 1884).

[4] Freshwater Diatoms, according to Pfitzer, seldom attain a length of $\frac{1}{8}$ mm., and are usually much smaller; some salt water forms are as much as 3 mm. long (*Synedra Thallothrix*).

of the Diatomaceae. Besides the ordinary rotation of protoplasm in their interior, Diatoms exhibit a creeping movement, by means of which they glide over fixed bodies or push small granules that are near them along their surface; this occurs only in a line drawn along the length of their wall, in which Schultze supposes slits or holes, through which the protoplasm protrudes; this has never been directly observed, but it is perhaps the cause of the gliding movement, which is referred by others to osmosis [1].

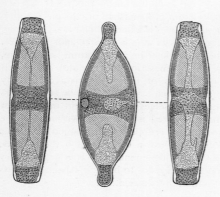

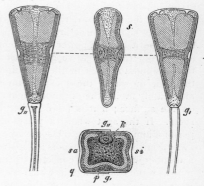

FIG. 9. *Anomoeneis sphaerophora* showing the surface of a valve in the middle figure (side view), and right and left the girdle (front view) answering to the right and left margins of the valves; the endochrome places are shaded; magn. 900 times. After Pfitzer.

FIG. 10. *Gomphonema constrictum* Ehrbg.; *s* view of valves (nucleus visible); g_i view of the girdle corresponding to the right, g_{ii} to the left margin of the valves; *q* transverse section through the middle of the cell, showing with unusual distinctness the composition of the silicified cell-wall of two halves, one overlapping the other (*sa* the larger, *si* the smaller valve); *k* the nucleus; *p* dense protoplasm; g_i g_{ii} the two girdle-surfaces. After Pfitzer.

The cells of the Diatomaceae live in fresh, brackish and salt water, either single or united in rows; some are borne either singly or a number together on gelatinous stalks (Fig. 10), or they are imbedded in a gelatinous mass, which in some species takes the form of regularly branching threads, as in *Schizonema*. They multiply by bipartition. When cell-division begins the two valves move apart from one another, and the contents divide into two daughter-cells, each of which forms a new valve on the plane of division; the inflexed margin (the girdle) of the new valve fits into the girdle of the old valve of the mother-cell; the old valve extends beyond the edge of the new valve, as a lid over the edge of a box. The two new valves of the two daughter-cells lie at first in contact with one another. Since, according to Pfitzer, the valves, which though highly silicified contain at the same time some organic matter, do not increase in size after formation, it is plain that the new ones must be smaller and smaller from generation to generation; when their size has reached a certain minimum, large cells, the *auxospores*, are again suddenly produced; the valves of the small cells separate, and the contents issue forth and increase in size by growth, or by conjugation and growth combined; the auxospores thus formed provide themselves with new valves. Since the large auxospores are somewhat differently shaped from their smaller mother-cells and primary mother-cells, cells differently shaped and with unlike lobes must necessarily result at first from their division, as happens also with the Desmids. The two valves moreover are always of unequal age.

As regards the mode of formation of the auxospores five types may be distinguished, in accordance with the views of Pfitzer and Schmitz.

The simplest type is seen in a simple *rejuvenescence* of single cells. An individual

---

[1] See Mereschowsky in Bot Ztg. 1880, p. 520.

cell casts off its two valves and begins to spread itself out and increase in size, being sometimes surrounded by a gelatinous envelope, sometimes not. At first naked, it soon appears encased in a thin non-silicious membrane, the *perizonium*. When the auxospore has reached its full size, it secretes two silicious valves one after the other within the perizonium which then disappears, while the new diatom continues to multiply by division into two till it reaches the minimum size, when the formation of auxospores again takes place. This is the mode of proceeding in the case of a considerable number of species, as *Melosira varians, Cyclotella Kützingiana, Cocconeis Pediculus*.

The second mode of formation of auxospores differs from the first only in this, that the protoplasmic mass of a mother-cell divides into two naked daughter-cells, which issue from the gaping valves of the mother-cell and develope each into an auxospore. This type is given by Smith and Lüders for *Rhabdonema arcuatum* only.

A third mode, common to very many diatoms, always shows two individual cells combining to form auxospores but without the occurrence of a real conjugation. Two cells lay themselves side by side and secrete a gelatinous substance which encloses the pair of cells in a common and usually ellipsoidal envelope. Then the two cells within the gelatinous envelope cast off their old valves, and so lie side by side as naked cells. In some cases the formation of the gelatinous envelope does not begin till after the valves are cast off. The two cells then lie naked, i.e. without cell-membranes, inside the gelatinous envelope, in some cases closely approximated to one another, in others on the contrary so separated from each other by tolerably thick layers of the jelly, that no contact takes place between them. Then both elongate and grow parallel and alongside of one another to the normal size of auxospores, and on their outer surface sooner or later appears a membrane of cellulose, the perizonium. Then each cell forms its two silicious valves and begins its usual course of development. Examples of this type are *Frustulia saxonica, Cocconema Cistula*, and others. It must remain a question in this case, whether the two cells exercise a material influence on one another, and if this influence is due to the exchange of some substance in solution ; if such an exchange takes place, it must be, as Schmitz remarks, when the two cells lay themselves side by side, but it has not yet been directly observed.

A fourth mode is exemplified according to the observations of Pfitzer and others in the genera *Himantidium, Surirella* and *Cymatopleura*. Two individuals here co-operate in the formation of one auxospore. The two cells, usually wrapped in a common gelatinous envelope, cast off their old valves and unite into a single naked mass of protoplasm which grows into an auxospore. In this case therefore the auxospore is formed by the *conjugation* of two gametes, and must consequently be called a *zygospore*.

Lastly, the fifth mode is where two cells, surrounded by a common gelatinous envelope, throw off their old valves and divide each of them transversely into two naked daughter-cells. Each pair of these four daughter-cells, lying opposite to one another, unite to form a single naked cell, which then grows into an auxospore. Thus it happens, according to Schmitz, with *Epithemia Zebra*. Here too there is a conjugation ; the auxospores are zygospores ; only they do not, as in the Conjugatae to be hereafter described, pass through a period of rest, but commence their further development at once.

Thus the formation of auxospores in the Diatomaceae varies in different species, and indeed within the limits of a single genus, *Cocconeis*. The question is, which of the five modes should be regarded as the original one. It is obvious that with our present knowledge we cannot decide this point with certainty; but my opinion is that the cases of apogamy mentioned above in other Thallophytes make it most probable in this case also, that the forms of asexual formation of auxospores must be derived as instances of apogamous suppression from the formation of zygospores. In the case of the third type the cells lay themselves side by side and empty their contents into the common gelatinous envelope, in others this proceeding does not occur, and each cell by itself forms an auxospore.

Besides the auxospores, which as has been stated do not pass through a period of rest, many Diatoms have also resting-cells which are usually spoken of as *craticular states*. The cells in this case form a double cell-wall, i.e. two new valves inside the old one.

III. SCHIZOPHYTA [1].

This class comprehends two divisions: one of forms containing chlorophyll, whose green colouring matter is mixed with a blue which is soluble in water (the Cyanophyceae), and one of forms without chlorophyll (the Schizomycetes). The former live chiefly in water or else in wet places, sometimes as pseudo-parasites; the latter are either true parasites, or they live on the moist surfaces of organic bodies, or they are found in fluids containing organic substances in solution, from which they derive their food, and which they decompose by causing putrefaction or fermentation.

The structure of the Schizophytes is always very simple, and in the simplest forms the cells are so small that they can as a rule be seen only under high magnifying power; the cell-wall and the cell-contents are often scarcely distinguishable from one another in the very minute forms; where this is possible, the contents are seen to be a homogeneous substance sometimes sprinkled with small granules; the cell-wall has a tendency to deliquesce into a thin jelly, in which the cells lie scattered about or disposed in order; sometimes the cell-wall is only swollen up and then is plainly seen to be stratified. No cell-nucleus is found either in the Cyanophyceae or in the Schizomycetes.

In the simplest forms the cells live isolated; when a cell divides, the halves grow to the size of the mother-cell, divide again, separate and live an isolated life by themselves [2]. In the more perfect forms the cells produced by division remain united, and according to the growth and the corresponding cell-divisions which ensue, either simple and often very slender rows of cells are formed, or thin plates, the cells from the mode of their division lying in one plane, or lump-like aggregations of cells from the growth and divisions of the cells taking place in all directions. It is only in the most highly developed species that the multicellular bodies assume a definite external form.

As a general rule the Cyanophyceae are larger and their cell-structure more perfect than in the Schizomycetes; here already on the lowest stage of the vegetable kingdom we see how a degradation of structure is usually connected with absence of chlorophyll.

The cells of a Schizophyte are usually exactly alike; but in some Cyanophyceae a few larger and differently coloured cells, termed *heterocysts*, are interposed at intervals between the other cells of a chain.

In most cases there is no distinction of base and apex, and therefore no definite direction of growth; it is only in the most highly developed forms that a base and an apex can be distinguished, and this is accompanied by a certain kind of ramification.

---

[1] [Zopf, Zur Morphologie der Spaltpflanzen, Leipzig 1883.—Schmitz, Fr., Die Schizophyten oder Spaltpflanzen (Act. Leopold. XIX. 1883).]

[2] Owing to this peculiarity the name of the group is derived from σχίζω, I divide, and φυτόν, a plant.

Swarm-cells, such as those of the higher Thallophytes, are found only in *Merismopedia*, a genus of Cyanophyceae, and perhaps in some other Chroococcaceae; but many Schizophytes possess the power of motion; they swim hither and thither, or the chains of cells which are spirally coiled turn on their own axis, or they can bend to either side, or they exhibit other movements.

The Schizophytes have no sexual organs. They multiply, as has been stated, either by division into two of isolated cells, or where the species form chains of cells, these break up into pieces, which have the power of motion and grow into new individuals. Besides this both Cyanophyceae and Schizomycetes have *resting-cells*,— isolated cells which have passed into a quiescent state, in which they may become dried up without losing their vitality. These resting-cells are usually distinguished by a thicker cell-wall and denser protoplasm, especially in the Cyanophyceae; the resting-cells of the Schizomycetes are very minute, and their structure therefore very difficult to determine. (See below.)

The Schizophyta then consist of the two following divisions:—

A. **Cyanophyceae.**
B. **Schizomycetes.**

A. CYANOPHYCEAE.

The Cyanophyceae[1] (Phycochromaceae) are of a bluish or verdigris green, or of some similar colour, due to a mixture of true chlorophyll and *phycocyan*, which latter, when diffused out of dead or ruptured cells, produces the blue stain on the paper on which filaments of *Oscillatoria* have been dried. Phycocyan, when extracted with cold water from crushed plants, gives a solution which is a beautiful blue in transmitted light, blood-red in reflected light[2]. If the crushed plants are heated with strong alcohol after the extraction of the colouring matter, a green solution is obtained which contains true chlorophyll and probably a special pigment, *phycoxanthin*[3]. The cells of the Cyanophyceae, according to Schmitz[4], have no nucleus; but there are granules distributed in the protoplasm which are probably composed of nuclear substance (nuclein). Propagation is entirely asexual, either by resting cells,—isolated cells rich in protoplasm, which secrete a thicker cell-wall and

---

[1] Nägeli, Einzellige Algen, Zürich 1849.—Fischer, Beiträge zur Kenntniss der Nostocaceen (Bern 1853).—De Bary, Beitrag zur Kenntniss der Nostocaceen, insbesondere der Rivularien (Flora 1863).—Bornet et Thuret, Notes algologiques, Fasc. I, II, Paris 1876 and 1880.—Janczewski, Observ. sur la reprod. de quelques Nostochacées (Ann. d. sc. nat. 5 sér. T. XIX).—[Id. Godlewskia, n. g. d'Algues de l'ordre Cryptophycées (Ann. sc. nat. 6th sér. XVI. (1883).]—Borzi, Note alla morfologia e biologia delle alghe Ficocromacee (Nuovo giorn. bot. Italiano, Vols. X and XI).— [Falkenberg, Die Algen im weitesten Sinne, in Vol. II. of Schenk's Handb. d. Botanik.—Tangl, Zur Morphologie der Cyanophyceen (Sitz. d. k. Akad. d. Wiss. in Wien, Mai 1883).—Zopf, Weit. Stütze f. meine Theorie v. d. Inconstanz d. Spaltalgen (Phycochromaceen) (Ber. Deut. bot. Ges. 1883).— Cooke, Brit. Freshwater Algae.—Hansgirg, Ueber den polymorphismus der Algen (Bot. Centralbl. 1885)].

[2] Cohn in Archiv f. mikrosk. Anatomie v. Schulze, III. p. 12, and Askenasy in Bot. Zeit. 1867, Nr. 29.

[3] Millardet u. Kraus in Comptes rendus, LXVI. p. 505.

[4] Unters. über die Struktur des Protoplasmas und der Zellkerne der Pflanzenzellen (Sitzungsber. der niederrh. Gesellsch. 13 Juli 1880).—[Hansgirg, Ein Beitr. z. d. Kenntn. d. Verbreitung d. Chromatophoren und Zellkerne bei d. Schizophyceen (Ber. Deut. bot. Ges. 1885).]

are able to pass through a period of rest; or in the species which form cell-filaments, such as the Nostocaceae, by *hormogonia*,—portions of filaments with power of motion, which become isolated, and after a period of rest grow into new individuals. I have besides seen the formation of swarm-spores in *Merismopedia*.

The Cyanophyceae fall into two divisions; in one of these, the Chroococcaceae, the cells lie, singly or a number together variously arranged, in a gelatinous envelope formed by the swelling up of the cell-walls; in the second division, that of the Nostocaceae, the cells are united into filaments.

1. The **CHROOCOCCACEAE** live as isolated roundish cells or in roundish families, whose cells are imbedded in amorphous mucilage or in the swollen walls of their

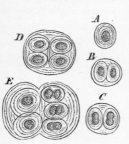

FIG. 11. *Gloeocapsa.*

mother-cells. They occur as gelatinous growths in damp places. Several genera with numerous species have been distinguished: *Chroococcus* and *Gloeocapsa* (Fig. 11), which divide in all directions, the latter imbedded in a stratified jelly; *Gloeotheca* in a similar jelly but dividing only in one direction; and *Merismopedia*, the cells of which divide crosswise and lie in a single plane.

2. The **NOSTOCACEAE.** The genus **Nostoc** may be taken as a typical example of this division. It forms lumps of mucilage or gelatinous nodular envelopes, which float in water or lie loose on damp earth or among mosses. Moniliform rows of round cells lie coiled up like snakes in the jelly; single larger cells, termed *heterocysts*, incapable of further development and having differently coloured watery cell-contents, are interposed at intervals in the chains. The filaments increase in length by the growth and transverse division of the individual cells, and thus add to the number of the coils in the jelly which they secrete. New colonies are formed, according to Thuret, in the following manner:—the jelly of the old colony becomes softened in the water, and the portions of the filaments that lie between the heterocysts creep out of the jelly, while the heterocysts themselves remain in it. Having come out into the water these portions of filaments, termed *hormogonia*, exhibit the movements of the Oscillatorieae; their escape from the jelly is probably brought about by these movements as well as by the liquefying of the jelly itself. The hormogonia may continue in motion for as long a time as one hour[1]. When they have come to rest they stretch themselves out and surround themselves with a gelatinous envelope. The roundish cells of the hormogonia now grow transversely, i.e. at right angles to the axis of the filament, and divide by longitudinal walls parallel to its axis; but the short filaments thus produced continue to be connected with one another at their extremities, and thus form the beginning of a single coiled nostoc-thread. Individual cells, disposed apparently in no definite order, become heterocysts. For the formation of spores certain cells—often all the cells of a

---

[1] These motile threads of *Nostoc* were seen by Janczewski to enter the young stomata of the under side of the thallus of *Anthoceros laevis*, where they develope into roundish coils. Such *Nostoc* colonies have long been known in cavities and in the tissue of certain Hepaticae (*Blasia* and *Anthoceros*), but they were usually regarded as endogenous gemmae of these species, till Janczewski pointed out their true nature. *Nostoc* also forms settlements in the large porous cells of the leaves of *Sphagnum*. The entrance of *Nostoc* into the parenchyma of the stem of a dicotyledonous plant *Gunnera* is effected, according to Reinke, in a different way; the deeper lying cells of the parenchyma of the circumference of the stem, which are themselves covered by layers of parenchyma, are densely filled with colonies of the Alga (Bot. Zeit. 1872, pp. 59 and 74). An *Anabaena* is found constantly in the cavities of the leaves of *Azolla* (Salviniaceae) in the earliest stages of the growth of the young plant; the filaments of the *Anabaena*, according to Berggren, attach themselves to the macrospores, and as soon as the embryo is formed they make their way into its leaves.

portion of a filament—are invested with a thick cell-wall and increase in size, their protoplasm becoming at the same time dense and of a yellowish-green colour. The exosporium bursts in germination, and each spore produces a new nostoc-thread which soon invests itself with an envelope of mucilage. In some cases, as in *Nostoc Linckia*, the young plant, instead of growing directly into a nostoc-thread as usual, changes its colour to yellow and becomes a hormogonium, which after passing through a period of rest again assumes the ordinary bluish green colour and developes into a nostoc-colony.

Besides the genus *Nostoc* just described there are the following subdivisions of the Nostocaceae.

a. The OSCILLATORIEAE. These are rigid cylindrical filaments of varying thickness, often extremely slender, and divided by very delicate transverse walls into disc-like cells. The cells are all alike, there being no heterocysts. The filaments are not straight, but somewhat twisted into a very oblique spiral ; they turn on their axis, and when growing together in large numbers (in water or on moist ground) become matted into balls or pellicles of a dark green colour ; a bunch of these filaments placed in water or on wet paper assumes a star-like arrangement in consequence of these movements, as Nägeli has shown [1].

b. The SCYTONEMEAE form branched filaments, consisting at least in their older portions of several rows of cells, and enclosed in thick gelatinous envelopes. Hetero-cysts, hormogonia and spores occur. To this subdivision belong *Scytonema, Sirosiphon,* and others. The mode of branching is peculiar ; any cell of a filament thrusts itself past the cell that stands above it, and grows out into a branch.

c. A distinct section of the Nostocaceae comprises those forms, in which the filaments end in a hair ; the cells toward the extremity of the filament become narrower and lose their protoplasm. The heterocysts are at the opposite end of the filament, which growing gradually thinner from above downwards takes the form of a riding-whip with a knob (the heterocyst) at the top. The branching is the same as in *Scytonema*. To this subdivision belong the RIVULARIEAE especially, together with some marine species. The Rivularieae form soft greenish-brown lumps of jelly which are found free floating or attached in calcareous waters. In the first case they are spherical in shape, in the second hemispherical, the smallest about half a millimetre in diameter, the largest the size of a hazel-nut. A large number of moniliform filaments with roundish cells lie radially disposed in the jelly. The filament increases in length by transverse division of its cells. The cell that lies immediately over the basilar heterocyst becomes a spore, and grows in breadth and especially in length ; its cell-contents become more dense, and it invests itself with a firm cell-wall. Ultimately the whole colony is broken up and the spores alone remain. These after a time germinate, dividing each into four to twelve shorter cylindrical pieces, each of which divides repeatedly till upwards of one hundred cells have been formed ; the cells then become rounded off and give the filament a moniliform appearance. The elongation of the filament bursts the wall of the spore, the upper end of the filament emerges, and the lower portion ultimately slips out of the sheath. The cells at the extremities of the thread become pointed, and finally the whole thread breaks up into several pieces, which crowd together into a bundle or tuft. Each portion of the filament now becomes elongated at one end into a segmented hair, while the cell at the other end forms the heterocyst. This tuft of filaments, the product of a germinating cell, represents once more a young rivularia-family, whose filaments are already enclosed in a jelly produced by the swelling up of the cell-walls. The multiplication of the filaments of a growing family is effected by 'apparent' branching (as in *Scytonema*), that is, one of the lower cells becomes a new heterocyst, while the portion of the filament between it and the old basilar cell grows into a perfect thread and takes up a position alongside of the mother-filament.

---

[1] [Hansgirg, Bemerk. über die Bewegungen d. Oscillarien (Bot. Zeit. 1883).]

B. SCHIZOMYCETES.

The Schizomycetes[1] or Fission-Fungi, known also as Bacteria, are closely connected by their morphological characters with the Cyanophyceae. They are distinguished from them by the entire absence of chlorophyll, which obliges them to feed only on organic substances. Bacteria are organisms which often lie on the very border line of visibility. They consist of short cells, whose diameter is sometimes $\frac{1}{500}$ of a millimetre, but usually considerably less. They are therefore easily confounded with inorganic granules, so that it is often necessary to establish their organic character by indirect methods; the most characteristic mark of distinction is their power of dividing and of manifesting active movements very different from the so-called molecular motion of minute particles of inorganic matter. Bacteria occur either isolated or in larger or smaller swarms, and are often united into threads or families. Many forms are motionless at all times, others display a more or less lively and spontaneous motility, due to the presence of cilia, which occur singly at the extremity of the rod-like organism; in other and filamentous forms the movements correspond to those of the Oscillatorieae. But the motile forms usually pass through stages of their life, in which they are motionless; the countless cells that lie close together usually secrete a mass of mucilage or jelly, the shape of which may be sharply defined or be quite irregular; these gelatinous colonies, which are often of considerable size, are known as *zoogloea*-forms.

The Schizomycetes are the causes of putrefaction proper and of the phenomena of fermentation in the wider sense of the term. They change the sugar of milk, for instance, into lactic acid, so that the milk becomes 'sour,' and the lactic acid by a further process into butyric acid, &c.; one of them excites ammoniacal fermentation in urine. They appear also as the causes of disease in living organisms; at least there are certain forms of disease, splenic fever for instance, in which the connection of these organisms with the disease as cause and effect has been established with certainty, while the reference to them of many other infectious diseases is to say the least highly probable. Some species are distinguished by their power of forming pigments. Thus *Micrococcus prodigiosus* forms at first on substances containing starch or albumen, as bread, potatoes and paste, small red points which afterwards enlarge into bright red patches. These patches are red masses of mucilage in which countless colourless micrococcus-cells are imbedded.

The Schizomycetes exhibit great variety of form, as may be gathered from what has been already said. It is to Cohn especially that we are indebted for a discrimination of these forms and their arrangement in genera, and we may recognise among them four main series, the spherical, the rod-like, the filiform, and the spiral.

---

[1] Cohn, Unters. über Bakterien (Beitr. zur Biol. d. Pflanzen, Bd. 1 and 2).—Brefeld, Unters. über die Schimmelpilze, IV Heft (*Bacillus subtilis*).—Nägeli, Die niedern Pilze in ihren Beziehungen zu den Infektionskrankheiten, München, 1877.—Zopf, Ueber den genetischen Zusammenhang von Spaltpilzformen (Monatsber. der Berlinischen Akad. 1881, p. 277 ff.); [also Die Spaltpilze, part of Vol. III of Schenk's Handb. d. Botanik.—De Bary, Vergl. Morph. u. Biol. d. Pilze, Mycetozen und Bacterien, Leipzig 1884, must be consulted for a succinct account of this group and its copious literature. Of more recent works may be mentioned here Prazmowski, Die Entwick. und Morph. des *Bacillus anthracis*, Cohn (Krakau 1884, extr. in Bot. Centralbl. XX. 1884).—Fisch, C., Ueber die systemat. Stellung der Bacterien (Biol. Centralbl. V. 1885).—Baumgarten, Ueber pathog. pflanzliche Mikroorganismen, II. Berlin, 1884.—Grove, Synopsis of the Bacteria and Yeast Fungi, London, 1884.—Klein, Micro-organisms in Disease, London, 1885].

1. To the first division belongs the genus **Micrococcus**, consisting of small roundish cells which divide in one direction only, and either separate after division or remain strung together like the beads of a rosary. The cells of *Sarcina,* which lives in the human stomach, on the other hand divide by walls crossing one another in three directions in space and continue united together into small bales.

2. Among the rod-like forms the genus **Bacterium** agrees in every respect with *Micrococcus,* except that the cells are not spherical but elliptic or shortly cylindrical.

3. In the third division we must distinguish first those forms which have straight filaments. If these filaments are slender, short and rod-like they are named **Bacillus,** if they are slender and long, *Leptothrix,* if stouter and long, *Beggiatoa*; a form with comparatively large filaments invested with a gelatinous envelope is known as *Crenothrix.* Some filaments are branched and are named *Cladothrix*; the mode of branching is as in the Cyanophyceae.

4. Short rigid filaments with few coils are named **Spirillum**; *Spirochaete* has very slender and not rigid filaments with many coils.

To these might be added a few more but less characteristic genera; the species are many in each genus, and are chiefly distinguished by their physiological effects.

Two views obtain with regard to the independence of the forms here briefly described. Cohn considers *Micrococcus, Bacterium, Bacillus* and their allies to be distinct genera, the several species of which exhibit distinct physiological activities. Nägeli on the other hand is of opinion that the number of species is small, and that each of these species passes through a definite and somewhat extensive cycle of forms, so that different species may appear in analogous forms and with a similar sphere of operation ; in other words, that one and the same species may appear according to the stage of its development as a *Micrococcus, Bacillus, Spirillum,* or *Cladothrix*[1]. This latter view finds support in some observations of Cienkowski, who noticed the breaking up of the filaments of *Cladothrix* and *Leptothrix* into small portions which then had the form assigned to the genus *Bacterium.* Still more important are the statements lately published by Zopf[2]. He observed that the cycle of development in the genera *Cladothrix, Beggiatoa* and *Leptothrix* is in fact such as was to be expected according to Nägeli's views. An example or two will make this plain. *Beggiatoa alba* is a very common form with long filaments imbedded in jelly, living chiefly in hot sulphur springs, where they decompose the sulphur compounds in solution in the water and give off sulphuretted hydrogen. These filaments divide into long rods, which divide again into shorter portions, and these by further transverse divisions become *Micrococci,* which swarm and form zoogloea-families. Elongation of the *Micrococci* leads to the formation of rods, which are either straight (*Bacterium*) or spiral (*Spirillum*) and can also assume the motile condition. After coming to rest they grow into filaments of *Leptothrix,* which may be bent into stiff spiral forms. *Cladothrix* also has a micrococcus-stage, from which shorter or longer rods are evolved, and these grow into leptothrix-like filaments either immediately or after having passed through the stage of swarming movement; finally the filaments branch in the same way as in the Cyanophyceae, and *Cladothrix* reappears. The filaments consist of longer rods, which separate by transverse division into shorter rods and ultimately into *Micrococci.* But under certain circumstances the cladothrix-forms as well as the leptothrix-forms may become swarming spiral forms, and these may appear as *Spirillum, Vibrio,* or *Spirochaete.* The spirally-twisted filaments break up into daughter-spirals which swarm by the aid of flagella, and these can themselves again divide. The *Micrococci* may also develope into zoogloea-forms which are branched like a tree.

---

[1] [Ray Lankester (Quart. Journ. Micr. Soc. 1873) pointed out the genetic relationships of Cohn's genera.]

[2] Zopf, Ueber d. genetischen Zusammenhang von Spaltpilzformen (Monatsber. d. Akad. in Berlin, 10 März 1881). It has yet to be determined whether the course of development as given by Zopf is common to all the forms of the Schizomycetes.

Bacillus subtilis[1], the species which has been most thoroughly investigated, will serve to illustrate the course of development, so far as it is known, in the Schizomycetes. It is one of the commonest species and lives naturally in fluid and semi-fluid substances. Its germs, like those of all Schizomycetes, become disseminated when the substratum dries up ; they rise into the air and are borne along by its currents. This species exists in the vegetative condition in the form of small rods, about twice as long as broad, which multiply by bipartition, the divisions either soon separating or cohering in the form of slender filaments. Each little rod can during its vegetative period assume the motile condition, and then has two delicate cilia, one at each extremity ; single filaments also may become motile. As soon as the nourishing substratum is exhausted, growth and division cease, and fructification begins by the formation of a spore in each rod in the following manner. Clearer points make their appearance in the middle of a rod, or towards an extremity, pointing to a denser accumulation of protoplasm at the spot. The whole cell-contents of the rod now gradually draw together to this spot and assume the form of an ovoid or oblong-cylindrical strongly refractive mass, which invests itself with a cell-wall from within outwards and so becomes a *spore*. After the spore is formed the rod swells slightly at the hyaline spot ; by-and-by the other parts of the rod disappear. In germination the spore becomes paler in colour at first and increases in size. Then exactly in the middle of the side of the somewhat elongated spore, a protuberance (the germ-tube) makes its appearance and lengthens rapidly, and soon separates by transverse division into daughter-rods.

The spores are so small, that their nature as vegetable organisms cannot be recognised by their outward appearance. They germinate immediately, requiring to pass through no period of rest. On the other hand, as Brefeld has shown, they offer unusual resistance to external influences. They are killed by boiling only when the process is continued for two hours ; a shorter time, such as a quarter of an hour, only excites them to more abundant germination. They are not readily affected by poisonous substances, though their development is hindered by addition of acids, especially mineral acids. Formation of spores has been ascertained to take place in a number of other Schizomycetes, e.g. in *Bacillus Amylobacter*, *Vibrio Rugula*, *Bacillus Ulna*[2], and is in fact a very general phenomenon, though the mode of proceeding sometimes varies slightly from that given above for *Bacillus subtilis*.

IV. ALGAE[3].

Under the term Algae are here included all the Thallophytes which contain chlorophyll, with the exception of the Cyanophyceae and Diatomaceae ; in two sections only of the Algae is the chlorophyll masked by another colouring matter. The Algae are not grouped together on account of this physiological character, but because the course of development of their forms, varied as it is, is yet essentially the same, the extreme forms being connected together by intermediate ones. The vegetative structure of the thallus is not less varied than the mode of sexual propagation ; in

---

[1] See Brefeld, Unters. über die Schimmelpilze, Heft IV.

[2] Prazmowski, Zur Entwicklungsgeschichte und Fermentwirkung einiger Bakterienarten (Bot. Zeit. 1879, p. 409).

[3] A succinct account of this group has lately been published by Falkenberg (Schenk's Handbuch der Botanik, II. Bd.). [See also Wille, Zur physiol. Anat. d. Algen (Bot. Centralbl. Vol. XXI. 1884), for a summary of investigations into the construction of Algae ; also Ferd. Hauck, Die Meeres Algen (Rabenhorst, Crypt. Flora v. Deutschland, 2nd Ed., Leipzig, 1883, Schmitz, Fr., Die Chromatophoren in Algen (Verh. d. naturh. Ver. Preuss. Rheinl. u. Westph. 1883), and Beitr. z. K. d. Chromatophoren (Pringsh. Jahrb. XV. 1884).]

each of the three subdivisions which are here distinguished, there are some forms with extremely simple, some with more or less complex vegetative bodies. The three subdivisions are the Chlorophyceae or green Algae, the Phaeophyceae or brown Algae, and the Rhodophyceae or red Algae or Florideae. Here too the appearance indicated by the name of these subdivisions, viz. the colouring of the cell-contents, is not the real ground of division, but the fact that in each of these groups we have before us a number of forms, in which the course of development is fundamentally the same, but with a certain amount of variation within the limits of each subdivision.

All the three groups have chlorophyll-corpuscles; but in the Chlorophyceae alone the green colour appears pure and unmixed, in the Phaeophyceae it is obscured by a brown, and in the Florideae by a red pigment.

1. The **Rhodophyceae** are distinguished by the fact that their male organs of fertilisation are small cells without the power of active movement (*spermatia*); the female organ, the *procarp* (see p. 7), consists of a receptive portion, the *trichogyne*, with which the spermatium coalesces, and of a carpogenous portion, the *carpogone*, which is excited by fertilisation to a process of vegetation, resulting in the formation of *carpospores*. The asexual organs of propagation, formed usually by division of a mother-cell into four parts (*tetraspores*), are also non-motile, being unprovided with cilia. The Florideae are for the most part inhabitants of the sea. *Swarm-spores* occur as a rule in both the other subdivisions; the male and female sexual elements (*gametes*) take also the form of motile cells in the simplest cases; in the higher forms the male gamete at least, the *spermatozoid*, is a swarming protoplasmic body.

2. The **Phaeophyceae** are known by the circumstance that the two cilia in all the swarm-spores are inserted laterally near the base of the pointed extremity. The species are all marine.

3. The **Chlorophyceae** have all swarm-spores; but these in some species have two cilia inserted at the tip of the pointed extremity, in others four or a circle of cilia at their colourless anterior extremity, or finally their whole surface is covered with cilia (*Vaucheria*). Some species live in fresh, some in salt water.

A. CHLOROPHYCEAE.

The Chlorophyceae may be distributed into several series of forms which are at the same time connected with one another in various ways; such are the Confervoideae with the two connected series of Conjugatae and Characeae, the Protococcaceae, the Volvocineae, and the Siphoneae; the essential point of distinction between the subdivisions is the structure of the thallus. The process of fertilisation within each ascends from the *isogamous*, i.e. the union of two gametes of similar form, to the *oogamous*, i.e. the coalescence of gametes of dissimilar form; the oogamous fertilisation is least distinctly marked in the Protococcaceae, where, as in *Phyllobium*, one small male motile cell coalesces with one larger female cell, the *oosphere*. In other respects each section has its own characteristic marks. The green colour of the Chlorophyceae is often changed in those of its cells which are passing through a period of rest, such as the zygospores and oospores, which then become red. The red colouring matter represents a modification of the chlorophyll, which Rostafinski considers to be a reduction-product of the latter, and to which he gives the name of *chloro-rufin*[1].

The cell-structure and manner of life vary much among the Chlorophyceae, but the structure of the thallus never reaches so high a stage with them as with the Phaeophyceae. Many species are unicellular, others consist of cell-filaments or single cell-surfaces; the Siphoneae exhibit unicellular tubular filaments which often attain to large dimensions, and have numerous nuclei in their protoplasm. Most of the Algae of this subdivision live in water; a few only are found in spots that are occasionally moistened with water, as *Chroolepus*, which grows on the stems of trees and on stones, and has the peculiarity, that its vegetative cells assume the red colour mentioned above. A certain number of Chlorophyceae live in cavities of plants of a higher order,—a mode of life adopted by them chiefly for the sake of shelter, and therefore named by Klebs 'Raumparasitismus[2].' Thus the zoospores of *Chlorochytrium* make their way into the tissue of species of *Lemna*, by inserting a process between the walls of two opposite epidermal cells and thus opening a passage for themselves into the substance of the plant, where they develope into a green spherical body. Other Protococcaceae make a home in the tissue of the leaves of various dicotyledonous water-plants. Filamentous Algae also have been known to adopt this mode of life. One of the Siphoneae, *Phyllosiphon Arisari*[3], lives in the intercellular spaces of the leaf of *Arisarum vulgare*, and moreover draws nourishment from the cells of the leaf, for the chlorophyll is consumed in the cells contiguous to the intercellular spaces which are occupied by the *Phyllosiphon*, and of their protoplasm there remains ultimately only a thin wall-layer. This then is a case not only of 'Raumparasitismus,' but of true parasitism, such as is known in the case of other chlorophyll-containing organisms (*Viscum, Thesium*, and some species of *Rhinanthus*). It may be remarked that the leaf-cells of *Arisarum* remain turgescent almost up to the moment when they have completely parted with the substances which they contained.

Classification of the Chlorophyceae[4]:—

1. **Siphoneae** (Coeloblastae). Thallus composed of tubes, undivided by septa, and lying free or interwoven with one another, and often attaining a high degree of morphological differentiation, as in *Caulerpa* with organs resembling stem, root and leaves. Sexual propagation the result either of conjugation of swarming gametes of similar form (*Acetabularia, Botrydium*), or of fertilisation of an oosphere (*Vaucheria*). The species live on land, and in fresh and salt water.

2. **Volvocineae.** Unicellular, or forming a pluricellular family. They have this peculiarity, that their cells move about by means of cilia during the vegetative stage; the families also which consist of a number of variously arranged cells have the power of free movement. Sexual propagation isogamous or oogamous.

3. **Protococcaceae.** Unicellular stationary Algae, isolated or united into families. Sexual propagation isogamous (*Hydrodictyon*) or oogamous.

---

[1] Rostafinski, Ueber den rothen Farbstoff einiger Chlorophyceen, &c. (Bot. Zeit. 1881, p. 461).

[2] [If a special term is necessary for such endophytic plants we may designate them 'aulophytes.']

[3] Kühn, Ueber eine neue parasitische Alge *Phyllosiphon Arisari* (Sitzungsber. der naturf. Ges. zu Halle, 1878).—Just, *Phyllosiphon Arisari* (Bot. Zeit. 1882, Nr. 11 ff.).

[4] [Klebs, Ueber d. Organis. ein. Flagellatengruppen u. d. Beziehungen z. Algen u. Infusorien (Unters. aus d. Bot. Inst. z. Tübingen, I. Heft 2, 1883). See also Biol. Centralbl. IV. (1883).]

4. **Confervoideae.** Thallus of cell-filaments or cell-surfaces. Asexual organs of propagation occur in all species in the shape of zoospores, which are formed either on the thallus or only after the germination of the sexually produced spores (*Sphaeroplea*). The Conjugatae and Characeae are connected with the Confervoideae, as collateral series of forms which have no zoospores.

1. SIPHONEAE[1].

The Siphoneae or Coeloblastae form a rather large group of Algae which are for the most part marine, and which, with all the differences of habit of the several species, have this character in common, that no septa as a rule appear in the tubes of which they are composed, except in the formation of organs of reproduction. Hence the vegetative body of these plants, which often attains to a considerable size, is not divided into single cells, but its cavity is continuous; and Sachs calls them therefore *non-cellular* plants growing without division into compartments, while others regard them for the same reason as *unicellular*. Numerous small nuclei[2] are always present in the protoplasmic lining of the cells, but this is a peculiarity which is by no means confined to the Siphoneae among the Algae. Asexual multiplication, in the species which have any form of it, is effected either by swarm-spores as in *Botrydium* and some species of *Vaucheria*, or by motionless cells as in other species of *Vaucheria*, while *Acetabularia* and a few species again of *Vaucheria* &c. have no asexual multiplication. The remarkable genus *Caulerpa* has neither sexual nor asexual reproduction so far as is at present known; it multiplies by separation of new shoots which form on the old plants.

The simplest structure of the vegetative body is found in *Botrydium*, a plant not uncommon on moist mud in ditches, &c. One portion grows above ground, the other beneath it. The former has the appearance of a green bladder, one to two millimetres in breadth, which grows narrower downwards till it passes into the rooting-portion, which is fixed in the ground and has an irregularly dichotomous branching-system. The genus *Vaucheria* has a similar but less largely developed rooting-portion; but the upper green portion of the thallus consists of variously branched filaments, often

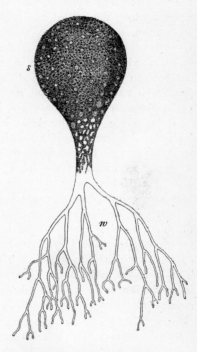

FIG. 12. *Botrydium granulatum*, an isolated young plant, magn. 30 times; *w* root system. After Woronin.

---

[1] Nägeli, Neuere Algensysteme, p. 58; also *Caulerpa prolifera* in Nägeli u. Schleiden, Zeitschr. f. wiss. Bot. 1844, Heft 1.

[2] Schmitz, Ueber d. Zellkerne d. Thallophyten (niederrh. Ges. 7 Juni, 1880, p. 7 of the reprint). —Strasburger, Zellbildung u. Zelltheilung, 3 Aufl. p. 65.

more than thirty centimetres long, with a number of spherical nuclei in the protoplasmic layer on the cell-wall. In *Bryopsis* the main axes bear secondary axes pinnately disposed, with limited power of growth. The lowest of these are thrown off after their cavity has been separated from that of the main axis by the formation of a gelatinous stopper, such as is not unfrequently to be observed in the Siphoneae. *Caulerpa*, on the other hand, has a tolerably thick creeping main axis, which in the case of *C. prolifera*, a not uncommon plant of the Mediterranean, bears branched rooting structures on its ventral surface, branches on its lateral surface, and on its dorsal surface broad leaf-like formations. Though often several metres long, it is not divided internally into compartments by cell-walls, but forms one continuous cavity, which is however crossed by bands of cellulose stretching from wall to wall to strengthen the thallus. The same purpose is attained in other species, whose thallus is an unusually long thin-walled and much-branched tube, by the branches being densely interwoven, the result being an algal body of some size with the appearance of true tissue-formation. This is the case with *Codium, Udotea* and *Halimeda*, the latter of which we may take as an example of the rest. This plant with the habit of an Opuntia (Fig. 13 *A*) appears to be formed of a number of separate parts with narrower bases all strung together, and with their outer surface more or less incrusted with lime. The longitudinal section (Fig. 13 *D*) however shows that the whole vegetative body is here also one branched unsegmented tube. The branches are especially crowded together towards the circumference, and thus form the compact outer layer of the thallus. In *Codium*, which has a similar formation of its tissue, the tubes swell out at the surface and form a palisade-like layer. These tubes are often separated from the inner filaments from which they spring by a diaphragm—a strongly refractive stopper, which first appears as a solid annular thickening on the wall and grows continually towards the inside till it closes the lumen of the tube. Another subdivision of the Siphoneae is distinguished by the verticillate arrangement of its branches, the further ramifications of which form umbels. This is the case with *Dasycladus* and *Acetabularia*. The latter resembles externally a small mushroom; on a thin lime-incrusted stalk is perched a small umbrella-like cap, which is divided into a large number of separate filaments by radiating walls that do not however quite reach the centre.

The development of **Acetabularia** is well known through the investigations of De Bary and Strasburger[1], and will serve as an example of the development of the isogamous Siphoneae. An important part of the plant in reference to the manner of growth, and one which has not yet been mentioned, is the basal portion first noticed by De Bary. The stalk has tuber-like organs of attachment at its lower extremity, but it rises from among them in the shape of a thin-walled vesicle with branches usually in the form of lobes. *Acetabularia* is a perennial plant, but each stalk with its cap is only annual. The cap with the upper part of the stalk dies at the end of its period of vegetation, and the lower part only remains; but the protoplasm retreats into the basal portion, especially that which was spoken of above as the vesicle, and fences itself off above by a transverse wall. In this condition the plant passes the winter. When the next period of vegetation begins, the transverse wall arches outwards and developes into a cylindrical tube growing out of the remains of the old plant, and this tube ultimately assumes the form of a cap-like shoot. This process is repeated during a series of years, probably till the

---

[1] De Bary u. Strasburger, *Acetabularia mediterranea* (Bot. Ztg. 1877, p. 713 ff.).

plant prepares for sexual reproduction, which comes to pass in a peculiar manner. A large number of thick-walled ellipsoidal *spores* are formed in the compartments of the cap, usually about one hundred on an average in each of the eighty compartments, eight thousand therefore in all. A cir-
cular discoid portion of its membranous wall with introverted margin covers one end of the ellipsoidal spore, like a lid pushed too far into a circular aperture, and immediately beyond its inwardly projected edge a delicate ring of ra-diating striae passes through the entire thickness of the wall from within out-wards. The area of wall-membrane thus sharply defined is afterwards cut off as a lid. Numerous swarm-cells, which are in fact *gametes*, are pro-duced in the spores. The lid of the spore being removed, the gametes are set at liberty, but they *conjugate* only when two different spores open at the same time ; there is therefore a sexual difference between the individual spores or sporanges, though there is no ex-ternal indication of this difference. As a rule only two swarm-cells conjugate, but clusters of conjugating organisms are also not infrequent. The *zygospore* becomes invested with a cell-wall and passes into the resting stage. In ger-mination a unicellular shoot is form-ed with one extremity narrowed and

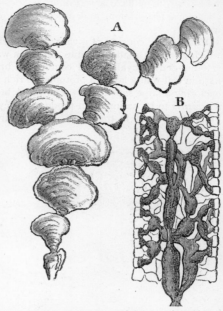

FIG. 13. *Halimeda Opuntia. A* thallus (nat. size) without the basal portion formed of interwoven filaments ; it is made up of separate members which spring from one another as in an Opuntia. *B* part of a longitudinal section ; the thallus consists of the ramifications of a tube.

conical, the other broader and rounded ; the latter is the base, the former the apex of the young plant which grows into a tube at first without a cap. The formation of the cap is always preceded by the production of some whorls of branched rays.

The development of **Botrydium**[1] agrees with that of *Acetabularia* in the circum-stance that spores are formed inside the mother-plants, and that the spores produce motile gametes. *Botrydium* also possesses the power of asexual multiplication in a remarkable variety of ways. The little plants can become *zoosporangia* in almost every stage of their existence and produce swarm-spores, which are distinguished from the gametes by having only one cilium. If the plantlets are in danger of being dried up, the whole of the protoplasmic contents migrates into the root-system and fragments into a number of portions which are separated from one another by cell-walls. Each of the cells thus formed can either behave as a zoosporangium, or germinate and pro-duce a tube which grows into a young *Botrydium*,—a proceeding which cannot here be described in detail.

Isogamous reproduction has also been ascertained in **Dasycladus**[2]. In this case the gametes are formed in sporangia, which arise in the place of one of the terminal rays of the verticillate branches, which are themselves also again branched. Only those gametes conjugate, according to Berthold, which come from different plants, so that a difference of sex appears to be indicated in this case also in the plants them-selves, or in all the sporanges of a plant.

[1] Rostafinski u. Woronin, Ueber *Botrydium granulatum* (Bot. Zeit. 1877, p. 649).
[2] Berthold in Bot. Zeit. 1880, p. 648.

Bryopsis and **Codium** are known to have two kinds of swarm-spores, small yellow and larger green ones, but no sexual act has at present been observed. If the supposition should be confirmed, that the smaller motile cells are male, and the larger female, we should then have a transition established to those Siphoneae in which there is oogamous fertilisation, and especially to *Vaucheria*, which as yet stands somewhat isolated.

Vaucheria[1] consists of a variously branched tube, sometimes thirty centimetres long, which grows in shade on damp soil, or in water both fresh and brackish. Its fixed end (rooting-end) is hyaline and contortedly branched. The free portion contains within its thin cell-wall a layer of protoplasm, rich in chlorophyll-granules and oil-drops, and enclosing a large sap-cavity. The oil-globules appear from Borodin's investigation of *V. sessilis* to be assimilation-products ; they lie outside the chlorophyll-bodies but are probably formed in them. The plants are produced at the commencement of the

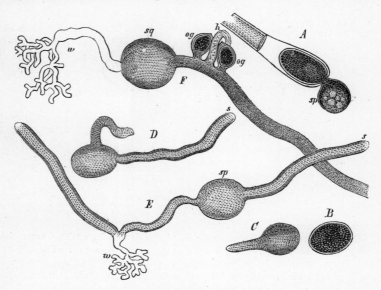

FIG. 14. *Vaucheria sessilis* (magnified about 30 times). Description in text.

period of vegetation in spring from oospores of the previous year, and in many species they propagate themselves at first asexually during several generations. The *brood-cells* which serve to this end are either obtained by simple abstriction of the ends of certain twigs, or they are large swarm-cells which escape from the tube, and have their whole surface clothed with very short cilia. The various species of *Vaucheria* show graduated transitions from the one of these forms to the other. For instance, in *V. tuberosa* branches swell up to a considerable size, become detached at the bases, and put out at once one or more germinating tubes. In *V. geminata* the contents of a

---

[1] Pringsheim, Ueber Befruchtung u. Keimung der Algen u. das Wesen des Zeugungsprocesses (Monatsber. der Berliner Akad. d. Wiss. 1855, and Jahrb. f. wiss. Bot. II. p. 470).—Schenk, Entw. der Fortpflanzungs-Organe u. Befruchtung von *Vaucheria geminata* (Verh. der physik.-med. Ges. zu Würzburg, Bd. VII. 1853).—Walz, Beitr. zur Morph. und Syst. d. Gatt. *Vaucheria* (Pringsheim's Jahrb. V. Bd.).—Woronin, Beitr. zur Kenntn. d. *Vauch.* (Bot. Zeit. 1869), and *Vaucheria de Baryana* (Bot. Zeit. 1880).—Stahl, Ueber d. Ruhezustände d. *V. geminata* (Bot. Zeit. 1879).—With respect to the nuclei see Schmitz und Strasburger, *loc. cit.*—Borodin, Ueber die Wirkung des Lichtes auf die Entwicklung von *V. sessilis* (Bot. Zeit. 1878, p. 497).

branch which has swollen to an oval shape are cut off behind by a cross-wall, and contract and form a new membrane, and the brood-cell thus formed is either set free by the decomposition of the mother-cell-wall, or falls off with it, and germinates after some days. The brood-cells of *V. hamata* are formed in the same way, but are thrown out with a jerk, lie quietly where they fall, and germinate during the ensuing night. In other species (*V. sessilis, sericea, piloboloides*) the contents of a branch are cut off behind by a septum, contract, and force their way out as a swarm-cell through a fissure at the extremity of the branch. The motion of a swarm-cell lasts only from half a minute to a minute and a half in *V. sericea*, in other species for some hours. In *V. sessilis* the rotation of the swarm-cell begins as it leaves the branch, and if the opening of the mother-cell is too small the swarm-cell breaks up into two portions, each of which becomes rounded off and is again a perfect swarm-cell; but the outer one swims away, the other remains rotating in the mother-cell. These motile cells are the largest known, being visible to the naked eye, and are thickly covered with cilia. Numerous nuclei may be seen in the superficial layer of their protoplasm, and a membrane is secreted on their surface while they are in the motile state.

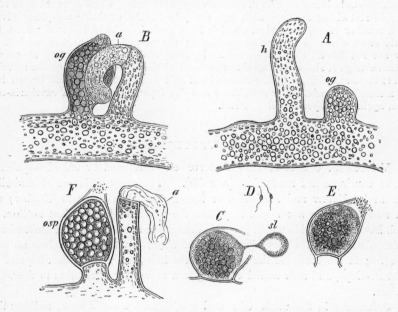

FIG. 15. *Vaucheria sessilis*. *A, B* formation of an antheridium *a* on the branch *h*, and of the oogonium *og*. *C* oogonium opened and ejecting a drop of mucilage *sl*. *D* spermatozoids. *E* collection of spermatozoids at the beak of the oogonium *F*; *a* an antheridium emptied of its contents, *osp* oospore in the oogonium. *A, B, E, F* from nature, *C, D* after Pringsheim.

The formation of the swarm-spores or brood-cells begins in the night, as is the case with most Algae and Fungi; they escape in the morning, and germination begins during the day or in the following night. In germination one or two green tubular cells are put out (Fig. 14, *C, D*), or a root-like organ of attachment is formed at the same time (*E, F, w*).—The oogonia and antheridia appear first as lateral protuberances on a filament containing chlorophyll (Fig. 14 *F*, 15 *A, B*), sometimes even on the germinating tube of a swarm-cell. All Vaucherias are monoecious, and the two kinds of sexual organs are usually close together. The *antheridia* (Fig. 15, *h, a*) are the terminal cells of slender branches, the contents of which, containing but little chlorophyll, produce a large number of small *spermatozoids* (Fig. 15, *D*), which escape by the bursting of the antheridial cell at its apex. In several species the antheridia are curved like a horn, in

[2]

others straight (*V. sericea*), or like a bent bag or pouch (*V. pachyderma*). In *V. synan-dra*, discovered by Woronin, from two to seven small horns are formed on the large ovoid terminal cell of a two-celled twig. The *oogonia* are thicker protuberances, densely filled with oil and chlorophyll (*og* in Fig. 15, *A* and *B*); they swell usually into an obliquely ovoid form, and their contents are at length cut off by a transverse wall (*F, osp*). The green coarse-grained mass collects in the centre of the oogonium, while a colourless protoplasm gathers at its apex, where the oogonium opens; at this moment the whole of the contents contract and form the oosphere, and in some species a colourless slime is expelled from the opening at the apex. After the entrance of the spermatozoids the oosphere invests itself with a thick wall, its contents become red or brown, and the oospore now begins its period of rest. The formation of the oogonia and antheridia begins in the evening, is completed during the next morning, and fertilisation ensues between ten and four o'clock of the same day.

It has lately been ascertained[1] that *Vaucheria* passes through resting stages of like character with those of *Botrydium*. The plant in these stages used to be described as a distinct genus under the name of *Gongrosira*. The tubes are divided by thick gela-tinous cross-walls into a number of separate segments (cells), which after the close of the period of rest either develope each into a vaucheria-tube, or their protoplasm divides into a number of separate pieces, which issue forth in a body invested with a thin pellicle or an envelope of mucilage, and then the several portions become isolated. They are not however swarm-spores as in *Botrydium*; but they creep about with constant change of shape on the substance on which they have settled, just like amoebae. Each of these amoebiform bodies rounds itself off into a green sphere and invests itself with a membrane, and either germinates and developes directly into a vaucheria-tube, or can again enter upon a period of rest.

2. THE VOLVOCINEAE[2].

The Volvocineae consist of cells that are either isolated or united together in gelatinous envelopes to form families (*coenobia*). These coenobia are either hollow spheres, as in *Volvox* and *Eudorina*, or four-cornered plates, as in *Gonium*; and though surrounded by a cell-wall they have the power of independent motion, for each cell has two long cilia which protrude through the cell-wall. The isolated cells of *Chlamydomonas* and *Chlamydococcus* swim about by this means like ordinary swarm-cells; in the coenobia the cilia of all the individual cells project beyond the common envelope, and their united efforts give a movement of rotation to the whole coenobium.

The differences in the mode of sexual propagation are still more striking than those in the structure of the plants themselves. The simplest case is where two swarm-spores of similar form unite with one another, as in *Pandorina* and species of *Chlamydomonas*; in other cases, as in *Eudorina* and *Volvox*, the male element is clearly distinguishable from the female.

---

[1] Stahl, Ueber die Ruhezustände der *V. geminata* (Bot. Zeit. 1879, p. 129).

[2] Pringsheim, Ueber Paarung der Schwärmsporen (Monatsber. der Berliner Akad. Okt. 1869).—Cohn, Entwicklungsgesch. der Gatt. Volvox (Cohn's Beitr. z. Biol. d. Pflanz. Bd. I).—Kirchner, Zur Entw. des *Volvox minor* (Cohn's Beitr. z. Biol. d. Planz. Bd. III).—Goroshankin, Die Genesis bei den Palmellaceen (Referat über diese Abhandl. in Bot. Jahresbericht, 1875).—Rostafinski, Quelques mots sur *l'Haematococcus lacustris* (Mem. de la Soc. nat. d. sc. nat. de Cherbourg, 1875, T. XIX).—Cohn u. Wichura, Ueber *Stephanosphaera pluvialis* (Nova Acta Leop.-Carol. Vol. XXVI).—De Bary, Bot. Zeit. 1853, Beilage, p. 73.—Rostafinski, in Bot. Zeit. 1871, p. 757.

Some examples will serve to illustrate the course of life of these plants.

The genus **Chlamydomonas** consists of isolated vigorously motile cells, which in the vegetative state multiply by division into two or four. In sexual reproduction the cells divide each into eight motile daughter-cells, provided with four cilia ; these daughter-cells are smaller than their parent-cell, and differ also from one another in size. These cells, according to Rostafinski, conjugate in precisely the same manner as that described by Pringsheim in the case of *Pandorina* (see below) ; the *zygospores* thus produced come to rest and grow for some weeks ; if they are then dried and again put into water, they divide repeatedly and form non-motile resting cell-families, identical with the old genus of the Palmellaceae, *Pleurococcus* [1].

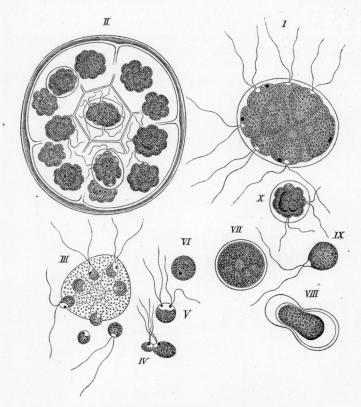

FIG. 16. Development of *Pandorina Morum*. *I*. a swarming family. *II*. a similar one divided into sixteen daughter-families. *III*. a sexual family, the cells of which are issuing from the gelatinous envelope. *IV*, *V*. pairing of the swarm-cells. *VI*. a zygospore just formed. *VII*. a fully developed zygospore. *VIII*. transformation of the contents of a zygospore into a large swarm-cell. *IX*. the swarm-cell free. *X*. young family formed from No. *IX*. After Pringsheim.

In **Pandorina Morum** (Fig. 16) the course of development was first observed in its entirety by Pringsheim, and the first example of the conjugation of swarm-cells was

---

[1] Goroshankin gives a different account of the process of conjugation in *Chlamydomonas pulvisculus*. In this plant male and female gametes are formed. The male smaller than the female ; eight male gametes are produced in a vegetative cell, but only 2–4 female. The pointed ends of the gametes meet, the cilia drop off, and a passage is formed at the anterior extremities of the two bodies, through which the protoplasm of the male cell finds its way to that of the female and unites with it to form a zygospore.

discovered by him in this plant. *Pandorina* (Fig. 16, *I*) is one of the commonest of the Volvocineae. The sixteen cells of a coenobium are closely packed together in the thin gelatinous envelope which surrounds them, and from which the long cilia project. In the *asexual multiplication* each of the sixteen cells divides again into sixteen smaller cells, which form themselves into a coenobium in the manner which will be described further on in the case of *Eudorina.* The sixteen daughter-families (Fig. 16, *II*) are set free by the solution of the gelatinous envelope of the mother-plant, and each of them, invested with an envelope of its own, grows to the original size of the mother-family. The *sexual reproduction* commences in the same way; but the gelatinous envelopes of the young families become softened, and the individual cells thus liberated move about freely by themselves (*III*); they vary very much in size, and are rounded and green at the posterior extremity, narrow and hyaline and with a red corpuscle at the anterior extremity, where are the two cilia. In the throng of swarm-cells pairs may be seen approaching and as if they were seeking for one another; these meet and come in contact with their pointed extremities, and coalesce into a body which has at first the

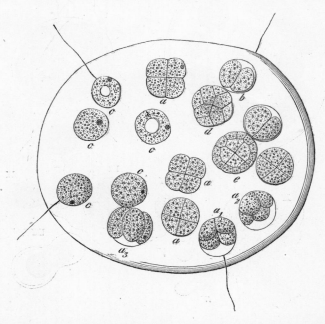

FIG. 17. *Eudorina elegans.* A coenobium in the act of forming daughter-coenobia, and with the gelatinous envelope of the coenobium swollen. The cilia are only visible here and there, each cell of the coenobia having two. At *c* the cells are still undivided, at *b* they are divided into two, at *a* into four; a_1 and a_2 are seen obliquely from above, a_3 from the side; *d* and *e* are more advanced stages of division; in the state represented at *c* the daughter-coenobium is already a concave disk and eventually becomes a hollow sphere by the folding over and union of its edges.

shape of an hour-glass (*IV*) and by degrees contracts into a sphere (*V*), in which the two red corpuscles and the four cilia at the enlarged hyaline end may be seen for a short time only. The process of conjugation occupies a few minutes, and then the zygospore is a spherical cell with a cell-wall (*VI*), which lies resting for some time and changes its green colour to a brick-red. If the dried spores, which have in the meantime increased considerably in size, are put into water, they begin to germinate after twenty-four hours; the outer layer of the cell-wall bursts, an inner layer protrudes, and is seen to contain two to three large swarm-cells; these finally escape, and after swarming for a short time become surrounded by a gelatinous envelope, and break up by repeated divisions into sixteen primordial cells, which now again form a family like Fig. 16, *I.*

Eudorina elegans[1], a species resembling *Pandorina* in appearance in many of the stages of its development, shows very great advance in the differentiation of the sexual elements. The coenobia are hollow bodies of ellipsoidal form with 16–32 (rarely only 8) cells enclosed in a common gelatinous envelope; each cell has two long cilia which protrude a long distance through holes in the envelope, a red eye-spot, and, in all the specimens which I have examined, a hyaline anterior extremity which is often rostrate. The plant multiplies itself copiously in the asexual manner, new coenobia being formed from the cells of the old ones, as in *Pandorina*. The cell-wall first swells up and separates from the protoplasm, which first divides into two parts, and then into four by a wall at right angles to the first. The young colony is next seen to separate into eight cells (Fig. 17, *c*), which are so disposed that the four middle ones form a cross; this arises from the circumstance that the walls of the quadrants are a little curved, and an anticlinal wall makes its appearance in each quadrant. Cells are then cut off from the

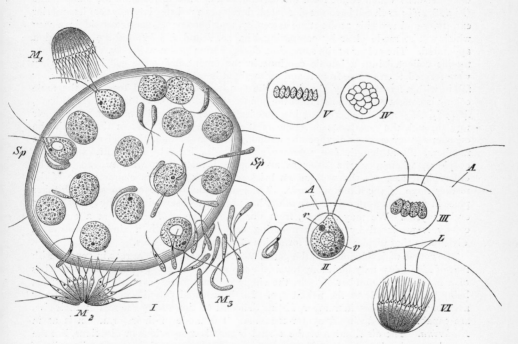

FIG. 18. *Eudorina elegans. I.* a female colony (coenobium). The walls between the several cells are swollen into a jelly. Each of the cells has two cilia, but they are not all visible. M_1, M_2, M_3 male coenobia; M_1 has just reached the female colony and caught its cilia in it, M_2 reached it earlier and its spermatozoids are separating from one another, M_3 has broken up into the separate spermatozoids, which are forcing their way into the gelatinous envelope of the female colony to lay themselves upon its cells (Sp. spermatozoids). *II.* mother-cell of a male colony; the swollen cell-wall is lifted off from the protoplasm; *A* outer surface of the coenobium, *r* red eye-spot, *v* contractile vacuole. *III.* a young male coenobium seen sideways, consisting of a cell-disk, the cells of which have been increased in number in *V.* *VI.* a mature male coenobium consisting of a bundle of spermatozoids, arranged like a bundle of cigars; each spermatozoid has two cilia at its extremity. The male coenobium is still enclosed in the swollen wall of the mother-cell, but is just setting itself in motion; it is subsequently set at liberty. *IV.* a young male colony seen from below.

outer side of the 'cross-cells' by periclinal walls, as is shown in Fig. 17, *d*, while the four inner cells do not again divide. In this way a disk of cells is formed,—the same arrangement of cells therefore which the coenobia of the genus *Gonium* present all their

---

[1] The following statements rest on observations made in 1878, and they agree entirely with the report on Goroshankin's Russian treatise (See Jahresbericht, 1875, p. 28), with the exception of some unimportant details.

life-long; but here the disk begins to deepen into a bowl, the edges draw together, close up and form a hollow sphere, which, as was said, consists of sixteen or thirty-two cells. When the several cells have developed their cilia, the young colony begins to move, and being set free by the dissolution of the envelope of the mother-colony, is able to produce new daughter-colonies in the evening of the day on which it was itself formed. Thus the coenobia have two distinct poles, one on which the four originally middle cells lie, and one where the edges of the disk unite in the formation of the sphere.

The sexual organs are dioeciously distributed, and the colonies are therefore male and female. The cells of the latter are only slightly distinguished from the vegetative cells. The cell-walls swell up, the several cells of the female colony, the *oospheres*, are thereby separated from each other, and are rather larger than the vegetative cells. The male colonies produce *spermatozoids*, the formation of which begins in the same manner as that of the asexually produced daughter-colonies. But in the case of the spermatozoids the daughter-cells which result from the division of a cell are disposed in the same plane (Fig. 18, *IV*) ; each cell becomes elongated, developes a red spot laterally near its anterior extremity and two cilia at the same extremity, and becomes a spermatozoid in a way which will be made clear by comparing Fig. 18, *I* and *III–VI*, and the explanation appended. The colour at the same time changes from green to yellow. The spermatozoids collected into a bundle continue in movement inside the cell in which they were formed, then escape from it and swim about in freedom as a male colony. If they fall in with a female colony, the cilia of the two become entangled together, the male colony is caught and held, and then the bundle of spermatozoids falls apart (see Fig 18, M_1, M_2, M_3), and the spermatozoids, now isolated, elongate still more and force their way through the gelatinous envelope of the female colony. When they reach the oospheres, they creep and grope about among them and attach themselves to them in numbers, till at length one spermatozoid mingles its substance with that of an oosphere, whereupon the latter as an oospore invests itself with two coats. The chlorophyll assumes the well-known brick-red colour, which is characteristic of the resting stage of the Chlorophyceae. The germination of the oospores, which takes place in the spring after their formation, has not been observed either by Goroshankin or by myself. We may assume, from our knowledge of *Volvox*, that a eudorina-colony is produced by each germinating oospore, and with a similar process of division to that displayed in the formation of the asexual colonies.

The course of development of the genus **Volvox**[1] itself, which agrees in general with that of *Eudorina*, may be briefly touched upon in this place. The coenobium consists of a much larger number of cells, the single volvox-spheres, even those of *V. minor*, being plainly visible to the naked eye. In the asexual colonies of *V. globator*, only a few of the cells, eight in number, distinguished at all times from the rest by their size, are capable of producing daughter-coenobia. The mode of their formation is as in *Eudorina*. The distribution of the sexual organs is monoecious or dioecious, but the sexual reproductive cells are always few in number among the many sterile cells of a coenobium. The bundle of spermatozoids is formed in the same way as in *Eudorina*; 32–64 spermatozoids proceed from one mother-cell. In shape, too, they are like those of *Eudorina*, but the cilia, according to Cohn, are inserted laterally, as in *Fucus*. The germination of the oospores is known only in *V. minor*. The outer coat of the spore bursts, and the protoplasm emerges surrounded by the swollen inner membrane. It divides at first into an eight-celled disk, which is transformed into a hollow sphere, the coenobium, in the manner described above in the case of *Eudorina*.

In the genera **Gonium** and **Stephanosphaera**[2] we may assume, with a high degree of probability, that the process of fertilisation is the same as in *Pandorina*, viz. by means of motile gametes of similar form.

---

[1] [Drude, Ueber Bau u. Entw. d. Kugelalgen *Volvox* (Abh. d. naturw. Ges. z. Dresden 1882).

[2] Hieronymus, G., Ueber *Stephanosphaera pluvialis*, Cohn (Cohn's Beitr. z. Biol. d. **Pflanz.** Vol. IV).]

If, in conclusion, we compare the mode of proceeding in the case of *Pandorina* with that in *Eudorina* and *Volvox*, it appears that the differences are connected chiefly with the form of the fertilising organs. Of the small coenobia in *Pandorina*, the cells of which become gametes, some are male, others female; therefore it is most probable that the gametes from one and the same coenobium do not conjugate together; in like manner the bundles of spermatozoids in *Eudorina* and *Volvox* are simply small male coenobia and are strikingly distinct from the female. In *Volvox* there is the further complication that most of the cells in a coenobium remain sterile and do not become sexual.—The term 'coenobium' is applied in one sense in the case of the Volvocineae and in another in that of the Hydrodictyeae (see the next section). It has been shown that the coenobia of *Volvox* are not formed by combination of originally separate cells, but by division of a single cell. The term admits of justification, if we bring into the comparison such Volvocineae as *Chlamydomonas*, which live as single isolated cells and agree entirely in structure with a cell of a coenobium of *Volvox*; the expression therefore is properly only comparative.

3. PROTOCOCCACEAE.

Under the name Protococcaceae we include a number of unicellular fresh-water Algae, which fall naturally into two sections, the Hydrodictyeae, in which several cells, originally separate, unite to form cell-families (*coenobia* or colonies), but have not, like the Volvoc ineae, the power of movement, and the Eremobiae, in which the isolated unicellular individuals live apart from one another often in the cavities of other plants, living in but not on their host ('Raumparasitismus.')

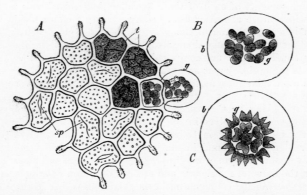

FIG. 19. *Pediastrum granulatum* (magn. 400 times). *A* a disk of cell adhering to one another; at *g* the innermost layer of the wall of a cell is just issuing from the cell, and contains the daughter-cells formed by division of the green protoplasm; at *t* various states of division of the cells; *sp* slits in the walls of cells which have discharged their contents. *B* the inner lamella of the wall of the mother-cell disengaged from the cell and much enlarged, *b* contains the daughter-cells *g*, which are in lively swarming motion. *C* the same family of cells four hours and a half after its birth, four hours after the small cells have come to rest; they have arranged themselves into a disk, which is already beginning to develope into such a one as *A*. After A. Braun.

a. HYDRODICTYEAE [1]. The genera **Pediastrum** and **Hydrodictyon** may be taken as representatives of this group. They have a sexual mode of reproduction, actually observed as yet only in *Hydrodictyon*, and an asexual. *Pediastrum* consists of

---

[1] On *Pediastrum*, &c. see Braun, Die Verjüngung in der Natur 1857, and, Algarum unicellularium genera nova vel minus cognita. Leipzig 1855.—Pringsheim, Ueber die Dauerschwärmer des Wassernetzes (Monatsbericht der Berlin. Akad. Dec. 1860).—The conjugation of the gametes of Hydrodictyon was observed by Suppanetz.

roundish disks containing a large number of cells (Fig. 19), which are either connected with one another with no intercellular spaces, or form a perforated disk.

The coenobia in *Pediastrum* are propagated by the formation of a large number of swarm-cells in each cell, which move about for some time within the mother-cell, and coming to rest arrange themselves in a definite order, which varies according to the species ; they then increase in size together and eventually multiply again in the same way, as Fig. 19 shows. Certain smaller swarm-spores have also been observed, which escape from the mother-cell, and, to judge by *Hydrodictyon*, must certainly be gametes.—In *Hydrodictyon utriculatum*, which occurs here and there in wet ditches, the full-grown plant, the coenobium, consists of a sac-like net several centimetres long, formed of a large number of cylindrical cells with their ends so united together as to form 4–6-angled meshes. In the ordinary mode of reproduction the green contents of one of the cells of a net break up into 7000–20,000 swarm-cells ; these exhibit the usual swarming motion inside the mother-cell, and coming to rest at the end of half-an-hour arrange themselves in such a manner that when they elongate they produce a net of the original form, which is set free by the dissolution of the wall of the mother-cell, and in three or four weeks attains the size of the parent-plant. The green contents of other cells of a mature net, on the contrary, break up into 30,000–100,000 smaller swarm-cells, which escape from the mother-cell at once and as they escape conjugate in pairs, seldom more together. The *zygospores* move freely about for a longer time ; on coming to rest they become spherical in form, secrete a firm cell-wall, and can remain in a dry state for the space of some months, if not exposed to the light. They begin slowly to grow again after several months' rest. After they have reached a considerable size their contents break up into from two to four large zoospores, which coming to rest after some minutes assume a peculiar angular form, and increasing considerably in size put out horn-like processes. The green parietal contents of each of these so-called *polyhedra* break up once more into zoospores, which move about for from twenty to forty minutes inside a sac, which is the swollen inner membrane of the polyhedron and protrudes from it. When they come to rest these cells arrange themselves within the sac, which eventually disappears, into a very small sac-like net composed of from 200–300 cells, which resembles in other respects the ordinary nets and gradually grows to their size. In many polyhedra smaller and more numerous zoospores are produced, which however unite in the same way to form a net.

b. Of the free-living Protococcaceae which do not form united colonies one species may be mentioned, which lives in the cavities of the tissues of other plants and has been recently and carefully investigated by Klebs[1]. **Chlorochytrium Lemnae** is a unicellular Alga that is found in the intercellular spaces of *Lemna trisulca*. Each individual, without previously multiplying by bipartition, produces zoospores which escape from the tissue of the *Lemna* and are enclosed in a gelatinous envelope. These zoospores are *gametes* and conjugate inside the gelatinous vesicle ; the *zygozoospores*, which have four cilia, escape into the water, and after swimming about there for a short time settle on the epidermis of *Lemna trisulca*, and always on the boundary line of two epidermal cells. Here they come to rest, invest themselves with a membrane, and put out a colourless process which thrusts apart the walls of the epidermal cells ; eventually the protoplasm of the zygospore passes into the process. This proceeding is repeated several times in the course of the period of vegetation. During the winter the chlorochytrium-plants inside a *Lemna* become resting cells, which in the ensuing spring again produce gametes.—Many Protococcaceae besides *Chlorochytrium* live within other plants and are well known ; **Phyllobium dimorphum** may serve as an example of them. This Alga is found in the tissue of the vascular bundles of the leaves of *Ajuga reptans* and other plants, but especially in *Lysimachia Nummularia*.

---

[1] Beiträge zur Kenntn. niederer Algenformen (Bot. Zeit. 1881, p. 249 ff.).

Its resting cells (compare *Chlorochytrium*) produce zoospores, some smaller, *micro-zoospores*, others larger, *macrozoospores*, which differ from each other in size only and perish if they remain isolated. They must conjugate with one another to bring about the commencement of a new generation ; a small male cell unites with a larger female cell, and their union produces a *zygozoospore*, which however has but two cilia because the small gamete with its cilia is swallowed up in the larger. If one of these zygozoospores, which retain the power of movement for some time, encounters a leaf of *Lysimachia*, it enters by a stoma and puts out a germinating shoot, which thrusts apart the cells of the leaf and reaches the foliar vascular bundles ; there it developes between the spiral elements, and its protoplasm gathers in its anterior extremity, which is now separated by a septum from the empty portion and developes into a new *Phyllobium*. Besides these gametes *Phyllobium* possesses also zoospores which are produced asexually in smaller resting cells, but which may be wanting.

As regards the mode of life of these endophytic Algae, we cannot attribute to them any form of parasitism that implies the receiving of nutriment from the host, for these Protococcaceae contain abundance of chlorophyll and can take up inorganic substances from the surrounding water ; moreover they grow quite as well inside dead plants, and appear to do no harm to their host ; they seek rather a sheltered place of growth and are therefore called by Klebs 'Raumparasiten.' (Compare the endophytic Algae of some of the *Muscineae* and of *Azolla*.)

To the above may be appended a brief notice of the PALMELLACEAE, a group of Algae the course of whose development is little known ; stages in the life of Confervoideae and Volvocineae resemble forms of the genus *Palmella* and have been supposed to be genera and species of the Palmellaceae. The Palmellaceae are like the simpler forms of the Protococcaceae in appearance, but their cell-walls produce a mucilage and their cells multiply by bipartition ; to them belong *Pleurococcus* (see under the Volvocineae), *Palmella*, *Hydrurus* consisting of slimy branching filaments which grow in mountain streams, and some others.

4. CONFERVOIDEAE.

The name Confervoideae or Confervaceae (Chlorosporeae) is given to certain Algae living mostly in fresh water in which the thallus is either a cell-filament or a cell-surface. Of the latter kind are the Ulvaceae, in which the thallus is either a single layer of cells, as in *Monostroma*, or a double layer, as in *Ulva*, and is often of some extent. The two layers of cells not unfrequently separate from one another, and the thallus thus becomes hollow (*Enteromorpha*). In the rest of the Chlorosporeae the thallus is a simple or branched row of cells ; if a number of filaments growing close together unite with one another, as in *Coleochaete*, they form a disk-shaped thallus which grows at its margin. In many of the plants belonging to this group, *Stigeoclonium* for instance, *Ulothrix*, *Ulva* and others, the thallus separates into isolated cells which resemble the genus *Protococcus*, or the cell-walls becoming largely mucilaginous the cells swell out into a spherical form and separate from one another, and thus assume the condition and appearance of a *Palmella*[1]. The cells thus isolated and imbedded in a jelly multiply by division. But these cells, to take the instance of the palmella-state of *Stigeoclonium*, do not produce a new *Stigeoclonium*

---

[1] Cienkowaki, Über d. Palmellaceen-Zustand von *Stigeoclonium* (Bot. Zeit. 1876).

directly, but swarm-spores which develope each into a new Stigeoclonium. *Zoospores* as asexual organs of reproduction are found in all the better known members of the group, though in some (*Sphaeroplea*) they only occur in the germination of the oospores.

The mode of sexual reproduction is not yet known in all the Confervoideae. In some it consists in the conjugation of motile cells of similar form (*gametes*), in other words there is an *isogamous* union of gametes; in others the gametes are distinguished into a smaller male motile-cell or *spermatozoid*, and into a larger non-motile female cell, the *oosphere*, which waits in a cell of the filament that produced it for the impregnation which makes it an oospore. Both modes of fertilisation may occur within one and the same subdivision; in the Ulothricaceae, for example, the genus *Ulothrix* is isogamous, *Cylindrocapsa* is oogamous.

A larger number of fresh-water Algae, and among them species the most widely distributed and most striking in appearance, belong to this group. They are evidently nearly related to the Siphoneae on one hand and to the Conjugatae on the other. The group called by Schmitz Siphonocladiaceae, to which the common Alga of fresh and salt water, *Cladophora*, belongs, is intermediate between the Confervoideae and the Siphoneae; they resemble the latter in the character of the protoplasm with its many small nuclei, but their thallus is multicellular. The power possessed by the thallus of breaking up into isolated Protococcus-like cells and of vegetating in this condition recalls the Protococcaceae, of which *Hydrodictyon*, for example, has the like cell-structure to *Cladophora*. The resemblance to the Conjugatae is rather one of habit; these Conjugatae, as has been already said, are a rather peculiar section of the Algae, though not quite so peculiar as the Characeae.

Certain families will now be described as examples of the course of development in the Chlorosporeae.

a. ULOTHRICACEAE. The thallus in this family consists of unbranched cell-filaments; each cell contains a chlorophyll-band running round the cell. The genus *Ulothrix*[1] has isogamous, *Cylindrocapsa* oogamous fertilisation.

Ulothrix has two kinds of swarm-spores; small ones with two cilia (*microzoospores*, which are gametes), and larger asexual ones with four cilia, the *macrozoospores*. The latter are formed singly, or two or four together, from the protoplasm of a cell of a filament; they escape through a hole in the cell-wall, enclosed in a vesicle which is the innermost layer of the wall of the mother-cell. Four zoospores, for instance, are formed by successive bipartition of the protoplasm of a cell, the central vacuole remaining behind as a hyaline bladder, as in many other similar cases. The zoospores are set free by absorption of the enveloping membrane; they are pear-shaped bodies, with four cilia at the colourless pointed extremity which in motion is the forward end, and with a red spot, the so-called eye-spot, on the side. The zoospores, when come to rest, fix themselves by their colourless extremity, secrete a cell-wall, and grow into a new Ulothrix-filament. The sexual zoospores, the *gametes*, are all of the same shape and size, and have only two cilia. They conjugate in pairs, the cilia being first of all entangled together; then they place themselves close to and finally unite with one another, the process beginning with the hyaline pointed ends. The *zygospore* thus formed moves

---

[1] Dodel-Port, Die Kraushaar-Alge, *Ulothrix zonata* u. ihre geschlechtliche Fortpflanzung (Pringsheim's Jahrb. f. wiss. Bot. X. p. 142).

about for some time by aid of its four cilia, then comes to rest, is invested with a cell-wall, and passes through a period of rest, during which it increases considerably in size. In the next period of growth, a number of swarm-spores are produced from the zygospore, but their escape from it has not yet been observed. The gametes of *Ulothrix* can also germinate without conjugation, in the same way as the macrozoospores, but they produce somewhat slenderer plants : the difference of sex is therefore not yet distinctly marked.—**Cylindrocapsa** has *oogamous* fertilisation[1]; the contents of a cell of a filament which swells out into a spherical shape is rounded off into an oosphere ; the small reddish male gametes (*spermatozoids*) make their way to it through an opening in the cell-wall and effect the fertilisation, no doubt by the coalescence of one or more of the gametes with the oosphere.—The same mode of fertilisation is found in the following group, which is composed of only one genus and one species ; it is represented by—

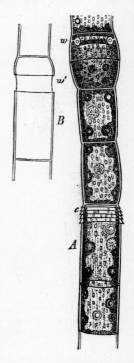

b. **Sphaeroplea annulina**[2], which consists in its fully developed state of cylindrical filaments divided by transverse walls into very long cells, in which green protoplasm encloses rows of large vacuoles and thus forms an encircling ring. In their vegetative state the cells are all alike; it is only when sexual reproduction begins that any difference appears, and then some cells produce only spermatozoids, others only oospheres ; a large number of the latter are formed in each cell by the breaking up of its contents after certain previous changes into roundish portions, each of which is marked by a hyaline spot. The *spermatozoids* are also formed in unusually large numbers by division of the contents of a cell, which has previously assumed a yellowish brown colour. In both kinds of sexual cells a number of holes are formed in the cell-wall by absorption, and through these holes the spermatozoids issue forth, and enter in crowds into the cells in which the oospheres are lying. To outward appearance therefore the antheridia and oogonia are alike, but the oospheres and spermatozoids are very unlike ; the latter are elongated, club-shaped bodies, with two cilia at their pointed end. The oospores invest themselves with a thick warted cell-wall, and assume a brick-red colour ; their further development begins in the following spring with the division of their red-coloured contents into a number of primordial cells, which escape from the oospore, move about by means of two cilia, come to rest, and then germinate. In this process the

FIG. 20. Portion of a filament of *Oedogonium* ; at *w* the cushion of cellulose, which in Fig. *B* has lengthened into a piece of the cell-wall *w'*; *c* the 'caps,' i.e. the projecting remains of the earlier cell-walls which split each time by an annular fissure on the outside of the cushion.

short fusiform cell grows out at both ends into a tube, in which the posterior and anterior extremities are exactly alike, and which shows therefore no distinction of base and apex. After considerable increase in size transverse septa appear and the tube becomes a filament composed of similar cells. The formation of (asexual) swarm-spores, with the exception of those produced by the oospores, is unknown in *Sphaeroplea*.

---

[1] Cienkowski, Zur Morphol. der Ulothricaceen (Mélanges biologiques de l'acad. de St. Petersbourg, T. IX. p. 534).

[2] Cohn, Ann. d. sc. nat. 4ᵉᵐᵉ série, T. V. 1856, p. 287.—[Rauwenhoff, *Sphaeroplea annulina* (Sitzgber. d. k. Akad. d. Wiss. z. Amsterdam, 26 Mai, 1883).—Heinricher, E., Zur Kenntn. d. Algengattung *Sphaeroplea* (Ber. d. deutsch. Bot. Ges. 1883, p. 433).]

c. The OEDOGONIEAE[1] include at present only the two genera **Oedogonium** and **Bulbochaete**. The species, which are numerous in *Oedogonium*, abound in fresh waters, and are fastened by an organ of attachment at their lower end to firm bodies, chiefly submerged plants. The thallus consists of unbranched filaments in *Oedogonium*, of branched ones in *Bulbochaete*, and the cells increase in length by intercalary growth : in *Bulbochaete* the terminal cells are prolonged into hyaline bristles. Increase in length of the cylindrical cells commences with the formation of an annular cushion of cellulose on the inner side of the cell close beneath its upper transverse wall (Fig. 20, *w*). The cell-wall parts at this spot by an annular split, and the ring of cellulose stretches, and thus a broad transverse zone is intercalated into the wall of the cell (Fig. 20, *B, w'*); this process is repeated always close beneath the older, short upper portion of the cell in such a manner

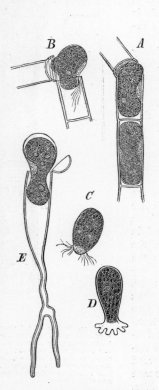

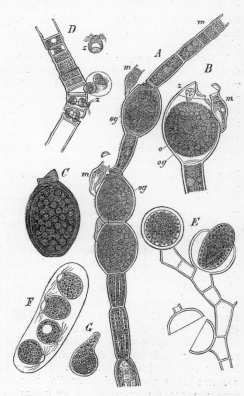

FIG. 21. *Oedogonium*, development of the swarm-spores (zoogonidia), (magn. 350 times). *A, B* swarm-spores being formed from older filaments. *C* free swarm-spore in motion. *D* commencement of germination. *E* a swarm-spore formed from the entire contents of a young plant the product of a germinating swarm-spore. After Pringsheim.

FIG. 22. *A Oedogonium ciliatum*, middle portion of a sexual filament (magn. 250 times) with an antheridium *m* at the upper end, two oogonia with oospores *og*, and the dwarf male *m*. *B* oogonium of *Oedogonium ciliatum* at the moment of fertilisation, *o* the oosphere, *z* the spermatozoid making its way in, *m* the dwarf male. *C* ripe oospore of the same plant. *D* piece of the male-filament of *Oed. gemelliparum*, *z* spermatozoids. *E* branch of a young plant of *Bulbochaete intermedia* after the winter's rest, with one oogonium above still containing the spore and one which has just discharged it. *F* the four zoogonidia produced from an oospore. *G* zoogonidia of an oospore come to rest. After Pringsheim.

that the new pieces form small projections at the upper end of the cell (Fig. 20, *A, c*), and give it the appearance of being made up of caps set one over another ; the lower end of

---

[1] Pringsheim, Morphologie der Oedogonieen in Jahrb. f. wiss. Bot. Bd. I.—De Bary, Ueber die Algengattungen *Oedogonium* u. *Bulbochaete*, 1854.—Juranyi, Beitr. zur Morphol. d. Oedogonieen (Pringsheim's Jahrb. Bd. IX).

the cell appears to be enclosed in a long sheath, the lower portion of the old cell-wall, and this portion in a cell so elongating is always separated from the upper portion which bears the caps by a transverse septum. In *Bulbochaete* the growth of all the shoots, even of the first that proceed from the germinating spores, and consequently the cell-multiplication also, is confined to the division of the basal cells, so that the cells of every shoot must be regarded as the basal cells of their lateral shoots. Each cell contains chlorophyll-corpuscles and a nucleus in a parietal layer of protoplasm. The swarm-spores, oogonia, and antheridia are formed from the cells of the filaments, which swell out into a more or less spherical shape only when oogonia are formed in them. The oospores remain at rest for a considerable time and give birth to swarm-spores (usually four in number) which produce asexual plants, that is plants producing only swarm-spores, from which similar plants proceed repeatedly, till at length the series is closed by the appearance of a sexual generation which forms oospores ; but the sexual plants, the female especially, produce swarm-spores as well. The sexual plants are either monoecious or dioecious, in many species the female plant produces peculiar bodies, termed *androspores*, which give rise to very small male plants (dwarf males) ; in *Oe. diplandrum* the androspores proceed from male plants. Several cycles of generation or only one may be completed in a period of vegetation. A *swarm-spore* is formed in an ordinary cell of a filament, sometimes even in the first cell (Fig. 21, *E*), by contraction of the whole of the cell-protoplasm ; the cell then parts across into two very unequal portions (as in the division of the cells), and the swarm-spore is set free (Fig 21, *A, B, E*), enveloped at first in a hyaline vesicle. Its hyaline end—the anterior end in the moving state—is furnished with a circlet of many cilia. This end lay laterally in the mother-cell, and when movement ceases it becomes the lower fixed end and developes into a rhizoid. The direction of growth therefore of the young plant is perpendicular to that of the mother-cell. The *spermatozoids* are similar in form to the swarm-spores, but much smaller (Fig. 22, *B, z*), and move about like them by means of a circlet of cilia. The mother-cells of the spermatozoids are cells of a filament, but shorter and less rich in chlorophyll than the vegetative cells ; they lie isolated or as many as twelve together one above the other in the filament. In most species every such mother-cell (antheridial cell) divides into two similar special mother-cells, each of which produces a spermatozoid ; the spermatozoids escape by the rupture of the mother-cell as in the case of the swarm spores (Fig. 22, *D*). The androspores from which the dwarf males proceed are formed in mother-cells like those of the spermatozoids, but there is no formation of special mother-cells ; they settle after swarming on a definite spot of the female plant, on the oogonium or near it, and there germinate and produce at once the antheridial cells and spermatozoids in them (Fig. 22, *A, B, m, m*). The *oogonium* is always developed from the upper daughter-cell of a vegetative cell which has just divided, and which enlarges immediately after division into a spherical or ovoid form. In *Bulbochaete* the oogonium is always the lowest cell of a fertile branch ; this is not opposed to the law of growth stated above, since the mother-cell of a branch is at the same time its basal cell ; the oogonium of *Bulbochaete* is never the first cell of a branch, for this always developes into a bristle. The oogonium first becomes filled more full of cell-contents than the other cells ; then just before fertilisation the protoplasm contracts and forms the oosphere, as in *Vaucheria*, the chlorophyll-granules being crowded together in its interior ; the part of the oosphere which is turned towards the place where the oogonium opens contains only hyaline protoplasm, and this is where impregnation takes place. The opening of the oogonium is affected in a variety of ways, in many species of *Oedogonium* and in all of *Bulbochaete* an oval hole is formed in the side of the cell-wall, through which the colourless portion of the oosphere protrudes in the form of a papilla in order to receive the spermatozoid. In other species (Fig. 21, *A, B*) the oogonium breaks across, as the cells do for the release of swarm-spores, and then the filament with its usually straight row of cells appears as if broken at the spot. From the lateral aperture there issues a colourless mucilage which forms itself under the eye

of the observer into an open beak-like canal (Fig. 22, *B*, *z*) through which the spermatozoid enters and coalesces with the hyaline portion of the protoplasm of the oosphere,
the two protoplasmic bodies and the nuclei uniting with one another. In *Oe. diplandrum*
the large spermatozoids display amoeboid movements, and creep round about the
oogonium till they reach the canal, through which they then slowly make their way.
Immediately after fertilisation the oospore invests itself with a cell-wall which like the
cell-contents is eventually coloured brown ; but in *Bulbochaete* the contents of the
oospore are a beautiful red. The oospore remains enclosed in the oogonium, which

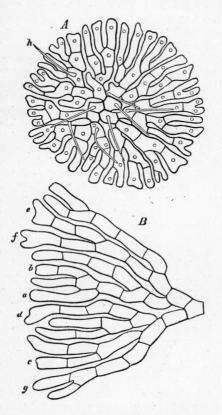

separates from the adjoining cells in the
filament and falls to the ground, where
the oospore passes through its period of
rest. When it awakes to new activity,
which may be within the vegetative period
in which it was formed, it does not itself
develope into a new plant, but its contents
issue forth from within the cell-wall
wrapped in a thin layer of jelly and divide
into four zoospores, which are set free by
the dissolution of the gelatinous envelope
and move actively about. After coming
to rest they grow each into a new plant.

d. The COLEOCHAETEAE[1] are distinguished from the Confervoideae which we
have been considering by the structure of
the oogonium, and by the peculiar formation of the fructification, which recalls that
of the Florideae. Entrance to the oosphere
is secured here, not as in *Oedogonium* and
Vaucheria by a short beak, but by a long
hair-like process from the oogonium, which
is open at the upper end. Fertilisation
takes place by means of spermatozoids
formed in special small branches or in
cells of the thallus which have undergone
division. The oospore becomes invested
by tubes which are branches from the
thallus, as in the cystocarp of many of the
Florideae, and then passes into the resting
stage. In the next vegetative period it
becomes by division of its contents a
parenchymatous body in which numerous
swarm-spores are formed, one in each
cell.

FIG. 23. *A Coleochaete soluta*, an asexual plant (magn. 250
times). *B* portion of a similar disk. The letters *a—g* show the
successive dichotomies of the terminal cells. After Pringsheim.

The Coleochaeteae are small chlorophyll-green fresh-water Algae (1–2 mm. in breadth),
composed of branched rows of cells. They are found in stagnant or slowly-moving water
fixed to submerged parts of plants, such as species of *Equisetum*, and form circular
closely attached disks or cushions ; their chlorophyll is attached to parietal plates or
isolated masses ; the genus *Coleochaete* (sheath-hair) derives its name from the circumstance that certain cells of the thallus form lateral colourless bristles which are
enclosed in narrow sheaths (Fig. 23, *A, h*). Comparison of the phenomena of growth
in the different species shows that there are two extreme cases, but these are connected

[1] Pringsheim, Beitr. z. Morphol. u. System. der Algen, III. die Coleochaeten (Jahrb. f. wiss.
Bot. II. Bd.).

by intermediate forms ; one extreme is exemplified in *C. divergens*, which as it de-velopes from the spore produces at first irregularly branched, creeping, segmented filaments, from which spring ascending branches that are also irregularly branched and segmented ; the thallus has no definite form. *C. pulvinata*, on the contrary, has the shape of a hemispherical cushion ; the segmented filaments which are the result of germination branch in one plane somewhat irregularly, but on the whole taking the form of a disk ; from them rise ascending, articulated branches, which are themselves again branched, and form the cushion. In the following species there are no ascending branches, but the others, which cling closely to the substratum, form a more or less regular disk, as in *C. irregularis*, where irregular ramifications lying in one plane fill up by degrees all the intervals, so that a layer of cells is formed almost without interstices ; on the other hand, in *C. soluta* (Fig. 23) dichotomous branching with corresponding cell-division begins in the two first daughter-cells of the germinating spore, so that a complete disk is early formed with radial bifurcations, which either lie loosely beside each other or are packed closely together. In the above species the branches arise laterally from cells of the thallus, never from the terminal cell of a branch ; in *C. soluta* dichotomy appears with the regular disk-like centrifugal growth, and this structure reaches its highest perfection in *C. scutata* ; the first cells produced in ger-mination remain laterally connected from the beginning and do not form isolated branches ; the young circular disk enlarges by growth at its circumference, the marginal cells dividing by radial and tangential walls. This growth may be reduced to the type of the foregoing ; the primary laterally united branches grow out radially with equal rapidity and become segmented by transverse walls (here tangential), whilst the expansion of the terminal cell of each radial row with its consequent radial segmen-tation corresponds with a dichotomy. The prevailing rule in the previously mentioned species, that only the terminal cell of a branch is divided by transverse walls, finds its expression in *C. scutata* in the marginal cells only of the disk being divided by tangential walls.

The reproduction of *Coleochaete* is effected by asexual *swarm-spores* and by sexually produced resting *oospores*. The oospores do not produce new plants directly, but several swarm-spores. The alternation of generation is as follows : the first swarm-spores, which issue on the commencement of vegetation in spring from the cells of the oospore-fructifications of the preceding year, produce only asexual plants, that is plants which produce only swarm-cells ; after a longer or shorter series of asexual generations there arises a sexual generation which is either monoecious or dioecious according to the species. One oospore is produced by fertilisation in the oogonium, and is enclosed in a peculiar cortical layer of cellular tissue ; the oospore developes into a fructification formed of parenchymatous tissue, and from its cells the first swarm-spores issue forth in the next vegetative period. Swarm-spores (Fig. 24, *D*) may be formed in any vegetative cell of the Coleochaeteae, but in *C. pulvinata* chiefly in the terminal cells of the branches. They are always the product of the whole of the contents of the mother-cell, and escape through a circular hole in the cell-wall. The *oogonium* is always the terminal cell of a branch, in *C. scutata* therefore the terminal cell of a radial row (Nägeli). The details of its formation are liable, according to the growth of the plant, to many though subordinate modi-fications. We will examine these details more closely in one species, *C. pulvinata* (Fig. 24). The terminal cell of a branch swells out and elongates at the same time into a narrow tube (*og* to the left in *A*), which then opens (*og″* to the right in *A*) and emits a colourless mucilage. The protoplasm of the swollen portion of the cell con-tains chlorophyll and forms the oosphere, in which a nucleus is visible. *Antheridia* are formed at the same time by the outgrowth in adjacent cells of two or three protu-berances from each (*an* in *A*), which are separated off by transverse-walls ; each flask-shaped cell thus formed is an antheridium, and its entire contents form a spermatozoid (*z*) of elliptical shape and with two cilia, which moves about like a swarm-spore; its entrance into the oogonium has not yet been observed. The result of fertilisation is that the contents of the oogonium clothe themselves with a cell-wall of their own, the oospore thus formed increases considerably in size, and the formation of the cortical layer (*r*) of the oogonium commences by the upward growth of branches from the supporting cell (*A, og″*); these branches cling closely to the oogonium, and send out branches of their own which also attach themselves closely to the oogonium and divide transversely; twigs also from other branches join in the formation (*B*). All this takes place in the period from May to July: while the contents of the rest of the cells of the plant eventually disappear, the rind of the fructification assumes a dark brown colour. The further development of the fructification begins in the ensuing spring; a parenchymatous tissue is formed in it by repeated bipartition of its contents; the cortical layer

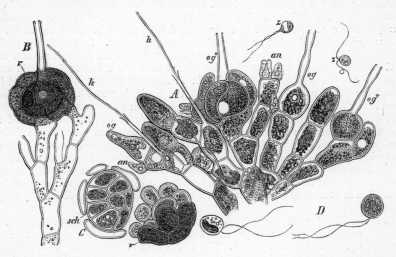

FIG. 24. *A* part of a fertile thallus of *Coleochaete pulvinata* (magnified 350 times). *B* ripe oogonium in its rind. *C* germinating fructifications of *C. pulvinata*, in the cells of which the swarm-spores are formed. *D* swarm-spores (*B—D* magn. 280 times). After Pringsheim.

bursts and is cast off (Fig. 24, *C*), and from each cell of the fruit proceeds an ordinary swarm-cell, which in its turn gives rise to an asexual plant. In *C. scutata*, which shows most variation from this course of development, the oogonia which are becoming invested with their cortical layer lie in the plane of the disk, and the antheridia are formed by division of cells of the disk into four.

Pringsheim has drawn attention to various points of affinity between the Coleochaeteae, Florideae, and Characeae, in his essay quoted above.

The Conjugatae and the Characeae must now be examined in connection with the Confervoideae.

CONJUGATAE.

The Conjugatae[1] consist of cells of limited growth, which multiply repeatedly and to an unlimited extent by bipartition; the cells thus formed live isolated or remain united in rows. The chlorophyll in these plants has a striking appearance, the corpuscles being disposed in parietal bands, in axile plates, or in pairs of stellate bodies. Conjugation takes place between ordinary vegetative cells, the contents of which coalesce in various ways. The body thus formed invests itself with a new cell-wall and

---

[1] De Bary, Unters. über die Fam. d. Conjugaten, Leipzig, 1858.

becomes a *zygospore*, which germinates after resting for some time; it differs essentially in form from the vegetative cell. There are no brood-cells. All the species of this group are fresh-water Algae.

De Bary distinguishes the following families :—

1. The MESOCARPEAE consist of cylindrical cell-filaments with an axile chlorophyll-plate, which as they lie parallel to one another either put out conjugating processes toward one another, or touch each other in spots where the filament is bent like a knee : the walls at the point of contact being absorbed, a broad canal for conjugation is thus formed, in which the protoplasm of the two conjugating cells collects ; and the space in which conjugation is effected being shut off by the formation of two or four transverse septa, its contents become a *zygospore*. This mode of formation obviously recalls the similar proceeding in the case of the Zygomycetes. The germination of the

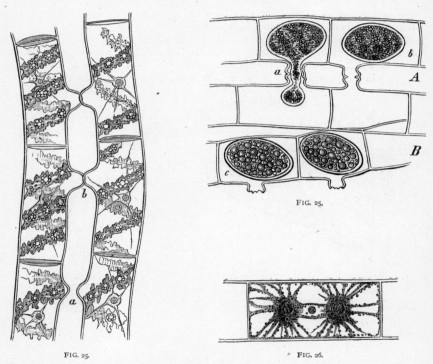

FIG. 25.   FIG. 26.

FIG. 25. *Spirogyra longata.* On the left, cells of two filaments preparing for conjugation ; they show the spiral chloropyll-bands, with grains of starch disposed here and there in them in rings, and small drops of oil. The nucleus in each cell is surrounded by protoplasm, threads of which pass to the cell-wall. At *b* preparations for conjugation. *A* to the right in the act of conjugating ; at *a* the protoplasm of one cell is just going over into the other, at *b* the two protoplasmic bodies have united ; in *B* the young zygospores are already invested with a cell-wall.

FIG. 26. A cell of *Zygnema cruciatum* with two stellate chlorophyll-corpuscles united by a bridge of colourless protoplasm, in which lies the nucleus.

zygospore produces directly a new cellular filament, in which the extremity that remains in the spore is the base, and the free extremity the apex ; but this distinction is not maintained, since all the cells are alike and multiply by growth and transverse division. The genera *Mesocarpus*, *Craterospermum*, and *Staurospermum* belong to this family.

2. The ZYGNEMEAE also consist of cylindrical cellular filaments with straight or spiral parietal chlorophyll-bands or stellate chlorophyll-corpuscles in pairs (Fig. 26). In conjugation two filaments place themselves parallel with one another, and their cells put out processes toward one another (Fig. 25), which meet and by dissolution of the walls

[2]   E

at the meeting-point form a somewhat narrow canal.   Since several cells of a filament usually conjugate simultaneously, they form altogether a ladder-like structure, in which the conjugation-canals represent the rungs.   When the canals are formed, the protoplasmic bodies of the two cells contract, and one of them glides over to the other through the canal and unites with it to form a rounded *zygospore*, which invested with a thick many-shelled wall remains lying within the much broader mother-cell-wall and does not germinate till it has passed through a long period of rest (Fig. 27) : here too there is at first a distinction of base and apex in the young plant, but this distinction disappears at a later period, as in the Mesocarpeae, since all cells are alike in form and behaviour during the time of vegetation.   The genera *Zygnema, Spirogyra, Mougeotia, Sirogonium, Zygogonium* belong to this family.

3. The Desmidieae[1] consist of cells that live isolated, or less frequently in rows which readily break up into separate cells and are embedded in mucilage.   The cells are cylindric or fusiform, and sometimes have horn-like processes ; or their general outline is circular or elliptic, divided by a deep constriction into symmetrical halves.   Where there is no constriction, the chlorophyll-body in the interior of the cell is symmetrically halved, or else the symmetry is indicated by the so-called amylum-bodies and the distribution of the starch-grains.   It is in accordance with this symmetrical formation that in the vegetative multiplication of the cells (individuals) a dividing wall appears in the plane of symmetry (or within the constriction when there is one) ; this

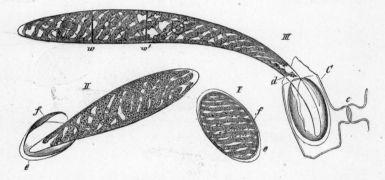

FIG. 27. Germination of *Spirogyra jugalis.* *I* resting zygospore. *II* commencement of germination of the same. *III* older germ-plant from a zygospore which was inclosed in the cell *c* of a filament, and in which the conjugation-tube is still to be seen ; *e* outer membrane of the spore, *f* yellowish-brown layer, *g* third and innermost layer of the cell-wall of the spore forming the germtube; *ww'* the first transverse walls of the germ-tube, the hinder extremity of which *d* grows out into a narrow process. After Pringsheim in Flora, 1852, No. 30.

wall parts into two lamellae, and thus the halves are separated ; a new half grows out at the place of separation and a new individual is thus formed complete and symmetrical like the original one.   The mode of formation of zygospores is the same as in the Zygnemeae ; but in the simplest cases, as in *Cylindrocystis* and *Mesotaenium* and others, where the conjugating individuals are of very simple form, the conjugation appears to be nothing more than a coalescence comparable with the pairing of the gametes of *Pandorina*, &c.   The zygospore either germinates directly or its contents produce two or more daughter-cells, each of which exhibits the vegetative multiplication described above.

These processes may be illustrated by the case of **Cosmarium Botrytis**, as portrayed by De Bary in Fig. 28.   The cells live isolated, and are divided by a deep constriction

---

[1] There is really no difference but that of habit between the Desmideae and Zygnemeae, and not that in all species ; the two families therefore cannot properly be separated from one another. [Fischer, A., Ueber d. Zelltheilung d. Closterien (Bot. Ztg. 1883, p. 225).]

into symmetrical halves (*X*), and are also compressed perpendicularly to the plane of constriction (*I*, *a*). In each symmetrical lobe are two amylum-bodies and eight chlorophyll-
plates, which curve and converge in pairs and run from two points of union to the wall.
In cell-multiplication the narrowest part of the constriction elongates a little, while the
external thicker layer of the cell-wall opens by a circular fissure. Then the two lobes
of the cell appear to have moved apart from one another and to be connected by a
short canal, whose wall is a continuation of the inner layer of the cell-wall of the two
lobes. Soon a transverse wall appears in the connecting canal, which divides the cell
into two daughter-cells, each of which is a half of the mother-cell. The transverse wall,
at first simple, now separates into two lamellae, which at once become convex towards
one another (*IX*, *h*). Each daughter-cell now possesses a small convex outgrowth
which increases in size and takes the form of a cell-lobe, so that each daughter-cell is
now composed of two symmetrical lobes (*X*). While the wall thus grows, the
chlorophyll-body of the older lobe also grows out into the new lobe. The two amylum-
bodies of the old cell-lobes elongate, become constricted, and divide each into two
bodies ; two of the four bodies pass over into the new lobes, and all four arrange

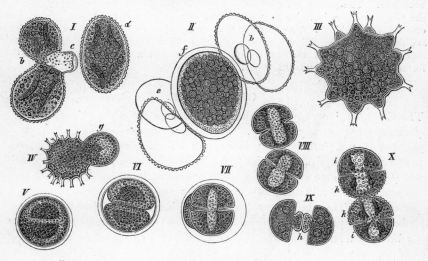

FIG. 28. *Cosmarium Botrytis. I—III* magn. 390 times, *IV—X* 190 times. After De Bary.

themselves in the former symmetrical manner. *Conjugation* takes place between pairs
of cells, which lie cross-wise enclosed in a thin jelly (*I*). Each of the two cells puts
out from its centre towards the other a conjugating process (*I*, *c*), and the two processes
meet and touch ; they are clothed with a delicate membrane, a continuation of the
inner layer of the cell-wall, the firm outer layer having burst asunder (*I*, *c*). The two
processes expand each into a hemispherical bladder and touch one another ; the wall that
separates them disappears, the contents unite in the broad canal thus formed, and the
protoplasm separates entirely from the cell-wall and contracts into a spherical body,
which now appears invested with a delicate gelatinous membrane (*II*, *f*) ; by its side
lie the empty cell-walls (*II*, *e*, *b*). The *zygospore* is now a round ball, and as it ripens
its cell-wall is differentiated into three layers, an outer and an inner colourless layer of
cellulose, and a middle layer which is firmer and brown. This stratified cell-wall now
forms spinous processes at several points on its surface, which are at first hollow, afterwards solid, and each of them produces a few smaller teeth at its extremity (*III*). The
starch-grains of the conjugated cells change in the zygospore into fatty substances.
At the commencement of germination the colourless inner layer of the cell-wall protrudes

through a broad fissure in the two outer layers (*IV*), and remains for a time as a thin-walled spherical body considerably larger than the zygospore itself. In it may be seen (*V*) imbedded in fatty protoplasm two chlorophyll-masses, which were distinguishable in the zygospore. The contents now contract and surround themselves with a new cell-wall (*V*), from which the former wall separates as a delicate vesicle. After a time the protoplasmic body becomes constricted in the middle, and separates into two hemispheres, each of which contains one of the two chlorophyll-bodies (*VI*). Each hemisphere is at first without a cell-wall and is again constricted; but this time the constriction does not reach to the middle, while the hemisphere changes its shape in other respects, and each finally appears as a symmetrically lobed cosmarium-cell (*VII*), which now assumes a proper cell-wall. The planes of the constrictions of both the cells cut the planes of division of the germ-cell produced from the zygospore at a right angle, and they are themselves also at right angles to one another; the two cells therefore lie across one another in the mother-cell. In each of them the contents arrange themselves in the manner above described; the wall of the mother-cell is absorbed, and the cells separate. All these proceedings are completed in from one to two days. The young cells, whose cell-wall is smooth on the outside, now divide in the usual manner, but the new lobes that are added are larger and rough on the outside (*VIII, IX, X*). The four daughter-cells of the two cells produced in germination are therefore of two different forms; two of them have equal, two unequal lobes; the latter yield always in division a cell with equal and a cell with unequal lobes, the former only cells with unequal lobes.

CHARACEAE.

The Characeae [1] occupy the highest place among the green Algae, and are not very closely allied to any of them. Their very complex structure gives them the appearance of small Cormophytes; their organs of fertilisation also show peculiarities of form and an amount of differentiation which we have not hitherto met with. Thread-like motile *spermatozoids* are formed in very peculiar *antheridia* (*globules*), and the oogonium is invested before fertilisation with five spirally twisted tubes, which spring from its pedicel-cell. The whole organ thus formed, that is, the *oosphere* with its enveloping tubes and the pedicel-cell, is termed the *oogonium* (*nucule*). The oosphere by fertilisation becomes a resting spore with a thick cell-wall, and in germination developes a *pro-embryo*, on which the sexual plant arises as a lateral shoot. Gonidia (swarm-spores &c.) are wanting, as they are in many species of *Vaucheria* and in the Conjugatae.

The Characeae are submerged water-plants, which are rooted in the ground and grow erect, attaining a height of one-tenth of a metre to a metre, and are rich in chlorophyll; their growth is slim, for the stems and leaves are not more than from one-half to two millimetres in thickness, and their structure is delicate, being strengthened sometimes by a deposit of lime on the surface of the plants. They are social plants and form close patches at the bottom of fresh-water and brackish lakes, ditches and streams; some grow in deep water, some in shallow, some in stagnant water and some in rapid streams; perennial species grow intermixed with annual.

---

[1] A. Braun, Ueber die Richtungsverhältnisse der Saftströme in den Zellen der Charen (Monatsber. der Berl. Akad. d. Wiss. 1852 u. 1853).—Pringsheim, Ueber die nacktfüssigen Vorkeime der Charen in his Jahrb. f. wiss. Bot. Bd. III. 1864.—Nägeli, Die Rotationsströmung der Charen (Beitr. z. wiss. Bot. Bd. III. 1860, p. 61).—Thuret, Sur les anthéridies des Cryptogames (Ann. d. sc. nat. 1851, T. XVI. p. 19).—Montagne, Multiplication des charagnes par division (Ann. d. sc. nat. 1852, T. XVIII. p. 65).—Göppert und Cohn in Bot. Zeit. 1849.—De Bary, Ueber die Befruchtung der Charen (Monatsber. d. Berl. Akad. 1874, Mai); and Zur Keimungsgeschichte der Charen (Bot. Zeit. 1875).

The species are many and are found in all parts of the world ; but they agree so closely with one another, that they may be all comprehended in two genera, *Chara* and *Nitella* ; these have been recently divided again each into two genera.

The germinating oospore does not produce a *sexual leafy plant* at once. At the apex of the oospore a small lenticular cell filled with clear finely granular protoplasm is divided off from a larger one which contains reserve food-material ; the latter is called by De Bary the *basal cell*, the former the first *nodal cell*, and from it the further development of the embryo plant proceeds. The basal cell suffers no further change beyond parting with its food-material ; the first nodal cell, on the other hand, divides by a vertical wall coinciding with the longitudinal axis of the oospore into two daughter-cells, each of which developes into a tube. One of these is the so-called *primary or main root* (Fig. 29, *w'*), the other the *pro-embryo*, which consists at first of a simple row of cells with limited apical growth. Two disk-like nodes are then formed in it, a rhizoid-forming-node (Fig. 29, *d*), and a stem-node (Fig. 29, *g*). The disk-shaped nodal cell is divided by longitudinal septa into two inner and six to eight peripheral cells. One of the latter, the first formed, is the growing-point of the Chara-plant, the others give rise to a few rudimentary leaves. Further details are given below.

The main shoot which bears the sexual organs has unlimited apical growth. It has an apical cell (Fig. 30, *t*) from which segments are cut off by transverse walls. Each segment is again divided by a transverse wall into two cells lying one above the other ; the lower of these (*g*) does not divide again, but becomes an internode, which may be 5–6 centimetres long ; the upper, while scarcely elongating at all, divides by a vertical wall into two halves, and in each half a whorl of peripheral cells (*b*, *b*) is formed by further successive (anticlinal) walls. From the node thus formed the leaves are developed, one from each of the peripheral cells, and the normal lateral twigs spring from the axil of the first or the first two leaves of the whorl. The development of the 4–10 leaves of the whorl repeats the processes of growth in the stem with some modifications ; but their apical growth is limited ; the apical cell ceases to divide after the formation of a definite number of cells, and grows into the usually pointed terminal cell of the leaf (Fig. 30, *A*, *b''*). Lateral leaflets (secondary rays) may spring from these leaves, in the same way as they were formed from the stem, and these secondary rays of a whorl may again produce rays of a higher order. The successive whorls of a stem alternate in such a manner, that the oldest leaves of a whorl, which have the branches in their axils, are arranged in a spiral line running round the stem. Each internode as a rule suffers a subsequent torsion in the same direction. A lateral shoot is always formed in the axil of the oldest leaf of a whorl in *Chara*, and in the axils of the two oldest leaves in *Nitella* ; the lateral shoots repeat the development of the main stem in every detail (Fig. 30). It has been already said that the segmentation of the leaves is like that of the stem ; they too consist of internodes which are at first very short (Fig. 30, *B*, *γ*), but are eventually much elongated, and are separated by short transverse disks, the leaf-nodes ; from these nodes the lateral leaflets (secondary rays) spring in successive whorls, which are not alternate, but are in a straight line one above

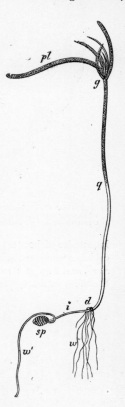

FIG. 29. *Chara fragilis*. Germinating-spore *sp*; *i, d, q, pl* together form the pro-embryo (*pl* is segmented, which is not clearly shown in the figure); at *d* are the rhizoids *w''*; *w* the so-called primary root; at *g* the first leaves (not a whorl) of the leafy plant, the second generation. After Pringsheim, magn. about four times.

another (Fig. 31, β). Every leaf begins with a node (the basal node) by which it is united with the stem-node, and each leaflet is united in the same way with its primary. These basal nodes are the starting-points for the formation of the cortex which covers the

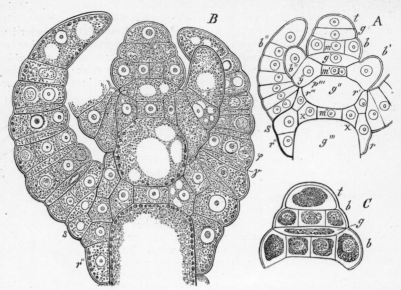

FIG. 30. *Chara fragilis*; longitudinal section through the bud; the cell-contents are left out in *A*, the finely granular substance in *B* is protoplasm, the larger bodies are chlorophyll-corpuscles; the formation of vacuoles may be observed; in *C* the cell-contents are contracted by solution of iodine. Magn. 500 times.

internodes of the stem in the genus *Chara*, but which is wanting in *Nitella*. Distinct cortical lobes run from the basal node of every leaf, one downwards and one upwards (Fig. 30, *r*, *r′*, *r″*, and Fig. 32); as many descending cortical lobes, as there are leaves in a whorl, meet therefore in the centre of each internode with the cortical lobes which ascend from the

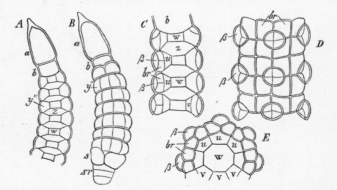

FIG. 31. Leaves of *Chara fragilis*; *a* terminal cell; *b* last cell but one of a leaf; *z* internodal cells of leaf; *w* cell of leaf-node; *y″* mother-cell of a lateral leaflet and its basal node, from which *v* and *u* (the connecting cells) are formed; *br* the basal node, which produces four simple cortical lobes and β the lateral leaflet. *A* and *C* in longitudinal section. *B* the entire young leaf seen from without with the stipule *s* and its descending cortical lobe *sr*. *D* middle portion of an older but still young leaf from without. *E* transverse section of a leaf-node of the same age as *D*.

whorl next below; but the number of the latter is one less, because the leaf, in the axil of which the lateral shoot arises, produces no ascending lobe. The cortical lobes close up together laterally and form a compact envelope round the internode, in the middle of which the ascending and descending lobes fit into one another like the elements of a prosenchyma. The cortex is formed at such an early period, that the internode is covered with it as it elongates, the cortical lobes following its growth accurately as it

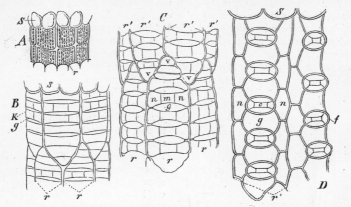

FIG. 32. Development of the cortex of the stem in *Chara fragilis*. *A* a very young internode of the stem with the lobes still unicellular *r*. *B—D* further development of the same ; *r, r* indicate everywhere the cortical lobes which ascend from the lower leaves, *r', r', r'* those which descend from the upper leaves ; *c, v* the apical cell of each cortical lobe ; *g, g,* its internodal cells ; *n, m, n* the formation of its node ; *v* in *D* the central cell of a cortical node. *S* denotes everywhere the unicellular stipular formations which spring in pairs from the bases of the leaves.

increases in length and thickness. Each cortical lobe grows like the stem by means of an apical cell forming transverse segments, from each of which cortical internodal and nodal cells are formed by repeated transverse division ; each of the latter divides by successive septa into an inner cell next the stem-internode and three outer cells, the middle one of which often grows out into the form of a conical point or knob-like projection, imitating a leaf ; the lateral outer cells of the node, on the other hand, follow the elongation of the internode upwards and downwards and grow into longer tubes, so that each cortical lobe consists of three parallel rows of cells, the middle row however having alternately short and long (internodal and nodal) cells. The cortical layer of the leaves which proceeds from the leaflets (secondary rays) is much more simple (Fig. 31, *br*). There are other leaf-like formations also which arise from the basal nodes of *Chara* and are called by Braun *stipules* ; they are always unicellular and either very short or long tubes, and are found on the inner and outer side of the base of the leaf (Fig. 41, *s*).

The nodes are the centres of formation for all the lateral members in the Characeae. The root-like structures (*rhizoids*) spring from the outer cells of the lower nodes of the main shoot ; they are long hyaline tubes, which grow obliquely downwards and elongate only at the apex. They form an outgrowth of flat cells on the circumference of

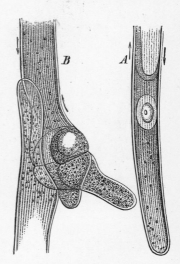

FIG. 33. Rhizoids of *Chara fragilis*. *A* extremity of a growing tube. *B* a so-called joint ; the lower part of the upper tube is branching. After Pringsheim, magn: 240 times. The arrows show the direction of the 'streaming' of the protoplasm.

the node, to which they are attached therefore by a broad base ; these bases divide again in the stronger rhizoids and give rise, especially on their upper margin, to small flat cells, from which thin rhizoids are then developed. The tubes of the rhizoids form only a few transverse septa, which lie far behind the growing apex and are oblique from the first. The two adjacent cells are placed one against the other like the soles of two human feet placed sole to sole. The branching proceeds only from the lower end of the upper cell (Fig. 33, *B*) ; a protuberance is formed which is cut off by a septum and then by further division produces several cells, which grow into branches ; these therefore are placed in a tuft on one side. The tubes of the rhizoids vary in length from several millimetres to more than two centimetres, and in breadth from one-fortieth to one-tenth of a millimetre.

The *vegetative (asexual) multiplication* of the Characeae proceeds for the most part from the nodes, and has three modifications: 1. Tuber-like bodies, the so-called *bulbils* or *amylum-stars* of *Chara stelligera* ; these are isolated subterranean nodes with much-shortened leaf-whorls of neat and regular construction, and with their cells densely filled with starch and other formative material ; shoots from them develope into new plants. 2. *Branches with naked base* of Pringsheim. These are formed on old nodes of *Chara* of the previous year's growth, or on nodes cut from the stem, in the axils not only of the oldest but also of the younger leaves of a whorl ; the chief difference between these and normal branches is that the cortical envelope is entirely or partially wanting in the lower internode and in the first whorl of leaves ; the cortical lobes which descend from the first node of the branch often separate from the internode and grow free, curling upwards ; the leaves of the lowest whorl often form no nodes. 3. *Pro-embryonic branches*. These grow beside the branches with naked base from the nodes of the stem, but they are essentially distinct from them, their structure being that of the pro-embryo which proceeds from the spore ; like the branches with naked base, they have only been observed on *Chara fragilis* and by Pringsheim. A cell of the stem-node grows out into a tube, whose apex is cut off by a septum ; the terminal cell elongates and fresh divisions are formed in it, till the apex of the pro-embryo consists at last of a row of from three to six cells. A new plant is developed from this pro-embryo,

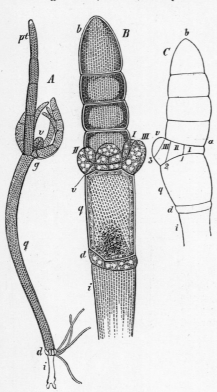

FIG. 34. *Chara fragilis. A* an entire pro-embryonic branch ; *i* the lowest colourless cell beneath the node forming rhizoids ; *q* the long cell which arises from the middle cell of the bud-rudiment ; *pt* the apex of the pro-embryo ; at *g* is the false leaf-whorl, *v* the bud of the second generation of the leafy plant. *B* upper part of a younger pro-embryonic branch ; *i, d, q* as before, *b = pt* in *A* ; *I, II, III* the young leaflets of the stem-node, *v* the bud of the leafy stem. *C* still younger pro-embryonic branch ; *i, d, q, b* as in *B* ; *v* the apical cell of the bud of the stem. After Pringsheim ; *B* magn. 170 times.

just as from the pro-embryo produced by the germination of the oospore. Beneath the apex of the pro-embryo (Fig. 34, *C, ab*) the tube swells, and the swollen part is cut off by a transverse wall, and forms a cell which Pringsheim terms the *bud-rudiment* (Fig. 34, *C*, from *a* to *d* inclusively). This cell divides into a short upper and short lower cell, with a middle one between them. The middle cell does not divide again, but grows into a long tube. The two other cells are the stem-node (Fig. 34, *a*) and the node from which rhizoids grow (Fig. 34, *d*). The stem-node divides first by a longitudinal wall into two halves. By successive longitudinal divisions, which start from the front wall and advance towards the hinder side, two interior cells and a ring of from six to eight peripheral cells are formed. The oldest of these is also the largest, for it grows more rapidly than the rest : it is the mother-cell and at the same time the first apical cell of the new *Chara*, the leafy plant with sexual organs. The other cells of the periphery may become the leaves at the angle where pro-embryo and Chara-plant join, which are usually only rudimentary; these are the small leaves surrounding the terminal bud of the stem which are shown in Fig. 34.

From the nodes forming rhizoids are also produced accessory pro-embryos, and in *Chara aspera* and others small white tubers formed chiefly by enlargement of the lower segment of a lateral rhizoid ; when the tubers germinate they develope accessory pro-embryos.

The antheridia and oogonia are always formed on the leaves ; the antheridium is the metamorphosed terminal cell of a leaf or lateral leaflet ; the oogonium in the

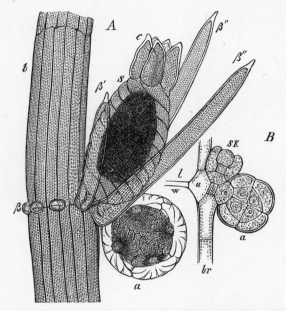

FIG. 35. *Chara fragilis.* A middle portion of a leaf *b* with an antheridium *a* and an oogonium *S*; *c* its crown ; β a sterile lateral leaflet ; β′ larger lateral leaflets beside the fruit ; β″ the bracteoles springing from the basal node of the sexual organs (magn. about 50 times). *B* a young antheridium *a* with still younger oogonium *sk* ; *w* the nodal cell of the leaf; *u* the point of union between this cell and the basal node of the antheridium ; *l* lumen of the leaf-internode ; *br* cortical cells of the leaf. Magn. 350 times.

monoecious species arises close beside it from the basal node of the leaflet in *Chara*, or from the last node of the primary ray which is crowned by a terminal antheridium in *Nitella*; the oogonium therefore is beneath the antheridium in the monoecious species of *Nitella*, above or beside it in *Chara*. This relation of proximity disappears in the dioecious species, but the morphological significance and position remain the same. We will examine both organs first in their mature state.

The *antheridia* (globules) are spherical bodies, from one half to one millimetre in diameter, at first green, afterwards red. The wall is formed of eight flat cells, four of which surround the free pole and are triangular, while the four at the opposite pole are four-angled and a little narrowed below. Each of these cells is a definite portion of the wall of the antheridium and is called a *shield* ; in the unripe state their inner wall is covered with green chlorophyll-corpuscles, which turn red as the antheridium matures ;

as the outer wall is free from them, the outside of the sphere appears clear and transparent (Fig. 35, *A*); folds of the cell-wall run from the circumference to the centre of each shield, and give it the appearance of being lobed in a radiate manner. A cylindrical cell projects inward from the centre of the inner wall of each shield almost as far as to the centre of the hollow sphere; this is termed the *handle* or *manubrium*. The flask-shaped cell (pedicel-cell) that bears the antheridium also intrudes into it, thrusting itself between the four lower shields. At the central extremity of each of the eight manubria is a roundish, hyaline cell, the *head-cell* (capitulum); the frame-work of the antheridium is thus composed of twenty-five cells. Each head-cell is surmounted by six smaller cells (*secondary head-cells*), and from each of these proceed four long whip-like filaments, the numerous coils of which fill the interior

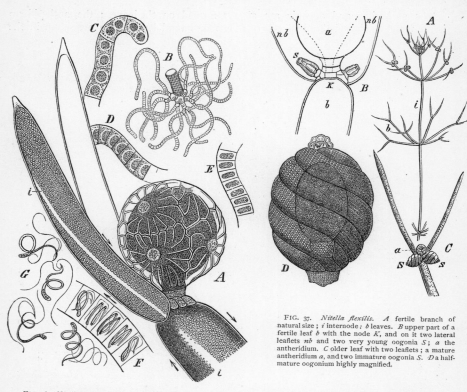

FIG. 37. *Nitella flexilis. A* fertile branch of natural size; *i* internode; *b* leaves. *B* upper part of a fertile leaf *b* with the node *K*, and on it two lateral leaflets *nb* and two very young oogonia *S*; *a* the antheridium. *C* older leaf with two leaflets; a mature antheridium *a*, and two immature oogonia *S*. *D* a half-mature oogonium highly magnified.

FIG. 36. *Nitella flexilis. A* a nearly ripe antheridium at the end of the primary leaf, beside it two lateral leaflets; *i* neutral zones; arrows show the direction of the 'streaming' of the protoplasm. *B* a manubrium with its head-cell and the whip-like filaments, in which the spermatozoids are formed. *C* extremity of a young filament. *D* middle portion of an older one. *E* one still older. *F* mature antheridial filament with spermatozoids *G*. *C—G* magn. 550 times.

of the antheridium (Fig. 36, *B*). Each of these filaments—about 200 altogether—is a row of small disc-shaped cells (*D*, *E*, *F*), the number of which amounts to 100-200. In each of these 20,000–40,000 cells a *spermatozoid* is formed, a thin, spirally twisted thread, thicker at its hinder extremity, and with two long delicate cilia at the other and pointed extremity (Fig. 36, *G*). When the antheridium is ripe the eight shields separate by the lessening of their spherical curvature, the spermatozoids escape from their mother-cells and move about in the water; the antheridia appear to break up usually in the morning, and the spermatozoids continue in movement for some hours, sometimes till the evening.

The *oogonium* (nucule) when fully grown and ready for fertilisation is of a longer or shorter ellipsoidal form, and is supported on a short cell serving as a stalk (the pedicel-cell), which is visible externally only in *Nitella* and consists of an axile row of cells closely invested with an envelope of five spirally twisted tubes. The whole may

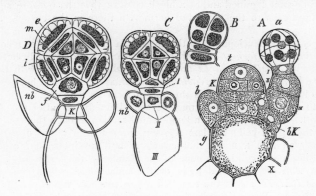

FIG. 38. Development of the antheridia in *Nitella flexilis.* At *B, C,* and *D* the protoplasm has been contracted by glycerine.

be described as a metamorphosed shoot, but this does not mean that the oogonium actually originates in the transformation of a shoot. The pedicel-cell answers to the lowest internode of a shoot and bears a short nodal cell, from which the envelope-tubes arise like a whorl of leaves. Above the nodal cell rises the peculiarly formed apical cell of the shoot, which is large in proportion to the other parts and ovoid. At its base immediately above the nodal cell a short hyaline cell is divided off at an early stage in *Chara* ; its place is taken in *Nitella* by a disc-shaped group of such cells, which Braun has called the 'Wendungszellen.' The large apical cell of the oogonium is filled with protoplasm and a number of oil-drops and starch-grains, but its apical region, the *apical papilla*, contains pure hyaline protoplasm. The tubes of the envelope, which are rich in chlorophyll, project above the apical papilla and support the *crown*, which is composed of five larger cells in *Chara*, of five pairs of small cells in *Nitella* : these cells were divided off by transverse septa from the enveloping tubes at an early period. Above the apical papilla and beneath the crown, which constitutes a compact lid, the five enveloping tubes form the *neck*, which encloses a narrow cavity, the *apical cavity* ; this is inversely conical above the papilla and grows narrower upwards, because the five segments of the neck project inwards and form a kind of *diaphragm*, through the central and very narrow opening of which communication is maintained

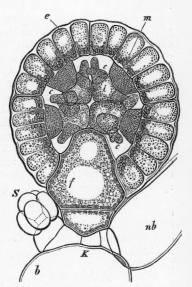

FIG. 39. More advanced state of the antheridium of *Nitella flexilis* magn. about 500 times.

with the upper roomy portion of the apical cavity. The cavity is closed above by the crown, but five lateral fissures appear between the neck-portions of the five tubes at the time of fertilisation and thus an opening is made to the outside ; through these fissures the spermatozoids find an entrance into the apical cavity, which is filled with hyaline mucilage, and make their way from thence into the oosphere, the wall of which has become mucilaginous in its upper part. After fertilisation the oospore becomes invested with a wall of cellulose and the chlorophyll-corpuscles of the envelope assume a reddish-yellow colour ; the walls of the enveloping tubes adjacent to the oosphere thicken and become lignified and of a black colour ; thus the oospore acquires a hard black coat, and falls to the ground to germinate there in the ensuing autumn or in the next spring.

The history of the development of the antheridia and oogonia is as follows.

The sequence in the *formation of the cells of the antheridium* has been fully described by A. Braun in *Nitella syncarpa* and *Chara Baueri* ; it agrees with that in *Nitella flexilis* and *Chara fragilis.*—In *Nitella* the terminal cell of a leaf becomes an antheridium ; the oldest leaf in a whorl is the first to form its antheridium, the others follow according to age ; the antheridia may be seen immediately after the appearance of the leaf-whorl. Fig. 38, *A*, gives a longitudinal section through the apex of a shoot, of which *t* is the apical cell ; the last segment formed from it has already divided by a transverse wall into a nodal mother-cell *K* and an internodal cell beneath it ; beneath the internodal cell is the node of the stem with the last whorl of leaves ; *b* is its youngest leaf, *bK* the basal node of the oldest leaf, which consists already of the segments *I, II, III* ; *a* is the terminal cell of this leaf which is being transformed into an antheridium. While the spherical antheridium is being formed, the leaf also suffers changes which should first be considered. The segment *III* becomes the first internode of the leaf, *II* the first node, which developes the lateral leaflet *nb* in *C* and *D*. The cell *I* divides into two (*C, I*), of which the lower remains short, while the upper grows into the flask-shaped cell *f* in Fig. 38, *D*, and Fig. 39.

The spherical mother-cell of the antheridium (Fig. 38, *A, a*) divides first by a wall, which is radial and vertical in relation to the axis of the branch, into two hemispheres, and these are converted into four quadrants by vertical walls at right angles to the first wall ; a third division, horizontal and at right angles to both the former walls, takes place in each of the quadrants and simultaneously in all four, and now the antheridium consists of four upper and four lower octants of a sphere. Contraction by means of glycerine shows distinctly that in each of these processes of division the protoplasm is completely divided before the appearance of the wall of cellulose (Fig. 38, *B*) ; the second division takes place even before the wall is developed between the two halves which were first formed ; it is possible to make the four quadrants contract before the wall between them is visible ; in Fig. 38, *B*, the third division has just taken place, the second vertical wall is already formed, the two quadrants there visible are already divided, but no horizontal wall is yet formed. Fig. 38, *A, a*, shows the eight octants with their nuclei in perspective. Each octant now first divides into an outer and an inner cell (Fig 38, *C*) ; the latter is again divided in all the eight octants, so that now each octant consists of an outer, a middle, and an inner cell (*D, e, m, i*). Up to this time the sphere continues solid, all the cells are in close contact with one another ; but now begins unequal growth and with it the formation of intercellular spaces (Fig. 39). The eight outer cells (*e*) are the young shields, the lateral walls of which showed at an earlier stage the radial infolding already mentioned ; they grow more strongly than the inner cells in a tangential direction, the outside of the sphere enlarging more rapidly than the inside ; the middle cells (*m*), the manubria, continue attached to the shields, but are separated from one another by the tangential growth of the sides of the shields ; they grow slowly in the radial direction ; the innermost cell (*i*) of each octant is rounded off into a head-cell. The cell (*f*) in Fig. 38, *D*, increases rapidly in size, thrusts itself between the four shields into the interior of the sphere, and becomes a flask-shaped cell, on whose apex the eight head-cells rest. Fig. 39 shows this condition of the antheridium in optical longitudinal section ; where the walls of the head-cells border on the intercellular spaces which are now formed and are filled with fluid, they put out branches (*c*) which become divided into cells by transverse septa and branch again ; these branches elongate by apical growth and form numerous transverse septa. The lowermost of these cells swell into a roundish shape and form the secondary head-cells, to which are attached the cylindrical filaments whose disc-shaped cells are the mother-cells of the spermatozoids (Fig. 39 and Fig. 36, *B, C, D, E*).

The antheridia of *Chara fragilis* are formed by the metamorphosis of the lateral rays (leaflets) which form the innermost row on a leaf (primary ray), and the development advances on it downwards, as Fig. 41 shows. The sequence in cell-formation and the growth are the same in all important respects as those of *Nitella*; the flask-shaped pedicel-cell is here set on a small cell wedged in between the cells of the cortex, the central cell of the basal node of the leaflet, which Braun says occurs even in sterile leaves, but which I have not been able to find there.

Development of the spermatozoids. The whip-shaped filaments in which the spermatozoids are formed have intercalary as well as apical growth, as is shown by the presence in the middle of young filaments of elongated cells with two nuclei, between which no division wall has yet appeared (Fig. 36, *C*); the longer the filaments grow, the more numerous are the septa, till at last the individual cells are only narrow discs. The further transformation of the contents of these spermatozoid mother-cells proceeds from

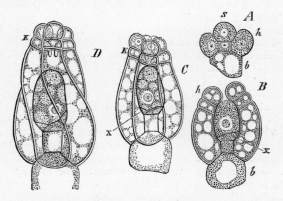

FIG. 40. Development of the oogonium of *Nitella flexilis* (see the text magn. about 300 times; *x* the 'Wendungszellen.'

the free end of the filament backwards; the spermatozoids are formed in basipetal order in each filament. The mode of formation has been recently investigated by Schmitz [1]. The nucleus is changed directly into the body of the spermatozoid; the peripheral layer becomes thicker and splits up into a thread of nuclear substance which is rolled inwards in a spiral manner, while the central part of the nucleus grows looser in texture and becomes a colourless vesicle; the anterior end that bears the cilia is according to Schmitz the only part of the spermatozoid that is formed from the protoplasm surrounding the nucleus, the largest part of it coming, as has been stated, from the nucleus. The spermatozoids begin to rotate before leaving the mother-cells, and escape from them after the breaking up of the antheridium; the thread-like body of the spermatozoid has 2–3 coils in *Nitella*, 3–4 in *Chara*; the posterior and thicker end encloses some glistening granules.

The *development of the oogonium* has been described at length by A. Braun; Sachs has also studied it in *Nitella flexilis* and *Chara fragilis*.—In *Nitella flexilis* the oogonium springs from the node of the leaf beneath the antheridium (Fig. 37, *B* and *C*), and begins to appear some time after it. Fig. 40 shows a very young oogonium whose pedicel-cell

[1] Untersuch. ü. d. Struktur d. Protoplasmas u. d. Zellkerne in Sitzgber. d. niederrhein. Ges. 13 Juli 1880, p. 31 of the reprint.

(A, b) bears the smaller nodal cell with the five rudimentary enveloping tubes (h), only two of which are here seen in longitudinal section ; above the nodal cell is the apical cell (s) of the shoot. (B) shows a further stage of development ; the first of the cells called by Braun the ' Wendungszellen' (x) has made its appearance, and two transverse septa have been formed in the upper portion of each of the enveloping tubes ; these short upper cells are raised by the intercalary growth of the tubes above the apical cell and form the crown K in C and D. The lower of these two cells puts out a process which projects inwards and downwards, as C and D show, so that the five lower crown cells together form a sort of weel (eel-basket) opening downwards. After a time the enveloping tubes begin to assume the spiral torsion, the coils constantly taking a more horizontal direction, while the apical cell of the shoot enlarges considerably and becomes the oosphere (Fig. 37).—The development and fertilisation of the oogonium in the genus *Chara* has recently been described at length by De Bary in *Chara foetida*. Here too, as in *Nitella*, it consists at an early stage in its existence of an axile row of three cells, and of five rows of two cells each forming an envelope round the former. The lowest cell of the axile row is the nodal cell : the second is here also always small and colourless and answers to the ' Wendungszellen' of *Nitella*, and, as De Bary's figures show, is cut off by an oblique septum from the base of the apical cell, which is now the third of the axile row. The apical cell, at first almost hemispherical, becomes ovoid-cylindrical and ultimately ovoid in shape ; until it reaches its full size its cell-wall is very thin and delicate ; its protoplasm is rich in drops of oil and starch-grains except at the apex, where there is a transparent terminal papilla, the receptive spot, with finely granular protoplasm ; in this state the apical cell of the oogonium is the oosphere. The five enveloping tubes are from the first closely applied to the apical cell ; after each has been divided in two by a transverse wall about half-way up, the upper cells thus divided off unite closely with one another above the apical cell ; the envelope is thus closed all round, at least in the case of *Chara foetida*, before the ' Wendungszelle' separates from the oosphere. The five upper cells of the envelope are at first of the same length as the five lower ; the dividing septa are about half-way up the oosphere ; but as the oosphere grows, the five lower cells grow into long tubes, which are at first straight and afterwards become twisted spirally round the oosphere. The five upper cells form the crown, which is raised some distance above the apex of the oosphere. Between the crown and the apex of the oosphere the tubes of the envelope grow inwards and increase in breadth, and form above the apical papilla of the oosphere a thick diaphragm open only in the middle, and separating a narrow space beneath the crown from a still narrower space above the oosphere. The cells of the crown form a lid over the upper space ; the upper and lower space communicate by the narrow opening in the diaphragm. De Bary finds a similar construction in *Nitella*. As soon as the oogonium has reached its full size, the small space above the diaphragm becomes enlarged by the elongation of the tubes between the diaphragm and the crown ; this portion of the envelope, thus late in enlarging, De Bary calls the *neck* ; at this part the five tubes separate from one another and form five fissures beneath the crown and above the diaphragm. Through the fissures the spermatozoids force an entrance in numbers into the apical space, which is filled with a hyaline mucilage ; that one or more find their way to the oosphere is rendered less doubtful by the circumstance, that the papilla at its apex is invested at this period with a very thin cell-wall or with none, as is shown by the extrusion of its contents into the apical space on very slight pressure.

Braun's account of the morphological value of the oogonium of *Chara* is fully confirmed by Fig. 41, A, which represents the lower portion of a young full-grown leaf of *Chara fragilis* with the adjoining piece of the stem and an axillary bud in longitudinal section : m is half of the nodal cell of the stem, i its upper, i' its lower internode ; sr a descending, y an ascending cortical lobe ; sr' the cortical lobe of the lower internode which descends from the leaf, rk one of its nodes ; i'' is the first internode of the axillary bud resting on the cell n, which connects the stem-node m with the basal node of the leaf.. The leaf shows three lower internodes z, z, z, which are at present short ; they may become six to eight times longer ; between them are the leaf-nodes w, w ; v, v are the cells which connect the leaf-node with the basal node of the leaflet β on the outer side of the leaf, a the corresponding cells on the inner side ; br the cortical lobes of the leaf, two of which ascend and two descend from each leaflet ; the lowest internode of the leaf is however covered only by descending lobes ; by the side of one of them is the stipule s ; x, x are the descending cortical lobes of the internodes of the leaf on their inner side, where the leaflets are transformed into antheridia a, a ; the ascending cortical lobes are wanting here, because one oogonium alway arises from the basal node of each leaflet (cp. Fig. 35, A and B). With respect to the origin of the oogonium, Braun says at p. 69 of the work cited above, that just as a twig springs from

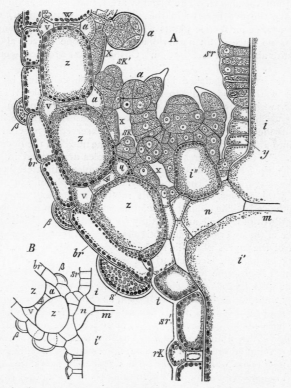

FIG. 41. *Chara fragilis.* *A* lower part of a fertile leaf, from the axil of which a lateral shoot is springing (see the text). *B* lower part of a sterile leaf without an axillary shoot (in longitudinal section).

the basal node of the leaf, so the oogonium springs from the basal node of a leaflet (in *Chara fragilis* of an antheridial twig, which there takes the place of a leaflet) ; as the branch-bearing leaf has no ascending cortical lobes, so the leaflet, which bears the oogonium, has none ; as it is the first leaf of the whorl on the stem which produces a branch in its axil, so it is the first (inner) leaflet of the whorl on the leaf with which the formation of the oogonium is connected. The basal node of the antheridial twig in *Chara fragilis* has, according to Braun, not four peripheral cells, as in sterile leaflets, but five ; one odd one above, the first formed, two lateral ones formed next, and two lower ones, the last formed. Of these five cells only the two lower become cortical cells (of the leaves) ; the upper, which is wanting in the sterile basal nodes, is the mother-cell of the oogonium ; the two lateral cells develope into leaflets, which are placed at the side between the antheridium and oogonium (Fig 35, *A*, *β″*) ; these are called by Braun *bracteoles*. The mother-cell of the oogonium grows out of the axil of the antheridial twig and divides by a transverse wall into an upper, outer, apical cell and into a segment, which divides in its turn by a wall parallel to the first into two discs (*sk* in Fig. 41, *A*) ; the lower cell does not divide, but forms the concealed pedicel of the oogonium and answers to the first internode of a branch ; the upper cell is of the nature of a nodal cell and divides by tangential walls into a circle of five outer and one inner cell (*s k′*) ; the former are the rudiments of the tubes which form the envelope, and whose origin agrees with that of the leaves.

A remarkable case of parthenogenesis has been observed by De Bary in *Chara crinita*[1]. Male plants of this dioecious species are extremely rare, and are known only in a few herbarium specimens. The oogonia are formed in the same way as in other Charas, and have the five fissures in the neck before fertilisation. Oospores were produced in abundance on female plants which were cultivated by themselves, and on which there was no trace of an antheridium ; scarcely one proved abortive, notwithstanding the entire absence of fertilisation. Oospores thus produced germinated in the usual manner.

The Characeae are distinguished by the size of their cells and by the simplicity of the relations of the single cells to the structure of the whole. The young cells have a nucleus, which always lies in the centre of the protoplasm filling the cell, and divides, as usual, previously to the division of the cell. In the internodal cells, which do not divide but elongate, Schmitz[2] has observed a peculiar fragmentation of the nucleus into a number of daughter-nuclei. The nuclei in the nodal cells suffer no further change. As the cell increases in size vacuoles are formed in the protoplasm which at first fills the cell completely, and these vacuoles ultimately become confluent and form a single large vacuole, the sap-cavity. The protoplasm, which covers the wall of the cell as a thick layer, now begins its rotating movement, choosing always the longest path in the cell. The chlorophyll-corpuscles, which now make their appearance, grow with the growth of the cell and multiply by repeated bipartition ; they adhere to the inner surface of the outermost thin motionless layer of protoplasm, and take no part in the rotation of the layers which lie further inside. With increase of growth in the cell the rotating protoplasm is differentiated into a watery and a less watery denser portion, the former having the appearance of hyaline cell-sap, in which the latter floats in the form of roundish lumps of varying size ; and as these denser masses are passively carried along by the rotating hyaline protoplasm, as can be seen by their tumbling over one another, the appearance is as though the movement of rotation was in the cell-sap. Along with the lumps of denser protoplasm of more irregular form are many spherical protoplasmic bodies, which are covered with fine rod-like projections and are known as *ciliated bodies* ('Wimperkörperchen'). The movement is, as Nägeli shows, most rapid next the motionless wall-layer, and grows gradually slower towards the inside ; hence the round masses floating in the thin rotating protoplasm tumble over one another, because they impinge with different portions of their surface on layers having different rates of speed. The chlorophyll-corpuscles are arranged according to the direction of the current in longitudinal rows along the layer of motionless protoplasm, and are often so thickly crowded together as to form a continuous stratum. They are absent only at the so-called *neutral zones* (Fig. 36, *i*). These mark the line where the ascending and descending portions of the rotating protoplasm of a cell flow alongside of one another in opposite directions, and where therefore there is rest. The direction of the movement of rotation in each cell stands in regular relation to that in all the other cells of the plant, and therefore to its morphological structure, as Braun has shown.

---

[1] See also Braun, Ueber Parthenogenesis bei Pflanzen (Abh. d. Berl. Akad. 1856, p. 337).

[2] Schmitz in Sitzungsber. d. niederrh. Ges. 4 Aug. 1879, p. 25 of the reprint.—Strasburger, Zellbildung. u. Zelltheilung, III. Aufl. p. 228.—Johow, Die Zellkerne von *Chara foetida* (Bot. Zeit. 1881, p. 729).

B. PHAEOPHYCEAE.

The Phaeophyceae, called also Melanophyceae or Brown Seaweeds, are a group in which the thallus is still more highly differentiated than in the Chlorophyceae, as is shown by the fact, that side by side with forms scarcely visible to the naked eye there occur genera, the dimensions of which are the largest to be found among the Algae and among the Thallophytes generally; *Macrocystis*, one of the Laminarieae, is said to reach a length of two hundred metres. Besides filamentous conferva-like forms such as *Ectocarpus*, the group contains others which like *Sargassum* show a differentiation into stem and leaf coinciding in outward appearance perfectly with that found in the higher plants. The sexual process has been examined in only a few genera and species; but what is known is sufficient to show that there is here the same advance from isogamous to oogamous fertilisation as in the Chlorophyceae. Notwithstanding the differences which present themselves on the one hand in the vegetative structure, on the other in the mode of fertilisation, the Phaeophyceae may be arranged in a series, beginning with *Ectocarpus* and ending with *Fucus*. The differences within the ranks of the Phaeophyceae are not so great as those which occur for instance in the Confervaceae and Volvocineae; their subdivisions therefore are to be regarded not as sharply defined groups, but as types which are for the most part connected with one another by intermediate forms.

The Phaeophyceae are all marine Algae[1]; the Alga from the Tegler See, described by A. Braun under the name of *Pleurocladia*, appears to agree in organisation with the Mesogloeae; but it is still imperfectly known, and moreover has not been found in recent times[2]. The Phaeophyceae have this in common, that besides their chlorophyll they contain a brown colouring matter, *phycophaein*, which conceals the green colour and is the cause of their peculiar brown tint, as phycocyan produces the verdigris-green tint of the Cyanophyceae. The structure also of their swarm-spores, which Thuret's researches made known to us, is characteristic of the Phaeophyceae; the cilia are inserted on the side of the colourless beak of the swarm-spore, not as in the Chlorophyceae on its point. In the lowest forms the sexual cells are uniform motile gametes (*Ectocarpus*), and these may germinate without conjugation. In *Cutleria* the gametes are of very different size, the male much smaller than the female, and the latter, soon losing its cilia, becomes a quiescent oosphere with which the male gamete coalesces. In *Fucus* the difference is still more striking; the male gametes are here small spermatozoids, and the female cell has lost its power of motion and is ejected from the oogonium, as an oosphere without cilia; fertilisation therefore takes place outside the plant which produces the sexual organs. Fertilisation of the oosphere in the oogonium, which is so common in the Chlorophyceae and is the universal rule in the Archegoniatae, is not found among the Phaeophyceae.

Putting aside the Tilopterideae, whose development is unknown, and the Dictyo-

---

[1] [See Flahault, Sur une Algue Phéosporée d'eau douce (Comptes Rendus, 1884).]
[2] As Professor Magnus kindly informs me.

taceae, in which the process of sexual reproduction is equally unknown, we may divide the Phaeophyceae into two groups [1];—

1. **Phaeosporeae** or **Phaeozoosporeae.**
2. **Fucaceae.**

1. PHAEOSPOREAE.

The Phaeosporeae [2] or Phaeozoosporeae are characterised by the circumstance that the propagative cells, whether sexual or asexual, are always swarm-spores of similar form and size. These are produced in sporangia of two kinds, the plurilocular and unilocular. The former are divided by cell-walls into a large number of small cells, each of which produces one swarm-spore; in the latter the protoplasm forms no cell-walls, but simply divides into a number of parts which escape as zoospores. The two kinds of sporangia differ usually in form; the unilocular are roundish or ovoid and usually dark-coloured bodies, while the plurilocular are more elongate-cylindrical. In some species it has been ascertained that the swarm-spores produced in plurilocular sporangia are sexually different and conjugate with each other (*Ectocarpus pusillus, E. siliculosus, Giraudia sphacelarioides, Scytosiphon*). On the other hand this has never been proved of the swarm-spores produced from unilocular sporangia, and these are most probably therefore asexual propagative cells. There are moreover Phaeosporeae, in which only one kind of sporangium is known; thus *Laminaria* has only the unilocular kind, *Scytosiphon* and *Phyleitis* only the plurilocular.

The course of development in the Phaeosporeae may be depicted in some of the better-known forms.

a. The ECTOCARPEAE (including the Mesogloeaceae and Desmarestieae) have in their simplest representatives, such as the genus *Ectocarpus* itself, a much-branched thallus consisting of single cell-rows, and with the growing-point not at the apex of the filaments but intercalary [3]; there is a row of cells beyond the growing-point, and these cells, in proportion as they become further removed from the growing-point, lose their protoplasmic contents and die off. The lateral branches on the main axis arise acropetally on the part of the filament behind the growing-point, that is, their succession is towards it [4]; but if the growing-point, as often happens in lateral branches, is quite basal, the lateral branches of successively higher orders arise in basipetal succession; in other words, their arrangement, with the exception of any that are adventitious, is always towards the growing-point. This intercalary mode of growth obtains also in many other Phaeosporeae, very plainly in *Giraudia sphacelarioides*, which may be regarded as a more highly differentiated *Ectocarpus*. In this species young lateral axes are simple cell-filaments, but eventually the cells at the upper end of the filament pass into the permanent state, and divide now only by longitudinal walls, so that a tissue is produced.

---

[1] [See also Rostafinski in Akad. d. Wiss. Krakau, 1881.]

[2] Thuret, Recherches sur les zoospores des Algues et les anthéridies des Cryptogames (Ann. d. sc. nat. Bot. iii. sér. T. XIV et T. XVI).—Derbès et Solier, Mém. sur quelques points de la physiol. des Algues (Suppl. aux comptes rendus des séances de l'acad. d. sc. T. I).—Goebel, Zur Kenntniss einiger Meeresalgen (Bot. Zeit. 1878).—Berthold, Die geschlechtl. Fortpflanz. der eigentlichen Phaeospor. (Mitth. aus der Zool. Stat. zu Neapel, Bd. II. 1881).

[3] Janczewski, Sur l'accroissement du thalle des Phéosporées (Mém. de la soc. nat. de Cherbourg, t. XX).

[4] Goebel, Ueber d. Verzweigung dorsiventraler Sprosse (Arb. d. bot. Inst. in Würzburg, Bd. II. p. 390).

The growing-point is at the base of the filament, which consists of a single cell-row, the cells of which continually divide and multiply; the uppermost divide by longitudinal walls and pass into the permanent state; in older filaments all the cells do so ultimately, and are then no longer capable of growth, but form a permanent cellular tissue. The forms known as Mesogloeae are only filaments of *Ectocarpus* of somewhat more complex construction; their branches are intertwined and often fused with one another by the conversion of their cell-walls into a mucilage, or, as in *Desmarestia, Stilophora,* &c., grow together into a tissue.

We have the authority of Goebel for a conjugation of similar gametes produced in plurilocular sporangia in the case of *Ectocarpus pusillus* and *Giraudia sphacelarioides;* Berthold[1] describes the same conjugation in *Ectocarpus siliculosus* and *Scytosiphon,* but with a difference. The conjugation in the two first cases is the same as in *Ulothrix* &c., and only gametes from different sporangia unite together. The following is Berthold's description of the process in *E. Siliculosus* and *Scytosiphon.* Some of the swarm-spores produced in the plurilocular sporangia are male gametes, others are female, and both are of the same shape and size. While the male cells are still moving actively about, the female early attach themselves by one of their cilia to some fixed body to which they draw closer up by shortening and finally drawing in the cilium entirely, the second cilium also being drawn in. In this way the female swarm-spore becomes the oosphere, with which a male swarm-spore may now coalesce. There is no receptive spot. Both kinds of gametes may germinate without conjugation, but the plants produced from the male swarm-spores are some of them very weakly. The zygospore or oospore also produces a young plant of *Ectocarpus* directly in germination.

b. The SPHACELARIEAE[2], in which no sexual process has hitherto been found, are chiefly distinguished from the Ectocarpeae by their mode of growth. The growing-point of the main and lateral axis is here terminal, and the summit is occupied by a large apical cell, which forms segments by transverse walls; further differentiation of tissue then takes place in the segments thus formed (Fig. 42), each segment-disc

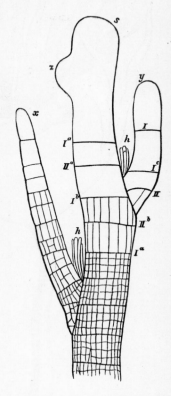

FIG. 42. Summit of a branch of the thallus of *Stypocaulon scoparium.* *s* apical cell (here the only growing part of the thallus) which is forming the rudiment of a branch at *z*; *y, x* older branches; *h* hairs. The apical cell is divided above its base by the walls I*a* and I*b*, and each segment is again divided by a transverse wall II*a*, II*b*, into two disc-shaped cells in which compartments are formed by longitudinal walls. After Geyler.

being divided by longitudinal walls. There are many interesting details in the structure of the thallus which we cannot enter into here. But it should be noticed (see Fig. 42) that in *Stypocaulon,* as Geyler has shown, the apical cell is as a rule the only growing part of the thallus; the lateral axes are formed on it, while these proceed in other

---

[1] That this observer saw no conjugation in the case of *Ectocarpus pusillus* does not prove that none takes place; we must wait for fresh investigations.

[2] Pringsheim, Ueber den Gang der morpholog. Differenzirung in der Sphacelarienreihe (Abh. d. Berl. Akad. 1873).—Geyler, Zur Kenntniss der Sphacelarieen (Pringsheim's Jahrb. f. wiss. Bot. IV. Bd.).—On the gemmae see Janczewski, Les propagules du *Sph. cirrhosa* (Mém. de la soc. nat. de Cherbourg, T. XVIII. 1872).

Sphacelarieae from its segments. It is remarkable that in some species (*Sph. tribuloides* and *Sph. cirrhosa*) short branches drop off from the thallus as gemmae, and that single cells in these gemmae develope into creeping filaments, on which new shoots of *Sphacelaria* are produced as lateral branches. The Sphacelarieae too not unfrequently have hair-structures with an intercalary growing-point, and there are also species of *Ectocarpus* with creeping primary filaments on which other sporangiferous filaments are produced as lateral axes; the growing-point in these creeping filaments is likewise terminal. The position of the growing-point therefore gives no clear distinction between the two groups of Phaeosporeae, nor does the higher differentiation of the tissue in the Sphacelarieae, for we have seen this exhibited in *Giraudia sphacelarioides*, one of the Phaeosporeae which is closely allied to the Ectocarpeae.

c. The LAMINARIEAE[1] occupy a peculiar position in the series. They are among the plants which attain the greatest length in the vegetable kingdom, as was stated above. Their thallus has a stalk of greater or less length, made fast to a substratum by root-like attachments which cling tightly to stones, stems of other Algae and the like, and ending above in a flat divided or undivided lamina. The stem in some species is of considerable thickness; in *L. Cloustoni* and *L. flexicaulis* it is not unusual to find stems with a diameter of three centimetres, in the Lessonieae it is said to reach twenty. This arises from the fact that the stem possesses secondary growth in thickness, which takes place in a meristem beneath the rind, which is

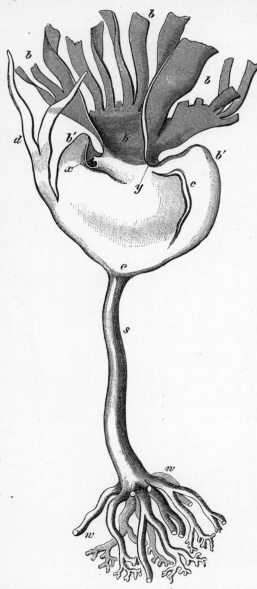

FIG. 43. *Laminaria Cloustoni*, a specimen engaged in renewing its lamina, about 3 times less than the natural size; *s* stalk; *w* root-like organs of attachment (some of their extremities cut off); *e* zone of vegetative growth; *b'* new lamina, which has already begun to split at *c*, and has split at *d*; *b* the old lamina above the new; the old decays and is cast off.

[1] Le Jolis, Examen des espèces confondues sous le nom de *Laminaria digitata*, suivi de quelques observations sur le genre *Laminaria* (Nov. act. acad. Leop. Carol. 1855, comptes rendus 1855).—Janczewski, Observations sur l'accroissement du thalle des Phéosp. (Mém. de la soc. nat. de Cherbourg, T. XX, 1875, p. 13 of the reprint).

not however very distinctly marked off from the older tissue. In the rind are gum-passages of similar structure to those in the Cycadeae. The part of the stem outside the central medulla consists of looser tissue in which the cells form filiform branches resembling the hyphae of fungi; these grow in between the cells of the medulla, the cell-walls of which swell up strongly, and force them apart.

The growing-point is intercalary, as in the Ectocarpeae, lying at the point where the stalk passes into the leaf-life expansion; here is found a meristem, where the increase of the stem in length takes place. In some Laminarieae, as *L. flexicaulis*, the flat expansion at the end of the stalk, which is of great length and breadth, is permanent and continues to enlarge as long as the individual lives. In other species the stem is perennial, but the leaf-like expansion is thrown off every year (compare the description of *Acetabularia* above). Fig. 43 is a representation of *L. Cloustoni*, which is on the point of throwing off its old lamina; this is shaded in the figure and marked *b b*. The growing-point is at *e*. From it has proceeded the broad plate between *e* and *b′ b′*, the new lamina. This plate is divided by longitudinal slits into separate strips in a palmate manner, as the old lamina was. Such strips are already separated at *d*, and a new slit is being formed at *c*. Other species (*L. saccharina*, for instance, which is found in the Atlantic and other seas, as *L. Cloustoni* is in the North Sea) have a very long and undivided expansion. In *Agarum* this is pierced by many roundish holes, and still more remarkable formations are seen in the great Laminarias of the southern hemisphere, as *Macrocystis*[1] and *Lessonia*, whose appearance cannot well be explained without figures. The only known organs of propagation are unilocular sporangia; a sexual process has not hitherto been observed, but must no doubt occur.

d. A sexual process has been certainly ascertained in the CUTLERIACEAE[2], which are really directly allied to the Ectocarpeae, and are removed from them here only because in their mode of fertilisation they afford a transition to the Fucaceae. This little group consists of two genera, *Cutleria* and *Zanardinia*; the development of the former only will be briefly sketched here, that of the latter must be alluded to only occasionally and for comparison's sake. The thallus of *Cutleria* is a broad flat fleshy many-layered expansion split at the margin into simple narrow segments. The growing-point is at the margin, but not on its outer edge. We get a good idea of this, if we suppose the margin of the thallus of a *Cutleria* to be composed of a number of filaments of *Ectocarpus* lying beside and in some places over one another, each of which has its own intercalary growing-point, and also lateral branches beneath it. But behind the margin the filaments grow together into a solid tissue, the origin of which from the coalescence of separate elements is no longer discernible. The sexual organs in *Cutleria* are dioeciously disposed, and antheridia are formed on some plants, oogonia on others; in *Zanardinia* they occur together on the same plant. Antheridia and oogonia form groups on the surface of the thallus and are branches of short cell-filaments which spring from the cells of the rind. Both take the form of plurilocular sporangia; but the compartments are smaller in the male than in the female. In each compartment of the female sporangium (*oogonium*) a large female swarm-cell is formed, in each compartment of the male sporangium (*antheridium*) two small male ones. Both the kinds of swarm-cells are set at liberty by the opening of the compartments of the sporangia; but the female cells soon come to rest, and assume the round form of an oosphere, in which a hyaline spot occupies the position of the colourless beak of the female swarm-cell and is the receptive-spot. A new *Cutleria* does not proceed directly from the oospore; this developes first of all into a row of cells and from that into a club-shaped mass of cell-tissue, on which eventually

---

[1] Wille, H., Zur Anat. von *Macrocystis luxurians*, Hook. fil. et Harv. (Bot. Ztg. 1884, 801).

[2] Reinke, Entwicklungsgesch. Untersuch. über die Cutleriaceen des Golfes von Neapel' (Nova Acta Leop. Car., Bd. XL.).—Falkenberg, Die Befruchtung u. d. Generationswechsel von *Cutleria* (Mittheil. aus der zool. Station zu Neapel, Bd. I. 1876.)—[Janczewski, Note sur la fécondation du *Cutleria adspersa* et les affinités des Cutleriees (Ann. Sc. Nat. 7 ser. XVI. 1883).]

flat creeping lateral branches are formed with a very different mode of growth from that of the sexual generation (Falkenberg, *loc. cit.*); for the growing-point in them is not formed by marginal filaments, whose hinder parts unite with one another, but by a connected row of marginal initial cells. How the upright thallus of *Cutleria* with its different mode of growth springs from the flat creeping shoots is not yet ascertained; perhaps by means of swarm-spores, which develope directly into a cutleria-thallus.

2. FUCACEAE[1].

The mode of fertilisation in the Fucaceae differs essentially from that of the Cutleriaceae in one point only, viz. that the oosphere has here entirely lost its power of motion, and is from the first a naked cell without cilia which is ejected from the oogonium by the expansion of the cell-wall of that organ. But in the structure[2], growth and articulation of the thallus the Fucaceae depart widely from the Cutleriaceae. As limited by Thuret they include a few genera of large marine Algae, in which the vegetative body, often many feet long, is of a cartilaginous texture and is attached by branched discs to stones and similar objects. It is only in *Fucus*, *Fucodium* (*Pelvetia*), *Himanthalia*, and some other genera that we can call the vegetative body a 'thallus;' in some genera, as in *Sargassum*, there is a distinction between stem and leaf equivalent to that in the higher plants. The growing-point is terminal in a depression of the apex, and the arrangement of its cells varies according to the statements of observers, in the different genera. The apical cell in *Sargassum*, *Cystosira*, and others is said to be tetrahedral. In *Fucus*, according to Rostafinski, the apex is composed of a number of cells ('initial cells') which are in shape four-sided truncated pyramids, and form divergent basal segments parallel to the basal surface, and lateral segments parallel to the lateral surfaces. The former are the rudiments of the cells of the medullary tissue, the latter chiefly of the rind.

The branching of *Fucus* is dichotomous, and the further development is often beautifully bifurcate, sometimes sympodial as in Fig. 44. The ramifications lie all in one plane having only some later displacements. The surface of the tissue consists of small closely-packed cells which form the rind, and continue capable of division longer than cells of the medulla. The innermost layers of the rind next to the elongated cells of the medullary tissue eventually produce lateral outgrowths in the shape of filiform branches, which grow in between the cells of the medulla and force apart those in which the walls have already become mucilaginous, so that the cells ultimately lie in a compact web of these filaments (compare the medulla of Laminarieae). The walls of the medullary cells are evidently formed of two different layers, an inner thin firm and compact layer, and an outer mucilaginous layer very capable of swelling, which fills the interstices of the cells and appears as a structureless 'intercellular substance.' This is obviously the cause of the slimy condition of Fucaceae that have lain for any length of time in fresh water. Portions of the tissue not unfrequently separate from one another in the interior of the thallus, and thus form cavities that are filled with air; these project as bladders on the outer surface, and

---

[1] Thuret, Recherches sur la fécondation des Fucacées (Ann. d. sc. nat. IV. sér. T. 2. 1854).— Pringsheim, Ueber Befrucht. u. Keimung der Algen u. d. Wesen d. Zeugungsaktes (Monatsber. d. Berl. Akad. 1855).

[2] Rostafinski, Beitr. zur Kenntn. der Tange, Heft I. 1876.—Reinke in Pringsheim's Jahrb. Bd. X.

serve as a floating apparatus for the thallus which is fixed at its base. In
Sargassum short lateral branches swell into bladders and look like stalked berries.

The Fucaceae have no asexual organs of reproduction, unless we reckon as such
the adventitious shoots which often appear at the base of the thallus, and according
to Reinke are formed endogenously on the filiform branches of the inner cortical
cells mentioned above.

The sexual mode of propagation on the other hand, as we know it from the
researches of Thuret and Pringsheim, is highly productive. The antheridia and
oogonia are formed in globular cavities (*conceptacula*), which appear many

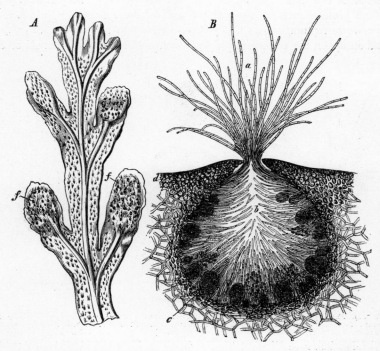

FIG. 44. *Fucus platycarpus*. *A* end of a larger branch (natural size); *ff* fertile branches. *B* transverse
section of a conceptacle; *d* the surrounding epidermal tissue; *a* hairs protruding from the orifice; *b* inner hairs;
c oogonia; *e* antheridia. After Thuret.

together and closely crowded at the end of the longer forked branches or of
peculiarly formed lateral shoots. These conceptacles are not formed inside
the tissue, but are depressions in its surface which are enclosed by the
surrounding tissue and so grown over that at last only a narrow opening remains
to the outside[1]. The cellular filaments, which produce the antheridia and oogonia,

---

[1] According to Bower, On the development of the conceptacle in the Fucaceae (Quart. Journal
of Microsc. Sci. 1880), the formation of the conceptacle commences with the dying away and disappearance of a cell belonging to the outer cortex; the growth of this cell was weak from the first.
[Valiante (Le Cystoseirae del Golfo di Napoli, Roma 1883) states that in *Cystosira* the development
of the conceptacle takes place by regular cell-division and growth in depressions which arise
acropetally at and near the vegetative point.]

spring from the cells that line the conceptacle. Many species are monoecious; both kinds of sexual organs are formed in the same conceptacle, as in *Fucus platycarpus* (Fig. 44); others are dioecious, the conceptacles of one plant containing only oogonia, of another only antheridia, as in *F. vesiculosus, serratus, nodosus, Himanthalia lorea.* Between the sexual organs in the conceptacles are numerous unbranched, long, thin, segmented hairs, which in *F. platycarpus* project in a tuft out of the mouth of the conceptacle. The *antheridia* are formed on branched hairs as lateral branches of the same; an antheridium is a thin-walled oval cell, whose protoplasm breaks up into a number of small *spermatozoids*; these are pointed at one end, and move about by the aid of two cilia; in their interior is a red spot. The *oogonium* begins as a papillose protuberance on a cell of the wall of the conceptacle, which is cut off by a transverse septum, and as it elongates divides into two cells, a lower, the stalk-cell, and an upper, the oogonium proper, which enlarges into a spherical or ellipsoid

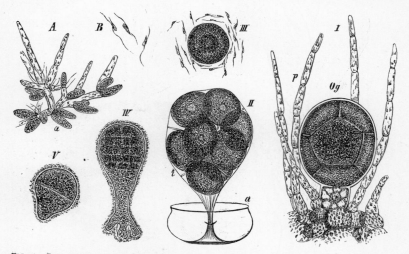

FIG. 45. *Fucus vesiculosus. A* a branched hair covered with antheridia. *B* spermatozoids. *I* an oogonium *og* after division of its contents into eight parts (oospheres), surrounded by simple hairs *p. II* oospheres preparing to escape; the membrane *a* has burst, the inner membrane *i* is ready to open (the two together are an inner shell of the cell-wall of the oogonium). *III* oosphere surrounded by spermatozoids. *IV* and *V* germination of the oospore, *B* magn. 330 times, the others 160. After Thuret.

shape and becomes filled with a dark-coloured protoplasm. This protoplasm continues undivided in some genera (*Pycnophycus, Himanthalia, Cystosira, Halidrys*), the contents of the oogonium forming one oosphere; in others (*Pelvetia*) it divides into two, or into four (*Ozothallia vulgaris*), or into eight (*Fucus*). Fertilisation takes place outside the conceptacle. The oospheres, enclosed in an inner membrane of the oogonium, are ejected and pass out through the opening of the conceptacle; the antheridia also are set free and collect in swarms before the opening, if the fertile branches are lying out of the water in a moist air; if they again come in contact with the sea-water the antheridia open and release the spermatozoids; the oospheres are also set free from their membranous envelope, which is now seen to be composed of two distinct layers (Fig. 45, *II*). The spermatozoids gather thickly round the oospheres, and fix themselves firmly to them, and when there is a sufficient number of them, their movements are so energetic that they set the large sluggish oospheres rotating, and this may continue for a half hour. Thuret leaves it uncertain whether spermatozoids penetrate into the oosphere; the analogy of the phenomena observed by Pringsheim in *Vaucheria* and *Oedogonium*, and of the sexual process recently and repeatedly observed, leaves no room for doubt that one or more of the spermatozoids mingle their substance with that of the naked sphere of protoplasm which forms the oosphere. Soon after these events the oospore becomes invested with a cell-wall, attaches itself to some object, and without passing through a resting period begins to germinate by elongating and dividing first by a transverse septum; this is followed by many other divisions, and the cellular body thus formed developes a hyaline root-like organ of attachment at the lower end, while the free thick end (Fig. 45, *IV*) is the growing apex. The development of a fertile thallus from the oospore has not yet been observed, and therefore the whole cycle of changes in the Fucaceae has not yet been certainly ascertained.

C. RHODOPHYCEAE OR FLORIDEAE[1].

The Florideae or Red Seaweeds, Rhodophyceae or Rhodospermeae, are chiefly distinguished from the two other large series of Algae, the Chlorophyceae and Phaeophyceae, by the mode of their sexual reproduction. In the two latter groups a zygospore or an oospore was produced by the union of one or more male sexual elements with a female; but the proceeding is different in the Florideae; in them there is found before fertilisation a unicellular or pluricellular female sexual apparatus, the *procarp*, which separates into two parts, each with a distinct function; the one is a receptive apparatus, the *trichogyne*, the other is excited by fertilisation to a vegetative process which ends in the production of spores. This part is called the *carpogone*, and may be composed of one or several carpogenous cells; the spores produced from it in various ways are known as *carpospores*, to distinguish them from the asexually produced *tetraspores*, which are usually formed by division of a mother-cell into four. Fertilisation is effected by passively motile male sexual cells without cilia, the *spermatia*[2].

The variety of forms in the Florideae is great, and the procarp in the different genera varies much in form, structure, and position on the thallus. One of the simplest cases is represented by the genus *Nemalion*, in which the procarp is unicellular (Fig. 49, *t, c*); the much elongated apex (*t*) in the figure is the trichogyne, the enlarged bulbous lower portion of the procarp is the carpogone (*c*). The spermatia

---

[1] Nägeli u. Cramer, Pflanzenphysiol. Unters. Zürich, 1855, Heft I; 1857, Heft IV.—Thuret, Recherches sur la fécondation &c. (Ann. d. sc. nat. 1855).—Nägeli, Neue Algensysteme, 1847; Id. in Sitzungsber. der Bayer. Akad. d. Wissenschaft. 1861, vol. II.—Bornet et Thuret, Recherches sur la fécondation des Floridées (Entdeckung der Befruchtung) (Ann. d. sc. nat., ser. 5°, T. VII. 1867, p. 137).—Solms-Laubach, Ueber d. Fruchtentw. von *Batrachospermum* (Bot. Zeit. 1867).—Bornet et Thuret, Notes algologiques, 1er fascic. 1876.—Janczewski, Notes sur le développement du cystocarpe des Floridées (Mém. de la soc. nationale d. sc. nat. de Cherbourg, T. XX).—Thuret, Études phycologiques, Paris 1878.—[F. Schmitz, Unters. ü. d. Befruchtung d. Florideen (Sitz. d. k. Akad. d. Wiss. z. Berlin, 1883); also Ann. and Magaz. Nat. Hist. 1884.—Schaarschmidt, Beitr. z. Entw. d. Gongrosiren, Klausenberg, 1883.—Sirodot, Les Batrachospermes, Organisation, Fonctions, Développement, Classification, Paris, 1884.]

[2] Once termed also spermatozoids, but this name is objectionable.

conjugate with the trichogyne, and their protoplasmic contents pass into it. The trichogyne itself is not excited by this union to further development, but it is first cut off from the carpogone by a transverse wall and then disappears. The carpogone, on the other hand, in consequence of the fertilisation puts out a number of shoots, which divide transversely and form cells, each of which is a carpospore and may germinate at once. The process of fertilisation is still more simple in the genera *Bangia* and *Porphyra*, as will be subsequently explained. With regard to the details of the process there is much yet to be learnt. In *Nemalion* and its allies the nucleus of the procarp-cell lies perhaps at first in the trichogyne, where it unites with the nucleus of the spermatium, and then passes downwards into the carpogone-portion. Where the trichogyne and carpogone are separated from the first by a transverse septum, the process must be complicated; but here too we must assume that the substance of the spermatium, which is first taken up by the trichogyne, is then conducted to the carpogenous cells.

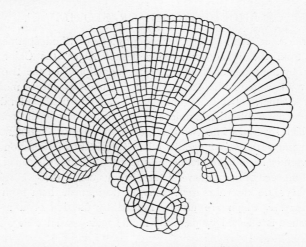

FIG. 46. Young thallus of *Melobesia Lejolisii* formed on the ellipsoidal germ-disk beneath. The periclinal walls are omitted in the portion of the figure to the right. After Rosanoff and Sachs.

The species in the group of the Florideae are extraordinarily numerous, and with some exceptions (*Batrachospermum, Lemanea, Thorea*, some species of *Chantrasia, Bangia* and *Hildebrandtia*) belong to the sea. In the living state they are usually of a red or violet colour, sometimes of a dirty green or blackish hue, as *Batrachospermum*. The green colour of the chlorophyll-corpuscle is masked by a red pigment[1]; but the absorption-spectrum of an alcoholic extract of chlorophyll from the Florideae is not quite the same as in phanerogamous plants. The red colouring matter is soluble in cold water; it is carmine-red in transmitted light, reddish yellow in reflected light (with a tinge of green in *Rythiploea*); the chlorophyll-corpuscles also show this fluorescence when the red colouring matter (*phycoerythrin*)

---

[1] Rosanoff in Comptes rendus, April 9, 1866.—Askenasy in Bot. Zeit. 1867.—Pringsheim, Ueber nat. Chlorophyllmodificationen u. d. Farbstoffe d. Florideen (Monatsber. d. Berl. Akad. Dec. 1876).

escapes from injured cells. The red and the green colours in the Florideae agree very closely in their optical properties.

The *thallus* consists in the simplest species of branched cell-rows, which elongate by growth at the apex with transverse segmentation of their apical cells. In many Ceramiaceae there is an apparent formation of tissue; branches from the mother-axes grow closely applied to them and invest them with a cortex; so that here, as in *Chara* and the Phaeosporeae, there are species in which tissue is formed by the coalescence of branches originally separate. In other Florideae the thallus is a cell-surface of one or sometimes several layers; in many *(Hypoglossum, Delesseria)* it assumes the outline of a foliage-leaf, and even shows venation (Fig. 47); in others, again *(Sphaerococcus, Gelidium)*, it is filiform or like a narrow ribbon, and is much branched *(Plocamium* and others). In all these cases the growth, according to Nägeli[1], is apical by means of an apical cell; in the simpler forms the segmentation is by transverse division, in others two to three rows of cells are formed by oblique septa. One section with many species, the Melobesiaceae, a subdivision of the Corallineae, has a disc-shaped thallus, which grows centrifugally at the circumference (Fig. 46), and adheres closely to the object on which it grows, usually larger Algae. These species have therefore some resemblance to *Coleochaete scutata*, but their thallus is many-sided, and its cell-walls are incrusted with lime. This feature is more evident in other Corallineae, the ascending branches of which have a number of initial cells, and not a single apical cell.

Asexual reproduction is effected by means of non-motile gonidia, four of which are often formed in one mother-cell, and are therefore called tetraspores, or more correctly tetragonidia; sometimes the mother-cell produces only one, sometimes two, sometimes eight gonidia; they are altogether absent in the Lemaneae. If the thallus consists of cell-rows, the tetragonidia are formed in the terminal cell of lateral branches; in other cases they lie imbedded in the tissue of the thallus, and not unfrequently in special branches of it and in large numbers (Fig. 48, *t*); these branches have been called *stichidia*.

FIG. 47. *Delesseria (Worm shjoldia) sanguinea.* Leaf-like thallus with disk of attachment; right and left are the bases of two other leaf-like branches.

The *sexual organs* are usually found on plants which do not form gonidia, and these plants are monoecious or dioecious; but both kinds do occur at the same time on the same plant, and in some species, as in *Polysophonia variegata*, not so uncommonly. The account which Sirodot gives of the fresh-water *Batrachospermum* is remarkable and requires further investigation. He says that the germination of the carpospores does not result in the direct production of a batrachospermum-plant, but

---

[1] Neuere Algensysteme, p. 248.

of a pro-embryo, which is formed of simple cellular filaments, and from its resemblance to the protonema of a moss might be called by that name. This protenema, which has sometimes been described as a distinct species of the genus *Chantransia*, produces unicellular gonidia,—small ovoid cells formed on the apices of branches, while the batrachospermum-plant itself, which springs as a lateral branch from the protonema

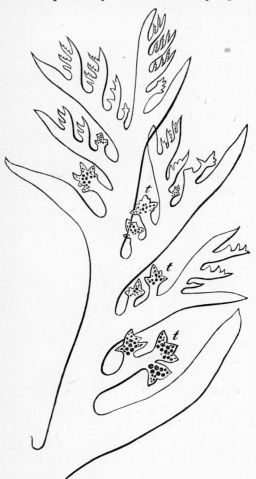

and has from the first a different structure, ramification &c., forms no gonidia. A similar pro-embryo, but without gonidia, occurs in the fresh-water *Lemanea*, a plant of somewhat complex structure which grows on stones in mountain-streams, while *Batrachospermum* occurs in the stiller waters of cold springs.

The spermatia are roundish cells with a thin cell-wall. In *Batracho-spermum*, according to Sirodot, they have the power of putting out a short tube in the direction of the tricho-gyne, when they are lying in its immediate proximity. Usually they attach themselves, one or more together, directly to the trichogyne and mingle their protoplasm with the protoplasm of that organ. The spermatia-cells which are formed in the tissue of the thallus are released by the conversion of the outer layer of the wall of the mother-cell into mucilage. In *Batrachospermum* the mother-cells of the spermatia are formed singly on the extremity of long, articulated branches; in the Ceramieae they are crowded together in large numbers on a common axis as the terminal cells of a system of very short branches; these groups of mother-cells of spermatia are

FIG. 48. *Plocamium.* Portion of a specimen with branches bearing tetraspores *t.*

called *antheridia* [better *spermogonia*]. In *Nitophyllum* they are crowded together on portions of the surface of the thallus which is formed of a single layer of cells; in the Corallineae they are formed in cavities that are grown over by the surrounding tissue.

We must not attempt in this place even a brief description of the several families of the Florideae, and indeed many of them have been as yet insufficiently investigated; only the most noteworthy phenomena in the formation of the procarp and in the process of fertilisation can be noticed in the following paragraphs.

The simplest mode of formation of procarp and carpospores is exemplified in the BANGIACEAE, which contain two genera, *Bangia* and *Porphyra*[1], the former consisting of cell-filaments, the latter of simple cell-surfaces. The spermatia are formed by the division of a cell of the thallus into a number of small daughter-cells ; the division is accompanied with loss of colour, and the daughter-cells are set free by the dissolution of the wall of the mother-cell. The procarp is distinguished from the vegetative cells of the thallus only by a small protuberance which represents the rudimentary trichogyne. After a spermatium has coalesced with this protuberance, the carpogenous cell, in this case almost the only representative of the procarp, divides into eight spores, and these are ejected from the mother-cell as round, naked protoplasmic bodies, which for a time display amoeboid motion, and then become invested with a cell-wall and germinate. It is evident that this case differs only in subordinate points from the mode of sexual reproduction in *Oedogonium*, for example, or *Sphaeroplea*. That the male element in *Bangia* is not a spermatozoid, but a non-motile spermatium, is connected with its mode of life, and, as regards the trichogyne, we find an arrangement for

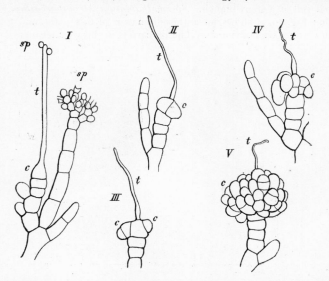

FIG. 49. *Nemalion multifidum*. *I* a branch with carpogon *c* and spermatia *sp*. *II*, *III* commencement of the formation of the fructification. *IV*, *V* development of the spore-cluster. *t* everywhere denotes the trichogyne, *c* the carpogone and fructification. After Thuret and Bornet.

conducting the male cell in *Oedogonium*, *Coleochaete*, and others ; that there is no open passage in *Bangia* is connected with the want of active movement in the spermatium, which would render special contrivances necessary if the spermatium was to find its way into such a passage. Then the fertilised carpogenous cell of *Bangia* behaves just like an oospore of *Oedogonium* &c., only that the latter when it has passed through its resting stage breaks up into a number of daughter swarm-cells, each of which produces a new plant. Besides the carpospores the Bangiaceae possess asexual gonidia formed by the division of a mother-cell into eight ; the fresh-water species[2] have only these asexually formed spores.

The NEMALIEAE also have a unicellular procarp, but they are distinguished from the Bangiaceae by the development of the trichogyne and by the production of spores

---

[1] Janczewski, Études anatomiques sur les Porphyra (Ann. d. sc. nat. sér. V. T. XVII).— Berthold, Zur Kenntn. der Bangiaceen (Mittheilungen der zool. Station zu Neapel, Bd. II).
[2] These grow in springs, on mill-wheels, and on the walls of canals, &c.

through a process of growth set up in the carpogone after fertilisation. This process has been already briefly described, but its characteristic features may be again noted in connection with the representation in Fig. 49. The figure shows in *I* to the left the unicellular procarp, with an elongated filiform upper part, the trichogyne (*t*), to the summit of which two spermatia are attached. After fertilisation the trichogyne is separated from the carpogone by a transverse septum (Fig. 49, *II*), and the latter becomes pluricellular by division; Fig. 49, *II*, shows one longitudinal wall which has appeared in it. The cells thus formed in the carpogone bulge outwards and form a compact mass of short branches (*IV, V, c*), which divide into cells that ultimately become carpospores. The trichogyne meanwhile disappears, as Fig. 49, *IV* and *V*, show. This cluster of spores, forming a very simple sporocarp (*glomerulus*), obtains in *Batrachospermum* a loose envelope by the upward growth of longer cells from beneath the carpogone.

In the CERAMIEAE, SPERMOTHAMNIEAE, WRANGELIEAE, and other subdivisions of the Florideae the procarp is a multicellular body before fertilisation, and is formed from the terminal cell of a short branch. *Spermothamnium hermaphroditum* may serve as an example; Fig. 50, *A* shows an antheridium (*an*) of this plant, and to the right of it a procarp with its trichogyne (*t*). The procarp is in this case terminal, being formed

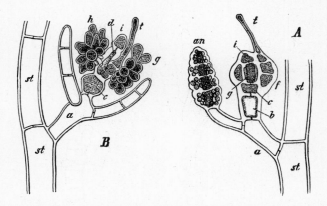

FIG. 50. *Spermothamnium hermaphroditum.* *A* a branch with the procarp (*t, f, g, i*) and an antheridium *an*. *B* after fertilisation, the sporocarp developing. After Nägeli.

from the three terminal cells of a branch. The upper of these (Fig. 50, *A, i*) and the lower take no part in the formation of the sporocarp, but remain as they were; the middle cell divides by longitudinal septa into five cells, a central and five peripheral cells. One of these five cells developes into a row of cells (Fig. 50, *A, f*), which bears the trichogyne (*t*) on its summit and is therefore called the *trichophore;* two of the lateral peripheral cells are the carpogenous cells (Fig. 50, *A, g*). As the two carpogenous cells are opposite to one another, only one can be seen in the side-view, and the fourth peripheral cell and the central cell have nothing further to do with the development of the sporocarp, but remain stationary. After fertilisation the two carpogenous cells divide and swell into small roundish heads, on the surface of which numerous crowded spores are formed (Fig. 50, *B*); the origin of these spores from two separate carpogenous cells is, according to Janczewski, no longer recognisable when the cluster of spores is fully formed. In other species of *Spermothamnium* (*Sp. flabellatum*) branches shoot out from the cell (*c*) and surround the sporocarp (*cystocarp*).

In other Florideae the branches which surround the fructification are united together into a more or less completely closed envelope, as in Lejolisia. Here the central cell (Fig. 51) of the procarp is the carpogenous cell, while the outer cells develope into segmented filaments and produce a closed envelope, which opens after a time at the apex, the trichogyne and trichophore being still to be seen outside it (Fig. 51, *tg*).—In the RHODOMELEAE the envelope of the fructification appears in its rudimentary form as a circular wall. We noticed a similar investment of the sexually generated spores in *Coleochaete*, a genus of the Chlorophyceae, while the oosphere of *Chara* has a similar covering before fertilisation ; but we shall lay no great stress on this difference, if we take into consideration analogous cases in other plants. For instance, the archegonia of *Marchantia* have an outer covering, which exists in a rudimentary form before fertilisation, but developes only after fertilisation, while the archegonia of *Jungermannia*, another of the Hepaticae, are invested before fertilisation and quite in-

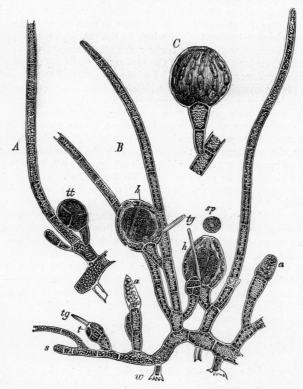

FIG. 51. *Lejolisia mediterranea*. *A* small piece of a creeping filament with a rhizoid and an erect branch, the lower cell of which bears a branch with tetragonidia *tt*. *B* a sexual (monoecious) plant ; *w* rhizoids of the creeping stem, the apical cell of which is at *s* and its erect branches bear the sexual organs ; *a a* antheridia, in which the axile cell-row is unfortunately not shown ; *tg* trichogyne beside the apex *t* of the fertile branch ; *h* the envelope of the sporocarp ; at *sp* a spore which has escaped from the sporocarp ; *C* an empty sporocarp, the outer covering of which is formed of cell-rows. After Bornet, Ann. d. sc. nat. 1859, magn. about 150 times.

dependently of it ; but in this case the outer covering encloses a whole group of archegonia ; similar cases might be adduced from the Phanerogams.

There are other Florideae in which the organs of fertilisation are of a more complex character. This is the case with the CORALLINEAE[1]. In this group, which includes the Melobesieae mentioned above, the walls of the vegetative cells are thickly incrusted with calcium carbonate. The thallus of the Melobesieae takes the form of creeping

---

[1] Solms-Laubach, *Corallina* (Aus Fauna u. Flora des Golfes von Neapel u. d. angrenzenden Meeresabschnitte, herausgeg. von d. Zool. Station in Neapel, IV. Monographie, Leipzig, 1881).

discs formed of one or more layers of cells ; the species of the genus *Corallina* have a cylindrical branched thallus with a group of initial cells of similar shape and size and not a single apical cell at the summit. Both the tetraspores and the sexual organs are found in special urn-shaped receptacles (*conceptacula*) formed by depression of the apex of a shoot, the two being on different plants. The procarps are formed from the cells which occupy the bottom of the conceptacles ; the development advances from the centre to the circumference. But while the trichogynes in the centre prepare for con- jugation by a club-shaped swelling at their apex and in other ways, the trichogynes at the margin of the disk formed by the procarps are fewer in number and shorter. Solms found no trichogynes in a receptive condition on the marginal procarps ; yet it is from the marginal procarps that spores are produced.

While in the majority of the Florideae one sporocarp (cystocarp) proceeds from each procarp, in *Corallina* only one fructification is formed in each conceptacle, but it is never- theless formed by the development of the whole of the procarps ; for after the fertilisa- tion of the central procarps with perfect trichogynes all the carpogenous cells of the pro- carps are fused into one by absorption of the separating walls. The carpogenous cell- fusion thus formed produces spores along its whole margin, and therefore from the car- pogenous cells of the marginal procarps which are fused in the general mass ; this happens in *C. mediterranea* in such a manner that from the indented undulating mar- ginal edge club-shaped cells grow out in large numbers, which are separated by a wall from the carpogenous cell-fusion and produce spores by transverse divisions. Thus while the central procarps have lost the power of producing spores but retain their receptivity, the converse has taken place with the marginal ones ; the spores proceed from their carpogenous cells, while their trichogynes are impotent.

The division of labour goes still further in **Dudresnaya**[1]. Here certain procarps have lost their receptive apparatus, the trichogyne, altogether, and their carpogenous cells are fertilised by other procarps, which have the receptive apparatus, but whose carpogenous cells produce no spores. The trichogyne of these procarps is the hair- like pointed terminal cell of one of the cell-rows that form the thallus. When the trichogyne has conjugated with the spermatia, or with one of them, long pluricellular tubes grow out of the trichophores. These tubes effect the fertilisation of the carpo- genous cells of the procarps which have no trichogynes; they lay themselves on them, the intervening portions of cell-wall are absorbed at the point of contact, and a portion of the contents of the fertilising tube passes into the carpogenous cell from which a sporocarp is then developed. A similar mode of fertilisation is found in *Polyides rotundus*, the Squamarieae, and others.

V. FUNGI[2].

The Fungi are chiefly distinguished from the Algae by the absence of chloro- phyll in their vegetative organs, in consequence of which they are dependent for their food on the organised substance of other plants or of animals. But it was pointed out in the general remarks on the Thallophytes that the Fungi are here considered separately from the Algae not on account of this physiological character, but because, with the exception of the Myxomycetes and Schizomycetes which have

---

[1] The essential points only in the process of fertilisation are given in the text; the details are of a more involved character. See Bornet and Thuret, *loc. cit.* [Also Berthol, Die Cryptonemiaceen, in vol. IV of the Mittheil. d. Zool. Stat. zu Neapel.]

[2] De Bary, Morphologie u. Physiologie der Pilze, Flechten, u. Myxomyceten, Leipzig, 1866. [See also his Vergleichende Morphologie u. Biologie der Pilze, Mycetozoen u. Bacterien, Leipzig, 1884, for a complete account of the group and its literature up to the present time.]—For special investi- gations see under the separate divisions.

already been described, they form a group of objects closely connected together by the history of their development, that is by their morphological characters[1]. The Fungi are marked by the peculiar structure of the elements of their thallus. The germinating spore developes into a branching tube with apical growth, which either remains undivided by transverse septa, as is also the case in the Siphoneae, or consists of cell-rows. These filiform fungal elements are called *hyphae*. It also frequently happens that Fungi, whose hyphae are originally unicellular unsegmented tubes, form irregularly disposed transverse septa when they come to produce organs of propagation. The unsegmented tubes in the Fungi as well as in the Siphoneae have numerous nuclei; but more than one nucleus may also appear in the cells of segmented hyphae. Among the Chytridieae, the simplest of the Fungi, are species in which the vegetative body has not yet acquired the characteristic hyphal structure, but is only a spherical or ovoid cell that soon turns to a zoosporangium. The higher forms of the same alliance (*Rhizidium, Cladochytrium*, &c.), on the contrary, have hyphae or elements very like hyphae. Deviations from the filamentous form of the hyphae occur also in other Fungi. In the Yeast-fungus, which consists of loosely connected branched rows of ellipsoidal cells and which multiplies by *sprouting* (*pullulation*) (Fig. 71), a cell forms a small protuberance usually at one end; this enlarges to the size of the mother-cell, becomes cut off from it by the formation of a dividing wall at the narrow point of junction, and finally separates from it entirely. Sprouting occurs also under certain circumstances in Fungi which have undoubted hyphae, such as *Mucor, Empusa muscae*. The Fungi have been divided according to the character of their vegetative organs into Fission-fungi (Schizomycetes, see above, p. 24), Sprouting-fungi (Yeast-fungi), and Spawn-fungi including all forms with hyphal growth, but these characters will not supply a general principle of division in any arrangement of the Fungi that keeps the whole course of their development in view.

The Fungi are either saprophytes and live on dead organic bodies, or are parasites. But one and the same Fungus may live in both ways. *Pythium De Baryanum*[2], for instance, is a frequent and destructive parasite on the seedlings of dicotyledonous plants, but it vegetates as readily in parts of dead plants or animals. A considerable number of parasitic Fungi, among them *Agaricus melleus* which lives on firs and other trees, have been successfully cultivated in suitable solutions containing of course organic substances, while Fungi that under ordinary conditions are saprophytes will in certain circumstances attack living plants; thus the germ-tubes of *Mucor, Penicillium, Botrytis*, &c., which cannot penetrate the uninjured rind of such fruits as apples and pears, can spread as parasites in the sound tissue of these fruits and bring about decay, if the rind is injured[3]. Other Fungi, on the contrary, are strictly confined to the one or the other mode of life. *Pythium vexans*, for instance, lives as a saprophyte in dead potato-tubers, but is not able to penetrate into the tissue of the living plant[4]. Parasitic Fungi find

---

[1] Our knowledge of the development of the Fungi is due especially to the labours of Tulasne, de Bary and his pupils. See also the literature cited below.

[2] De Bary, Zur Kenntniss d. Peronosporeen (Bot. Zeit. 1881, p. 521 ff.).

[3] Brefeld, Ueber d. Faulniss d. Früchte (Bot. Zeit. 1870, p. 281).

[4] De Bary, *loc. cit.*

[2]

their way into the plants or animals which supply them with nourishment in various ways; sometimes they pierce through the outer skin, sometimes they enter by the stomata. Many Fungi, as *Ustilago*, make their way into the plant only in its earliest stage and then grow luxuriantly throughout the growing plant; the greater number are not limited to any definite stage in the life of their host. There are Fungi living a peculiar kind of life, that cannot be called parasitic, in association with other organisms which contain chlorophyll and therefore assimilate carbon; these, together with the Algae round which they weave their hyphae, form a large and very distinct class of Thallophytes, the Lichens. This social life of Fungi with Algae is called by De Bary *symbiosis*[1], and will be described at greater length below. The great majority of Lichen-fungi belong to the section Ascomycetes, but it has been recently shown that a Basidiomycete is the Fungus in the Lichen-genus *Cora*.

The Fungi, like the Algae, have as a class both sexual and asexual propagative cells; but a large number of Fungi have only the asexual forms (*gonidia*, *conidia*); in some there occur peculiar phenomena of abortion in the sexual organs, and in many species, as in the Uredineae, the sexual process is not yet cleared up[2]. The branches of a hypha that has proceeded from the germination of a propagative cell usually manifest a division of labour; some penetrate into the substratum and spread abroad there in search of food, while the others grow at the expense of the organs from which they sprang. The hyphae which spread in the substratum as organs for obtaining food form the *mycelium* (spawn), and answer as regards their function to the root-like structures (rhizoids), for example, of *Chara*. If special branches of the hyphae serving for reproduction are present on the mycelium, they are called carpophores. Both the mycelial threads and the carpophores may be simple hyphae, as in the Filamentous-fungi, or a number of hyphae and their branches unite into a closely-woven tissue and form compact bundles of filaments, the individual elements in which are more or less intimately associated by the union of their walls. For instance, the large asexual carpophores (fructifications) of the Cap-fungi or Mushrooms, ordinarily regarded as the whole Fungus because the slender mycelium is hid in the substratum, are formed of interwoven hyphae. *Agaricus melleus* mentioned above has bundles of mycelial filaments formed by the union of many individual hyphae, which were supposed to be a distinct genus, *Rhizomorpha*, before it was recognised that they belonged to *Agaricus melleus*. Similar bundles though less conspicuous occur in many other Fungi. The peculiar bodies named *sclerotia*, resting states of the mycelium found in many Fungi, are formed in the same way. These sclerotia are small tuber-like bodies of varying size, which are able to remain for some time in a dormant condition and especially to withstand the effects of desiccation, and then under more favourable conditions to enter on a further course of development. They consist of a cortical layer and an inner compact tissue, with cell-walls that are often thick and of a cartilaginous consistence, so that their origin from separate hyphal branches woven together is often no longer perceptible in the mature state. Another kind of union of the

---

[1] [Lichens illustrate one form of symbiosis only. The term is applicable to all conditions in which dissimilar organisms live together.]

[2] [See Marshall Ward, On the Sexuality of the Fungi (Q. J. M. S. April, 1884).]

hyphae of the mycelium has been several times observed, especially in plants cultivated in artificial solutions; the cell-walls are absorbed at the points where two filaments touch one another, and the filaments thus communicate with one another. This proceeding is obviously distinct from the phenomena of sexual reproduction observed in the conjugation of the Zygomycetes.

It is through the *gonidia* that Fungi are most abundantly reproduced. These are either non-motile cells, or *zoogonidia* (swarm-spores); the latter are found in Fungi that live in water. Both kinds of gonidia may occur in nearly allied plants. *Pythium*, for instance, has zoogonidia, the rest of the Peronosporeae non-motile gonidia. The non-motile cells are the result of abjunction, or of the division of the contents of a mother-cell that has swollen into a spherical form. The most prevailing mode of formation is abjunction; examples are seen in *Cystopus* (Fig. 56, *B*), in the Basidiomycetes (Fig. 90), and in the Uredineae (Fig. 85), where cases of the formation of gonidia by abjunction are represented. In all of them the end of the mother-cell or the process or protuberance formed on it is abjointed from it by a parting wall as a daughter-cell, which developes into a gonidium and finally drops off. The process is repeated in *Cystopus;* when one gonidium has been formed another is formed beneath it, and in this way gonidia-chains are produced on the summit of the mother-cell, which is called a *basidium*, in the wider sense of the term. The *aecidiospores* of the Uredineae (Fig. 85), the gonidia of *Penicillium, Erysiphe* (Fig. 65) and others are formed in the same way. The gonidia of the Basidiomycetes are formed on the swollen club-shaped terminal cells of branches of the hyphae. These cells are termed basidia in the more restricted sense and put out narrow pointed processes, *sterigmata* (Fig. 90, *B*), the extremity of which swells into a ball and enlarges, and is then abjointed as a gonidium. When this is done the basidium disappears, for in this case there is no repetition of the process of formation and abjunction. The gonidia of the Uredineae (the *uredospores* and the *teleutospores*) are formed by the delimitation by a transverse septum of the upper portion of a cylindric somewhat club-shaped mother-cell (Fig. 85, *II* and *III*), the mother-cell serving as a stalk to the gonidium which does not drop off of its own accord. Lastly, the gonidia of *Mucor* are minute cells produced in large numbers inside hemispherical stalked sporangia, and are set free by the dissolution of the wall of the sporangium. The cells forming gonidia are either free and isolated, as in the last-mentioned case, or they form either by themselves or in combination with sterile hyphae an aggregate of cells which is termed the *hymenium*, a name usually applied to a layer of hyphae bearing propagative cells, whether asexually or sexually produced. The sexual mode of formation of spores, so far as it presents any peculiarity, will be described below.

SYSTEMATIC ARRANGEMENT OF THE FUNGI[1]. The Fungi include a number of forms, in which the course of development resembles that of *Vaucheria, Oedogonium*, and other genera of the Chlorophyceae; the germinating spore, whether zygospore or oospore, produces a thallus consisting of free hyphae not interwoven with one

---

[1] De Bary, Grundlagen e. Natürl. Systems d. Pilze in Beitr. zur Morphol. u. Physiol. d. Pilze von de Bary u. Woronin, IV. Reihe, p. 107. [Also De Bary, Vergl. Morph. u. Biol. d. Pilze etc., Leipzig 1884.]

another, which, if it runs its full course, ultimately produces zygospores or oospores, having in most cases previously given birth asexually to brood-cells (gonidia, zoogonidia). From the germinating spore a new thallus is developed either directly or indirectly through a previous formation of gonidia (or zoogonidia), a variation which may depend sometimes on outward circumstances. These Fungi, viz. the Zygomycetes, Peronosporeae, and Saprolegnieae, are named Phycomycetes on account of their affinity with the Algae, with which they might naturally be classed as forms without chlorophyll[1]. Their thallus, like that of the Siphoneae, consists of unsegmented tubes, in which however transverse septa sometimes appear. The mode of fertilisation is either isogamous or oogamous. The gametes, with the exception of the spermatozoids of *Monoblepharis* described by Cornu, are not motile. The Ascomycetes are nearly related to this group, as has been already stated in the introduction (p. 8), their archicarps in their simple form showing a very close resemblance to the sexual organs of the Peronosporeae. The difference in *Podosphaera*, for example, is, that the contents of the female cell (the archicarp) do not form an oosphere as in the oogonium of the Peronosporeae, but the fertilisation takes effect on the still quite small undifferentiated archicarp-cell, which then grows and eventually forms the ascus, after a stalk-cell has first been divided off from it. That the process is more complicated in other Ascomycetes has been stated above. Gonidia also are found in the Ascomycetes answering to those of the Peronosporeae; the more simple instances of these, as in the Erysipheae, closely resemble what we find for instance in *Cystopus*.

The Uredineae have the same course of development as the Ascomycetes. Their fructifications known as aecidia correspond to the fructifications with asci of the Ascomycetes, only the spores are not formed in asci but by abjunction. The first stages in the development of these fructifications are unknown, but it is probable that they are sexually generated; beside them a number of gonidial forms are found in the typical Uredineae, and are known as uredospores, teleutospores, and sporidia.

Lastly, the Basidiomycetes are Fungi, which have no fructifications corresponding to an ascus-fructification or aecidium, at least none such are known; they have only gonidiophores with gonidia which correspond with those in the Uredineae and Ascomycetes. Among the Uredineae too there are species, from whose course of development the aecidium has dropped out, and which are propagated only by gonidia. With the above-named Fungi are associated a few smaller groups, but we will not go further into the detail of their affinities, which are in many points still very doubtful; among them are the simple forms with which the following account begins[2]. The order in which the groups are taken is:—

1. **Chytridieae.**
2. **Ustilagineae.**
3. **Phycomycetes.**
4. **Ascomycetes.**
5. **Uredineae.**
6. **Basidiomycetes.**

---

[1] See Sachs, Lehrb. d. Bot., 4th ed.

[2] The account here given has in view only the more important species, in which the developement is more accurately known.

1. CHYTRIDIEAE.

The Chytridieae[1] are Fungi of the most simple organisation. There is an advance within this group from unicellular forms without a mycelium to others which possess a mycelium. Reproduction is effected by means of swarm-spores, which usually have but one cilium. Resting cells are also found in many species, which germinate and become sporangia producing swarm-spores. A sexual process has been described only in the case of *Polyphagus Euglenae*, in which according to Nowakowski a zygospore is formed[2].

Chytridium has no mycelium, but consists of single cells which live on or within the plant that feeds them. The cells after reaching their full size become zoosporangia. The swarm-spores have only one cilium, which is in front or at the hinder end in the peculiar backward hopping movement which they exhibit. The plants live on living or dead organisms in water and are parasitic on other Fungi and on Algae.—The genus **Rhizidium** has the rudiment of a mycelium in the form of slender branched root-like processes on the cell which produces the swarm-spores, and from which the mycelium is separated by a transverse wall.—**Cladochytrium**, on the other hand, has a distinct delicate filiform mycelium which proceeds from cells that produce zoospores, and bears new zoosporangia. The Cladochytrieae are parasites on water or marsh Phanerogams, for instance on *Menyanthes*.

The genus **Protomyces**[3] comes near to the Chytridieae. The mycelium of *Protomyces macrosporus*, composed of segmented filaments, is parasitic on the stems and leaf-stalks of *Aegopodium Podagraria* and other Umbelliferae, and causes peculiar marks on them like weals. Single cells of the mycelium swell into tough-walled resting spores, which germinate in the spring following their formation. An inner membrane protrudes from the outer, and its contents form a number of small cylindrical rod-like bodies, spores, which however have no cilia. These are set free and conjugate in pairs, forming by their union an H-shaped body. A germ-tube grows out from one of the two united spores, and forces its way into a healthy plant of *Aegopodium*, and there produces a mycelium which again generates resting-spores. No gonidia have been observed.

2. USTILAGINEAE.

The Ustilagineae[4] are parasites which live inside land-plants, some in their intercellular spaces only (Entyloma), while some penetrate the walls of the cells of the

---

[1] A. Braun, Ueber Chytridium, eine Gattung einzelliger Schmarotzergewächse (Abhandl. d. Berl. Akad. 1856).—Nowakowski, Beitr. z. Kennt. d. Chytridiaceen, I, II, in Cohn, Beitr. zur. Biol. d. Pflanz., Bd. II. [In De Bary, Vergl. Morph. u. Biol. d. Pilze, Mycetoz. u. Bact., Leipzig 1884, p. 184, the literature up to 1884 will be found.]

[2] [Now known in other forms; see de Bary; also Fisch, C., Beitr. z. Kenntn. d. Chytridiaceen, Enlangen, 1884; Borzi, Nowakowskia (Bot. Centralbl. XXII (1885).]

[3] De Bary, Beitr. z. Morph. u. Phys. d. Pilze, I Reihe (Abhandl. d. Senckenberg'schen Ges. zu. Frankf. a. M., V. Bd. 1864; [see also Vergl. Morph. u. Biol. d. Pilze, Mycetozoen u. Bacterien, Leipzig 1884, p. 199, for the literature].

[4] The position of the Ustilagineae is still unsettled even after the latest investigations, but at present it seems most natural to connect them with the Chytridieae. See Tulasne, Mém. sur les Ustilaginées comparées aux Uredinées (Ann. d. sc. nat. 3 ser. t. VII), and 2de Mém. sur les Ured. et les Ustilag. (Ann. d. sc. nat. 4 ser. t. II).—De Bary, Unters. ü. d. Brandpilze, Berlin 1853; Id. *Protomyces microsporus* (Bot. Ztg. 1874, p. 81); [also De Bary, Vergl. Morph. u. Biol. d. Pilze, Mycetozoen u. Bacterien, Leipzig, 1884, p. 200, where further literature is quoted.]—Wolff, Beitr. z. Kenntniss d. Ustilag. (Bot. Ztg. 1873).—Woronin, Unters. ü. d. Ustilag in De Bary u. Woronin, Beitr. z. Morph. u. Phys. d. Pilze, V. Reihe, 1882 (Abh. d. Senck. Ges. zu Frankfurt a. M.).—[Weber, Ueber den Pilz der Wurzelanschwellungen v. Juncus biformis (Bot. Zeit. 1884).]

parenchyma. The pathological appearances produced by them have long been described as Smut or Bunt, and the Ustilagineae themselves are known as Smuts or Bunt-fungi. They sometimes attack their host in certain parts only; *Entyloma* for example produces small pustules on the leaves of species of *Ranunculus* (*R. repens*) and *Calendula ;* sometimes they penetrate into the seedling and spread through the whole of the growing plant, and end by forming their resting-spores in special places in the plant. Thus *Tilletia Caries* forms its spores only in the ovary of the wheat-plant, while the mycelium penetrates through the whole of the plant; *Ustilago antherarum* forms them in the anthers of the Sileneae, and *U. Carbo* in the inflorescences of various grasses. The resting-spores form in most cases a black dust, produced oftentimes in considerable quantity in parts of the host which swell with the disease;

this may be well seen in *Zea Mais* when attacked by *U. Maidis.* The phenomena in the germination of the resting-spores will be described under the several genera. Besides the resting-spores some forms (*Tubercinia*, some species of *Entyloma*) have also gonidia formed by abjunction on gonidiophores which project above the surface of the host.

FIG. 52. *Tilletia Caries*, germination of the resting-spores. *p* the promycelium, *s* sporidia (commencement of the formation of sporidia at *a*), *s'* secondary gonidium, *x* a delicate germ-tube from a primary sporidium. Magnified 460 times. After Tulasne.

The species of **Entyloma** appear as parasites on *Calendula officinalis, Ranunculus repens,* &c.; spots and weals on the parts attacked show the presence of the parasite. The slender colourless hyphae with a few delicate transverse septa grow in the intercellular spaces of the host. Single cells intercalated in the hyphae swell into a spherical shape and become resting-spores, which ultimately fill the intercellular space with their thick masses; their cell-wall is differentiated into layers (episporium and endosporium). The germination of the resting-spores of *Entyloma* (e.g. *E. Calendulae*) agrees entirely with that of the spores of the following species.

The rest of the Ustilagineae differ from *Entyloma* as regards their vegetation in not attacking small portions only of the plant, but in spreading through it; they enter the plant at its earliest stage and their mycelium grows as it grows. The genera *Tilletia, Urocystis,* and *Ustilago* are suitable examples. Fig. 52 shows the germination of the spore of **Tilletia Caries.** The spore has put out a short blunt germ-tube of limited growth, the *promycelium.* A whorl of thin pointed branches, the *sporidia,* is formed at its apex. Before the sporidia drop off from the promycelium, they conjugate in pairs by means of a protuberance (Fig. 52, *b*). The sporidia thus united in pairs, put out a germ-tube (Fig. 52, *s'*), which forces its way into the host, or becomes club-shaped at its extremity and gives off a secondary sporidium by abjunction (Fig. 52, *s'*), which then forms a germ-tube to penetrate into the host. *Tilletia Caries* causes the disease in wheat known as 'Bunt.' The germ-tubes penetrate into the young wheat-plant and grow up with it. The mycelium is at first very inconspicuous and consists of thin delicate filaments; when it reaches the inflorescence it ramifies copiously, makes its way into the blossoms, and takes possession of every part up to the wall of the ovary. It is in the flowers only that the resting-spores are formed, one on the end of each branch of the mycelium; the exosporium has reticulate thickenings in *T. Caries,* while it is smooth in *T. laevis.*—**Urocystis** is distinguished by the peculiar behaviour of its spores. These appear as enlargements of certain branches of the threads of the mycelium, and occur singly or in groups; then special branches of the mycelium grow at an early period round the group of spores, or the single spore, and form an investment for it; the cell-wall of the spores is thick and of a brown colour. *Urocystis occulta* is a parasite on the leaves and stems of rye. The mycelium vegetates at first in the intercellular spaces of the plant, but afterwards pierces the cell-walls. Germination is similar to that in the two species above described, only the H-shaped union of the sporidia occurs but seldom.— The genus **Ustilago**, on the other hand, shows a difference in the mode of germination. *Ustilago Tragopogonis* (Fig. 53, *B*) developes in germination a promycelium which is divided by transverse septa. The sporidia are formed on the cells of the promycelium and conjugate in pairs. The promycelium of *U. longissima* (Fig. 53, *A*) is a narrow cylindrical tube, from the apex of which a sporidium is abjuncted which varies in shape from fusiform to cylindrical. The spores of *U. Carbo* (Fig. 53, *C*), on the other hand, put out a short cylindrical tube, which forms sporidia either at the extremities of small lateral branchlets, or by dividing by transverse septa into cylindrical cells. When the spores are being formed the mycelium gives off an unusually large number of branches, which become divided by transverse walls into many cells, and each of these cells is separated eventually from the rest and becomes a spore. The spores are formed in huge numbers, the part of the plant in which this takes place being much deformed and swollen, and the black spore-dust taking the

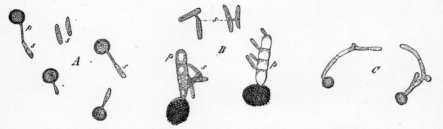

FIG. 53. Germination of resting-spores of *Ustilago*. *A Ustilago longissima* Tul. magnified nearly 700 times. *B Ustilago Tragopogonis*, magn. 390 times. *C Ustilago Carbo* Tul. magn. over 390 times; *p* the promycelium, *s* sporidia. After De Bary.

place of the whole of the inner tissue; plants of maize attacked by *Ustilago Maidis* show these effects in the most conspicuous manner. *U. Carbo* produces the 'Smut' of various grasses, as oats and barley.

Woronin has recently given an account of the development of **Tubercinia Trientalis**, an interesting species which is parasitic on *Trientalis europaea*. In this case also the mycelium spreads through the intercellular spaces, but it possesses organs of suction (*haustoria*) which penetrate into the cells and there ramify. *Tubercinia* produces gonidia as well as resting-spores, and multiplies largely by their means. The gonidiophores appear as a cottony covering on the underside of the leaves in spring. The threads of the mycelium all develope towards the underside of the leaf and send out branches at right angles to its surface, which pass through the stomata or between the cells of the epidermis and project beyond the surface of the leaf. These branches either become gonidiophores at once or they spread over the surface of the leaf and put out branches which become gonidiophores. A pear-shaped gonidium is formed at the extremity of the gonidiophore, and when this drops off, another is formed, and then another, till the protoplasm of the gonidiophore is all used up. The gonidia put out germ-tubes in water, and these either form secondary gonidia by abjunction or make their way at once into a leaf of *Trientalis*. In three weeks at most after the sowing of the gonidia on a healthy leaf of *Trientalis* black spots appear on it, indicating the presence of resting-spores. These resting-spores are collected into a roundish cluster, and are enclosed in an envelope which shows no structure, but is probably formed of swollen hyphae pressed together. Each spore germinates in autumn in the same way as the spores of *Entyloma* and *Tilletia*. The sporidia produced from the promycelium conjugate in pairs, and one of the two united sporidia forms a secondary sporidium, which may however be formed directly on a sporidium which has not conjugated. The secondary sporidium puts out a germ-tube, which penetrates into young and sound plants of *Trientalis* now in their winter rest. The mycelium formed in the plants spreads during the next year in the new shoots, and developes gonidia on their leaves. While the mycelium produced from the resting-spores thus spreads through the whole plant, that which comes from the gonidia is confined to certain spots on the leaf.—Of other forms it remains to mention **Thecaphora hyalina.** The resting-spores collected into clusters produce a promycelium which is divided by transverse septa. The cells of the promycelium do not however form sporidia (gonidia), as we saw in *Ustilago*, but develope into filaments, which conjugate in pairs when they meet ; one of the filaments then puts out a new germ-tube.

3. PHYCOMYCETES[1].

Under this designation De Bary includes the nearly allied groups of the Zygomycetes, Peronosporeae, and Saprolegnieae. Their mycelium is copiously branched, and its hyphae are usually without division-walls. The sexual propagation is isogamous in the Zygomycetes, oogamous in the Peronosporeae; the Saprolegnieae have lost the power of conjugation, apogamy having established itself, as will be shown below. Asexual propagation is by non-motile gonidia or by zoospores according to circumstances. The Entomophthoreae are probably allied to the Zygomycetes.

I. **ZYGOMYCETES.** The mycelium is a much-branched tube (Fig. 54, *Bm*), in which transverse septa are formed only when the plant is fully grown and is preparing for sexual and asexual propagation. Numerous small nuclei are enclosed in the protoplasm, as is the case with the Siphoneae[2]. The branches of a mycelium in the Zygomycetes are all the product of a germ-tube from a brood-cell, and can in the course of a few days cover a space of several square centimetres. The Zygomycetes live on organic substances, for example on and inside fruits, on bread and glue, or even on saccharine fluids or dung, from all of which the branches of the mycelium take up their food ; many species grow as parasites on their relatives, withdrawing the contents of their cells by means of organs of suction (*haustoria*) (Fig. 55, *h*).

Asexual reproduction and multiplication of the mycelia can go on for an unlimited number of generations before favourable conditions occur for the formation of organs of conjugation, that is, for sexual reproduction. The asexually produced brood-cells are formed in two ways. In the Mucorineae thick branches grow from the mycelium and rise erect into the air to a height of some centimetres, and finally swell into a globular shape at their free extremity (Fig. 54, *Bg*)[3]. Numerous roundish brood-cells are produced from the contents of this globular cell ; they are set free by the bursting of its wall, and germinating at once produce mycelia. In the two other families, the Chaetocladieae and Piptocephalideae, erect gonidiophores branch copiously above and form numerous brood-cells (*stilogonidia* or gonidia) by abjunction at the ends of their branches, and these produce new mycelia directly as in the Mucorineae. Besides these normal asexual

---

[1] De Bary, Beitr. z. Morph. u. Phys. d. Pilze, I. (Abh. d. Senckenb. nat. Ges. in Frankfurt a. M. (Syzygites)); [see also Vergl. Morph. u. Biol. d. Pilze, Mycetoz. u. Bacter., Leipzig 1884, p. 170, where additional literature is quoted].—Brefeld, Unters. ü. d. Schimmelpilze, Heft II, IV (where other works on the subject are given).—[Zopf, Zur Kenntniss d. Phycomyceten, Halle, 1885.]

[2] Schmitz, Ueber d. Zellkerne d. Thallophyten (Abh. d. Niederrh. Ges. 1880).

[3] [Errera, Die grosse Wachsthumsperiode bei den Früchtträgern von *Phycomyces* (Bot. Zeit. 1884).]

organs of propagation, the mycelium not unfrequently produces the so-called *gemmae* by the division of its tubular branches by tranverse septa into short members, which round themselves off and can under favourable circumstances give rise to new mycelia. In this way is explained the production of the so-called mucor-yeast by *Mucor race-mosus*, the resemblance of which to true yeast is increased by the fact, that when placed in an unfavourable nutrient solution it can multiply by sprouting. *Mortierella* also produces similar gemmoid bodies.

Under special circumstances the mycelium is able to attain the morphological

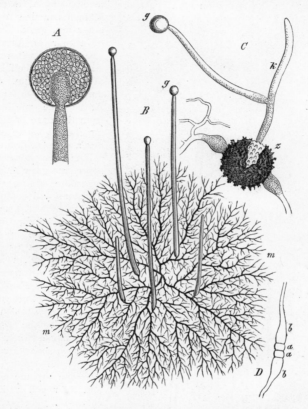

FIG. 54. *B* mycelium (3 days old) of *Phycomyces nitens* grown in a drop of mucilage with a decoction of plums ; the finest ramifications are omitted ; *g* the gonidiophores. *A* a gonidiophore of *Mucor Mucedo* in optical longitudinal section. *C* a germinating zygospore *s* of *Mucor Mucedo* ; the germ-tube *k* puts out a lateral gonidio-phore *g*, In *D* are conjugating branches *b b*, the extremities of which, *a a*, though they have not yet coalesced, are already cut off by transverse walls ; the zygospore is formed from the coalescence of the cells *a a*. *A*,*C*,*D* after Brefeld greatly magn., *B* from nature slightly magn.

conclusion of its development by forming *sexual organs* ; thicker club-shaped branches arise on adjacent branches of the mycelium which cross one another ; the apical cells meet and unite by the solution of their cell-walls at the point of contact (Figs. 54 and 55 *Z*), after a transverse septum has formed in each tube right and left of the point of conjugation; the protoplasm aggregates in the chamber thus cut off and by considerable growth of the whole separated chamber (Fig. 54 *C*), or of its middle portion only (Fig. 55 *Z*), a comparatively large *zygospore* is formed, the thick outer wall of which is usually dark-coloured and furnished with knobs or spike-like projections[1]. The zygospore

[1] [Bainier, Nouv. observ. sur les zygospores des Mucorinées (Ann. sc. Nat. 6me. sér. XIX).].

rests for a considerable time and then germinates ; the product of germination depends on the supply of nutriment ; if it is placed in a nutrient solution at the moment of germination it produces a mycelium ; otherwise it forms a gonidiophore at once, and its gonidia then produce new mycelia. In both cases the outer wall bursts and the inner protrudes in the form of a tube.

Brefeld has recently discovered a specially interesting mode of formation of fructification in **Mortierella.** This plant has very large gonidiophores, which have their base enveloped in the tissue of the mycelium, and on which thousands of gonidia are formed as in *Mucor.* In the formation of a zygospore the club-shaped extremities of two filaments incline towards one another and meet, like the two legs of a pair of forceps. The two sexual cells, which are of unequal size, are cut off from the rest of the mycelium, and their contents combine to form a zygospore. At the same time hyphae grow out from the base of the cells supporting the zygospore and unite with other adjacent branches of the mycelium to envelope the young zygospore, and grow as it grows. The zygospore attains considerable dimensions and compresses the hyphal tissue which surrounds it, and which grows more dense and compact from the branching of the hyphae, till at length it encloses the zygospore in a membranous capsule of woven threads, the outside of which is still a loose hyphal tissue. The growth of the envelope comes to an end with the maturity of the zygospore, which has a single wall of cellulose, there being no exosporium or endosporium ; the hyphae composing the envelope assume a darker colour and their cell walls become cuticularised. The germination of the zygospores has not been observed. The formation of the fructification recalls that of *Coleochaete,* where too the oospore is surrounded by tubes which shoot forth from the cells bearing the oogonium.

FIG. 55. *Piptocephalis Freseniana. M* a piece of the mycelium of *Mucor Mucedo,* on which the mycelium *m m* of *Piptocephalis* lives ; *h* the haustoria which have penetrated into the filament of *Mucor* ; *c* a gonidiophore ; *ss* the two conjugating branches of the mycelium which form the zygospore *Z.* After Brefeld ; *c* magn. 300 times, the rest magn. 630 times.

The Zygomycetes may be divided in the present state of our knowledge into three sub-divisions, distinguished by the mode of formation of their gonidia.

a. The MUCORINEAE, including *Mortierella, Choanephora,* and some others. The gonidia are formed in the genus *Mucor* inside globular sporangia borne on long stalks, and are set free by the bursting or the solution of the frail wall of the capsule ; in *Pilobolus* the wall is firmer, and parts at the base when the capsule is mature, and is flung away to some distance with the spores. *Mucor Mucedo* is one of the commonest of moulds, and is to be found on fruits, bread, dung, even inside old nuts and apples into which the mycelium finds its way.—*Mucor stolonifer* covers in a short time large patches of the like substrata, the mycelium forming long stolon-like branches, which fix themselves root-wise at their extremities and form gonidiophores with small black heads. The mycelium has been known to penetrate the shell of a freshly laid hen's egg and form gonidial capsules in its air-space.—*Phycomyces nitens* is known by its violet-coloured gonidiophores which are from ten to fifteen centimetres in height.— The genus *Thamnidium* forms an ordinary capsule at the top of its tall gonidiophore, and lower down whorls of small branches with small capsules containing only a few gonidia.—The genus *Pilobolus* is almost certain to make its appearance if fresh horse-dung is put under a glass cover.

b. The CHAETOCLADIEAE. The genus *Chaetocladium* is parasitic on *Mucor*. If the germ-tubes from the gonidia of *Chaetocladium* encounter a filament of *Mucor*, they form an open communication with it and develope at the point of union a cluster of branches, some of which grow on into other mucor-filaments, while others form organs of propagation. The gonidia in this case, as in the following sub-family, are not formed in a sporangium (*gonidangium*) but by abjunction. The gonidiophores form whorls of branches, and some of the lateral branches swell out and form on their surface slender protuberances (*sterigmata*), and from the apex of each of these a gonidium is abjointed. The formation of the zygospore is as in *Mucor*.

c. The PIPTOCEPHALIDEAE are distinguished by the circumstance that the young zygospore developes at a distinctly defined and localised growing-point which soon disappears, and a simple process of division then takes place (Brefeld). The point of union of the two conjugating cells bulges outwards, the convexity quickly enlarges into a spherical form, and the mass of dense protoplasm moves into it. Then the curved posterior part of the zygospore (Fig. 55, *s*) is cut off from the spherical portion, which is now the resting spore of the Fungus (Fig. 55, *Z.*) *Piptocephalis* is parasitic on *Mucor*, and is represented in detail in Fig. 55.

The small group of the ENTOMOPHTHOREAE is allied to the Zygomycetes[1]. These are parasites on living animals, which they usually kill in a short time. The only two genera are *Empusa* and *Entomophthora*; resting-spores are known in the latter, and these, according to Nowakowski, are the result of conjugation.

Empusa. The best known species is *Empusa muscae*, which is often the cause of an epidemic among houseflies in autumn. The Fungus rapidly multiplies its cells by sprouting, after the manner of the Yeast-fungus, in the fatty substance of the fly and thus kills it. Then the isolated cells put out tubes which pierce through the skin of the fly, and form gonidia by abjunction from their extremities in the open air, one from each filament. These gonidia are abjected with some force, and when one alights on the lower side of the hinder part of the fly's body it can penetrate through its skin and infect the whole insect. Usually, however, the gonidia, smeared with a sticky substance obtained from the protoplasmic content of the ruptured gonidiophore, light first when abjected in the neighbourhood of the spot where the infected fly has fixed itself, and there give rise to secondary gonidia which are also flung off with force. The gonidia in this case form a white deposit in the neighbourhood of the dead flies. Resting-spores are not known in *Empusa*, but they are found in the next genus.

Entomophthora attacks various insects and their larvae; the best known is *E. radicans*, which in some years causes an epidemic in the caterpillars of the cabbage-butterfly. In this case too the gonidia put out germ-tubes which penetrate the skin of the caterpillar; but the further development in the body of the

---

[1] Brefeld, Unters. über d. Entw. d. *Empusa muscae* u. *E. radicans* (Abhandl. d. naturf. Ges. zu Hall, XII Bd., where older literature on the subject is given); Id. Unters. über d. Schimmelpilze IV. Heft, p. 97, (*Entomophthora radicans*); [also Untersuch. aus d. Gesammtgebiete d. Mykologie IV. (1884) Entomophthoreen].—Nowakowski, Die Kopulation bei ein. Entomophthor. (Bot Zeit. 1877, p. 217).—[See also De Bary, Vergl. Morph. u. Biol. d. Pilze, Mycet. u. Bacterien, Leipzig 1884.]

insect is different. The germ-tube does not swell, as in *Empusa*, into a globular cell
which afterwards sprouts like the cells of the yeast-plant, but developes into a much-
branched mycelium divided by transverse septa, which in the space of five days
usually spreads entirely through the fatty substance of the caterpillar and so wastes it,
that the lightly-stretched skin of the insect ultimately contains nothing but a dense
hyphal tissue with the tracheae and intestines. The fungus-mummy is then secured to
the substance on which it lies by tufts of hyphae which break through on the under
side, while a number of branches of the mycelium come out through the upper surface,
ramify and give rise at the extremity of every branch to a gonidium which is abjected
and can infect a healthy insect in the same way as in *Empusa*. After a series of
asexual generations resting spores make their appearance ; their presence in the dead
caterpillar is shown by its not stiffening in death, but continuing flaccid. According to
Nowakowski these spores are formed by conjugation ; two cells put out processes
towards one another, as we see in the Conjugatae, and these processes unite. On one
of them, or on some portion of the conjugating cells, a protuberance is formed into
which the protoplasm moves ; the protuberance becomes globular in form (zygospore) [1],
and being cut off by a transverse septum becomes the resting spore, the germination of
which has not yet been observed ; it has a very thick cell-wall which is differentiated
into an exosporium and an endosporium.

2. The **PERONOSPOREAE** [2], according to De Bary's latest researches, include the
genera *Pythium*, *Phytophthora*, *Peronospora*, *Sclerospora* and *Cystopus* ; they are for
the most part parasites living in the interior of living plants, though the genus *Pythium*
contains species which can live as saprophytes as well as parasites ; *P. De Baryanum*,
for instance, often attacks and kills the seedlings of Dicotyledons, but can vegetate
equally well in dead plants and animals ; *P. vexans*, on the other hand, lives as a
saprophyte in potato-tubers, but cannot penetrate into the tissue of the living plant.
Peronospora and *Cystopus* inhabit the juicy parenchyma of living Dicotyledons ; the
much and irregularly branched mycelium spreads widely in their intercellular spaces,
thrusts a number of suckers (*haustoria*) into the parenchymatous cells of the host, and
takes their contents for its own support. The vegetative body, the mycelium, is at first
a single tube which is not divided by transverse walls, and numerous nuclei may be seen
in its protoplasm. At a later period, when the organs of propagation are being formed,
transverse walls are found in it at irregular intervals. At the beginning of the period of
vegetation propagation is effected almost exclusively in the asexual way by the formation
of non-motile gonidia or of swarm-spores, in *Pythium* of swarm-spores. Ultimately,
under suitable conditions of nutrition, oospores are formed sexually ; in many species
of *Pythium* indeed they may make their appearance quite at the commencement of the
vegetative period. When swarm-spores are formed in *Pythium* the whole of the protoplasm of the usually spherical sporangium issues forth and then divides into a number
of swarm-spores. *Pythium De Baryanum* has not only these zoosporangia but also
resting gonidia, which are of exactly the same appearance as the zoosporangia but do
not produce swarm-spores ; they persist after the vegetative portion of the Fungus has
died away, and develope germ-tubes in germination ; in this case then zoosporangia

---

[1] Brefeld (Schimmelpilze, Heft IV.) does not consider the process in the formation of the resting
spores to be the same as that in the formation of zygospores in the Mucorineae, &c., but to be an asexual
one, because the resting spores are formed also on filaments which have not conjugated with
others, and coalescence occurs on purely vegetative branches of the mycelium of many Fungi.

[2] De Bary in Ann. d. sc. nat. 4ᵉ série, T. XX ; Id., Untersuch. über die Peronosporeen u.
Saprologieen u. die Grundlagen eines natürlichen Systems der Pilze, in De Bary u. Woronin, Beitr.
z. Morph. u. Phys. d. Pilze IV. Reihe (Abdr. a. d. Abh. d. Senckenberg. nat. Ges. Bd. II. Frankfurt
1881) ; Id. Zur Kenntn. der Peronosporeen (Bot. Zeit. 1881); [also Vergl. Morph. u. Biol. d. Pilze
Mycet. u. Bacterien, Leipzig 1884.—Marshall Ward, Observations on the genus *Pythium* (Q. J. M. S.
Oct. 1883).]

and gonidia are, as comparison with the other species shows, equivalent formations which behave differently according to the external conditions. *Pythium*, which lives both in water-plants (Algae and others) and in succulent land-plants (seedlings, &c.), discharges the contents of its gonidia (zoosporangia) while they remain on the mycelial tube which produced them ; in *Peronospora* and *Cystopus*, on the contrary, the gonidia at the extremities of branches of the mycelium germinate only after having been separated from them.

In *Peronospora*, a genus with many species, long slender branches of the mycelium push through the stomata of the host into the open air, where they ramify and form a comparatively large roundish-elongate gonidium at the extremity of each branch. In *Cystopus*, on the contrary, a number of short club-shaped branches (Fig. 56, *B*) appear close together on the parasitic mycelium beneath the epidermis of the host, and each

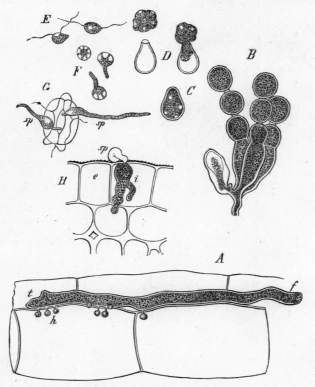

FIG. 56. *A—G Cystopus candidus. H Phytophthora infestans. A* branch of mycelium growing at the apex *t* with haustoria *h* between the cells of the pith of *Lepidium sativum. B* branch of mycelium bearing gonidia. *C—E* formation of swarm-spores from gonidia. *F* swarm-spores germinating. *G* swarm-spores germinating on a stoma and piercing the epidermis of the stem of a potato at *H.* After De Bary, magn. about 400 times.

of these forms at its free extremity a row of round gonidia, a gonidia-chain, till at last the multiplication of these gonidia bursts the epidermis and they issue forth as a white dust. The behaviour of the gonidia in germination varies. In certain species of *Peronospora*, as *P. infestans, P. nivea*, if the gonidia on separating from the parent plant fall into a drop of water (dew, rain), their contents break up into a number of zoogonidia and disperse (Fig. 56, *C, D*) ; in *P. pygmaea* the whole of the protoplasm escapes from the gonidium and forms a roundish cell which at once developes a germ-tube. In a third and fourth section of the genus the gonidium puts out a tube at once, and either at a fixed spot, as in *P. gangliformis*, or at any point, as in *P. parasitica, P. calotheca*,

Alsinearum and others. In the genus *Cystopus* either all the gonidia are alike, that is, they all produce swarm-spores when they have fallen into a drop of water (*C. candidus*), or the uppermost gonidium in a chain puts out a germ-tube, if it is capable of germination, while the other cells of the chain produce swarm-spores (*C. Portulacae*).

When the swarm-spores come to rest they settle on the cuticle of the host and become invested with a delicate cell-wall; in *Phytophthora infestans* they insert a slender germ-tube directly into a cell of the epidermis by piercing the cell-wall; the tube thus introduced (Fig. 56, *H*) receives the whole of the protoplasm of the swarm-spore, and having pierced through the inner wall of the epidermal cell reaches an intercellular space, where the development of the mycelium then begins. On the other hand, the swarm-spores of *Cystopus* place themselves near the stomata of the host and send their

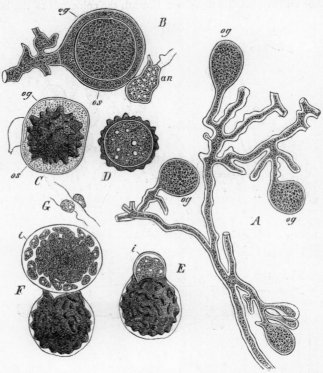

FIG. 57. *Cystopus candidus.* *A* mycelium with young oogonia. *B* oogonium *og* with oosphere *os* and antheridium *an*. *C* ripe oogonium. *D* ripe oospore. *E, F, G* formation of swarm-spores from oospores; *i* endosporium. After De Bary, magn. 400 times.

germ-tubes through the opening (Fig. 56, *G*) directly into the intercellular spaces. If the mycelium is once established in the parenchyma of the host, it grows vigorously and often spreads through the whole plant, and protrudes the branches which produce the gonidia at various points in stem, leaf or inflorescence into the open air. The mycelium may also live through the winter inside the host, as *Phytophthora infestans* inside the potato-tuber, and spread again in the next spring in the young shoots. The sexual organs of *Peronospora, Phytophthora, Cystopus,* and others, are formed inside the host, outside it also in the saprophytic species of *Pythium.* A portion of a branch of the mycelium, either the extremity or not unfrequently a part between the two extremities, swells into a globular form, and the protoplasm moves into the swollen part. The *oogonium* thus formed is then cut off by one transverse wall, if it is at the extremity of the branch, by two if in any intermediate portion of it, from the rest of the branch (Fig, 57, *og*). Then near it begins the formation of antheridia ; usually a lateral protuberance, like the rudiment of a branch, makes its appearance on the filament that bears the oogonium or on an adjacent branch of the mycelium, and grows in a curve in the direction of the oogonium. Its extremity which is in contact with the oogonium is now divided off by a transverse wall, and forms the *antheridium* (Fig 57, *an*). The processes of formation of the oosphere and of fertilisation have been recently made known to us by the researches of De Bary. The interior of the oogonium is at first uniformly filled with dense finely granular protoplasm. But the whole contents of the oogonium are not employed to form the oosphere, as is the case in the Saprolegnieae. The dark granular portion of it retreats from the periphery and collects into a ball (Fig. 57, *os*), the outer surface of which is separated by a broad interval from the wall of the oogonium. This ball is the *oosphere*, and its granular mass is bounded by a layer of thinner hyaline protoplasm. The portion of the protoplasm which is not expended in forming the oosphere is called the *periplasm*[1], and remains as a pale turbid substance, with fine granules unequally distributed through

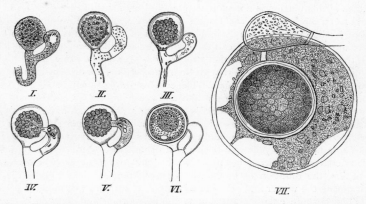

FIG. 58. Formation of oospores and fertilisation in the Peronosporeae. *I–VI. Pythium gracile*, successive states of an oogonium. *I* Oogonium full-grown, to the right an antheridial branch applied to it but not yet divided off. *II*. Antheridium cut off by a transverse wall *III*. Formation of spherical oosphere complete in the oogonium ; a narrow zone of periplasm lies between the oosphere and the wall of the oogonium. *IV*. The antheridium has put out the fertilisation-tube ; a clear receptive spot may be seen in the oosphere. *V*. Passage of the gonoplasm from the antheridium to the oosphere. *VI*. Ripe oospore invested with a thick cell-wall, almost entirely filling the cavity of the oogonium, the figures magn. about 800 times. *VII. Peronospora arborescens* ; an oogonium with an antheridium applied to it, which has put out a fertilisation-tube. The oospore is invested with a thick cell-wall, and outside it is a comparatively broad zone of periplasm ; the periplasm is contracting to form the episporium round the oospore ; magn. 600 times. After De Bary.

it, filling the space between the oosphere and the oogonium (Fig. 58, *II, VI, VII*). From this stage the course of procedure varies somewhat in the different genera of the group. We will take *Pythium* first, and especially *P. De Baryanum* (Fig. 58, *I–VI*). As the oogonium is formed changes also begin in the antheridium, in preparation for fertilisation. At a spot in the surface of the antheridium, where it impinges on the oogonium, there appears a blunt cylindrical or conical protuberance, the *fertilisation-tube*, which grows through the wall of the oogonium straight towards the oosphere, till its extremity is in close contact with it. The tube at first contains only homogeneous protoplasm ; but as soon as its surface impinges distinctly on the oosphere, a sudden separation is visible in the protoplasm of the antheridium. A thin layer, the *periplasm*, remains, lining the wall of the antheridial cell[2]; the larger part, the *gonoplasm*,

---

[1] It corresponds to the portion of the protoplasm not used to form the oosphere but ejected from the oogonium in *Vaucheria*.

[2] This circumstance too finds its parallel in the antheridia of *Vaucheria*, where a large part of

moves in the form of a band of irregular thickness into the central space. Then begins a movement of the gonoplasm through the tube into the oosphere, till it has all made its way into it ; the movement is slow, and the transit lasts from one to two hours. When the transit begins, the more granular portion of the protoplasm of the oosphere draws back from round the point of contact with the fertilisation-tube, leaving a narrow hyaline spot free, the *receptive spot.* The particles of the gonoplasm enter one after another into the substance of this spot, then move towards the dark granular substance and disappear in it. Here therefore fertilisation is effected by the union (conjugation) of two masses of protoplasm. After fertilisation has taken place the oospore is seen to be invested with a coat of cellulose, the periplasm of the oogonium shrinks to a loose sac, and the wall of the oogonium remains intact till the germination of the oospore. Sometimes more than one antheridium pours its gonoplasm into one oosphere, as in the case of *P. proliferum.*

In *Phytophthora omnivora*, a parasitic plant which attacks many Phanerogams, no separation of the contents of the antheridium into gonoplasm (the only portion employed in *Pythium* for fertilisation) and periplasm is to be seen ; a very small portion of the contents of the antheridium passes over as gonoplasm into the oosphere, and the appearance of this portion is not such as to make it evident that it had been previously separated from the rest ; but the transit is plainly seen. The same is the case with *Peronospora* ; but here only very minute quantities of the contents of the antheridium pass over into the oosphere, nor can the transit be actually seen. In the nearly allied group of the Saprolegnieae fertilisation appears no longer to take place, as will be seen by the account to be given below, although the sexual organs are present in many cases in the same form as in the Peronosporeae. The cellulose-wall of the ripe oospore is differentiated into a thick outer layer, the episporium, and a thin inner layer, the endosporium, and the contents are composed of a central portion rich in oil, and an outer granular protoplasm surrounding it, which shows in one place a small hyaline spot. The oospore of *Peronospora* and *Cystopus* has an additional envelope formed from the periplasm, which hardens into a firm deep yellowish-brown coat fitting close to the oospore, and having its surface coarsely and irregularly tubercled. The oospores enter when mature on a period of rest, the duration of which varies in different species; usually they remain dormant during the winter and germinate in the next spring. The mode of germination varies. The oospore enlarges and bursts the episporium and puts out a germ-tube, which may remain shorter than the diameter of the oospore or exceed it several times in length. This germ-tube either becomes a zoosporangium (*Cystopus*, Fig. 57, *F*), or it ramifies and forms several sporangia, or, if it falls upon a suitable substratum, it grows at once into a mycelium. These different modes of germination may occur in one and the same species, according to the supply of nutriment (see above under *Mucor*) ; but some species are limited to one mode.

3. The **SAPROLEGNIEAE**[1] include the genera *Saprolegnia, Achlya, Dictyuchus* and *Aphanomyces; Pythium* was till quite recently placed in this group but now ranks wth the Peronosporeae, from which the Saprolegnieae differ in growth and in the mode of propagation. The Peronosporeae are chiefly endophytic parasites ; in the Saprolegnieae the spore settles on the outside of the substratum and sends out one germ-tube

---

the protoplasm not expended in the formation of the spermatozoids is ejected; compare also the development of the spermatozoids in *Chara* and the Vascular Cryptogams, where it is really only the nuclear substance of the mother-cells that is used to form them. Perhaps the gonoplasm of the antheridia of the Peronosporeae consists chiefly of nuclear substance.

[1] De Bary, Beiträge &c., IV. Reihe, and Unters. ü. d. Peronosporeen u. Saprolegnieen (Abh. d. Senckenb. nat. Ges. Bd. XIII. pp. 225–370, Frankfurt 1881) ; [also Vergl. Morphol. u. Biologie der Pilze, Myceotozoen u. Bacterien, Leipzig, 1884]. Pringsheim, Jahrb. Bd. I, II, IX. Other works in De Bary, *loc. cit.* Schmitz, Ueber die Zellkerne der Thallophyten (Niederrh. Ges. 1880).

which grows away from it into the air, and another which penetrates it; the former grows rapidly in length and thickness and puts out a number of branches near its base (Fig. 59); the latter forms copious slender ramifications which spread through the substratum like rhizoids. Rhizoids are also formed on the branches outside the substratum, and penetrate into it (Fig. 59). Finally, the Saprolegnieae usually cover animal or vegetable organisms, dead insects especially, which have fallen into the water, but sometimes fishes also, with dense radiating tufts of filaments. Each individual plant, which branches in a shrub-like manner outside the substratum and is fixed in it by rhizoids, is composed at first of an unsegmented tube, in which irregularly disposed transverse septa are eventually formed. Asexual propagation is effected not by motionless gonidia but by swarm-spores, as might be expected in plants living in the water. The swarm-spores are formed on branches the contents of which have been isolated by transverse walls. Sometimes several such transverse divisions arise, and then every cell can produce swarm-spores. The swarm-spores are formed by simultaneous division of the contents of a cell into a great number of parts, each of which has a nucleus (Fig. 60, *A*). Then the cell opens at its apex, and the spores are ejected and

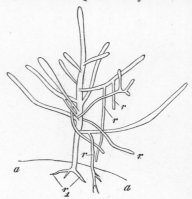

swarm in the water and disperse; or they remain at first heaped in a non-motile state before the aperture of the cell, and each spore clothes itself with a delicate membrane, which it soon however casts off and swarms away (Fig. 60, *B*). In some cases the swarm-spores, which are usually separated from one another in the mother-cell by films of granular protoplasm with a capacity of swelling, become invested with delicate membranes while they are still in the mother-cell and form a kind of parenchyma there, and escape by swarming through a number of holes in the mother-cell. These various modes of forming spores, which have been used to distinguish genera and species, may occur together, as Pringsheim has shown, on the same plant, as in the genera *Saprolegnia* and *Achlya*. When the spores have swarmed out of the terminal cell of a branch in *Saprolegnia*, the transverse septum arches outward and grows into

FIG. 59. A plant of *Achlya prolifera*, twenty-four hours old, grown from a zoospore on the larva of a gnat (after de Bary). The surface of the larva is indicated by the line *aa*, the plant is attached to it by the primary rhizoids *r₁*. The portion of the germ-tube outside the substratum has put forth branches like a tree, and the branches send down secondary rhizoids (*r*) into the substratum.

a new receptacle which takes the place of the one just emptied; in *Achlya* a new lateral branch is formed beneath the septum and becomes a new zoosporangium. The swarm-spores when they germinate give rise to plants of the same kind, which on a nidus, such as a dead fly, form at first only asexual organs of propagation, zoosporangia. Sexual organs make their appearance only towards the close of the period of vegetation, and in their regular and perfect form upon the same plant as the zoosporangia. The oogonia and antheridia are of the same form as in the Peronosporeae. The former usually arise as spherical swellings of the extremities of branches, but not unfrequently on some point in the middle of a tube. The formation of the oosphere is not as in the Peronosporeae; the whole of the protoplasm of the oogonium is used up for this purpose, and there is therefore no separation of periplasm. Only one oosphere is formed in the oogonium of *Aphanomyces*, in others two or more; their development runs through three stages, the aggregation, the separation, and the rounding off; but we cannot describe these processes here in detail. The antheridia are formed at the same time as the oogonia. Thinner branches arise usually on the filament that bears the oogonium, and grow towards the oogonium and attach themselves closely to it. The terminal cell cut off at the extremity of such a branch by a transverse wall is

[2]

the antheridium.   The sexual process was first fully described by De Bary in this case, as in that of the Peronosporeae.   **Saprolegnia ferax** may serve as an example.   In this species the smaller oogonia contain only one oosphere, the larger from ten to twenty.   The wall of the oogonium is marked with roundish unthickened areas (pits), but the antheridia send their tubes through the thickened as well as the unthickened portions of the wall ; there is therefore no morphologically definite spot for the attachment of the antheridium to the oogonium.   The oosphere has in its centre a clearer spot, the nuclear spot, which is probably only a nucleus ; its outer surface is formed of a thin pellicle free from granules.   The volume of the oosphere shrinks in the process of formation ; there is therefore a loss of water.   The oospheres when formed lie as spherical bodies in the centre of the oogonium, in which there is then nothing but the oospheres and some water.

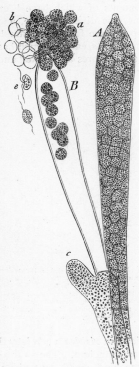

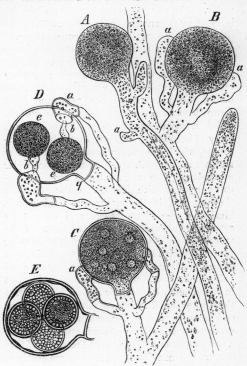

FIG. 60. Two zoosporangia of *Achlya*. *A* still closed. *B* open to discharge the spores; *a* spores ejected but still resting, *c* swarm-spores, which have left their membranes at *b* behind them. Magn. about 300 times.

FIG. 61. Oogonia and antheridia of *Achlya lignicola*, growing on wood in water ; course of development according to the letters from *A* to *E* ; *a* the antheridium, *b* its tube forcing its way into the oogonium. Magn. 550 times. Compare the text.

Meanwhile the contents of the antheridium have been differentiated into a layer of protoplasm lining the walls of the cell and a central watery portion.   Then the antheridia begin to put out tubular processes at the point of contact with the oogonium, each antheridium producing two or three such tubes ; these are the fertilisation-tubes, which penetrate through the wall of the oogonium.   If there is only one oosphere in the oogonium, the tube grows up to it and attaches its extremity firmly to it ; after a few minutes a protuberance appears at the margin of the point of contact of the fertilisation-tube and the oosphere, and rapidly develops into another tube, which at first travels over the surface of the oosphere but eventually takes another direction.   If there are more oospheres than one, and only one tube enters the oogonium, it grows towards the nearest oosphere ; the second tube, the protuberance just mentioned, then grows over the first oosphere and travels on to the second, and so on. The granules in the protoplasm of the oosphere withdraw in many cases from the spot where the tubes touch the oospheres, but the extremity of the tube in contact with the oosphere always appears to be perfectly closed ; there is no opening to be seen in it and no passage of the contents of the antheridium into the oosphere, as in *Pythium* and other cases. Nevertheless the oospheres show the usual signs of maturation ; they become invested, for instance, with a wall of cellulose which eventually is differentiated into an exosporium and an endo-sporium. The same course of things is seen in *Achlya prolifera* and *A. polyandra* as in *Saprolegnia ferax*. In other individuals of *Saprolegnia* the antheridium becomes firmly attached to the wall of the oogonium, but no fertilisation-tubes are formed, or they do not reach the oospheres. Finally, there are found not a few individual plants of *Saprolegnia ferax*, *S. asterophora*, *Achlya spinosa* and *Aphanomyces*, on which no antheridia are formed, but in which the oospheres pass without the co-operation of antheridia through all the stages of development observed when antheridia and fertilisation-tubes are present with them. It appears then that a process of fertilisation, such as takes place in the Peronosporeae and most distinctly in *Pythium*, does not occur in the Saprolegnieae, and that this is a group of plants which has lost the power of sexual propagation ; the phenomena of conjugation having disappeared, they have fallen into the conditon of apogamy. And if we consider the Peronosporeae and the Saprolegnieae in series together, we have a highly interesting view of the way in which this condition has been gradually introduced ; it is here given in de Bary's own words.

1. One end of the series is formed by species of *Pythium*, in which the larger part of the protoplasm of the antheridium passes over as gonoplasm into the oosphere, when an opening in the delicate cell-wall of the fertilisation-tube has established a communication with the oosphere. In other words, conjugation takes place between the oosphere and the contents of the antheridium.

2. In *Phytophthora* a very minute portion of protoplasm, but one that can still be followed with the eye, passes through the fertilisation-tube from the antheridium to the oosphere. In this case too there must be a narrow opening in the tube.

3. In *Peronospora* the presence of such an opening is not to be directly recognised, nor can the protoplasm of the antheridium be distinctly followed in its passage into the oosphere. But the complete agreement of the other points observed in this case with what has been ascertained in the case of *Phytophthora* makes it highly probable that the passage of a very minute portion of protoplasm does take place in *Peronospora* also. Whether the protoplasmic matter passes through a narrow or a wider opening in the wall of the tube, or by osmosis through the interstices of its micellar structure, must for the present remain unsettled.

4. In certain species or individuals of *Saprolegnia*, *Achlya* and *Aphanomyces* there is close contact between tube and oosphere, but there is no apparent opening or passage of the contents of the antheridium into the oosphere.

5. There are other individuals of *Saprolegnia*, as *S. torulosa* and *S. asterophora*, in which the antheridium becomes firmly attached to the wall of the oogonium, but either no fertilisation-tubes are formed, or those which are formed do not reach the oospheres.

6. Finally, oogonia and oospores are produced without the formation of antheridia.

The germination of the oospores agrees with that which has been given above for the Peronosporeae, that is, the oospore with all its protoplasm first forms a short germ-tube and then becomes a zoosporangium ; or all the protoplasm passes into the germ-tube, which is then cut off by a transverse wall and becomes a zoosporangium, but may if sufficiently well fed ramify and form several typical sporangia and then disappear ; or, lastly, the germ-tube developes without a previous formation of zoosporangia into a vegetative thallus, which only when it has reached its normal form and size produces zoospores and oogonia. *Achlya polyandra* and various species of *Saprolegnia* show all three modes of germination according to circumstances ; *Achlya spinosa* has only the third, *Phytophthora omnivora* only the second, &c.

4. ASCOMYCETES[1].

The Ascomycetes are an extensive group of plants of very complex structure, whose specific peculiarities will be further discussed below. They are as a group distinguished by having their spores formed in *asci*, that is, the spores are in most cases developed from the protoplasmic contents of club-shaped tubes or globular sacs. In their simpler forms they have some resemblance through the formation of their fructification to the series of the Peronosporeae. If we take, for instance, the formation of fructification in *Podosphaera*, we see two small lateral branches spring from the place where two filaments of the mycelium cross each other, one forming an ellipsoid cell which is separated off from its mycelium by a transverse septum (Fig. 63, *w*), and

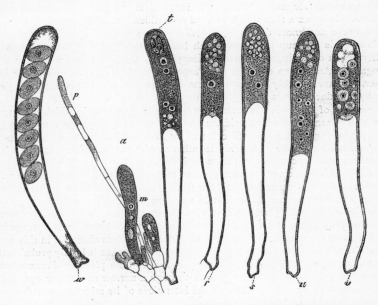

FIG. 62. *Peziza (Pyronema) confluens. a* small fragment of the hymenium, with *p* a paraphysis and three young asci, *m*. *r—w* full grown asci, the order of development according to the letters; in *r* the nucleus still undivided, in *s* two nuclei formed by division of the inner nucleus, in *u* and *v* further multiplication of nuclei. *w* ascus with ripe spores. After de Bary, magn. 390 times.

the other a slenderer lateral branch from the other mycelial filament, which is closely applied to the ellipsoid cell and a small obtuse cell cut off by a septum close beneath its summit (Fig. 63, *m*). The further development shows what is in itself obvious, namely that these organs bear the greatest resemblance to those which make their appearance in the sexual reproduction of the Peronosporeae; the slender branch answers to the antheridial branch there, the cell separated off at its extremity to the antheridium, the broader ellipsoid cell to the female organ, the oogonium. The branch of the thallus that corresponds to the oogonium (Fig. 63, *w*) is named by De Bary[2], for reasons to be discussed presently, the *archicarp* (*ascogone*); the antheridium, or

---

[1] [De Bary, Vergl. Morphol. u. Biol. d. Pilze, Myceotozven, u. Bacterien, Leipzig, 1884.]
[2] Beitr. z. Morphol. u. Physiol. der Pilze, Heft. IV.

antheridial branch was formerly called the *pollinodium.* The sexual function of these two organs, the antheridium and the archicarp, that is, a transference of fertilising matter from the former to the latter, has not been ascertained in this genus any more than in the Saprolegnieae, and it probably does not take place; it is probable, that is, that the organs actually existing and homologous with those of the Peronosporeae have lost their function. But the archicarp does not behave as an oogonium in respect to the differentiation of its contents; that is, no oosphere is formed in it, but, in consequence perhaps of a fertilising operation of the antheridium on its contents, it developes into an ascus by the division of a part of its protoplasm into a number of round bodies, each of which becomes invested with a cell-wall and forms an *ascospore.* Moreover, hyphae springing from beneath the basal wall of the archicarp and also from the antheridial branch grow up round the archicarp at an early period; the hyphae are divided into cells by transverse walls and form a compact envelope round the young ascus (compare the zygospore of *Mortierella,* p. 90). *Podosphaera* is one of the Erysipheae. In other members of that family the ascus-fructification contains several asci, which grow from a multicellular archicarp (Fig. 63, *F, w*); in this case it is a stout segmented hyphal branch, which

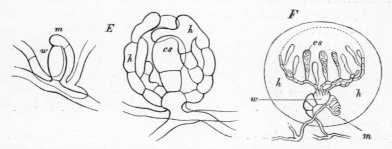

FIG. 63. Enlarged diagrammatic representation of the development of the fructification in some Ascomycetes. *E Podosphaera. F Ascobolus; w* archicarp (ascogone), *m* antheridial branch, *cs* asci, *h* envelope of the sporocarp formed of sterile branches. After de Bary and Janczewski.

gives rise to the fertile filaments (asci) that ultimately produce the spores; for this reason the archicarp is also called an *ascogone.* The archicarp and the antheridial branch sometimes differ little from each other in size; sometimes, as in *Gymnoascus,* they are of exactly the same size; usually the archicarp is the larger of the two and is multicellular, while the antheridium is a slender branched tube, always distinguished from the archicarp by the fact that it is from the latter only that the fertile ascogenous hyphal branches arise. The sterile tissue of the fructification springs from the cell that bears the archicarp, and sometimes from other adjoining cells. The antheridial branch either lays its whole length along the archicarp, or it touches with its apex only the anterior and sometimes much elongated portion of the archicarp. It has been already said that in members of this group there is no apparent and direct transference of protoplasm between the antheridial branch and the archicarp, both organs continuing closed; and usually it is not the part of the archicarp actually touched by the antheridial branch but a part nearer its base from which the fertile filaments of the fructification afterwards spring; this recalls a similar fact in the formation of the fructification in the Florideae. There is still greater agreement in respect to the mode of formation of the fructification between the Florideae and that section of the Ascomycetes, which by a peculiar association with certain Algae form the organisms known as Lichens. (See below, and for the Basidiomycetous lichens, p. 114). In these, as in the Florideae, we find male organs of fertilisation, the *spermatia*, produced in special receptacles, *spermogonia*. The archicarp (ascogone) moreover developes, as in the Florideae, a special receptive apparatus, the *trichogyne*, with the apex of which the spermatia conjugate, as in the Florideae. In this case therefore there is no antheridial branch; the spermatia perform its functions.

In contrast to this case of sexual production of the fructification in the Ascomycetes, many others have recently become known to us, in which there is no trace of sexual organs, archicarp or antheridial branch, preceding the formation of fructification, and therefore no distinction between sterile and fertile hyphae in the fructification. So it is in *Pleospora herbarum*[1], *Chaetomium*[2], *Peziza Fuckeliana*, *tuberosa* and *sclerotiorum*[3]; the sclerotia of the last-named, for example, are formed by the active growth of shoots from branches of the hyphae simultaneously over broad patches of mycelium, and the cup-shaped fructifications arise from inside the sclerotia during their further development in the form of dense tufts of hyphae. The parts that bear and produce the asci are in this case hyphae, which differ from the adjacent sterile hyphae only in having asci formed as branches on them. In these Ascomycetes then the retrogression has gone so far that the sexual organs, the archicarp and the antheridial branch, are no longer formed; just as we saw in the Saprolegnieae that the formation of antheridial branches had entirely ceased in individuals of several species, and yet the oospores continued to be formed as in all the rest. We shall make acquaintance presently with a similar case of loss of conjugating power, *apogamy*, among the Ferns.

Fig. 62 gives a clear idea of the formation of the spores in the ascus[4]. In the young ascus (Fig. 62, *m*, *r*) there is a nucleus which divides in two; the two parts separate (Fig. 62, *s*), and each divides again; each of the four parts divides once more, and thus there are now eight free nuclei in the ascus. Cell-formation about them now takes place (Fig. 62, *r*), each becoming surrounded with protoplasm which forms a membrane on its outer surface. There is little protoplasm in the ripe ascus besides that which forms the spores; almost all has been used in forming the spores.

With respect to the structure of the fructification, it is to be remarked that there are some species in which we can scarcely say that there is any fructification. This is the case in *Gymnoascus*, where the asci spring from branches of the mycelium which are not united into a fructification distinctly delimited, and surrounded by a coherent envelope; and there is even less appearance of a fructification in *Exoascus* and the Yeast-fungi, which, as reduced Ascomycetes, will be considered at the close of this

---

[1] Bauke, Zur Entwicklungsgeschichte d. Ascomyceten (Bot. Ztg. 1877, p. 313).

[2] Zopf, Unters. ü. *Chaetomium* (Bot. Ztg. 1879, p. 73).

[3] Brefeld, Bot. Unters. ü. d. Schimmelpilze, IV.

[4] De Bary, Ueber d. Fruchtentwicklung d. Ascomyceten, p. 34.—Strasburger, Ueber Zellbildung u. Zelltheilung, III. Aufl. p. 49 ff.—Schmitz, Sitzungsber. d. niederrh. Ges. Aug. 1879, p. 20 of the reprint. Compare also the formation of spores in *Exoascus* and *Tuber*.

section. In all other Ascomycetes a fructification of more or less complex structure and composed of numerous hyphae is formed on the mycelium. It consists of two essentially distinct parts, a sterile part which is sometimes of considerable size, and a fertile part which produces the spores. If the hyphae in the fertile part form a continuous layer, this is called the *hymenium*. In it are usually found, together with the asci, a number of unicellular or multicellular hair-like sterile branches of the hyphae, called *paraphyses*. The Ascomycetes may be subdivided according to the character of the fructification. In the Discomycetes the fructification is a roundish often stalked disk or bowl (Fig. 64, *A*) in which the hymenium forms the exposed concave upper surface. The fructifications, on the contrary, of the Pyrenomycetes are not exposed but open only by a narrow canal or aperture to the outside, and consist of an outer wall and an interior part chiefly composed of hymenial tissue lining the inner surface of the wall. In a third subdivision, the Cleistocarpous Ascomycetes, the asci are inside the closed envelope of the fructification and are set free by its decay or in some other way. Finally, the Tuberaceae are known by their subterranean tuberous fructifications in which the hymenium is inclosed in sinuous cavities (*Tuber*).

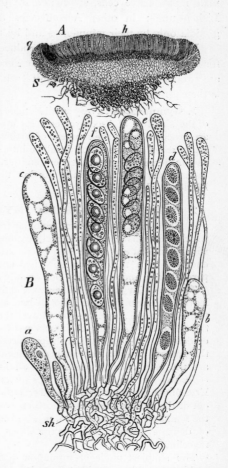

FIG. 64. *Peziza convexula.* *A* vertical section through the whole fructification; *h* hymenium, *S* sterile tissue surrounding the hymenium like a cup at the margin *q*. At its base fine filaments grow out between the particles of the soil. *B* a small portion of the hymenium; *sh* subhymenial layer of closely woven hyphae; *a—f* asci of different ages, between them thinner filaments (the paraphyses) containing red granules. *A* magn. about 20 times, *B* 550 times.

The number of spores formed in an ascus varies much; in the Truffles there are two to three, in other kinds four, most frequently eight spores. The *ascospores* have always a firm cuticularised outer membrane, the exosporium, which is usually beset with small protuberances, raised edges, or spike-like projections. An inner membrane, the endosporium, bursts or breaks through the exosporium in germination and developes one germ-tube or several together, and these give rise to the mycelium. The mycelium in many cases produces *gonidiophores*, as in the Peronosporeae, on which gonidia are formed and abscised; and several of our commonest moulds are nothing but gonidial forms of Ascomycetes, among them *Penicillium glaucum*, *Eurotium Aspergillus glaucus*, and *Botrytis cinerea*, which last belongs to *Peziza Fuckeliana*. Besides the gonidiophores certain special receptacles are often found with or on the fructifications, in which gonidia of varying size are produced (*stylospores* in *pycnidia*, and *spermatia* in *spermogonia*). It has been shown in several cases that the pycnidia belong to Fungi which are parasitic on the particular Ascomycete; in others that the pycnidia make their appearance as a further form of gonidial fructification in the Ascomycete. A variety of formations seem to have been included under the term spermogonia; true spermogonia, receptacles in which male reproductive cells, spermatia, are produced, are known only at present in the Lichen-fungi; in other Ascomycetes the spermatia are distinguished from the gonidia only by their minuteness and by their being incapable of germination.

Pycnidia as well as the gonidia produced on free gonidiophores may be wanting, as, for instance, in *Tuber*; but in many species, as in the moulds just mentioned, they are produced in enormous quantities, while the sporocarps are seldom formed; this is the case with *Penicillium*.

1. **Gymnoascus**[1], a very small Fungus growing on the dung of horses and sheep, is one of the simplest of Ascomycetes. Its mycelium bears numerous sexual organs, which are exactly alike at the moment of fertilisation. After fertilisation the archicarp divides into a series of cells which develope into short branched filaments with the eight-spored asci in dense masses at their extremities. The investment of the fructification is only rudimentary, and the fertile portion therefore is naked, as in the simplest of the Florideae (*Nemalion*).

2. CLEISTOCARPOUS ASCOMYCETES.

a. The ERYSIPHEAE[2] form globular fructifications on the surface of the substances which they inhabit. These fructifications are usually so small as scarcely to be seen with the naked eye, while the mycelia attain to a considerable size; the fructification is enclosed in a thin hollow spherical envelope having a superficial layer of pseudo-parenchyma, and containing one or only a few asci which spring from the archicarp.

The genus **Erysiphe** (Mildew), which has many species, is found on the surface of the leaves and green stems of Dicotyledons and a few Monocotyledons; the much-branched filaments of the mycelium spread over the epidermis, often crossing one another and at the same time sending their suckers (haustoria) at many points into the cells of the epidermis. The mycelia are reproduced by gonidia, which are abjointed in rows on the summit of erect unbranched filaments (Fig. 65, *I*); these organs of propagation are the only ones at present known in many species, as for instance in *Erysiphe* (*Oidium*) *Tuckeri*, the Fungus which causes the grape-disease.—In many others of the Erysipheae the sexually produced fructifications are easily found; filaments often grow out of the rind of these fructifications which either lie close along the substratum like the filaments of the mycelium, or stand up clear from it in various forms like a clothing of delicate hairs. The fructifications and the gonidia are formed on the same mycelium.

The simplest mode of formation of fructifications is seen in Podosphaera. The archicarps and antheridial branches are formed close together, and touching one another from the first, at spots where the filaments of the mycelium cross (Fig. 65, *III*); both are small lateral branches; the one that becomes the archicarp (*c*) enlarges into an ovate shape and is delimited above its base by a transverse wall; the one that produces the antheridial branch (*p*) bends over the apex of the archicarp and a cell is cut off there by a transverse wall. After 'fertilisation' has been effected, filaments grow up from beneath the basal wall of the archicarp and also from the

---

[1] Baranetzky in Bot. Ztg. 1872, No. 10.

[2] Tulasne, Selecta fungorum Carpologia, I. Paris 1868.—De Bary, Beitr. z. Morph. u. Phys. d. Pilze, III, 1870 (Abh. d. Senckenb. Ges. zu Frankfurt a. M.) [Marshall Ward, On the morphology and development of the perithecium of *Meliola* (Phil. Trans. Roy. Soc. 1883).]

antheridial branch (*IV, h*) in close contact with the archicarp and unite in an arch over its apex; the filaments then become pluricellular by transverse divisions, and close up laterally, forming a pseudo-parenchyma. As the investment increases in size it puts out short branches from its inner side, and these fill up the now enlarged space between it and the archicarp which has as yet grown but little larger (see Fig. 65, *V, h*). Then the still unicellular archicarp begins to enlarge and is divided by a transverse septum into a lower and an upper cell; the former may be considered to be the simplest case of an ascogenous filament, the apical cell of which becomes an ascus at once (*V, a*). Eight spores arise by free cell-formation in the protoplasm of the ascus, which increases in size and ultimately fills up the space inside the envelope, and will slip out from it if the fructification is squeezed (*II, a*). In other Erysipheae, as *E. Umbelliferarum, communis, lamprocarpa* and others, where the fruits contain several asci, the archicarp, here too at first unicellular, grows inside the envelope to a long, thick, curved filament, which is divided by several transverse septa; then several of the cells thus formed put out short lateral branches, and these produce the asci.

The Erisypheae with several asci furnish a transition to the Eurotieae, in which the

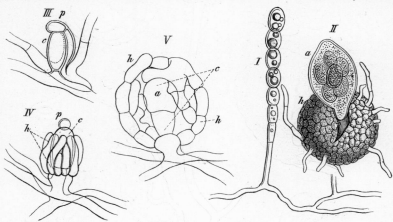

FIG. 65. *I, II Podosphaera pannosa. I* Gonidiophore, with gonidial chain. *II* Ripe fructification after Tulasne. *Podosphaera Castagnei. III* Archicarp and antheridial branch. *IV* the same at commencement of the formation of the fructification. *V* the young fructification; *c* archicarp, *p* antheridial branch, *h* envelope of the fruit, *a* the single ascus. After de Bary, magn. 600 times.

archicarp elongates considerably before fertilisation, and in doing so is twisted like a corkscrew.

b. The history of the development of **Eurotium repens** and **Eurotium Aspergillus glaucus** has been described in detail by De Bary. Both these species live in decomposing organic substances of very various kinds, and especially in preserved fruit. In the latter case the fungus covers the surface of the fruit with a delicate white flocculent mycelium, from which gonidiophores soon begin to rise in large numbers; these swell at their upper extremity into a globular form, and from the upper half of the globe a number of conical projections, the *sterigmata*, arise, closely crowded and radially disposed. Each of these projections gradually produces a long chain of greenish gonidia, and at length the head of the gonidiophore is covered with a thick layer of them. During the production of the gonidia sexual organs are being formed on the same mycelium. The archicarp is the corkscrew-like extremity of a branch of the mycelium (Fig. 66, *A, as*), the turns of which approach nearer and nearer to each other, till at length they touch and form a hollow screw (*C, D*). During this proceeding about as many delicate transverse septa make their appearance as there are turns of the screw, namely, from five to six. Two slender branches then shoot out from two opposite spots on the lowest turn of the archicarp, and grow up outside the screw; one of them grows faster than the other, reaches the uppermost turn, and applies its apex closely to it (*B*). This branch is the antheridial branch, and conjugation takes place between its apex and the apex of the archicarp, the cell-wall becoming dissolved at the point of contact and the protoplasmic contents of the two cells coalescing. Soon after this new filaments shoot out from the lower part of the antheridial branch and of the archicarp; these increase in number, attach themselves closely to the screw (*C*), and ultimately completely invest it. Then a layer of polygonal cells is formed out of these filaments by means of transverse divisions, and this layer forms the envelope of the archicarp. Next the cells of the layer grow out on its inner side and the papillae thus formed are divided off by transverse septa (*E*), and while the envelope increases in size the space

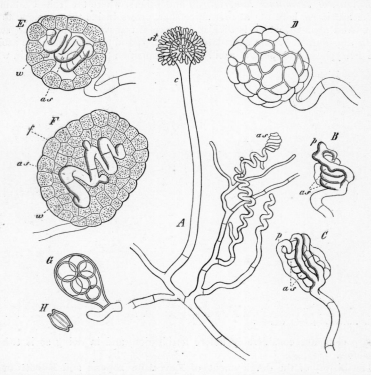

FIG. 66. Development of *Eurotium repens*. *A* small part of a mycelium with the gonidiophore *c* and young archicarps *as*. *B* the spiral archicarp *as* with the antheridial branch *p*. *C* the same with the filaments beginning to grow round it to form the wall of the perithecium. *D* a perithecium seen from without. *E*, *F* young perithecia in optical longitudinal section; *w* parietal cells, *f* the filling tissue (pseudo-parenchyma), *as* the archicarp. *G* an ascus. *H* an ascospore. After de Bary. *A* magn. 190, the rest 600 times.

which it encloses is also enlarged and is filled up with the papillae, which are closely packed and grow up to the archicarp and between the turns of the screw which are now further apart; then this new growth of filaments divides by the formation of transverse septa into a number of cells of equal diameter, and finally the space between the envelope and the turns of the screw is filled with a pseudo-parenchyma, the filling-tissue. During these proceedings numerous transverse walls are formed in the archicarp, and a number of branches are put out from its cells, which grow in every direction between the cells of the filling-tissue, form septa and ramify; their ultimate ramifications are the asci (*G*), which consequently owe their origin to the ascogone fertilised by the antheridial branch. These interior changes are accompanied by a considerable increase in size of the whole structure, the *perithecium*. During the development of the asci the filling-tissue becomes looser, its cells become round and capable of swelling, lose their oily contents, and finally disappear; their place is occupied in the ripe fructification by the eight-spored asci. As the perithecium increases in size the cells of its walls enlarge and become covered with a sulphur-yellow coating which acquires a considerable thickness and is formed probably of some resinous or fatty substance; they finally collapse and dry up. The asci disappear, and at length the perithecium consists only of the brittle yellow covering and the mass of spores, which it encloses, and a slight pressure is sufficient to release them. The mycelium too, like the perithecium, is overlaid with a coloured substance, but in this case it is of a chestnut colour, and the perithecia show on it as yellow granules individually visible to the naked eye. The ripe spores have the form of biconvex lenses (*H*); in germination the endosporium which developes the young germ-tube swells strongly and bursts the exosporium in two halves. The mycelium produced by the ascospores, like that which proceeds from the gonidia, gives rise first to gonidiophores and then to perithecia; but there is no true alternation between a sexual and an asexual generation.

c. The mycelium of **Penicillium glaucum** grows on almost all organic substances, even on fluids, on which it forms a dense felted covering. Erect branches rise from the mycelium, which ramify in a penicillate manner and produce at their extremities long chains of greenish gonidia, which are almost everywhere disseminated through the air and account for the very general and spontaneous appearance of the Fungus.

Penicillium forms its fructification only in the absence of air and light; under these conditions the tolerably conspicuous gonidiophores are not produced, and as the fructifications are small yellowish bodies no larger than pins' heads, they were overlooked till Brefeld succeeded in raising them by artificial cultivation. 'The mycelia[1] must be cultivated on a substratum, on which by help of abundant supplies of food and avoidance of all disturbing causes it can reach its highest point of vegetative development. This may happen in from seven to ten days from the sowing of the spores. Then suitable methods must be adopted to hinder the access of atmospheric oxygen and the consequent exhaustion of the mycelia by the production of gonidiophores. As these conditions are not usually fulfilled in nature, it is no wonder that only the asexual reproduction of *Penicillium* has hitherto been known.

'The sexual organs of *Penicillium* agree in essential points with those with which De Bary has made us acquainted in *Eurotium*, and consist of a corkscrew-shaped archicarp and an antheridial branch disposed in a similar manner with reference to the archicarp. Here too the archicarp is closely invested with filaments which grow up from beneath it; but the archicarp itself grows at the same time and sends out branches which make their way in among the filaments of the envelope.

'When now an envelope of from eight to fifteen layers of filaments encloses the growing archicarp, no new layers are formed, only there is some further development of the old filaments. This consists chiefly in copious division of the filaments, and the cells thus formed expand and close up into a tissue. This gradual formation of tissue at first impedes and at last stops the advance of the ascogenous threads; but they can be plainly seen in a median section as stout hyphae arranged concentrically. During the formation of this tissue the cells expand, but not uniformly, to six or eight times their previous size, and

---

[1] The account in the text is almost entirely taken from the 4th Ed., in which the preliminary communication of Brefeld in Flora 1875 is printed word for word. A fuller account will be found in his 'Schimmelpilze,' Heft II. Brefeld has since then come to the conclusion that the processes in the formation of the sporocarp of *Penicillium* are not a sexual act, but a vegetative growth, and has even applied this view to cases where, as in the Erysipheae, an archicarp and an antheridial branch are plainly distinguishable. The homology of these organs however with similar ones in the Peronosporeae, putting their function out of sight, may be considered as demonstrated by De Bary's recent researches; *Penicillium, Peziza Sclerotiorum* &c. are, as was stated above, retrograde forms.

finally their cell-walls become much thickened.   This thickening begins simultaneously at two points, inside in the ascogenous hyphae, and outside in a zone which lies some cell-layers deep beneath the periphery.

'The fructification, which is now detached from the mycelium and is of the size and colour of a coarse yellow grain of sand, is in this state a sclerotium ; the outer surface is composed of from two to four layers of cells which are longer in the tangential direction and of a yellow-brown colour.   These are followed by large cells more radially disposed, which diminish in size from without inwards, and are traversed by stiff ascogenous hyphae disposed in the tissue and looking like much-branched passages.

'The sclerotium if kept dry will go through a resting stage of more than three months without losing the power of germination, but if it is placed on damp blotting paper, a further development of the ascogenous hyphae takes place after a period of from six to seven weeks ; they again assume the appearance of living hyphae and divide into short cells, and each cell can produce a shoot which divides at once into a thick and a thin filament.   The thick filaments have to do with the formation of the fructification, the thin ones consume the surrounding tissue and supply food to the thick ones.   The thin filaments are less branched and have no partition-walls ; the thick ones form numerous lateral branches closely following one another just beneath their apex, and have a septum between every two branches.   These branches form a continuous chain of asci, and each ascus forms eight spores.   The further development concludes with the absorption of all the tissue inside the brown envelope ; the ripe asci, the hyphae from which they sprang, and the filaments that supplied them with food disappear ; and finally, after a period of from six to eight months, the sclerotium, though not changed in outward appearance, is only a vesicle containing a dense mass of countless bright-yellow spores.

'Each ascospore under proper cultivation developes a mycelium, which is in every respect the same as that produced from a gonidium and is marked out by the very characteristic gonidiophore ; the origin of each gonidiophore can be traced back through the mycelial filaments to a single spore.

'If the sclerotium loses the power of germination through being too much dried or through age or other disturbing causes, that is, if the ascogenous filaments inside it are dead, single cells of the tissue will sometimes germinate.   The germ-tubes protrude through fissures in the sclerotium and produce the usual gonidiophores on its surface. Here the physiological distinction, or rather the contrast between the ascogenous filaments and the tissue that surrounds them, is still more clearly shown."

3. The **PYRENOMYCETES**[1] produce their long club-shaped asci, which usually contain eight spores, inside small roundish or flask-shaped receptacles known as *perithecia* ; the outer covering of the perithecium, especially when it is free and isolated, as in *Sphaeria* and *Sordaria* and others, is composed of a firm tissue of pseudo-parenchyma which is usually of a dark colour.   Inside this there is in its early state a delicate transparent tissue containing no air, which is eventually supplanted by the asci and paraphyses ; these have their origin in a hymenium which lines the wall of the perithecium or occupies its base only.   The perithecium is either open from the first, as in *Sphaeria typhina* and *Sordaria*, or it is at first closed and afterwards forms a canal-like aperture clothed with hairs through which the spores escape, as in *Xylaria*.

In a number of species (the Sphaeriae simplices, such as *Pleospora* and *Sordaria*) the free perithecia grow singly or in groups on the inconspicuous filamentous mycelium,

---

[1] Tulasne, Selecta fungorum carpologia, Paris, 1860–65.—Woronin u. De Bary, Beitr. z. Morph. u. Phys. d. Pilze, Frankfurt 1870, [and De Bary, Morph. sc. d. Pilze, 1884, p. 200].—Fuisting in Bot. Zeit. 1868, p. 179.—Bauke, Beitr. z. Kenntn. d. Pycniden (Nova Acta Leop. Car. 1876).— Bauke, Zur Entwicklungsges. d. Ascomyceten (Bot. Zeit. 1877).—Zopf, Die Gonidienfrüchte von *Fumago* (Nova Acta Leop. Car. 1879); [Id., Zur Kenntn. d. anatom. Anpass. d. Pilzfrüchte an die Funktion der Sporenentleerung. Halle, 1884.]

which lives usually on dead but sometimes also on living plants. We know chiefly from Woronin's researches into *Sphaeria Lemaneae* and *Sordaria*, that in this case each perithecium owes its origin to an archicarp and represents therefore a whole fructification. But in other Pyrenomycetes, *Xylaria* for instance, a *stroma* is first developed on the mycelium, a structure which may be cylindrical or pileus-like or cup-shaped or branched and shrub-like, and is composed of compact and apparently homogeneous tissue. In this structure numerous perithecia are afterwards formed. In such cases, if retrogressive metamorphosis has not gone to such a length that archicarp and antheridial branch are no longer to be seen in connection with the formation of the sporocarp, it remains uncertain whether the stroma is merely a peculiar form of the mycelium and sexual organs are formed in it which give rise to as many perithecia, or whether the stroma itself is the product of a sexual act performed on the filamentous mycelium and is to be regarded therefore as a fructification which subsequently forms its asci in a number of perithecia ; the latter is the more probable alternative, since in *Claviceps* the stroma comes from a sclerotium which is the product of a sexual act; the sclerotia of *Peziza* however should be compared.

The asexual reproductive cells, the gonidia, are produced in the Pyrenomycetes not only from the mycelium but also and especially from the stroma, and in *Penicillium* even from the wall of the perithecium. They are formed on longer or shorter hyphal branches in large numbers, smaller and larger ones sometimes on the same species. It was stated above that the receptacles known as pycnidia and spermogonia, which also produce larger and smaller gonidia, are structures of varying significance ; they sometimes belong to the species on which they appear, sometimes are parasitic. There are in *Fumago*, as Zopf has shown, intermediate forms between gonidiophores and pycnidia, and at the same time the formation of pycnidia in this case is instructive, because it shows that they may be produced in different ways on the same species, through true tissue-formation as well as by the interweaving of hyphae.

The Fungus which produces the Ergot, **Claviceps purpurea,** may be chosen for a more detailed description. Its growth begins with the formation of a filamentous mycelium, which settles on the surface of the ovary of the Gramineae, especially of Rye, as it lies enclosed between the paleae, covers it with a thick felt and penetrates into a part of its tissue, sparing the apex and often other parts. In this way a soft white felted mycelium takes the place of the ovary and roughly retains its shape, the style being often borne on the top. The surface of the hyphal tissue is marked by deep furrows and forms an abundance of gonidia on basidia disposed radially ; the gonidia issue forth from between the paleae imbedded in slimy matter. In this state the Fungus used to be considered a distinct genus and was called *Sphacelia*. The gonidia may germinate at once, and again give off gonidia by abstriction, and these, according to Kühn, can again at once produce sphacelia in other grass-flowers. When the formation of gonidia is at its height the mycelium of the sphacelia forms at the bottom of the ovary a thick belt of more compact hyphae, which is at first surrounded by the looser tissue of the sphacelia ; this is the commencement of the *sclerotium* or *ergot*; its outer surface soon turns dark-violet, and it grows into a horn-shaped body which is often an inch long. Meanwhile the sphacelia ceases to grow, its tissue dries up and is ruptured below by the sclerotium and carried up on the apex of the latter, crowning it with a tall cap and finally dropping off. The mature and hard sclerotium now remains in a state of rest till the autumn and most frequently till the following spring, when the formation of the fructifications begins if the sclerotium lies on moist ground (Fig. 67, *A*). The stromata arise beneath the outer wall of the sclerotium by the formation of numerous crowded branches at certain points on the central hyphae ; the tuft of branches bursts through the wall and developes into a stroma consisting of a long stalk and a small globular head. In the head are formed a number of flask-shaped perithecia (Fig. 67, *B*), which in this case have no bounding wall. Each perithecium is filled from the bottom with many asci, in each of which several slender filiform spores (Fig. 67, *D*) are produced. These spores swell at various points in damp air and put forth germ-tubes ; if these find their way to the young flowers of the Rye or some related grass, they de-

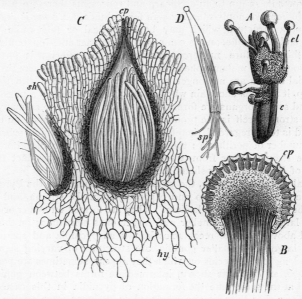

FIG. 67. *Claviceps purpurea.* *A* a sclerotium (Ergot) forming stromata *cl*, nat. size. *B* upper part of a stroma in longitudinal section ; *cp* the perithecia slightly magn. *C* a perithecium with the surrounding tissue highly magnified ; at *cp* its orifice, *hy* hyphae of the head of the stroma, *sh* epidermal layer of the same. *D* an ascus ruptured and discharging its spores. After Tulasne ; *C* and *D* highly magnified.

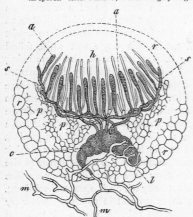

FIG. 68. Enlarged diagrammatic section of the fructification of *Ascobolus furfuraceus*; *m* mycellum, *c* archicarp, *l* antheridial branch, *s* ascogenous tubes, *a* the asci, *rp* the tissue of the fructification from which the paraphyses *h* proceed. Designed from Janczewski's figures.

velope in them into sphacelia, as Kühn informs us, and thus complete the cycle of development.

4. DISCOMYCETES[1]. In order to give as clear an illustration as possible of the mode of formation of a perfect fructification in this section, we may take as the next example **Ascobolus furfuraceus** as described by Janczewski. Fig. 68 gives a vertical section through the entire fructification of this Fungus, which is still connected with a portion of the mycelium; the figure is diagrammatically drawn to simplify it and at the same time make it complete. The archicarp *c* and the antheridial branch *l* are formed on branches of the mycelium *m*. The former consists of a row of broader but shorter cells, and is much curved. The antheridial branch with its slender branchlets lays itself across the anterior portion of the archicarp and closely embraces its cells. As the result of fertilisation one of the middle cells of the archicarp, which is also known as the ascogone, grows more vigorously than the rest,

---

[1] De Bary, Ueber d. Fruchtentwickl. d. Ascomycet. Leipzig, 1863.—De Bary u. Woronin, Beitr. z. Morph. u. Phys. d. Pilze, Frankfurt 1866, 2ᵉ Reihe (Abh. d. Senck. Ges.)—Tulasne in Ann. d. sc. nat. 1866, V. ser. t. VI. p. 217.—Janczewski in Bot. Zeit. 1871, No. 18.—Brefeld, Bot. Unters. über die Schimmelpilze, Heft. 4.

becomes round, and shoots forth a number of filaments, from which the asci eventually arise. In the meantime a cluster of filaments has grown up from the hyphae that bear the sexual organs and has entirely invested the archicarp ; these filaments are the large sterile portion of the fructification, the hyphae of which form a pseudo-parenchyma. Fig. 68 shows this cortical covering at *r*, and at *p p* its inner portion with diagrammatic indication of the sterile hyphae. The ascogenous filaments from the archicarp continue to grow, and form a layer *s s*, the subhymenial layer, inside the fructification, and send thicker club-shaped cells upwards ; these are the asci in which the spores are formed. In this way a hymenium *s a* is produced and is completed by the sterile hyphae sending a number of parallel branches, the *paraphyses*, in between the asci ; the paraphyses therefore belong to the sterile portion of the fructification. Ultimately the cortical envelope opens at the apex, the hymenium comes to lie on the surface and spreads itself flat out as in Fig. 69 *A*, in order to release the spores from the asci.

The history of **Peziza confluens,** in which the sexuality of the Ascomycetes was first

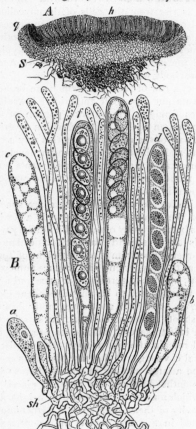

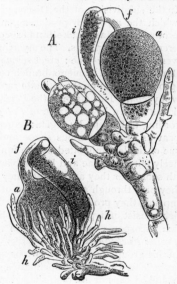

FIG. 69. *Peziza convexula. A* vertical section of the entire fructification, magn. about 20 times; *h* hymenium, the layer in which the spore-producing tubes lie; *S* the sterile tissue of the fructification, which surrounds the hymenium like a cup at its margin *q*; at its base fine filaments proceed from the tissue *S* and grow between the particles of the soil. *B* a small portion of the hymenium magn. 550 times; *a—f* spore-producing tubes (asci); between them slenderer tubes, the paraphyses, in which are red granules.

FIG. 70. Sexual apparatus of *Peziza confluens*. In *B* fertilisation is being followed by the formation of hyphae *h*, from which the fructification is developed. After Tulasne very highly magnified.

discovered by De Bary, is shown by his observations, as supplemented by Tulasne, to be as follows. The mycelium grows on the ground ; ascending branches with many ramifications arise on special parts of its hyphae ; the sexual organs are formed on the extremities of the ramifications in large numbers and close together in rosettes. The terminal cells of the stouter branches swell into ovoid vesicles (Fig. 70, *a*), and these put out processes which are usually curved (*f*) ; each of these vesicles is an archicarp. From one of the cells of the same branch beneath the archicarp grows a club-shaped antheridial branch (*i*), which unites its apex with the process from the archicarp. Thereupon numerous slender hyphae shoot forth (*h*) from the main filament that bears the rosette of sexual organs, and grow round them and wrap them in a thick felted tissue. This tissue constitutes the body of the fructification, on the upper side of which closely crowded hyphae arise at once to form the hymenial layer. Finally the fructification takes the form of a peziza-cup, as shown in Fig. 69, and produces the ascospores in its hymenium.— Woronin made similar observations on **Peziza granulosa** and **P. scutellata.** In these plants branches divided into three or more cells rise from the cells of the mycelium, and their terminal cell enlarges to a spherical or ovoid form but puts out no process ; from the cell beneath it spring two or more slender tubes which embrace the other, and the sexual apparatus thus formed becomes closely invested by numerous hyphae which grow up from beneath it ; out of these the peziza-cup is developed.—In **Ascobolus pulcherrimus** the archicarp is a vermiform body which Tulasne calls the *scolecite* ; this is a branch of the mycelium, and consists of a row of short cells which are broader than those of the mycelium. Adjacent filaments put out small antheridial branches, the terminal cells of which attach themselves firmly to the anterior portion of the scolecite ; and this together with the fertilising organ is then invested with a covering of branched hyphae derived from the adjacent part of the mycelium ; in this way a coil of hyphae is formed with the scolecite inside it, and this structure at length developes into the cup-shaped fructification. In all these cases the ascogenous filaments have not been observed to originate in the archicarp, but their resemblance to the previous and following examples leave this point no longer in doubt.

In the subdivision of the Discomycetes which we are considering there are species in which the mycelium produces gonidia, and the immature fructification is a resting sclerotium. **Peziza Fuckeliana** especially has been carefully observed by De Bary with reference to these points. The mycelium of this fungus is found in autumn on dead moist leaves of the grape-vine : erect segmented filaments rise from it to the height of some millimetres ; these filaments branch copiously at their upper end and produce numerous ellipsoidal gonidia on the ultimate ramifications, which can germinate at once and form new mycelia. This stage of the *Peziza* was once supposed to be an independent plant and was known by the name of *Botrytis cinerea.* Sclerotia are subsequently formed, according to Brefeld, by vegetative growth of shoots on the mycelium. These sclerotia appear as weals of various shape and from a half to several millimetres broad in the tissue of the leaf inhabited by the fungus and remain after its decay ; they consist of densely felted hyphae and have a black cortical covering. If they are placed on moist earth soon after they are formed, they develope a large number of gonidiophores ; but if they pass through a resting-state of some months' duration, and are then placed on damp soil, they produce small stalked cups which may be a centimetre in height, and which consist of hyphal tissue ; the shallow cavity of these cups bears a hymenium in which ascospores are formed, as is represented in Fig. 69 ; this is the fructification of *Peziza Fuckeliana.*

In this group are included various other genera with small fructifications, and also the Morchelleae, Helvelleae, Spatularieae and *Geoglossum*, in which the fructifications are like stalked caps or are club-shaped or of some similar form ; these often attain a very considerable size and have the hymenium spread over large portions of their surface.

5. The **TUBERACEAE**[1] have subterranean tuber-like fructifications. The mycelium spreads in the ground and perhaps lives parasitically on the roots of trees, as Reess has

---

[1] Tulasne, Fungi hypogaei, Paris, 1851.—De Bary, Morph. u. Phys. d. Pilze, p. 90 ff.—Reess, Ueber d. Parasitismus von *Elaphomyces granulatus* (Bot. Ztg. 1880, p. 730) ; Id. Ueber *Elaphomyces* in Ber. Deutsch. Bot. Ges. 1885. [Hesse, R. Cryptica, eine neue Tuberaceengattung (Pringsh. Jahrb. XV. 1884). See also Frank's interesting paper, Ueber d. Ernährung gewisser Bäume durch Pilze in Ber. Deutsch. Bot. Ges. 1885].

recently shown to be the case with the genus *Elaphomyces*[1]. The mycelium of this Fungus is parasitic on the outer layers of the roots of pines and produces dichotomous branching in them of an abnormal kind. Neither the formation of gonidia, nor the germination of the ascospores have been observed. The tuber-like fructifications with their asci are either attached to the mycelium by a distinct basal portion, as in *Terfezia* and *Delastria*, or are enclosed in the young state by the mycelium, as in *Tuber*; in the mature state the mycelium has disappeared and the fructifications lie in the ground detached and without their former investment, but covered by a cortical layer, the *peridium*, which is usually a thick compact mass of pseudo-parenchyma. The spores which are produced inside the fructification are set free by its decay. The interior is occupied by winding chambers which are covered by the broad hymenial layers and separated by barren portions. The spores in an ascus are not formed simultaneously but at different times in a way not yet understood, and the number varies, being usually four, but often less. There are intermediate forms between the Discomycetes and the Tuberaceae.

6. There remain to be noticed certain Fungi which are classed with the Ascomycetes as doubtful or very degenerate forms, in which the spores are formed in an ascus, but the asci are not produced in a fructification but are free branches of the mycelium. Among these are *Exoascus* and the Yeast-Fungi.

Exoascus[2]. *Exoascus Pruni*, which occasions the malformation known as bladder-plum in the fruits of *Prunus domestica*, *P. insititia* and other species, may serve as an example of this genus. The mycelium consists of unbranched hyphae with transverse septa, and grows from the parts round the fruit and the adjacent branches into the young fruit, spreading there between the cells and ultimately occupying the whole of it. In consequence of this fungus-growth the fruits increase to an abnormal size ; the part which usually forms the juicy flesh swells up, and the tissue inside it, where the stone should be, does not develope, but in its place there is a cavity, the so-called 'pocket.' At length the hyphae beneath the surface of the fruit put out branches, which grow perpendicularly to the surface and raise up the cuticle. Each of these branches elongates into a club-shaped tube which bursts through the cuticle, parts off a stalk-cell at its basal extremity by a transverse septum, and becomes an ascus. Eight spores are formed in an ascus. The spores sprout in germination, like the cells of the yeast-plant. How the Fungus finds its way into healthy trees is not known.

The YEAST-FUNGI[3], in the narrower sense of the term, belong to the genus *Saccharomyces*, and are distinguished by their power of exciting alcoholic fermentation in saccharine fluids. *Saccharomyces* is a typical unicellular Fungus. Its cells are roundish or ellipsoidal in form and consist of a delicate cell-wall and vacuolated protoplasm. A nucleus has not been observed in them[4]. Their mode of multiplication

---

[1] The relations of this genus to the genus *Tuber*, and its connection with the Tuberaceae, still require investigation.

[2] De Bary, *Exoascus Pruni* u. d. Taschen oder Narren d. Pflaumenbäume (Beitr. z. Morph. u. Phys. d. Pilze, I, in Abhandl. der Senckenberg. Ges. in Frankfurt a. M., V. Bd. 1864),—[also Vergl. Morph. u. Biol. d. Pilze, Mycetozoen u. Bacterien, Leipzig, 1884. Fischer, Ueber die Pilzgattung Ascomyces (Bot. Zeit. 1884).]

[3] Nägeli includes the Schizomycetes under the term 'Hefe' (Yeast-fungi), which applies to all organisms which excite fermentation and putrefaction in contradistinction to inorganic ferments (see Nägeli, Theorie d. Gährung., München 1879).—Rees, Bot. Unters. ü. d. Alkoholgährungspilze, Leipsic 1860. The extensive literature on the subject of fermentation cannot be further noticed here, [but see De Bary, Vergl. Morph. u. Biologie d. Pilze, Mycetozoen u. Bacterien, Leipzig, 1884, for an account of this subject and the more important literature ; also Schutzenberger, Les fermentations, 4th edition, Paris 1884.—Reess, Ueber d. systemat. Stellung d. Hefepilze (Bot. Zeit. 1884).—Hansen, Vorläuf. Mittheil. über Gährungspilze (Bot. Centralbl. XXI. 1884).—Kny, Die Beziehung des lichtes z. Zelltheilung bei Saccharomyces Cerevisiae (Ber. d. Deut. Bot. Ges. 1884).—Grove, Synops. of the Bacteria and Yeast-Fungi (London, 1884)].

[4] [The presence of a nucleus has been observed; see Schmitz, Ueber d. Zellkern d. Thalloph. (Niederrh. Ges.)].

by sprouting is characteristic of the yeast-cells. Each cell in a fermentable solution puts out at one or more points in its circumference a small knob-like protuberance, which increases in size and by constriction and the formation of a parting wall at its base is delimited from the mother-cell. Then the daughter-cell either separates at once from the mother-cell or continues united to it for some time ; if the latter happens while many generations of daughter-cells are produced, the result is the formation of chains of cells (*sprout-chains*) (Fig. 71, *d*). If yeast-cells are cultivated on the cut surface of pieces of potato, turnip, &c., single cells are converted into asci, in which from two to four ascospores are formed. These can germinate at once by the production of the characteristic yeast-sprouts : they can also retain the power of germination for a longer time. It is only in solutions in which the fermentation is sufficiently active that the yeast-cells can do without the free oxygen which is necessary for the life of other

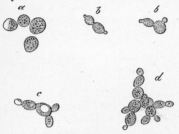

FIG. 71. *Saccharomyces cerevisiae. a* isolated cells, *b,c,d* smaller and larger aggregations of sprouts, the cells of which multiply by sprouting. After de Bary. Magn. 390 times.

Fungi and of all plants ; where sugar is wanting in a solution they cannot live without the access of free oxygen, but they can grow in solutions which do not contain oxygen provided they contain sugar. Oxidation by the free oxygen of the atmosphere however is favourable to their fermentive activity, and the fermentive activity of a cell promotes its growth under all circumstances. The yeast-like sprouting which may be observed under certain circumstances in some species of *Mucor*, as in *Mucor racemosus*, must not mislead us into confounding those forms with the true yeast-cells of the genus *Saccharomyces* ; they too have the power of setting up a weak alcoholic fermentation in fluids which contain sugar[1].

7. **LICHENS.** Since the researches[2] of Schwendener, with which must be associated those of Bornet, Stahl and others as confirming and extending them, it can no longer be doubted that the Lichens are genuine Fungi of the division of the Ascomycetes with a few genera belonging to the Basidiomycetes, as *Cora* and *Rhipidonema*, and that they are distinguished by a remarkable parasitism. The host-plants are Algae, growing as a rule in damp situations, but belonging to a variety of groups, frequently to the Chroococcaceae and Nostocaceae, still more frequently to the Palmellaceae, sometimes to the Chroolepideae, rarely to the Confervaceae. The Fungi which form Lichens occur only as parasites on certain species of Algae[3], while the Algae which are attacked by them, and which when united with the Fungi are called *gonidia*, are also known in the free state and separate from the Fungi. Where the Alga which is attacked by the Lichen-fungus is a filamentous Alga and the hyphal tissue is developed only in small quantity, as in *Ephebe* and *Coenogonium*, the true state of the case is at once apparent ; and ever since Lichens of this sort have been more accurately known, the suspicion has been entertained that they were in fact Algae attacked by Fungi. Even before this time attention had been repeatedly called to the identity of the gonidia of the Collemaceae with rows of cells of the Nostocaceae ; but in

[1] Brefeld, Untersuch. ü. Alkoholgährung in Verhandl. d. phys. Med. Ges. zu Würzburg, 1874.

[2] Tulasne, Mémoire pour servir à l'histoire organogr. et physiol. des Lichens (Ann. d. sc. nat. 3° série, T. XVII).—Schwendener, Unters. ü. d. Flechtenthallus in Nägeli's Beitr. z. wiss. Bot. 1860 u. 1862; —Id., Laub- und Gallertflechten (Nägeli's Beitr. z. wiss. Bot. 1868);—Id., in Flora, 1872, Nr. 11–15, and Ueber d. Algentypen d. Flechtengonidien. Basel 1869.—Bornet, Recherches sur les gonidies des lichens. Ann. d. sc. nat. T. XVII. 1873.—Stahl, Beitr. z. Kenntn. d. Flechten. Leipzig 1877 and 1878. Other works are cited in the text. [See also De Bary, Morph. u. Biol. d. Pilze, &c., 1884.—Marshall Ward, On the structure, development and life-history of a tropical epiphyllous Lichen (Strigula complanata, F.) in Trans. Linn. Soc. Lond. Bot. II. part 6. 1884.—Neubner, Beitr. z. Kenntn. d. Calicien (Flora, 1883).—Fünfstück, Beitr. z. Entwicklungeschichte der Lichenen (Jahrb. d. K. bot. Gartens z. Berlin, III. 1884).]   [3] See however what is said below of *Arthonia*.

this case the food–supplying Alga usually undergoes considerable change of habit, at least in the outlines of its form, by the influence of the Fungus that preys upon it, just as *Euphorbia Cyparissias* suffers from the aecidium that lives on it. The greater part however of the Lichen-fungi employ as their hosts the Chroococcaceae and Palmellaceae which form coatings and cushions on moist soil, on the bark of trees and on stones. The tissue of the Fungus grows so copiously around and among the cells and cellfamilies of these Algae, that the latter at length appear to be merely dispersed through the compact hyphal tissue, or to form a distinct layer, the *gonidial layer*, in it. The Algae thus completely enclosed by their parasites are not impeded in vegetative growth or multiplication, though they are subject to other disturbances of their development; but if they are freed from the Fungi which are assailing them, they proceed with their normal development, and they have been several times known to form zoogonidia.

We will first of all consider the Lichen as a whole, as it presents itself in nature, where the Alga which supplies the nutriment appears under the name of gonidium as an element in the construction of its thallus, and will afterwards examine further into the algal nature of the gonidium. The thallus in the Lichens is often a crust overlaying

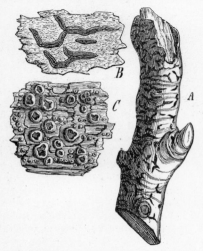

FIG. 73. A piece of the foliaceous thallus of *Peltigera horizontalis*; *a* the apothecia, *r* the rhizines. Natural size.

FIG. 72. *A* and *B Graphis elegans,* a crustaceous Lichen on the bark of *Ilex aquifolium. A* natural size. *B* slightly magnified, *C* another crustaceous Lichen, *Pertusaria Wulfeni.* Slightly magnified.

FIG. 74. A gelatinous Lichen, *Collema pulposum.* Slightly magnified.

stone and bark, or insinuating itself between the laminae of the bark of woody plants and sending out its fructifications only above the surface. These *crustaceous* Lichens are so closely attached to the substratum, at least on their under surface, that they cannot be removed from it entire and without injury to the thallus (Fig. 72, *A, B, C*). These forms pass by intermediate steps into the *foliaceous* Lichens, in which the leaf-like thallus forms flat, often crisped expansions, which can be removed in their entirety from the substances on which they have grown, the soil, stones, moss or bark being fastened to them only in places by special organs of attachment, named *rhizines*. The foliaceous thallus not unfrequently attains considerable dimensions, measuring sometimes in the large species of *Sticta* and *Peltigera* a foot in diameter and a half to one millimetre in thickness, and then inclines to assume on the whole a circular outline and has rounded indented lobes at the growing margin (Fig. 73, and Fig. 74). A third form of the Lichen-thallus, which is also connected by intermediate forms with the previous ones, is seen in the *fruticose* Lichens, which are attached to the substratum at one point only and by a narrow base, and grow upwards from it with a branching shrubby habit.   The branches of the thallus are either flat and

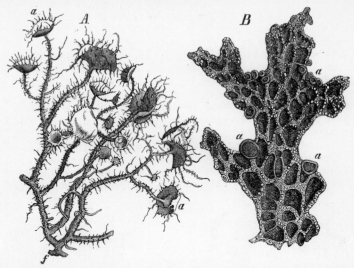

FIG. 75.   *A. Usnea barbata*, a fruticose Lichen, natural size.   *B* piece of the thallus of *Sticta pulmonacea*, a foliaceous Lichen, natural size, seen from below ;   *a* apothecia, *f* the disk in *A* by which the Lichen is attached to the bark of a tree.

ribbon-like, very similar to the lobes of many foliaceous lichens, or they are slender and cylindrical (Fig. 75, *A*).   In *Cladonia* and *Stereocaulon* we have not so much intermediate forms between the foliaceous and fruticose thallus, as a combination of the two, where there is at first a small foliaceous expansion, and then a cup-shaped or branched and shrub-like thallus proceeding from it.

The thallus of Lichens may be dried till it is ready to be ground into powder without losing its vitality ; if it is then soaked in water, it usually acquires the consistence of leather, and is tough and elastically flexible ; but there are a number of genera, remarkable also on other accounts, in which the thallus in the soaked state is slippery and gelatinous ; these *gelatinous* lichens form cushion-like masses with a wavy surface, and in growth approach sometimes the fruticose and sometimes the foliaceous lichens ; *Collema* is a typical lichen of this kind (Fig. 74).

The arrangement of the gonidia and the hyphae in a thallus may be such, that these two elementary forms seem to be distributed in it uniformly and in equal proportions, as in Fig. 77 ; in

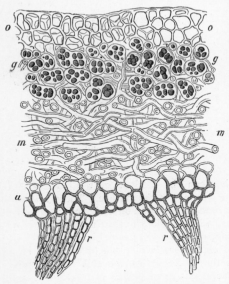

FIG. 76.   *Sticta fuliginosa*, transverse section through the foliaceous thallus, magn. 500 times ;   *o* rind- (epidermal) layer of the upper side, *u* that of the under side, *rr* rhizines or attaching structures which spring from the epidermal layer, *m* the medullary layer, the filaments of which are to be seen in longitudinal and transverse section ; the upper and under rind also consist of hyphae, but their short cells have much broader lumina and are connected together without interstices, forming a pseudo-parenchyma ; *g* the gonidia with their light-green protoplasm shaded dark ; each gelatinous envelope encloses several gonidia formed by division.

this case the thallus is said to be *homoiomerous*; or the gonidia are crowded together in one layer (Fig. 76), so that the hyphal tissue is divided into an outer and an inner or into an upper and a lower layer as the case may be; the tissue of the thallus is therefore stratified, and such Lichens are said to be *heteromerous* (Figs. 76 and 79).

The mode of growth, the branching and outward form of the thallus may either be determined by the gonidia, so that the hyphae play only a subordinate part in the formation of that body, or the hyphae determine the form and the mode of growth, while the share of the gonidia in the formation of the tissue is subordinate. The former case occurs in only a few Lichens, the latter is the ordinary mode of growth in typical lichens, especially in those of the heteromerous kind. In many homoiomerous gelatinous Lichens (Fig. 77) it seems to be doubtful, whether the change in the outward form proceeds more from the gonidia or from the hyphae. This relation between the gonidia and the hyphae, which is morphologically and physiologically important, will be made sufficiently clear by examination of Figs. 78 and 79. Fig. 78 is an optical longitudinal section of a branch of **Ephebe pubescens**; the large gonidia are shaded, the delicate hyphae are indicated by the letter *h*. The branch elongates by growth at the apex and by corresponding transverse division of a

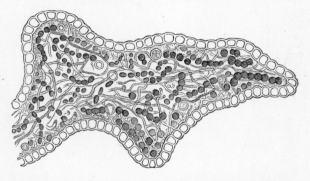

FIG. 77. *Leptogium scotinum*, vertical section of the gelatinous thallus, magn. 550 times; an epidermal layer clothes the inner tissue, which consists for the most part of formless and colourless jelly, in which the coiled strings of gonidia lie; single larger cells of the strings (the limiting cells) are of a lighter colour; between them run the slender hyphae.

gonidium *gs*, which is the apical cell of the branch; the cells derived from the gonidium at the apex divide in a plane parallel to the longitudinal axis of the branch, and further divisions then take place in different directions, and thus groups of gonidia are produced at a considerable distance from the apex of the branch. The slender hyphae reach in the figure up to the apical cell; in other cases they come to an end some way below the apical gonidium, and only a few single filaments grow inside the gelatinous envelope, which is evidently produced from the gonidia, and follow the longitudinal growth of the branch. It is only at some distance behind the apex of the branch that the hyphae send out lateral branches which penetrate between the gonidia and gonidial groups by growing through their softened mucilaginous cell-walls. Thus the whole form of the branch, its growth in length and thickness, is determined by the gonidia; the hyphae with their small number and delicacy scarcely cause any change of importance either in the external form or in the interior structure of the branch. The same thing appears plainly in the formation of the lateral branches of the thallus of *Ephebe pubescens*; one of the outer gonidia elongates in a direction at right angles to the axis of the main branch of the thallus and becomes the apical cell of the lateral branch, producing new cells by transverse divisions, as is shown in Fig. 78, *a*; branches of the hyphae at that spot turn in the same direction and behave in the same way towards the new apical cell as they have been shown to behave towards the apical cell of the main branch.—**Usnea barbata**, a fruticose Lichen, forms a much-branched shrub-like thallus, resembling that of *Ephebe pubescens*; in this case also the branches of the thallus elongate by apical growth (Fig. 79, *A*); but this is not effected by means of the gonidia as in *Ephebe*, nor usually by a single cell, but the hyphae, which run parallel to each other in the branch, and incline towards one another at its extremity, elongate individually by apical growth of the terminal member, and thus co-operate in bringing about longitudinal growth at the apex of the branch; this growth is supplemented by an intercalary growth further behind due to intercalary elongation of the hyphae and the interpolation of branches of the hyphae in different directions.

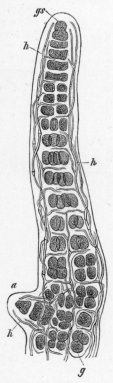

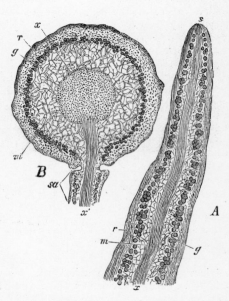

FIG. 78. A branch of the thallus of *Ephebe pubescens*, magn. 500 times; see the text.

FIG. 79. *Usnea barbata. A* optical longitudinal section or a slender branch, softened in potash solution. *B* transverse section of an older thallus-stem with the basal portion of an adventitious (soredial) branch *sa*, magn. 300 times; *s* apex of the branch, *r* the rind, *x* the axial medullary bundle, *m* the loose medullary tissue, *g* the gonidial layer.

The hyphae lie so close together that they form a compact mass without interstices; but at some distance behind the apex of the branch the hyphal tissue is differentiated into a dense rind formed of fibres interwoven on all sides, an axile longitudinal bundle of closely packed filaments, and between them a layer of looser texture with air-conducting interstices. At the place where this differentiation of the hyphal tissue begins behind the apex, there the layer of gonidia terminates; this layer is composed of small roundish green cells, which, as they multiply by division, form small groups; these groups are themselves disposed in a mantle-like layer lying between the rind and the tissue beneath (see the transverse section *B* in Fig. 79). Single gonidia only lie behind the growing apex of the branch, and by their subsequent division the cells in the gonidial layer are increased in number. It is plain then that in *Usnea barbata* the growth in length, the growth in thickness, and the internal differentiation of the tissue must be wholly put to the account of the hyphae, and that the gonidia behave as a foreign addition to the hyphal tissue. In accordance with this the formation of new branches originates with the hyphae and not with the gonidia. The branching may be dichotomous, and if so, the apical members of the hyphae incline towards two points lying near each other and then grow on in corresponding directions, so that the two equal forks form an acute angle. Adventitious lateral branches arise behind the extremity of the thallus by the fibres of the rind forming a new apex and growing in an outward direction ; there are gonidia also to be found behind the apex of the new branch ; the base of the branch sends fibres of the tissue beneath the rind and an axile bundle into the mother-branch, and thus the corresponding forms of the tissue of the two are united together. The growth of *Usnea* may be compared in its essential points with the growth of the stroma of *Xylaria* ; the gonidia are here a subordinate element in the formation of the whole ; and the strands of the Rhizomorphae, which will be described later on under the Basidiomycetes, supply, as Brefeld has pointed out, an instance of still closer analogy amongst the Fungi.—In many crustaceous Lichens the thallus has as a rule no certain outline ; there is no such definite external form as in the cases which we have been considering ; the thallus appears to be composed of groups of gonidia somewhat irregularly disposed and of hyphae growing among and between them. In others however, such as *Sporastatia morio, Rhizocarpon subcentricum, Aspicilia calcarea*, the thallus forms lobed disks, which expand by centrifugal growth at the margin ; the growing margin is composed of hyphal tissue only, and groups of gonidia appear first at separate spots further inwards, that is, nearer the centre, and spread by degrees. The rind-tissue shows indentations at the circumference of the spots where the gonidia are collected, and isolated scale-like bits of a true lichen-thallus are in consequence formed upon a fibrous substratum known as the *hypothallus*[1].

Some of the Lichens which live on the bark of trees, the GRAPHIDEAE especially, exhibit peculiarities, which Frank[2] has recently investigated. They pass through two different states in their existence ; 'one in which they are without gonidia and consist only of hyphae, and one in which they are typical Lichens composed of hyphae and gonidia.' In the first state the hyphae of *Arthonia vulgaris* and *Graphis scripta* form inside the outermost corky layer of the periderm of the trees which they inhabit a tolerably close and coherent felt of extremely delicate hyphae, which spread irregularly and in every direction among the cells of the tissue, forming a homogeneous substratum and causing certain changes in the appearance of the periderm. This layer of hyphal tissue grows centrifugally in breadth, and eventually forms the marginal zone of the thallus. The thallus is produced by the intrusion into the hyphal tissue of gonidia belonging to the algal genus *Chroolepus*, a filamentous Alga very nearly related to *Cladophora*, and whose cells are usually coloured with a red oil. It is only after the entrance of the gonidia that a fructification is formed. But all the Lichens that live in cortical tissue, which Frank calls 'hypophloeodic Lichens,' are not of this kind. *Lecanora pallida* makes its way into the cortex with the first gonidia that are attacked by the hyphae, and obtains the rest of the gonidia by multiplication of the original ones. The genus *Arthonia* above mentioned has also species which have no gonidia ; while *A. vulgaris* has gonidia, *A. punctiformis* is without them and is therefore a true Fungus.

That the Lichens are simply Ascomycetous Fungi which live in association with Algae may be considered to be proved by the facts which have now been recounted.

---

[1] See Schwendener in Flora, 1865, Nr. 26.

[2] Frank, Ueber d. biolog. Verhältnisse d. Thallus einigen Krustenflechten in Cohn's Beitr. z. Biol. Pflanzen, II. p. 213.

An interesting example of the formation of the thallus of a lichen is given in Stahl's description of the behaviour of the *hymenial gonidia*. These are small gonidia derived from the ordinary gonidia of the thallus, and found in the perithecia, for instance, of *Endocarpon pusillum* in the intervals between the asci, and in the jelly produced in the cavity of the perithecium by the swelling of the walls of emptied asci. The gonidia of *Endocarpon* belong to the algal genus *Pleurococcus*. The hymenial gonidia are specially and clearly distinguished from the gonidia of the thallus by their minute size. The spores are set free from the perithecium simultaneously with the hymenial gonidia, and are closely encircled by them. The spores if sown on glass or some other substance germinate at once and their germ-tubes attach themselves to the gonidia. Striking changes are now perceived in the gonidia ; they increase considerably in size and add largely to the amount of chlorophyll which they contained—both the result of the influence of the Fungus. Other germ-tubes strike downwards into the soil and are the first 'rhizines.' In the young thallus thus formed the separation into the various layers is only gradually effected, the portion of the thallus which is above the ground being at first only a mingled collection of gonidia and hyphae with scarcely any intervals between them. If the hymenial gonidia vegetate apart from the hyphae, they remain much smaller and multiply by divisions, the direction of which is different from that of the gonidia of the thallus and agrees with that of the algal cells known as *Stichococcus* ; the larger gonidia on the contrary, when vegetating in freedom, agree in this respect with the gonidia of the thallus which are a form of *Pleurococcus*. The hymenial gonidia of *Endocarpon pusillum* are employed in a still more remarkable way by the spores of a small lichen, *Thelidium minutulum*, which occurs with *Endocarpon*, in the formation of its thallus ; in this case we have an ascomycetous Lichen constructing its thallus with gonidia obtained from another species. The part of the thallus of *Thelidium* which has gonidia is of very reduced size, and forms a kind of appendage only to the rest of the mycelium which runs through the substratum and on which the perithecia are formed. In the earlier experiments of Rees, Treub and Bornet, in which the spores of lichens were brought into connection with the Algae which corresponded with their gonidia, the Fungus spun its threads round the Algae, but no perfect thallus was formed like that produced in Stahl's experiment ; at the same time the influence of the Ascomycete on the gonidia was very clearly shown.

Formation of spores. The spores of Lichens are formed in fructifications, which are known as *apothecia*, and which resemble the fructifications of the Discomycetes or those of many Pyrenomycetes. The apothecia are formed inside the tissue of the thallus and emerge from it at a later period, when they either spread out the flat surface of their hymenial layer to the open air (*gymnocarpous* Lichens), or allow their spores to escape by an orifice (*angiocarpous* Lichens). In all Lichens without exception the apothecium with all its essential parts from first to last is produced from the hyphal tissue only ; it is the Fungus alone which forms the fructification ; the food-supplying Algae, the gonidia, either take no part in it or a very unimportant part ; the tissue of the thallus with its gonidia merely grows up like a wall round the apothecium and partly encloses it (Fig. 80), or grows more luxuriantly underneath the apothecium and raises it as on a stalk above the surrounding thallus. The only exception to the endogenous origin of the apothecium is to be found in *Coenogonium* and similar forms, in which such a mode of formation is impossible, because the hyphae form only a thin layer about the filamentous Alga that does duty for gonidia ; these species plainly confirm what Schwendener's researches have demonstrated, that the fructification in the Lichens belongs exclusively to the hyphal tissue.

The apothecia of all the Lichens that have been sufficiently investigated are the result of a sexual act which agrees in many points with that of the Florideae. In both cases there are *spermatia* which conjugate with a *trichogyne*, and a multicellular conducting tube brings about the impregnation which causes the asci to grow out from the third part of the female organ. The spermatia are produced in special receptacles, the *spermogonia*; these are cavities in the thallus, which are round or flask-shaped or contorted, and densely lined or almost filled with *sterigmata*. The spermatia are obtained by abscision from these sterigmata in large numbers, and escape by a narrow opening in the spermogonium.

The following details of the development of the apothecium are taken from the gelatinous lichen **Collema microphyllum**[1]. The thallus forms a rim round the ripe sporocarp, which therefore has an *excipulum*. The sporocarp consists of a firm outside covering and a looser substance within. The apothecium in its earliest stages exactly answers to the procarp of the Florideae, and is at first a stout lateral branch on a hypha of the thallus. The basal portion is twisted like a corkscrew, and above it is a long process which reaches the surface of the thallus and terminates above it in a short point. The screw-twisted portion is the *ascogone* (archicarp), the pluricellular filament which surmounts it is the trichogyne or trichophore-apparatus (compare the Florideae). There are usually two and a half to three coils in the ascogone, and a larger number of cells, on the average twelve. The number of cells in the trichogyne varies with its length. It passes through the surface of the thallus

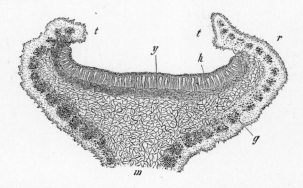

FIG. 80. Vertical section of the gymnocarpous apothecium of *Anaptychia ciliaris*; *h* the hymenium, *y* the subhymenial layer (and excipulum); all beside belongs to the thallus of which *m* is the medullary layer, *r* the rind, *g* gonidia: at *tt* the thallus forms a cup-like border round the apothecium. Magn. about 50 times.

and terminates above it in a short point. The trichogynes appear only on the side of the thallus which is exposed to the light.

Admission of water causes the spermogonia to set the spermatia at liberty, and these are spread over the surface of the thallus by the water-drops and so come in contact with the sticky surface of the process of the trichogyne. Conjugation takes place between them and the trichogyne, but it is not easily seen, owing to the extreme minuteness of the objects. The ascogone is invested by a coil of the surrounding hyphae, and its cells at the same time increase in size and multiply by intercalary growth. The asci now grow out as lateral branches from the ascogone (archicarp), while the rest of the parts constituting the apothecium are produced by a process of vegetation which takes place on the hyphae adjacent to the ascogone. Thus the young apothecium is composed of three elements: 1. The ascogenous filaments; 2. the paraphyses, a system of hyphae running parallel to one another and at right angles to the surface of the thallus and divided by transverse septa; 3. the pseudo-parenchymatous tissue, the 'excipulum proprium,' enclosing the other two. Fig. 81 gives a section through the apothecium of another Lichen, *Anaptychia ciliaris*; the explanation attached to the figure will be a sufficient description of the different parts.

---

[1] Stahl, Beiträge, Heft I.

The trichogyne also suffers characteristic changes in consequence of fertilisation. While the cells of the ascogone increase in size, those of the trichogyne lose a portion of their original volume; the transverse septa swell up into thick strongly refractive nodes, so that the trichogyne which was before of uniform thickness assumes a nodose appearance; the protoplasmic contents of its cells also become brown. The phenomena of reproduction are quite similar in other Collemaceae. *Physma compactum* is peculiar in one respect; the apothecia are formed in the tissue which constitutes the envelope of the spermogonia. From the base of this receptacle hyphal filaments grow up and form procarps. This species may therefore be said to be

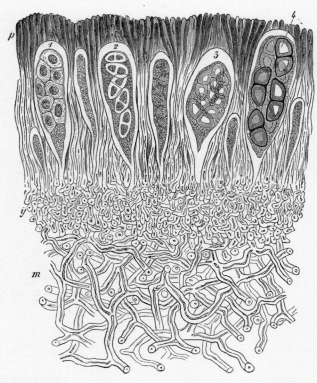

FIG. 81. *Anaptychia ciliaris*, a small portion of the apothecium in vertical section; *m* medullary layer of the thallus, *y* the subhymenial layer, *p* paraphyses of the hymenium; between them are the asci in different stages of development; in 1 the young spores are not yet septate, in 2—4 the spores are more advanced; the protoplasm in which they are imbedded is contracted by the drying up of the Lichen before the preparation was made. Magn. 350 times.

hermaphrodite, since spermatia and carpogone are derived from common hyphal layers. The envelope of the apothecium in this case is not as in *Collema* a result of fertilisation, but was in existence before as the envelope of the spermogonia.

The club-shaped spore-sacs (asci) of the Lichens resemble those of the Pyrenomycetes and Discomycetes in every important point; their wall is often very thick and has great power of swelling; the spores too (Fig. 82), as in the Fungi just mentioned, are the result of a process of free cell-formation, in which a portion of the protoplasm, and often a considerable portion, remains unused. The normal number of the spores is eight, sometimes only one to two, as in *Umbilicaria* and *Megalospora*, from two to three or four to six in some species of *Pertusaria*; some hundreds even are found in one ascus in *Bactrospora*, *Acarospora*, and *Sarcogyne*. The spores show a considerable variety of structure, though this is similar in general to that of the Ascomycetes; they are often septate and multicellular, like those of many Pyrenomycetes; the exosporium is usually smooth and often variously coloured.

The spores are set at liberty when water finds its way to the hymenium; they are suspended in the fluid which fills the ascus and are discharged with it when the ascus bursts at its apex; the discharge is probably the effect of the swelling of the paraphyses, and of the capacity for swelling possessed by the wall of the ascus itself.

The germination of the spores consists in the development of a hyphal filament from the endosporium of each cell of a spore; the filament branches and spreads over its moist substratum. The germination of the very large spores of a few genera, *Megalospora*, *Ochrolechia*, and *Pertusaria*, is peculiar; the spores are unicellular and filled with drops of oil (Fig. 82, *A*, *B*), and each may put out as many as a hundred

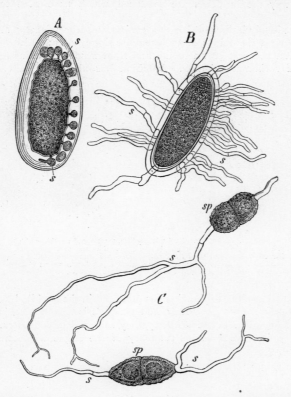

FIG. 82. Lichen-spores germinating. *A* optical longitudinal section of spore of *Pertusaria communis* after lying thirty-four hours in glycerine; *s* first beginnings of the germ-tubes. *B Pertusaria lejoplaca*, spore with numerous germ-tubes, after de Bary, magn. 390 times. *C* germinating septate spores of *Solorina saccata*. After Tulasne.

germ-tubes from different points in its circumference. The formation of each tube begins with the appearance of a canal in the endosporium, which enlarges from within outwards; the protoplasm passes into it and becomes invested with a very delicate membrane, which then grows in the outward direction in the form of a tube (Fig. 82, *A*, *B*).

Besides their spores Lichens possess organs named *soredia*, which assist materially in their multiplication. The soredia are single gonidial cells or groups of gonidia, which, when wrapt in hyphal tissue and set free from the thallus, are able at once to grow into a new Lichen-thallus; they issue from the thallus of non-gelatinous Lichens as a fine powder, sometimes forming thick cushion-like masses on them, as in *Usnea, Ramalina, Evernia, Physcia, Parmelia, Pertusaria,* and others. In the thallus of a heteromerous lichen the soredia are formed in the gonidial layer, where single gonidia, or a number of them together, become surrounded by hyphae which cling closely to them and form a fibrous envelope for them; the gonidia divide repeatedly, and each daughter-cell is again invested with hyphal threads, and by the frequent repetition of this process the soredia collect in large numbers in the gonidial zone, and at length rupture the thallus. When thus released the soredia may go on multiplying outside the thallus, or under favourable circumstances each soredium or a number of them may develope into a new thallus (Fig. 83). Schwendener says that this can take place in *Usnea barbata* when the soredium is still in the mother-thallus, and that in this way the branches are produced, which have been termed 'soredial branches.'

It has been already intimated that the *gonidia*, the other element which unites with the Fungus to form the thallus of a Lichen, are simply Algae which the ascomycetous Fungus has attacked and grown round, and from which it obtains food, being incapable itself of carbon-assimilation. Attention has also been called in connection

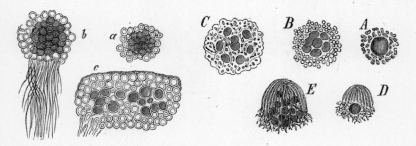

FIG. 83. *A—D* soredia of *Usnea barbata. A* a simple soredium, consisting of a gonidium with hyphae woven round it. *B* a soredium in which the gonidium has multiplied by division. *C* a group of simple soredia formed by hyphae forcing their way between the gonidia. *D* and *E* germinating soredia; the hyphae form an apex, the gonidia are multiplying. *a—c* soredia of *Physcia parietina. a* with an envelope of pseudo-parenchyma *b* the envelope producing attaching filaments. *c* a young thallus, developed from a soredium, magn. 500 times. After Schwendener.

with the hymenial gonidia to the changes produced in the gonidia by the Fungus. If the hyphal tissue in *Physcia, Evernia,* and *Cladonia* is decomposed in water, and the gonidia thus enabled to vegetate at liberty, they will produce zoospores.

The following is Schwendener's summary of the Algae which are employed as Lichen-gonidia:—

I. Algae with bluish-green cell-contents (Phycochromaceae).

Name of Alga-group.	Name of the Lichens in which the Algae occur as gonidia.
1. Sirosiphoneae	*Ephebe, Spilonema, Polychidium.*
2. Rivularieae	*Thamnidium, Lichina, Racoblenna.*
3. Scytonemeae	*Heppia, Porocyphus.*
4. Nostocaceae	*Collema, Lempholemma, Leptogium, Pannaria, Peltigera.*
5. Chroococcaceae	*Omphalaria, Euchylium, Phylliscum.*

II. Algae with chlorophyll-green cell-contents (Chlorophyceae).

6. Confervaceae	*Cystocoleus.*
7. Chroolepideae	Graphideae, Verrucarieae, *Roccella, Lecanora* sp. *Coenogonium.*

8. Palmellaceae . . . . . . Many fruticose and foliaceous Lichens.

    Cystococcus humicola . . *Physcia, Cladonia, Evernia, Usnea, Bryopogon, Anaptychia.*

    Pleurococcus . . . . . *Endocarpon* and various crustaceous Lichens.

9. Coleochaeteae (*Phyllactidium*)[1] .*Opegrapha filicina.*

The influence of the hyphae of the Fungus on the gonidia has been already alluded to in the description of the hymenial gonidia. This influence is different in different species. It is often scarcely perceptible, especially if the gonidia are unicellular Algae, but very striking sometimes and especially in the case of filamentous Algae, using that term in the widest sense. The filaments become crooked, divide into short pieces, or separate into single cells, as in *Opegrapha varia*, the gonidia of which belong to the filamentous Alga *Chroolepus*. At the margin of the thallus there are

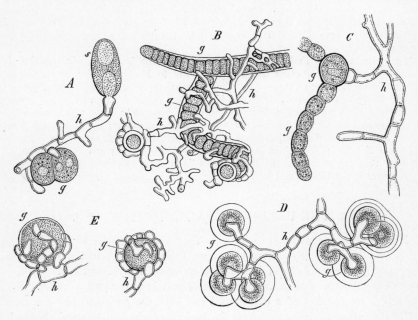

FIG. 84. Examples of various Algae which are employed as the gonidia of Lichens. *h* indicates always the hypha of the Fungus, *g* the gonidium. *A* germinating spore *s* of *Physcia parietina*, the germ-tube of which adheres closely to *Protococcus viridis*. *B* a filament of *Scytonema* with hyphae of *Stereocaulon ramulosus* twined round it. *C* from the thallus of the Lichen *Physma chalazanum*; a hyphal branch is entering a cell of the nostoc filament (gonidium). *D* from the thallus of the Lichen *Synalissa symphorea*; the gonidia are the Alga *Gloeocapsa*. *E* from the thallus of the Lichen *Cladonia furcata*; the gonidia which are being surrounded by the hyphae are the cells of *Protococcus*. After Bornet. *A, C, D, E* magn. 950, *B* 650 times.

perfect filaments of *Chroolepus* still to be seen; but as they become surrounded by the hyphae they break up into short pieces or into single cells. On the other hand, we find in old specimens of *Op. varia* that the gonidia have reassumed their normal appearance; they elongate, form straight filaments, and produce the zoosporangia of the algal genus *Chroolepus*. The gelatinous investment possessed by many Algae which serve as Lichen-gonidia disappears in the Lichen-thallus. Among the most remarkable are the cases where the branches of the hyphae penetrate into the gonidia, as in *Arnoldia* and *Physma* (Fig. 84); this gave occasion to the old and erroneous notion that gonidia

---

[1] The systematic position of this Alga is still uncertain owing to our ignorance of its organs of reproduction; the vegetative state however resembles *Coleochaete,* and like it forms broad disks on leaves and other objects.

were produced by hyphae. The gonidia in the cases cited, that is the cells of the nostoc-chains which supply the gonidia, increase in size, alter their form, and become invested with a thick cell-wall, such as is not observed in cells not pierced by the hyphae ; finally they lose their colour and disappear. In other cases too it would seem that gonidial cells are really destroyed by the Fungus.

But the gonidia in their turn exercise an influence on the hyphae ; if a hypha comes into contact with an Alga, it is excited by it to vigorous growth, as shown by a rapid increase in the number of its cells and the formation of numerous branches, which grow round the Alga (Fig. 84). An analogous growth will be described further on in discussing the peculiar symbiosis of certain Algae and Hepaticae (see p. 23). It is remark-able that in some Lichens two different Algae are found serving as gonidia in the same Lichen-thallus. The Algae which supply gonidia are all widely disseminated ; *Proto-coccus*, *Nostoc*, *Scytonema*, and their allies are found almost everywhere on the trunks of trees, on stones, on the ground and elsewhere. This explains the great prevalence of lichens, as well as the fact that they usually are the first forms of organic life that appear on the fresh surfaces of rock or other material. On this point Bornet's writings should be consulted.

The genera **Cora** and **Rhipidonema,** which have been already mentioned, are distinguished from all other Lichens, according to Mattirolo[1], by the fact that the Fungus in them is not an Ascomycete but a Basidiomycete, and other cases of the kind will probably be discovered. The genus *Cora* is a tropical lichen living on trees, with the surface of its membranous thallus marked in concentric zones ; its gonidia belong to the genus *Chroococcus*, those of *Rhipidonema* to *Scytonema* ; the hymenium is on the under side of the thallus and consists of basidia producing each one spore. The habit of these lichens places them nearest the basidiomycetous genus *Stereum*. It is obvious that the existence of these forms is a new and interesting proof of the correctness of the view here taken of the origin of the Lichen-thallus.

5. THE UREDINEAE (AECIDIOMYCETES)[2].

If we confine our attention in this as in the preceding groups to the forms whose development is thoroughly known to us, we find in respect to the phenomena of propagation two extreme cases ; in the simplest case the mycelium bears a fructifica-tion corresponding to that of the Ascomycetes and known as an *aecidium*, which in its mature state consists of a cup-shaped envelope, the *peridium*, and a hymenium occupying the bottom of the cup, from the basidia of which spores are obtained one after another by abscision (Fig. 85). The spores thus formed (*aecidiospores*) germinate immediately and produce a short filament consisting of a few cells, which

---

[1] Contribuzioni allo studio del genere *Cora* Fr.—Nuovo giornale Italiano Botanico, Vol. XIII, No. 4. Ottob. 1881 ; [see also Biol. Centralblatt, I. Feb. 1882.—Johow, Die Gruppe d. Hymeno-lichenen (Pringsh. Jahrb. XV. 1884).]

[2] Tulasne, Ann. d. sc. nat. 3e série, T. VII, and 4e série, T. II.—De Bary, Unters. ü. d. Brand-pilze, Berlin 1853.—De Bary, in Ann. d. sc. nat. 4e série, T. XX, und Monatsber. d. Berl. Ak. 1865.—Reess, Die Rostpilzformen d. deutschen Coniferen, Halle 1869 (Abh. d. naturf. Ges. Bd. XI).—Winter, Die Pilze (Rabenhorst's Kryptogamenflora, II. Aufl.) ;—Id., Zusammenstellung d. ü. d. Wirthwechsel d. verschied. Formen bekannten.—De Bary, *Aecidium abietinum* (Bot. Zeit. 1881). [Id., Vergl. Morph. u. Biol. d. Pilze, p. 308 (literature).—Plowright, Life-history of *Aecidium Belli-dis*, DC. (Journ. Linn. Soc. vol XX). Id., *Mahonia aquifolium* as a nurse of the wheat mildew (*Pucc. graminis*), and On the life-history of the dock Aecidium (*Aec. Rumicis*, Schlecht) (Proc. Roy. Soc. Lond. vol. xxxvi) ; also On the life-history of certain British heteroecismal Uredines (Q. J. M. S., Jan. 1885).]

soon ceases to grow, but forms instead on short slender branches smaller propagative cells, termed *sporidia*, which fall under the general conception of a gonidium as it has been defined above. The germinating filament which produces the sporidia is a *promycelium*. The sporidia in their turn put forth germ-tubes, which penetrate through the epidermis-cells into the tissue of a host, and there give rise to a mycelium which subsequently produces aecidia. In this case, which is represented by *Endophyllum Sempervivi*, there is a single alternation of generations, in which the alternating generations are the mycelium and the fructification (aecidium), with the slight variation that the spores produce the mycelium with the intervention of a promycelium and its sporidia. The other extreme occurs in *Aecidium Berberidis* (*Puccinia graminis*), *Aecidium Leguminosarum* (*Uromyces appendiculatus*), and others, where new mycelia are produced directly from the aecidiospores without the intervention of a promycelium; but these mycelia do not produce aecidia, but roundish gonidia on crowded cushion-like basidia; and by means of these gonidia, which are known as *uredospores* and can germinate at once, the mycelium is repeatedly reproduced during the period of vegetation; at a later period propagative cells of another kind, the *teleutospores*, make their appearance in the generations termed the *uredo* generations, and these do not germinate till the following year, when they produce promycelia, from the sporidia of which arise the mycelia which bear the aecidium.

A comparison of the second case with the first shows that in the former between the production of the aecidiospores and of the promycelium certain generations have been interposed, in which the organs of propagation (gonidia) are termed uredospores and teleutospores.

Even in these well-known forms of the Uredineae a sexual act has not yet been observed, but its existence must be considered as highly probable after what is now known of the origin of the apothecia of the Lichens; moreover *spermatia* are found in the Uredineae formed in special receptacles, the *spermogonia*, and they usually appear before the aecidia; it is highly probable that the spermatia, here as in the Lichens, perform the part of male organs, and if so the aecidia, the most complex product of the development, must be considered to be sexually produced. Then the aecidium will answer to the apothecium of the Lichens, or to the perithecium of the other Ascomycetes, the aecidiospores to the ascospores, and the uredospores and teleutospores will be, as has been said, different forms of gonidia. Experience has shown that the genera are most suitably named after the forms which bear teleutospores, from which the genera *Puccinia, Uromyces, Coleosporium, Melampsora* and others are already designated.

The gonidial forms known as uredospores and teleutospores are not found in all the genera of the Uredineae; both are wanting, as has been stated, in *Endophyllum*; the uredospores are absent in *Roestelia*; both occur in *Puccinia graminis*, *P. sessilis*, and others.

In many species the development is but imperfectly known, some of its stages being as yet undiscovered; but there are some in which the process is in fact simplified. There are for instance genera in which only teleutospores are known, but which reproduce themselves to an unlimited extent by their means without the appearance of an aecidium; such are *Puccinia Malvacearum* and *P. Dianthi*, *Chrysomyxa Abietis*, and others. The layer of spores in *Chrysomyxa* bursts through the epidermis of the acicular leaves of the pine in spring, and the teleutospores develope promycelia as they lie, and these form sporidia, the germ-tubes of which penetrate into the young leaves and spread through them, and this mycelium gives rise in the next year to new teleutospores. We must suppose that these genera have lost the aecidia out of the course of their development and have retained only the gonidia. The Basidiomycetes, to be described further on, afford a still more remarkable instance of a Fungus reproducing itself only by gonidia. It must be mentioned here that such species as *Puccinia graminis* supply a transition from the Uredineae which have aecidia to those which have not, in so far as the aecidia are of rare occurrence with them, while gonidia are formed in abundance.

The spermatia are produced in peculiar receptacles, the spermogonia (Fig. 85, *sp*) containing small branches of the hyphae, from which the spermatia are abscised. It has been already intimated that they are very probably to be regarded as male organs of fertilisation.

The Uredineae are found exclusively in living Phanerogams, usually in the stem and leaves or sometimes in the living cortical tissue of trees, as the Conifers; the spreading of the mycelium in the intercellular passages of the host does not necessarily disturb the growth of the plant; but it sometimes disfigures it, as when *Aecidium elatinum* causes the 'witches' brooms' in fir-trees; sometimes the mycelium is confined within narrow limits in the host, as *Aecidium Leguminosarum*; more often it spreads widely in it, as *Aec. Euphorbiae cyparissiae, Endophyllum Sempervivi*. The fructifications as well as the gonidial forms (uredospores and teleutospores) are formed beneath the epidermis of the host, and break through it when they are ripe and so come to the surface.

Some of the well-known species which have gonidia use the same host for all the stages of their development, as *Aecidium Leguminosarum* and *Aec. Tragopogonis*; in others the different reproductive forms develope only on different hosts; thus the aecidia of *Puccinia graminis (Aec. Berberidis)* are formed only on the leaves of *Berberis vulgaris*, while the uredospores and teleutospores occur only on grasses (De Bary, *loc. cit.*); in the same way the large aecidia of *Roestelia cancellata* are found only on the leaves of the Pomaceae, and their teleutospores only on species of Juniper. Such species are termed *heteroecious (metoecious)*, to distinguish them from those first named, which are *autoecious*.

The sporidia produced by the promycelium, whether it proceeds from the aecidio-spores, as in *Endophyllum*, or from the teleutospores, send their germ-tubes through the walls of the epidermis into the interior of the host; but the germ-tubes from the aecidiospores and the uredospores travel over the epidermis till they find a stoma and make their way through it to the intercellular spaces. *Endophyllum Sempervivi* is an exception to this rule, inasmuch as its aecidiospores produce promycelia, and *Puccinia Dianthi*, in which the sporidia from the promycelium of the teleutospores send their germ-tubes into the tissue of the host through the stomata, is also an exception.

The germ-tubes of both uredospores and teleutospores issue from them at spots previously prepared, where the cuticularised outer coat (the exosporium) is absent or very thin; three to six such perforations are found in the equator of each uredospore, one in each cell of a teleutospore. The teleutospores are single in *Uromyces*, two united together in *Puccinia*, three so united in *Triphragmium*, four in *Phragmidium*; they usually rest for some time before germinating in the spring, but they sometimes germinate immediately after their formation, as in *Roestelia* and *Puccinia Dianthi*.

For a more detailed account of the development of these Fungi I choose **Aecidium Berberidis**, whose uredo-form causes 'Rust' in wheat, and which is also known from its teleutospore-form as *Puccinia graminis*.

On the leaves of *Berberis vulgaris* yellowish swollen spots are found in spring, where delicate mycelial filaments have formed a dense felt between the cells of the parenchyma (Fig. 85, *A* and *I*, the dotted portion between the cells being the mycelium); in these swollen spots are the spermogonia, which make their appearance somewhat earlier, and the aecidia. The spermogonium (*I, sp*) is an urn-shaped receptacle in an enveloping layer of hyphal tissue; hair-like filaments line the cavity, and bursting through the epidermis of the leaf project like a brush beyond the mouth of the spermogonium; the bottom of the spermogonium is covered with short hyphae, the extremities of which give off by abscision a number of small spore-like bodies, the spermatia; it has been already said, that the part played by the spermatia in the further development of

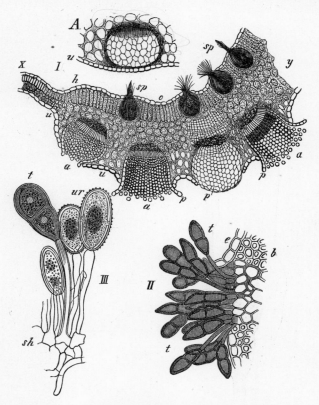

FIG. 85. *Puccinia graminis. A* portion of a transverse section of a leaf of *Berberis vulgaris* with a young aecidium. *I* transverse section of leaf of *Berberis* with spermogonia *sp* and aecidia *a; p* the peridium; the leaf is abnormally thickened between *u* and *y*, its natural thickness being seen at *x. II* a number of teleutospores on a leaf of couchgrass; *e* its ruptured epidermis, *b* its hypodermal fibres, *t* teleutospores. *III* part of a group of uredospores *ur* and a teleutospore *t; sh* subhymenial hyphae. *A* and *I* from nature, slightly magnified, *II* magn. 190 times, and *III* magnified 390 times. After De Bary.

the Fungus is not known. At a later period the aecidia (*I, a, a*) make their appearance, usually on the underside of the leaves; they lie at first beneath the epidermis of the leaf, forming tuber-like bodies composed of parenchymatous tissue (*A*), and like the spermogonium enclosed in an envelope of delicate hyphae. In the mature state the aecidium ruptures the epidermis of the leaf and forms an open cup, the wall of which (the peridium *p*) is a layer of hexagonal cells arranged in rows and produced from basidial hyphal branches at the bottom of the cup. The bottom of the cup is occupied by a hymenium, the hyphae of which turn their apices outwards and continually form fresh spores by abjunction ; the spores, at first polyhedral from mutual pressure, become afterwards round and separate from one another at the mouth of the cup (*I, a*) ; the peridium itself looks like a peripheral layer of similar spores, which however remain united ; like the spores they contain red granules.   The aecidiospores thus produced on the leaves of *Berberis* develope a mycelium only when they germinate on the surface of the blade or stem of one of the Gramineae, *Triticum* for instance or *Secale*. Then the germ-tubes penetrate through the passage of the stomata into the parenchyma of the plant, and the mycelium which they produce there forms uredospores (*III, ur*) in from six to ten days on branches (basidia) which are crowded together more or less erect on the cushion-like knots of mycelial filaments lying beneath the epidermis.   The uredospores too have the red granules, and may be seen with the naked eye forming together

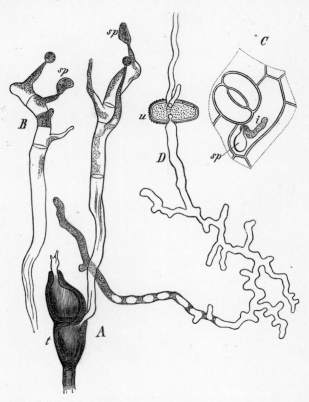

FIG. 86. *Puccinia graminis*. *A* germinating teleutospore *t*, the promycelium of which is forming the sporidia *sp*. *B* a promycelium (after Tulasne). *C* a piece of the epidermis of the under surface of a leaf of *Berberis vulgaris* with a germinating sporidium *sp*; *i* its germ-tube which has penetrated the epidermis. *D* a germinating uredospore fourteen hours after being sown in water. After De Bary, l.c.   *C, D* magn. 390 times, *A, B* more highly magn. than *C* and *D*.

long narrow red cushions on the leaves and spikelets of grasses.   The uredospores are scattered on the rupture of the epidermis and germinate in a few hours on the surface of gramineous plants (Fig. 86, *D*), and on these plants only they develope new mycelia, which again produce masses of uredospores in from six to ten days ; these spores also send germ-tubes through the stomata into the interior of the host.   While the Fungus in its uredo-form thus produces many generations of plants in a summer on the Gramineae, the formation of a new form of gonidium commences in the older clusters of uredospores.   By the side of the roundish unicellular uredospores appear long two-celled teleutospores (*III, t*), and soon the formation of uredospores ceases altogether; teleutospores only are henceforth produced (*II*), and with this the period of vegetation closes. The teleutospores remain in a resting state on the grass-stems during the winter and germinate in the spring; then they send out of their two cells short septate germ-tubes, the promycelia (Fig. 86, *A, B*), the terminal cells of which at once produce sporidia on slender branches. But these sporidia only develope a new mycelium when they germinate on a leaf of *Berberis*, and their germination is different from that of other forms of spores, because the tube, like that of the Peronosporeae, pierces the epidermal cell (*C, sp* and *i*) and passes through it and into the parenchyma; there it developes a mycelium which causes the swelling of the leaf with which we set out, and then produces aecidia and spermogonia.

The genus **Gymnosporangium** has no uredospores; its aecidia, which are known by the name of *Roestelia*, appear in July and August on the leaves, leaf-stalks, and fruits of the Pomaceae (*Pyrus, Cydonia, Sorbus*), and have the shape of long-necked flasks, which open by slits at the top or at the side and are sometimes as much as eight millimetres in length. The chains of spores have a peculiarity, not however entirely confined to them; a sterile cell, which subsequently disappears, lies between every two fertile cells. The masses of teleutospores in *Roestelia* (*Gymnosporangium*) appear in spring before the aecidia on species of *Juniperus* in the form of lumps of mucilage which may be round, conical, club-shaped, tongue-shaped, pectinate or palmate, and yellow or brown in colour; these contain closely crowded basidia, which spring from the mycelium beneath the epidermis of the leaves and in the cortical tissue of the branches and produce the teleutospores. The teleutospores resemble those of *Ae. Berberidis*, and like them produce promycelia, the sporidia from which develope into *Roestelia* with aecidia on the leaves of the Pomaceae.

6. THE BASIDIOMYCETES[1].

To this division belong the largest and handsomest Fungi, the fructifications of which, the well-known 'mushrooms,' produce gonidia. The early stages in the life-history of these fructifications, before imperfectly known, are now cleared up by the researches of Brefeld. The peculiar feature in these plants is that no sexually-produced fructification, corresponding to the ascus-fructification of the Ascomycetes, is to be found, or at least has yet been found, at any stage in the course of their development; for the massive structures of closely-interwoven hyphal tissue, on which the basidiospores are formed, are not comparable with the fructifications of the Ascomycetes, but are simply large gonidiophores (carpophores). The spores, which are known as *basidiospores*, germinate, and produce a mycelium, on which new gonidiophores (the stalked *pileus* in one section of the Basidiomycetes) are formed by the branching and interweaving of hyphae either directly, or indirectly after intercalation of a sclerotium. Besides these large gonidiophores the mycelia of many genera also bear gonidiophores, termed by Brefeld 'Stäbchenfructificationen' (rod-fructifications); these consist of short branches of the mycelium from which small gonidia-like rods ('stäbchen') are abscised, but which have lost the power of germination except in the lowest group of the Basidiomycetes, namely the Tremellineae.

Though there is more than usual variety in the outward form and interior structure of the fructifications of the Basidiomycetes, yet the formation of the spores themselves follows a common type; certain branches of the fertile hyphae swell into

---

[1] De Bary, Morphol. u. Physiol. der Pilze, Leipzig 1866, [and Vergl. Morph. u. Biol. d. Pilze, 1884].—Brefeld, Untersuch. ü. d. Schimmelpilze, III. Heft.

club-shaped form and become sporiferous *basidia*; each basidium produces two or more, usually four, sometimes eight spores simultaneously; for this purpose it sends out short slender branches which at first look like papillae, the *sterigmata*, and these swell at their free extremity into a round or ellipsoidal shape; the swollen part becomes invested with a firmer cell-wall, and is now a spore on a slender pedicel, and ultimately drops off.

The basidia are produced simultaneously in great numbers, and are usually crowded together and parallel to one another; in this way hymenia are formed, which in the Hymenomycetes have sterile filaments (*paraphyses*) between the basidia, like those of the Discomycetes. The Basidiomycetes are divided into *gymnocarpous* and *angiocarpous* forms, according as the hymenia cover free outer surfaces of the fructification, or line cavities in its inner tissue or are otherwise disposed inside it.

Most Basidiomycetes live on humus or soils containing humus, or their mycelia are developed in old wood or in the bark of the stout stems of living trees; small forms make use of fallen leaves, rotting branches, and similar matter as a substratum. A few only are true parasites on living plants.

The following account will serve to draw attention to some of the most dissimilar and morphologically most important fructifications.

1. **Exobasidium Vaccinii**[1] shows the simplest mode of fructification. The mycelium is parasitic in the leaves and stems of *Vaccinium vitis idaea*, and forms a hymenium of closely-packed four-spored basidia directly on the surface of the organs which it has attacked.

2. The **TREMELLINEAE** growing on dead wood or on old stems of living trees form fructifications of gelatinous consistence and often indefinite form, appearing usually as thick wavy coatings. Slender hyphae spread through the jelly and form hymenia on its surface. The mode of forming the spores is more complicated than in other Basidiomycetes[2].

3. Among the **HYMENOMYCETES**[3] those which form a cap (*pileus*), the Cap-fungi, are the best known and the most common. The structure which is usually called the Fungus or mushroom is the gonidiophore, and springs from a mycelium which vegetates in the ground or on wood or some other substance. The pileus is usually but not always stalked. The hymenial layer is on projecting portions of the substance of the pileus on its under surface, and these projections are of various form; in the genus *Agaricus* they are numerous vertical gills (*lamellae*) running in a radial direction from the stalk (*stipe*) to the margin of the pileus; in *Cyclomyces* similar lamellae form concentric circles; in *Polyporus* and *Daedalea* they are connected together so as to form a network; in *Boletus* they form closely-packed vertical tubes, which in *Fistulina* are isolated; in *Hydnum* the under side of the pileus is beset with soft dependent spikes, like icicles, which carry the hymenium on their surface. In many cases the fructification is naked, in others a veil which is subsequently torn away stretches across the under side of the pileus (*cortina, velum partiale*), or pileus and stipe are enveloped in a similar wrapper (*volva, velum universale*), or lastly in some species, as *Amanita*, both membranes are present. These veil-formations are connected with the entire growth of the fructification; the species with a naked pileus are by their nature gymnocarpous, the veiled species afford a transition to the angiocarpous

---

[1] Woronin, in Ber. d. naturf. Ges. zu Freiburg i. Br., Bd. IV. 1867.

[2] Tulasne, in Ann. d. sc. nat. 3ᵉ sér. T. XIX, and 5ᵉ sér. T. XV.—Brefeld, *loc. cit.* III. Heft.

[3] [De Bary, Vergl. Morph. u. Biol. d. Pilze, 1884, p. 366 (literature).]

fructifications of the Gasteromycetes; this is especially the case with *Amanita*.—
Agaricus variecolor (Fig. 88) is to a certain extent an intermediate form between
those with a naked pileus and those with the velum universale. The fructification first
appears on the mycelium as a slender conical body (*a* and *b*) formed of parallel hyphae
with apical growth (*c*); at an early period an outer hyphal layer is distinguishable, forming
a loose envelope round the whole body; after a while the growth at the apex ceases;
the hyphae bend outwards beneath the summit (*II, III*) and thus form the pileus (*IV*),
the margin of which grows centrifugally; the lamellae make their appearance on its
under surface, and as the margin of the pileus advances further from the stipe, the loose
peripheral layer becomes stretched into a velum universale.—The common mushroom,
Agaricus campestris, affords an example of the formation of a stalked pileus with a
velum partiale. Fig. 89 *A* gives a small portion of the widely spreading and reticulately
anastomosing mycelium (*m*), on which a number of fructifications are being formed;

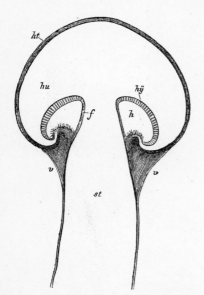

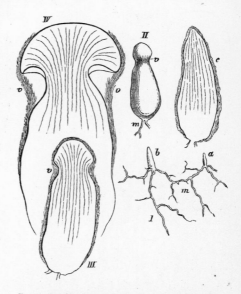

FIG. 87. Gonidia-producing fructification of *Boletus flavidus* in longitudinal section, slightly magnified; *st* stipe, *hu* pileus, *hy* hymenium, *h* the cavity beneath the hymenium, *ht* the separable superficial layer of the pileus, *f* the continuation of the hymenial layer on the stipe.

FIG. 88. *Agaricus variecolor*. *I* mycelium *m* with young gonidiophores *a* and *b* (nat. size); *c* longitudinal section of one of them magnified. *II* an older fructification with commencement of the formation of the pileus. *III* the same in longitudinal section. *IV* a pileus in a more advanced state; *v* the velum. The lines in the longitudinal sections show the course of the hyphae.

these are at first pear-shaped solid bodies (*l*) composed of young uniform hyphae,
and each of these bodies is a rudimentary stipe, from the upper part of which
the pileus will be developed. At an early period the hyphal tissue gives way in such a
manner as to form an annular air-cavity beneath the summit of the stalk (*II, l*); this
cavity enlarges with the growth of the whole body, its upper wall forming the under
side of the pileus, from which the radial hymenial lamellae grow in a downward
direction and fill up the cavity (*III, l*). The hyphae run from the base of the stipe to
the margin of the pileus and form the outer wall of the cavity; the central portion of the
stipe (*IV, st*) elongates, while the distance between it and the margin of the pileus continually increases. By this growth the hyphae beneath the cavity which contains the
lamellae become stretched and separate from the stipe from below upwards, and now
form a membranous veil (*V, v*) running beneath the lamellae from the upper part of the
stipe to the margin of the pileus, into which the hyphae are continued. When at length

the pileus is spread out horizontally by the stretching of the tissue, the membrane (the velum partiale) parts from its margin and hangs down like a frill on the stalk.

It was said above that the hymenium covers the surface of the lamelliform, conical, or tubular projections on the under side of the pileus. A tangential section of the latter gives in all three cases much the same result as is seen in Fig. 90, which is taken from *Agaricus campestris. A* is a piece of a tangential section of the disk of the pileus, *h* the substance of the pileus, *l* the lamellae. *B* is a portion of one of the lamellae more highly magnified to show the course of the hyphae; the body of the lamella *t*, called the *trama*, consists of rows of elongated cells which spread right and left from the median plane of the trama to its margins, where the hyphal cells are short and round,

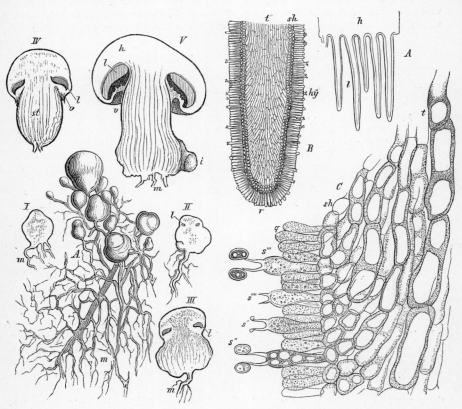

FIG. 89. *Agaricus campestris*, nat. size. See the text.

FIG. 90. *Agaricus campestris*, formation of the hymenium. *A* and *B* slightly magnified, *C* a part of *B* magn. 550 times. The portion marked with fine dots is protoplasm.

and form the *subhymenial layer* (*sh B* and *C*); from these short cells spring club-shaped tubes *q*, placed close to one another and perpendicularly to the surface of the lamella, which together constitute the hymenial layer (*B, hy*). Many of these tubes are sterile and are named *paraphyses*, others produce the spores and are the *basidia*. Each basidium in this species produces only two spores, in other Hymenomycetes usually four. The basidium sends out first of all as many slender branches, *sterigmata s'*, as there are spores to be formed; each of these branches swells out at its extremity, the swelling enlarges and becomes the spore (*s", s"'*), which drops from the stalk on which it was formed, and leaves it behind (*s""*).

I will add one remark only on the structure of the tissues in this group, namely that in the fructifications of many of the Agaricineae, *Lactarius* for example, single much-branched hyphae become laticiferous tubes, which give out large quantities of latex if the tissues are injured.

If we compare the course of development of the Basidiomycetes with that of the group last described[1], we find that it agrees with that of the species among the Uredineae which like *Chrysomyxa Abietis* have lost the aecidium, the counterpart of the fructifications of the Ascomycetes, and are propagated only by gonidia, and in the case of *Chrysomyxa* and others by one form only of gonidia, the teleutospore.

To this preliminary account of the structure of the fructification of the Hymenomycetes we will append as an example the history of the development of **Coprinus stercorarius** as it is given by Brefeld. The basidiospores germinate at once when sown in a decoction of dung as a nutrient solution, and the germ-tube issues forth at the end of the spore opposite to the sterigma, where there is a small pore. The mycelium which is now developed is filiform and copiously branched, with frequent coalescence of cells, such as occurs not unfrequently in other mycelia. Rudiments of fructifications make their appearance in from nine to twelve days on older parts of the mycelium, being formed immediately on single mycelial filaments in small, poorly-fed plants ; in plants of more luxuriant growth sclerotia are usually first formed. These originate in the dense interweaving of branches of the hyphae, which form at first a closely-tangled mass with the interstices filled with air. In a few days the sclerotium, the size of which depends on the supply of food, has arrived at the resting state ; it has a colourless inner tissue, and a black rind the cells of which are united into a firm tissue. Where the rind is removed, the part of the inner tissue that is laid bare assumes the character of a rind. In germination the peripheral cells of the rind sprout and form on their surface small flake-like bodies which are rudimentary fructifications. A single one outgrows the rest, which then cease to develope. The formation both of the sclerotia and of the fructifications is therefore purely vegetative, and the sclerotia here are merely resting mycelia, not as in *Penicillium* a resting state of the fructification.

The stipe is for a time very short in the young fructification, the pileus being developed before it. Rhizoids are formed in the basal part of the stem, at every point which comes into contact with a suitable object. The development of the pileus terminates with the formation of the rhizoids ; the stalk elongates to more than ten times its former length and the pileus then discharges its spores.

The formation of sclerotia as here depicted may however be omitted, as happens when the plants are starved, e.g. when grown on a microscopic slide. In this case the fructifications are developed on single filaments of the mycelium as adventitious shoots, which make their appearance on the mycelium produced from a single spore in limited numbers, the maximum being twenty. A hypha branches, and its branches ramify, and the ramifications gather into a coil or cluster. This hyphal coil forms inside it a nucleus of false tissue, the first rudiment of the stipe, and on the outside an envelope of hyphae. Where the rudimentary stipe passes into hyphae, at its upper end therefore, an extremely active formation of new hyphae takes place, from which the pileus is ultimately developed ; these hyphae grow close together and expand. The elements of the whole of this rudimentary structure are closely confined within a definite limited space, and the inner portion becomes separated off from the whole mass as the young pileus. This rudimentary pileus enlarges by marginal growth and is enveloped in the volva, which is the external portion of the rudimentary fructification and consists of hyphae loosely intertwined. The volva continues to be developed from the hyphae which were not directly used in the formation of the stipe, so that this envelope surrounds the young fructification as a velum universale. Then the lamellae make

---

[1] De Bary, *Aecidium abietinum* in Bot. Zeit. 1879, pp. 828–843.

their appearance as longitudinal projections on the inner (under) surface of the pileus. On the surface of the lamellae are the extremities of hyphal filaments, arranged regularly like a palisade, and perpendicularly to the middle, radially-disposed hyphae, of which they are the branches. These palisade-cells form the hymenium; the basidia with the spores proceed from them, but the basidia are not all fertile; the larger number are sterile paraphyses, and some which swell up into a spherical form are distinguished as *cystidia*. The basidia are usually cylindrical, and four new growing-points, the sterigmata, appear simultaneously on the apex of each; the sterigmata elongate a little and then terminate in a fine needle-point, which swells into a small globe and as it enlarges becomes ovoid in shape. The contents of the basidia pass into the swollen part, which is then separated off from the sterigma by a dividing-wall, and the spore is formed. Meanwhile all parts of the pileus have expanded, and its superficial cells have become thickened to form an outer coat. Then follows a rapid development of the stipe; the pileus is raised higher into the air, its tissues expand, and it discharges its spores.

Some further mention may be made here of Brefeld's interesting experiments. He showed that if the fructifications that are beginning to form on the sclerotia are removed, new ones are formed on them in almost unlimited numbers. If the pileus is removed in a young fructification, a new rudimentary fructification is formed by vegetative growth on the cut surface of the stalk from any of the superficial cells, and unites without break of continuity with the old stump and developes perfectly upon it. 'Every cell of the vegetatively produced fructification, every cell of the stipe, every hypha of the pileus, of the lamellae, of the hymenium has the power of growing out into a fructification.' In the same way young fructifications, if detached and placed in a nutrient solution, grow out into mycelial filaments, and pieces cut out of older fructifications will do the same. The germination of the sclerotia is materially promoted by light. The development of the pileus is hindered by darkness, but the stipe attains a considerable length.

It appears then that the sclerotia of *Coprinus stercorarius* are resting states of the mycelium, and pass immediately after their formation into a state of rest. It is otherwise with the Rhizomorphae which are the sclerotia of **Agaricus melleus.** These are root-like branched structures composed of strands of mycelial filaments, which are parasitic on the pine and give rise there to peculiar formations ('Harzsticke'), as Hartig has shown[1]. Hartig was the first to discover that *Rhizomorpha* belonged to *Agaricus melleus,* and his statements have been since confirmed and supplemented by Brefeld. The formation of the Rhizomorphae on the mycelium produced by the germination of the spores of *Agaricus melleus* begins in the same way as that of sclerotia of *Coprinus stercorarius*. But the Rhizomorphae do not pass at once into the resting stage; they are sclerotia with growing-points, and consist of a brown rind surrounding an internal mass of tissue in parts not in contact with a nourishing substance. The apex of the sclerotial strand is its growing-point, inside which new formations take place, and consists of extremely small cells connected together without interstices and perfectly alike at the summit of the growing-point, though the existence at this point of a true tissue cannot be certainly proved. The Rhizomorphae have been seen making their way into the pine. If the species lives beneath the bark (*Rh. subcorticalis*), its rind does not turn brown, the constituent elements multiply indefinitely at its circumference, and hence it attains a considerable thickness and an indefinite breadth. It remains plastic, altering its form at pleasure at any point, being sometimes thin as a needle, sometimes of enormous thickness, sometimes round, sometimes flat. With the extinction of the growing-point the Rhizomorphae enter upon the true sclerotial condition. The fructifications of *Agaricus melleus* are developed directly from the Rhizomorphae. A number of the inner hyphae begin to sprout, break through the rind, and commence the formation of the fructification.

---

[1] R. Hartig, Wichtige Krankheiten d. Waldbäume, Berlin 1874.

Brefeld has also followed the germination of **Coprinus lagopus**. The mycelium has at first no septa ; these make their appearance at a later period. One peculiarity is that little rods are detached from special branches of the mycelium, and these were sometimes erroneously described as spermatia, male organs of reproduction. They do not germinate, and therefore Brefeld regards them as rudimentary gonidia, a view which is supported by the fact that very similar objects make their appearance in the germination of the Tremellineae, only in the latter case they are capable of germination.

Amanita muscaria forms a transition from the gymnocarpous Basidiomycetes to the Gasteromycetes ; the lamellae are not formed in *Amanita* as in *Coprinus* on the free inner surface of the pileus, for none such exists while the pileus is being formed, but in ventral hyphae which are common to the stalk and the pileus ; the separate parts are formed inside the uniform tissue of the rudimentary structure, and the young pileus is therefore enveloped in a large volva.

4. The **GASTEROMYCETES**[1] agree with the gymnocarpous Hymenomycetes in the mode of forming their spores (they often produce eight on one basidium), but their fructifications are all angiocarpous, the hymenia being produced inside the fructification which is at first spherical ; the spores are disseminated by remarkable differentiations of layers of tissue and the growth of certain masses of hyphal tissue, or by simple rupture of the outer layers (*peridia*). The nature of these processes which are more than usually various in outward appearance may be rendered intelligible by two examples. The first is taken from the delicate Nidularieae. In **Crucibulum vulgare**[2] the mycelium forms a small white flake of branched hyphae, which spreads on the surface of wood. On it are formed by copious branching small roundish compact knots, the rudiments of the fructifications ; each of these round bodies increases in size by the introduction of new hyphal branches and gradually assumes a cylindrical form. A section through one shows the following layers of tissue ; a middle lighter zone of hyphae concave above

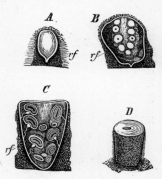

FIG. 91. *Crucibulum vulgare. A, B, C* slightly magnified in longitudinal section. *D* the entire nearly mature Fungus in its natural size.

divides a lower outer portion from an upper and inner (Fig. 91, *A*) ; the outer layer becomes the ' cup ' of the fruit (*C, B, D*), and soon shows two secondary zones which pass into one another above ; the outer is brown and dense, and passes on the outside into the loose hyphae which form the hair-like covering of the fructification. The middle separating layer of the rudimentary fructification, shown clear in Fig. 91, grows to considerable dimensions, and forms a kind of sac enclosing the inner layer as far as to the upper portion which passes directly into the dome-like summit. The whole mass of the middle layer becomes converted into a gelatinous tissue. In the inner tissue-layer isolated portions begin at an early period to look darker (the lighter parts in Fig. 91, *B*), while the rest becomes gelatinous. The nests which are thus formed are the 'sporangia' or *peridiola*. The middle layer then diminishes in thickness and is reduced to a narrow girdle, an inner lining of the outer layer. A cavity forms in the middle of each sporangium and is covered by the hymenium. Each sporangium (Sachs called them spore-forming nests) is therefore lined on the inside with a hymenial layer (Fig. 92) formed of paraphyses and basidia, the latter producing each four spores on small stalks, the sterigmata. If the sporangia are coloured, they are surrounded by two brown membranes which enclose a mass of central tissue resembling a sclerotium. Then the

---

[1] [De Bary, Vergl. Morph. u. Biol. d. Pilze, 1884, p. 367 (literature).]
[2] Sachs in Bot. Zeit. 1885.—Brefeld, *loc. cit.*

cup opens at its top, its edges turn over, and the sporangia sink to the bottom, where they lie free, not being, according to Brefeld, connected with the wall at any point (ac-

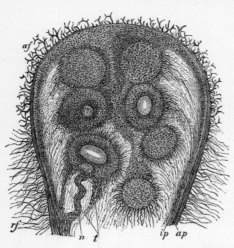

cording to Sachs (Fig. 91 and 92) they are fastened to the wall by cords of hyphae) ; they have only a projecting white coil of hyphae fixed like a peg in the centre. If we imagine the sporangia closer together and in greater numbers and with less thick walls, we shall have the roundish cell-like loculaments which occur in the fructifications of such Gasteromycetes as *Octaviania, Scleroderma,* and others.

Still more remarkable are the changes produced by differentiation of the inner tissues in the Phalloideæ ; we will here call attention to the main points only in the development of **Phallus impudicus**. The germination of the spores has not yet been observed. The young fructification, which is formed on the stout strands of the subterranean perennial mycelium, is here, as in the Nidularieæ, at first an aggregate of uniform filaments, in which differentiation begins and advances with the growth. Fig. 93

FIG. 92. *Crucibulum vulgare.* Upper part of the longitudinal section through a young fructification magnified, nearly corresponding to *B* in Fig. 91. The section is seen by transmitted light ; the dark parts in the interior are those in which air exists between the hyphae ; in the light parts a transparent mucilage free from air has been formed between the hyphae. The light parts in this figure are the dark parts in the preceding one.

gives a longitudinal section of a fructification when it has reached the size and shape of a hen's or goose's egg. At this time the tissue consists of separate portions, which may be distributed into four groups : 1. The *peridium,* composed of the outer, firm, dense, white membrane *a,* an inner white and firm but thin membrane *i,* and a thick layer of hyphal tissue which has become mucilaginous, the gelatinous layer *g.*   2. The spore-producing apparatus, the *gleba, sp,* bounded on the outside by the inner peridium, *i,* on the inside by the firm and dense membrane, *t ;* from this membrane walls are seen stretching outwards, connected with one another so as to form a honey-comb structure and dividing the gleba into numerous compartments, in which are the fertile hyphae ; on the hyphae are the basidia each of which produces four or more spores, and the number of the whole is so great that the dark-green gleba appears when ripe to consist only of spores.   3. The *stipe, st,* composed of air-containing tissue which forms numerous narrow compartments as yet very small ; the stalk is hollow, that is the axile portion of its tissue has been changed into a deliquescent mucilage ; the passage

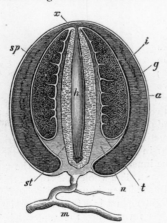

FIG. 93. *Phallus impudicus,* a nearly mature specimen just before the elongation of the stalk *st,* in longitudinal section one half the nat. size ; *a* outer layer of the peridium, *g* its gelatinous substance, *i* the inner peridium, *st* the stalk of the pileus *t* not yet elongated, and with white ridges forming a honey-comb structure on its surface, *sp* the dark green mass of spores (gleba), *h* cavity of the stalk filled with watery jelly ; *n* the cup in which the base of the stalk remains fixed after the elongation, *x* the spot where the inner peridium is detached by the elongation of the stalk, *m* thread of the mycelium.

thus formed is open above in many individuals, in others closed by the inner peridium. 4. The *cup, n ;* this is a low, broad column of firmer tissue, the outer portion of which connects above with the inner peridium, while it sends at the same time a layer of yielding consistence in between the stalk and the inner membrane of the gleba (*t*); its base is continuous with the outer firm peridium. This is the condition of the fructification when the spores reach maturity; to disseminate them the stalk (*st*) elongates greatly, the peridium bursts at the apex, the gleba separates from the inner peridium which tears away at *x*, while the membrane *t* has parted below; in this way the gleba is lifted up on the summit of the stalk high above the peridium, the stalk reaching a height of from six to twelve inches; the elongation of the stalk is caused by the enlargement of its compartments, which is such as to give it in its final condition the appearance of a sponge with large pores; it increases also proportionately in thickness. The hyphae of the gleba now deliquesce, and the mass of spores falls in drops of a thick tough mucilage, and ultimately nothing remains of the gleba but the membrane *t* with its comb-like walls, which hangs down like a frill from the apex of the stalk and is called the pileus. The details of these processes are subject to many variations in the different species of the Phalloideae : Corda, l. c., and De Bary, l. c., should be consulted with respect to them.

SECOND GROUP.

THE MUSCINEAE[1].

THE Hepaticae (Liverworts) and the Musci (Mosses), which are included under the term Muscineae, are characterised by a very distinctly-marked alternation of generations. The sexual generation which is rich in chlorophyll and self-supporting is not produced directly from the germinating spore, but a simpler structure, in the Mosses usually of a confervoid character, called the *protonema*, is first produced, and on this the sexual generation arises as a lateral or terminal shoot, which in the Hepaticae is often not very clearly distinguished from the protonema.

Fertilisation in the female sexual organ of the first generation gives rise to a second generation, a structure of a totally different character, exclusively intended for an asexual production of spores; this structure is not organically connected with the previous generation, but it derives its sustenance from it, and in outward appearance is simply its 'fruit,' like the smaller fructifications of the Thallophytes. To call attention to the peculiar nature of this sporocarp and to exclude all false comparisons[2], Sachs has proposed to call it a *sporogonium*.

The **SEXUAL GENERATION** (*oophore, oophyte*) produced from the spore with the intervention of a protonema in the Muscineae is either a flat leafless thallus, as in many of the Hepaticae (twisted in the form of a corkscrew in *Riella*), or a slender often much-branched leafy stem; in both cases, which are connected by very gradual transitions, numerous hair-like structures (rhizoids) are usually formed, which fix the thallus[3] or the stem to the surface on which it grows. In many cases the vegetative body is scarcely a millimetre in length, in others it grows into copiously branching forms from ten to thirty centimetres long or even more; the duration of its life is limited to a few weeks or months in only a few and these the smallest species; in the majority it may almost be said to be unlimited, for the thallus or leaf-bearing stem continues to grow at the apex or by means of new shoots, termed *innovations*, while

---

[1] See my treatise on the Muscineae in Schenk's Handbuch der Botanik, II. Bd., pp. 315–402, [also Encyc. Britann. 9th ed.].

[2] It would be incorrect, for instance, to regard the 'moss-fruit' as morphologically equivalent to the sporocarp of the Marsiliaceae or to that of the Phanerogams.

[3] The thallus, or thallus-like stem of many Hepaticae was formerly called a frond (*frons*); but the term is synonymous with thallus and therefore superfluous.

the oldest parts behind die off. In this way the branches become ultimately independent plants; this together with multiplication by gemmae, stolons, detached buds, the change of rhizoids into protonema (in the Mosses) not only contributes to multiply the number of individuals by asexual means to an extraordinary degree, but is also the chief cause of the social growth of these plants; many Mosses, even such as only rarely bear 'fruit,' may in this way form close and extensive patches, *Sphagnum*, for example, *Hypnum*, *Mnium*, and others.

The sexual organs are termed antheridia and archegonia. The *antheridium* when mature is a spherical, ellipsoid or club-shaped body with a short or long stalk, the outer cell-layer of which forms a sac-like wall, while the small cells enclosed by it, which are very numerous and crowded, each produce a *spermatozoid*. The spermatozoids are set at liberty by the rupture of the wall of the antheridium at its apex; they are spirally twisted threads with a thicker posterior and a sharply pointed anterior extremity, and on the latter are two long delicate cilia, the vibrations of which cause the movement of the spermatozoid. The female organs, which have been named *archegonia* since Bischoff's time, are, when their oosphere is ready for fertilisation, flask-shaped bodies which swell out into a pouch, the *venter*, above their narrow base and end above in a long *neck*. The tissue of the wall of the venter surrounds the *central cell*, out of the lower and larger portion of which the *oosphere* is ultimately formed[1]. A central row of cells is continued above this and runs all the way through the neck up to the *lid-cells* ('stigmatic cells' of authors) which lie on its apex. The cells of this axile row, which are known as *canal-cells*, are disorganised before fertilisation and changed into mucilage, which at length issues forth from the neck and forces the four lid-cells asunder; thus an open passage is formed leading to the oosphere and enabling the spermatozoids to reach it.

The origin of the sexual organs of the Muscineae varies in different species; in the thalloid forms of the Hepaticae they proceed from superficial cells of the thallus or thallus-like decumbent stem behind the growing apex, or on special metamorphosed branches as in many Marchantieae, but both antheridia and archegonia are formed in the leafy Jungermannieae and in the Mosses from the apical cell of the shoot or from its segments; in this case they may stand in the place of leaves or of lateral shoots or even of hairs; thus the antheridia in *Radula* are formed in the axils of the leaves, in *Sphagnum* in places where branches usually appear, in *Fontinalis* as apical growths and at a later period in place of leaves; in like manner the first archegonium on fertile shoots of *Andreaea* and *Radula* is formed from the apical cell, the later ones from its last segments; the same is probably the case with *Sphagnum*.

Antheridia and archegonia are usually produced in considerable numbers close beside one another, and in the thalloid forms of the Hepaticae are generally surrounded by later outgrowths of the thallus. In the leafy Jungermannieae and in Mosses it is usual for several archegonia to have an envelope of leaves round them, which is called a *perichaetium*; in the Mosses the antheridia also are grouped together in this way, and sometimes antheridia and archegonia are combined, but in the Jungermannieae and Sphagnaceae the antheridia occur singly. *Paraphyses*, in the form either of cell-filaments or of narrow leaf-like cell-surfaces, frequently accompany

---

[1] The archegonia are therefore oogonia of somewhat more complex construction.

the sexual organs, especially in the leafy species. Besides these forms of envelope the Hepaticae (not the Mosses) have often another called the *perigynium*, which grows up as a circular wall from the thallus at the base of the archegonia, and at length surrounds them like an open sac.

The **ASEXUAL GENERATION** (*sporophore, sporophyte*, the moss-fruit or *sporogonium*) is formed from the oospore in the archegonium: by repeated cell-divisions it is transformed into an ovoid embryo and grows at its apex, which is the pole turned towards the neck of the archegonium.

The sporogonium lives almost entirely at the cost of the vegetative body on which the archegonium is placed; it is physiologically the asexual, spore-producing generation, and parasitic on the sexual generation. The venter of the archegonium, in which the oospore lies, grows broader as it follows the growth of the embryo, and in this condition is called the *calyptra*. In *Riccia*, the lowest form in a series of Hepaticae, namely the Marchantiaceae, the sporogonium remains all its life inclosed in the calyptra. The spores are set at liberty by the decay of that portion of the thallus in which the sporogonium is immersed. In other Hepaticae also the embryo, the young sporogonium, passes the larger part of its existence in the venter of the archegonium. In *Pellia epiphylla*, for example, one of the most common of our thalloid Jungermannieae, the sexual organs are ripe and fertilisation takes place in May. The embryo requires the whole summer for its full development, and by the autumn is in all essential points mature; but it is not till the next spring that by sudden and vigorous elongation of the stalk it bursts through the calyptra and disseminates its spores, a proceeding which is completed in a few days. In *Anthoceros* the sporogonium has not so short a life, owing to the power of intercalary growth at its base; while ripe spores are being disseminated from its upper part, new ones are being produced below, and this may go on for a long time; there are foreign species which may in this way develope sporogonia seven centimetres long. In the Hepaticae the calyptra is broken through, as we have seen, and remains as a sheath at the base of the sporogonium; but in the Mosses the elongated fusiform embryo tears the calyptra at the base and carries it up with it in different forms as a cap on its apex. The sporogonium of some Mosses requires more than a year for its full development, as in certain species of *Polytrichum*, and in *Hypnum crista castrensis*.

The special function of the sporogonium is to produce spores. This function is performed in the simplest manner in *Riccia*, where the embryo is fashioned into a round cellular body, all the cells in which, with the exception of the layer which forms the wall, become spore-mother-cells producing each four spores. But in the higher forms the sporogonium is made up of distinct parts; a *foot* or *stalk*, which often thrusts itself into the tissue of the vegetative body, and a *capsule* in which the spores are formed. The differentiation inside the young capsule into the cells from which the spore-mother-cells are formed, and the cells which are employed to construct the wall or for any other purpose, takes place very early. The group of cells from which the spore-mother-cells are formed may be named, both here and in the Vascular Cryptogams, the *archesporium*. This is generally one layer of cells, but, according to Leitgeb, it consists in many of the Jungermannieae of several cell-layers one above another. In *Riccia* and the Mosses spore-mother-cells only proceed from the archesporium. But in most of the Hepaticae a number of the cells remain sterile and either serve only as nutrient cells to the spore-mother-cells which by degrees consume the food-material stored up in them, as happens in *Riella*, or develope into fusiform *elaters* with spiral thickenings, whose function it is to loosen the spore-masses at the dissemination of the spores.

The spores of the Muscineae are formed by fours through division of the mother-cell into four after previous bipartition of the nucleus; the mother-cells were previously connected with one another and with the surrounding cell-layers into a tissue, but become isolated before the spores are formed. The mature spores have a thin cuticle, the *exosporium*, beset with small excrescences, which is ruptured in germination by the inner layer of the cell-wall, the *endosporium*, and contain a colourless protoplasm, chlorophyll-corpuscles, starch and a fatty oil.

There is less variety in the construction of the tissues in the Muscineae than in the Thallophytes. In the latter the more complex tissues are the result either of the interweaving or concrescence of originally separate elements or of cell-division, but the latter is the only mode found in the Muscineae and in the forms above them. But the anatomical differentiation is still very simple; all the cells of the vegetative body are alike, as in many of the thalloid Jungermannieae, or an assimilating tissue-system is differentiated from a conducting tissue, as in the Marchantiaceae. The small stem of the leafy forms has usually a thickened cortical layer, and in the Mosses often an axile bundle of elongated cells, such as forms the ' midrib' in many thalloid species. In the most highly developed forms bundles of narrow cells from the nerves of the leaves join on to the bundle in the stem. Peculiar mucilage-passages are found in the thallus of *Fegatella*, elongated isolated fibre-strands in that of *Preissia*, both genera of the Marchantiaceae.

CLASSIFICATION OF THE MUSCINEAE. The sexual generation is developed from the spore, after previous formation of a protonema which in many of the Hepaticae is not sharply distinguished from the plant formed upon it; it is longer lived than the asexual generation and is the self-supporting vegetative body in these plants, and is either a flat thallus with dichotomous ramification, or a filiform stem with two to four rows of leaves. Vascular bundles are absent. The archegonia and antheridia, except in the simplest thalloid forms, are structures of cellular tissue, stalked and usually free, though sometimes becoming immersed in the thallus by subsequent luxuriant growth of the adjacent tissue. The central cell of the archegonium produces the oosphere by rejuvenescence of its protoplasm into a primordial cell. The spermatozoids are threads coiled spirally with two cilia at the anterior pointed extremity. The second or asexual generation, the sporogonium, is formed from the oosphere within the venter of the archegonium; the venter grows rapidly as the oosphere developes and is thus transformed into the calyptra. The sporogonium is not self-supporting but derives its nourishment from the sexual generation, and has the appearance of being an appendage of it; it is usually a stalked capsule, in which, in every genus except *Archidium*, an archesporium is differentiated, from which the spore-mother-cells are formed either directly or after further divisions; the spores are formed by division of the mother-cells into four parts.

1. **Hepaticae** or **Liverworts.** The first or sexual generation is formed from the spore with the intervention of a protonema which is usually small and unimportant; it is either a flat dichotomously-branched thallus, or a filiform stem with two to three

rows of leaves; this vegetative body is usually spread out on the ground or some other substratum and clings closely to it, and where the stem grows free, the tendency to the formation of an upper and an under side is still plainly expressed; the growth is therefore always decidedly dorsiventral, except in the thalloid genus *Riella* and the foliose genus *Haplomitrium*. The second generation, the sporogonium, remains inclosed till the spores are mature in the calyptra, which is in most cases at length ruptured at the apex and remains as an open sheath at the base of the sporogonium, while the free capsule opens longitudinally above it to discharge the spores. The spore-mother-cells are formed from all the cells inside the single layer which forms the wall of the capsule; or certain cells lying among and between the others are developed as elaters, and this is the more common case.

2. **Musci** or **Mosses**. The sexual generation is developed from the spore with the intervention of a protonema, which is usually formed of branched rows of cells, but is sometimes a flat expansion, and often continues to live and grow independently for a considerable time, even after it has produced leafy moss-stems from lateral buds. The vegetative body is never a thallus, but always a filiform stem with two, three, or four rows of leaves, usually without distinct bilaterality, and monopodially never dichotomously branched. The second generation, the sporogonium, only begins its development in the calyptra, which is then usually torn away below at the *vaginula*, and is carried up as a cap on the top of the sporogonium; the capsule which now becomes fully developed produces the spores from an internal layer of tissue, while a large central mass of tissue remains sterile and constitutes the *columella*, which disappears in the ripe capsule; in *Archidium* there is no appearance of a columella. The wall of the capsule has a strongly developed epidermis, the upper portion of which separates as a lid (*operculum*) from the lower portion, the urn or *theca*, in order to release the spores.

HEPATICAE[1].

Except in two genera, *Riella* and *Haplomitrium*, the *vegetative body* in the Hepaticae is always decidedly dorsiventral, its free side, which is turned to the light, having a different organisation from that of the shaded side which is turned towards the substratum, and often clings closely to it.

In most families and genera the vegetative body is a broad flat or crisped plate of tissue, varying from a few millimetres to several centimetres in length. In the simplest case it is a thallus with no leaves or leaf-like appendages, as in *Anthoceros*,

---

[1] Mirbel, Recherches anat. et phys. sur la *Marchantia polymorphe* (Mém. de l'Acad. d. sc. de l'Instit. de France, T. XIII. 1835).—Bischoff, Bemerk. ü. d. Lebermoose, vorz. u. d. Gruppen d. Marchantiaceen u. Riccien (Nova acta Akad. Leop. Car. 1835, Vol. XVI. p. 2).—Gottsche, Ueber *Haplomitrium Hookeri* (Nova Acta, Vol. XX. pars 2).—Nägeli in Zeitschrift für wiss. Bot.— Gottsche, Lindenberg u. Esenbeck, Synopsis Hepaticarum, Hamburg, 1844.—Hofmeister, Vergl. Unters. 1851.—Kny, Entw. d. laubigen Lebermoose (Jahrb. f. wiss. Bot. IV. p. 64), und Entw. d. Riccien (Jahrb. Bd. v. p. 359).—Thuret in Ann. d. sc. nat. 1851, T. XVI. (Antheridien).—Strasburger, Geschlechtsorgane u. Befruchtung bei *Marchantia* (Jahrb. f. wiss. Bot. VII. p. 409).—Janczewski, Vergl. Unters. ü. d. Entwicklungsgesch. d. Archegoniums (Bot. Zeit. 1872, Nr. 21 ff.)—Leitgeb, Unters. u. d. Lebermoose, Heft 1-6, 1874-1881.—Kienitz-Gerloff, Vergl. Unters. ü. d. Entwicklungsgesch. d. Lebermoossporog. (Bot. Zeit. 1874 and 1875).—[Vochting, Ueber d. Regeneration d. Marchantieen (Pringsh. Jahrb. xvi. 1885).]

Metzgeria, Aneura, Pellia, and others. Rhizoids appear on the shaded side, and near the apex in most species club-shaped papillae which secrete mucilage; a layer of the cellulose beneath the thin cuticle in these papillose hairs swells considerably and bursts the cuticle, and the mucilage is spread over the growing point, which is thus covered by a layer of this substance and protected from the danger of desiccation[1]. In place of these simple hairs some species have lamelliform outgrowths which may be called scales; such structures are found in the Marchantieae which are distinguished for their high anatomical differentiation. *Blasia* too has a riband-like stem with two rows of leaves on its under surface (*amphigastria*) in the form of small denticulate scales; but it also has leaves inserted parallel to the longitudinal axis of the stem, which at first sight look like projections from the flat stem and were formerly so described[2]. Next to *Blasia* comes the genus *Fossombronia* with its stem not broadly expanded but much flattened on the upper face, and on each side a row of obliquely inserted leaves. These forms together make up the *thalloid,* or as it was once called the *frondose,* division of the Hepaticae, as opposed to the *foliose* Hepaticae of the family of the Jungermanniaceae; in this latter division, which includes also the thalloid forms *Aneura, Blasia, Fossombronia* and some other genera, the vegetative body is a slender filiform stem bearing sharply differentiated leaves (*Jungermannia, Radula* and *Frullania*). There are three rows of these leaves, two on the sides, and one on the face turned towards the substratum; the last, the *amphigastria,* are smaller than the others and are sometimes reduced to hair-like structures, or they are wanting, as in *Jungermannia bicuspidata* and others. It has been already stated that the two divisions of the Hepaticae are connected by intermediate forms affording easy transitions. The leaves of all the Hepaticae are simple cell-surfaces, and have not even the mid-rib which is common in the leaves of the Mosses. The anatomical structure of the stem and thallus is extremely simple. An epidermis differentiated from the tissue beneath it is found only in the Marchantieae, and the epidermis of this family has stomata of a peculiar kind. Peculiar slits for the secretion of mucilage occur on the under side of *Anthoceros*; otherwise the differentiation of tissue is confined to the appearance of elongated cells in the midrib of the thalloid forms, as in *Blasia. Preissia* has thickened fibres, the extremities of which overlap like the sclerenchyma-fibres in

FIG. 94. *Riella helicophylla.* Plant in its natural aspect. growing erect and secured by rhizoids at its base. It consists of an axis and the wing which is wound round it in a spiral. From the Exploration scientifique de l'Algérie.

---

[1] In *Anthoceros* the mucilage is formed not from the hairs, but in the intercellular spaces of the under side of the thallus, which open to the outside by slits (mucilage-slits); see also below.

[2] [These appear to be the 'pistilla' of Sir W. J. Hooker in his British Jungermannieae, the 'pistilla sterilia' of the Synopsis Hepaticarum of Gottsche, Lindenberg, and Nees ab Esenbeck.]

the higher plants; *Fegatella conica* has a thallus traversed by bundles of mucilage-cells; these cells occur singly in others of the Marchantieae.

It is not the young Liverwort that proceeds directly from the germinating spore but a *protonema* of simple structure, on which the sexual generation then arises as a lateral shoot or in direct continuance of its growth; in the latter case the sexual generation is not so sharply contrasted with the protonema as it usually is in the Mosses. In *Aneura* a tube proceeds from the germinating spore and divides by transverse septa. When several have formed, an oblique wall appears in the terminal cell, and then a second in the opposite direction, and we have the apical cell of the thallus of *Aneura*. The spores of *Pellia* and sometimes those of *Fegatella* go through the first stages of germination while still in the sporogonium, as many spores of lichens do inside the ascus. They develope into an ellipsoidal green cellular body with a more transparent cell at one end, and this cell becomes the first rhizoid, while the further development of the young plant begins at its other end. The mode of germination in the foliose species *Radula* and *Frullania* is similar; the spores are as usual unicellular before germination[1]; the protonema which proceeds from them is a cake-like cell-surface, and the first bud of the leafy stem is formed out of one of the marginal cells. The rest of the foliose forms also proceed from thalloid protonemas. In *Lophocolea* and *Chiloscyphus* the spores have a finely granular exosporium and put out a tube which becomes a cell-row by transverse division. The original walls of the spores can be recognised in a terminal or other cell of the filament thus produced. The rudiment of the young plant is formed in the terminal cell of the filament, which is sometimes also branched. A wall inclined towards the axis of the filament appears in this cell, and commences the formation of the apical cell, which is a three-sided pyramid in the foliose forms. The course of proceeding in the formation of the leaves well deserves notice; the two lateral rows of leaves first make their appearance, and after them the leaves on the under surface, the amphigastria. The lateral leaves also only gradually acquire their ultimate form; the first are only short cell-rows, the later gradually assume the form of the fully developed leaves. This phenomenon—the appearance of leaves of simpler form in germination—is one of frequent occurrence in the Phanerogams. Many other foliose Jungermannieae resemble *Lophocolea* in these points, only instead of the filaments we find in many of them a protonema of usually irregular shape. The Marchantieae send out a germ-tube which grows towards the light, swells at its apex, and expanding in a direction at right angles to the direction of the light forms a disk, and the young plant developes from marginal cells of this disk.

The apical region of every shoot lies in most thalloid Hepaticae in an anterior indentation, produced by the more rapid growth in length and breadth of the tissue-cells which have been formed right and left from the segments of the apical cell, where there was one, while the cells lying behind the apical cell in the line of the axis of the shoot grow more slowly in length. The normal branching, which in a great majority of cases is a bifurcation, also takes place within this indentation. The apex first becomes broader, then a central portion of the tissue shoots out before the rest (Fig. 95, M_1, M_2), and is known as the middle lobe. In this way the original growing point is divided into two new points, and the middle lobe unites in itself the

---

[1] [On spore-structure see Leitgeb, Ueber Bau u. Entwickl. d. Sporenhaüte, 1884.]

beginnings of the lateral margins facing towards each other of the two daughter-shoots, which separate from one another as growth continues. When the bifurcating shoots grow longer, the middle lobe appears as the re-entering margin of the older bifurcation (Fig. 96, *f*). *Symphogyna* and *Umbraculum* have shoots, the rudiments of

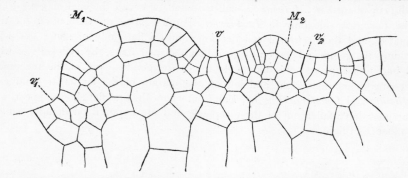

FIG. 95. *Aneura multifida.* Apex of a thallus in the act of dividing or branching; *v, v₁, v₂* apical cells of the three shoots formed by the branching of the primary apex, *M₁, M₂* intermediate lobes separating the apices of the shoots.

which appear at the growing point and on the ventral (under) side of the thallus also, and the same proceeding is observed in many Marchantieae (*vide infra*). The filiform stem of the foliose Jungermannieae ends in a bud as a more or less projecting vegetative cone with an apical cell which is a very convex three-sided pyramid. The branching is here always monopodial and very varied, as will be shown more fully below.

The arrangement of the cells in the apex is different in different genera. While the foliose forms have always, as has been said, an apical cell which is a three-sided pyramid, the thalloid forms, *Metzgeria* for instance and *Aneura*, have what is known as the wedge-shaped apical cell or some complicated forms of it, into which we must not enter further here since they show nothing essentially characteristic.

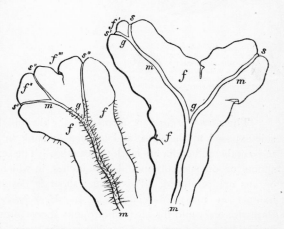

FIG. 96. *Metzgeria furcata,* magn. about 10 times, the upper side seen to the right, the lower to the left of the figure; in the midrib, *s, s', s''* the apical region, *ff* wing-like expansion formed of a single layer of cells, *f', f'', f'''* its development with the branching of the plant (middle lobes).

Asexual propagation is often effected in the Hepaticae by the dying away of the stem behind, by which the shoots lose their connection and become independent; adventitious shoots from cells of older portions of the margin or of the midrib, where as in *Metzgeria* there is a midrib, become detached in the same way. Leitgeb says that these adventitious shoots of the midrib of *Metzgeria* may also be formed endogenously. In foliose forms adventitious shoots are found on older leaves and on the stems. Copious propagation by gemmae occurs in many species and is very characteristic;

in many of the foliose Jungermannieae, *Madotheca* for instance, simple cells become detached as gemmae in numbers from the margins of the leaves; in *Blasia, Marchantia* and *Lunularia* special receptacles are formed on the upper side of the flat shoots which is turned towards the light; these receptacles are flask-shaped in *Blasia*, broadly cup-shaped in *Marchantia*, half-moon-shaped with the enclosing projection on the posterior side only in *Lunularia*. Papillae arise on the bottom of these receptacles, and their terminal cell developes into a flat body of some size, which constitutes the gemma; between them are club-shaped hairs, the cell-walls of which swell into mucilage, and this ultimately forces the gemmae out of the receptacles. There are indentations right and left on the margin of the lenticular gemmae of *Marchantia* and *Lunularia* (Fig. 98, *VI*), from which the first flat shoots appear, when the gemmae have fallen out of the receptacle and are exposed on damp ground to the influence of light.

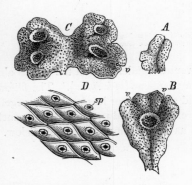

FIG. 97. *Marchantia polymorpha*, slightly enlarged. *A, B* young shoots. *C* the two shoots from a gemma with receptacles; *v, v* the apical region in a depression in the margin of the thallus. *D* a piece of the epidermis seen from above; *sp* stomata on the rhomboid plates more highly magnified.

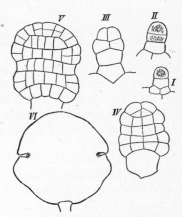

FIG. 98. Development of the gemmae of *Marchantia*.

The *sexual organs* are formed in the thalloid Hepaticae on the upper side, the side exposed to the light, and are usually sunk in the tissue of the thallus; in *Anthoceros* the antheridia are in closed cavities. The sexual organs are either on ordinary shoots or on specially modified branches, in which further growth ceases after the organs are produced. This sexual shoot is developed in a peculiarly remarkable manner in many Marchantieae. In *M. polymorpha* special shoots of singular form rise erect into the air (orthotropous shoots) from the prostrate stem, bearing the antheridia on the upper side, and the archegonia on the under side (though placed originally on the upper side), and these shoots are distributed monoeciously or dioeciously. We find such shoots in simpler form in thalloid Jungermannieae, as in *Aneura,* where certain shoots are retarded in their growth and so come to be lateral or to be placed on the ventral side of the branch-system, and these produce antheridia or archegonia. In *Metzgeria* the sexual shoots spring from the midrib and grow in so concave a form for the protection of the sexual organs on their dorsal face, that they have the appearance of a leaf-like envelope. Most other thalloid forms, as has been already said, protect the sexual organs by sinking them in cavities produced by the more rapid growth of the tissue immediately around them, and which often have only a narrow opening to the outer air. Fig. 99 is an example of such cavities.

In the foliose Jungermannieae the origin of the antheridia and archegonia is very various, and the organs in these also have different forms of envelope; about which more will be found in the detailed descriptions of the different families.

The *antheridium* in its mature state consists of a stalk and the spherical or ellipsoid body; the former is usually short if the antheridium is sunk in the tissue, longer if it is free, and is composed usually of from one to four rows of cells. The body of the antheridium consists of a wall of one layer of cells, containing chlorophyll; the whole of the space enclosed by it is densely filled with the mother-cells of the spermatozoids, which are discharged when water finds its way into the antheridium by the parting of the cells of the wall at the apex, or sometimes, as in *Fossombronia*, by the entire separation of these cells from one another.

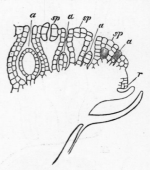

The small spermatozoid-mother-cells discharged at intervals and in great numbers from the antheridium become isolated in the water, and the spermatozoids issue from them as slender threads from one to three times spirally twisted, and with two long and very delicate cilia at the anterior extremity, by means of which they move about in the water and turn on their own axis; they usually drag a small and delicate vesicle attached to their hinder end. The development of the spermatozoids agrees, as far as we at present know, with that described by Schmitz in *Nitella* and elsewhere [1]; that is, they are formed chiefly from the nucleus of the mother-cell, which grows more dense towards the circumference and splits up into the screw-thread of the spermatozoid, while the central and looser part forms the vesicle above mentioned.

FIG. 99. Anterior margin of the young male cap-like sexual shoot of *Marchantia polymorpha*; *r* the growing margin; *a, a, a* the antheridia in different stages of their development; *sp* the stomata over the air-cavities between the antheridia. After Hofmeister, magn. 300 times.

The order in which the cell-divisions follow one another in the formation of the antheridium varies, according to the statements of observers, in the different genera; but in all the first rudiment is always a papillose protuberance on a cell, the papilla being then separated by a transverse septum. The papilla thus separated divides into a lower and an upper cell; the former produces the stalk and the latter the body of the antheridium, that is the wall-layer and the spermatozoids [2].

The order in which the cell-divisions follow one another in the formation of the *archegonium* is essentially the same in the different families. Like the antheridium the archegonium first appears as a papilliform outgrowth of a superficial cell, which, in the case of the first of a group of archegonia in *Radula*, is the apical cell of the shoot. The papilla is cut off by a transverse septum, and in *Riccia* is at once itself the mother-cell of the whole archegonium; in other species it first divides transversely

---

[1] For *Pellia* see Goebel, *loc. cit.*

[2] [Satter, Beitr. z. Entwicklungsg. d. Lebermoos-Antheridiums (Sitz. d. K. Acad. d. Wiss. Wien, 1852).]

into an upper and a lower cell, the latter of the two becoming the stalk, the former the archegonium itself. The mother-cell of the archegonium then first divides by three longitudinal walls into three outer cells, and one central cell which overtops them; the three outer next form five or six envelope-cells by radial longitudinal walls, while the central cell divides by a transverse wall into an upper cell, the lid-cell, and

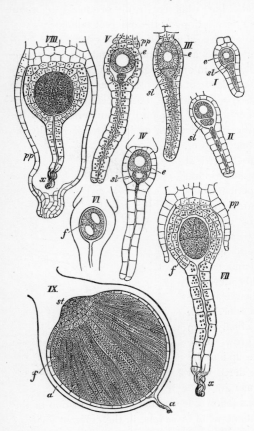

an inner (lower) cell. When the whole structure has grown somewhat longer, it is divided into two stories, the six envelope-cells and the innermost cell each dividing transversely. The lower story becomes the *venter*, the upper the *neck* of the archegonium. The inner cell of the venter, the *central cell*, increases considerably in size, and a transverse wall divides it into a lower and larger cell, the *oosphere*, and an upper and smaller cell, the *ventral canal-cell*. Meanwhile the upper story, the neck of the archegonium, elongates, and the middle cell divides at the same time into four, eight, or sixteen long narrow cells, the *neck canal-cells*. The wall of the venter, which is of one or two layers of cells, is completed by further longitudinal and transverse divisions in its outer cells, while the wall of the neck, consisting ultimately of five to six longitudinal rows of cells, is developed by transverse divisions of the outer cells of the neck, and the lid-cell divides into five or six cells forming the lid (stigma of authors) of the neck. Meanwhile the original stalk-cell of the archegonium divides by longitudinal walls which cross one another and by transverse walls. During the rejuvenescence and rounding off of the oosphere in the central cell, the longitudinal walls of the neck canal-cells and the trans-

FIG 100. Later stages in the development of the archegonia and formation of the sporogonium of *Marchantia polymorpha*, I—VIII magn. 300 times, IX about 30 times. I and II young archegonia. III, IV after the dissolution of the axile row of neck-cells. V just ready for fertilisation. VII, VIII the cells of the orifice of the neck x shrivelled after fertilisation, the embryo f showing the first divisions. In these figs. sl is the lowest cell of the axile row and the last to dissolve into mucilage, the ventral canal-cell; e in I—IV is the central cell, e in V the oosphere before fertilisation, pp in V, VII, and VIII the developing perigynium. IX is the unripe sporogonium in the venter of the archegonium which has developed into the calyptra; a the neck of the archegonium, f wall of the capsule, st its stalk; inside the capsule are the young elaters like long threads arranged radially, with the spores between them.

verse wall beneath the ventral canal-cell swell up into mucilage, which forces out the protoplasm of all the canal-cells through the opened lid at the apex of the neck (Fig. 100).

The *second generation* (*sporophore, sporophyte*), the sporogonium or sporocarp, is formed and reaches its full development inside the venter of the archegonium, which grows in size as the sporogonium grows, and from this time bears the name of *calyptra*; it is only in *Anthoceros*, where the archegonia are sunk in the thallus, that a proper calyptra is not formed. The stalk of the sporogonium some-times penetrates into the tissue of the vegetative body of the first generation; papillae shoot out from it, especially in the Anthoceroteae; these like the papillae of roots are concerned with the supply of food.

The outer form and the structure of the sporogonium is very different in different groups. In the Anthoceroteae it is in the mature state an elongated pod, which projects above the thallus and opens by two valves; in the Riccieae it is a thin-walled capsule quite filled with spores and with the calyptra sunk in the thallus; in the Marchantieae it is a shortly stalked sphere, which encloses elaters as well as spores, and either bursts irregularly after it has broken through the calyptra, or opens by a circular slit from which a lid falls off; in the Jungermannieae it matures as in the other families inside the calyptra, but ultimately breaks through it and appears as a sphere on a long and delicate stalk. The capsule when mature consists in the Jungermannieae, as in the Marchantieae and Riccieae, of a single layer of cells, but it opens by four stalked lobes disposed crosswise, on which the elaters remain suspended. The elaters here, as in the Marchantieae, are long fusiform cells, with one to three brown spiral bands as thickenings on the inside of the stout colourless outer layer of the wall.

The course of *development of the sporogonium* is marked by not unimportant variations in the several groups, in connection especially with the origin of the tissue which produces the spores, i.e. the differentiation of the archesporium, while there is a general agreement among them with regard to the course of cell-formation in the embryo. There is at the same time a continuous series within the group of the Hepaticae from the simple embryo of the genus *Riccia* to the more highly developed embryo of the Anthoceroteae. The embryos of *Riccia* (Fig. 101, *A*) are spherical and divided at first into octants. Further divisions then appear by which a peripheral layer of cells, the wall of the sporogonium, is separated from the central tissue, which becomes in its entirety spore-mother-cells, and each of these cells pro-duces by division four spores. The wall of the capsule eventually decays. But further differentiations are found even among the Riccieae. Sterile cells, not em-ployed in the formation of spores, which may be regarded as analogous to elaters, are found in *Corsinia*, and the genus *Boschia* has undoubted elaters; and in these two genera, as in the nearly allied Marchantieae, there is already a distinction in the sporogonium between stalk and capsule. This distinction is introduced in the Marchantieae (but not in the two genera of the Riccieae just mentioned according to Kienitz-Gerloff) by the first wall formed in the oospore which is at right angles to the axis of the archegonium (Fig. 101, *B*); the upper cell, which is towards the neck of the archegonium, developes into the capsule, the lower forms the stalk which is as yet but small. Here too, as in *Riccia*, the young embryo divides into octants, of which the four upper become the capsule, consisting of a layer of cells forming the wall and the inner cells from which the spores and elaters proceed. The elaters have pointed extremities and lie between the single or double rows of the spore-mother-cells. In the Jungermannieae the oospore is first divided by a wall at right angles to the axis of the archegonium into a lower and an upper cell; both the capsule and the stalk proceed from the upper cell, while the lower cell appears as an appendage or foot (Fig. 101, *a*) at the end of the stalk, though in many cases it undergoes some further divisions.   A somewhat older embryo shows in its upper portion a cellulose skeleton formed of a number of transverse tiers, which consist each of four cells in the form of quadrants of a cylinder, while the apex is occupied by four cells in the form of octants of a sphere.   It is from these latter that the capsule proceeds in the simpler cases, such as *Pellia, Frullania, Lejeunia*, a wall-layer being separated off by four periclinal walls from four inner cells, the *archesporium* (Fig. 101, *C*). But in most cases the tier of cells adjoining the four upper cells also takes part in the formation of the capsule.   The part beneath the capsule, in which the separate tiers

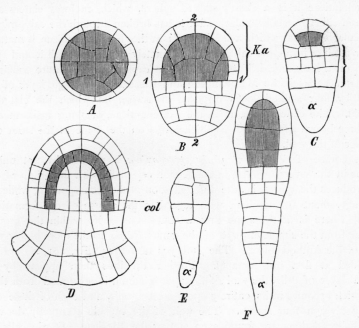

FIG 101. Development of the embryo of the Liverworts more or less diagrammatically represented. The cells from which the sporogenous tissue is formed are shaded. *A Riccia*, in which all the cells except those of the parietal layer are devoted to the production of spores. *B Marchantia*; the oosphere is divided by the first wall, formed in it after fertilisation, into a lower portion which becomes the stalk and an upper which forms the capsule *Ka*. *C Pellia epiphylla*; *a* appendage of the embryo, the archesporium is composed of four cells, of which two are visible. *D Anthoceros*; the archesporium is a bell-shaped cell-layer; *col* the columella. *E Jungermannia bicuspidata*. *F Radula complanata*; the archesporium consists of more than four cells. The bracket in Fig. *C* indicates the portion of the embryo from which the stalk of the sporogonium proceeds. After Kienitz-Gerloff and Leitgeb.

are still visible, becomes the stalk, and its basal portion often swells up into a thickened foot.   The spore-chamber as it grows becomes round, and the stalk elongates very considerably when the capsule is mature, and lifts it into the air.   The development of the embryo in *Anthoceros* is most unlike that of the other genera ; its first stages are the same as in the Jungermannieae ; the embryo consists of two to three tiers of cells disposed as quadrants.   In this case there is no stalk, but a foot proceeds from the lowest tier, and the capsule from the two upper, or from the one upper tier.   The cells of this tier are divided by periclinal walls into inner and outer cells.   But while in the rest of the Hepaticae the outer cells form the wall and the inner the archesporium, it is not so in *Anthoceros*; there the inner cells form a column of sterile tissue, the *columella* (Fig. 101, *D col*), and the archesporium is cut off from the outer cells by further periclinal divisions, and is thus a layer of cells in the form of a bell with the mouth downwards, a form which recurs among the Mosses in the Sphagnaceae and Andreaeaceae. In Fig. 101 *D* the layer outside the archesporium, the wall-layer, has divided again. Further growth consists only in the further development of the tissues thus formed. The sporogonia of *Anthoceros* have besides an intercalary growth at their base which continues for a long time. The upper part of the capsule may have opened for some time and discharged its spores, while no spore-mother-cells even have been formed in the lower part; the capsule of *A. giganteus* reaches a length of seven centimetres. The genus *Notothylas*, one of the Anthoceroteae, has capsules with a columella, and other capsules in which the columella is much less distinct or not formed at all; in the latter case the sterile cells form a chambered tissue which fills the inside of the capsule, and the spore-mother-cells lie in its cavities. By the formation of capsules without columellas *Notothylas* is connected with the rest of the Hepaticae, where also there are forms in which the sterile cells of the capsules are not developed into elaters, but act as cells of nutrition expending the food-material stored up in them in promoting the development of the spores[1]. Smaller deviations in the formation of the embryo, especially such as are caused by unequal development of separate parts, must remain unnoticed in this place[2].

The Hepaticae may be divided into two series with intermediate forms in either series:—

1. SERIES OF THE JUNGERMANNIEAE.
   { (*a*) **Jungermannieae.**
   { (*b*) **Anthoceroteae.**

2. SERIES OF THE MARCHANTIACEAE.
   { (*a*) **Riccieae.**
   { (*b*) **Marchantieae.**

SERIES OF THE JUNGERMANNIEAE.

(*a*) The **Jungermannieae**, alike from the number of their species and the frequency of their occurrence, are much the largest group of the Hepaticae. It was stated above that two subdivisions may be founded on the difference in the character of their vegetative organs, namely the thalloid and the foliose; it was pointed out at the same

---

[1] The orientation of the columella of *Notothylas* differs rom that of *Anthoceros*, inasmuch as in the latter the columella is a secondary product of differentiation inside the spore-chamber.

[2] If we take a survey of what has been said above, we shall see that, as Leitgeb has pointed out, four types may be distinguished in the development and structure of the sporogonium.

a. The sporogonium is differentiated into a layer of cells forming the wall and into an inner space filled with spores only (Riccieae, in the narrower sense).

b. The cells of the inner space are divided into fertile cells which form spores, and sterile cells which serve to feed the spores (*Corsinia*, Rielleae, *Notothylas*).

c. The cells of the inner space which remain sterile become elaters (most Hepaticae).

d. The axis of the capsule is traversed by a cellular column, the columella, which is surrounded and arched over by the spore-forming layer (Anthoceroteae, but for *Notothylas* vid. sup. under *b*).

time that transitional forms between the two are not wanting. Leitgeb has divided the Jungermannieae into two groups distinguished by the position of the female sexual organs, the *acrogynous* and the *anacrogynous*. In the first the growth of the shoot is terminated by the appearance of the archegonia, which are formed in immediate proximity to the apical cell; in many cases an archegonium is formed from the apical cell itself. To this group belong all leafy forms with radial structure, with the exception of *Haplomitrium Hookeri*, which differs from it in other respects also. In the second group the archegonia do not rise either on the apex or very near it, but, *Haplomitrium* only excepted, on the back of the shoot, which usually continues to grow after their formation, though the growth of sexual shoots is sometimes cut short, as in *Metzgeria, Aneura, Blasia* and some others.

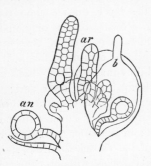

FIG. 102. Sexual organs of *Radula complanata; ar* archegonia, *an* antheridia, *b* leaf. After Hofmeister.

The sexual organs are distributed monoeciously or dioeciously, and are formed in the thalloid genera on the dorsal surface of the shoot. They are here protected by an envelope, formed either by the curvature of the shoot itself, as in *Metzgeria*, or by the turning up of the lateral edges of the shoot, or by peculiar outgrowths of the thallus, as in the Haplolaeneae and Diplomitrieae. In the foliose (acrogynous) Jungermannieae the sexual organs are formed on the apex of main shoots or of special small sexual branches which are often on the ventral surface and endogenous in their origin. The antheridia are usually in the axils of the leaves, singly or several together. The archegonia appear, usually in numbers, on the apex of the shoot, either on one which bears antheridia lower down, or on special female branches which are so deeply

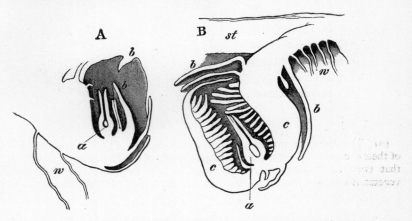

FIG. 103. *Calypogeia Trichomanis.* Longitudinal section of young sexual branches; *w* rhizoids, *a* archegonia, *b* leaves of the branches, *c* wall formed by the branch which has become cup-shaped, *st* primary stem on which the branch arises. In *A* the branch is still young; it has thrust itself obliquely into the ground and has then become curved upwards. After Hofmeister. magn. 200 times.

excavated in the Geocalyceae, that the archegonia are sunk in a deep pitcher-shaped hollow, a development which is specially striking in *Calypogeia* (Fig. 103). Where the archegonia are not enclosed in this manner, they have an envelope formed of the adjacent leaves, a perichaetium, and usually a second envelope is found, the perigynium, which lies as a membranous growth round each archegonium. These processes are minutely described by Leitgeb in the case of *Radula complanata*.

Both the main and the lateral shoots bear as a rule both kinds of sexual organs ; such a shoot is always for a long time purely vegetative, and then for a while forms antheridia, and finally a group of archegonia ; sometimes but less often it recurs to the vegetative state after producing antheridia. The antheridia in *Radula* stand singly in the leaf-axils, and are entirely inclosed in the hollow formed by the great concavity of the lower lobe of the leaf ; they arise from a club-shaped protuberance in a cell of the rind of the stem at the base and in front of the leaf. The group of archegonia in *Radula* is always at the extremity of the main shoot or of a lateral one, and consists of from three to ten archegonia in a perigynium, which is itself enveloped by two leaves. The archegonia and perigynium are both developed from the apical cell of the shoot and from its three latest segments. The archegonia are formed from the apical cell itself and the acroscopic portions of the lateral segments, the basiscopic portions and the ventral segment being applied to the formation of the perigynium ; their further development has been already described.

The branching of the thalloid forms was briefly noticed above ; that of the foliose

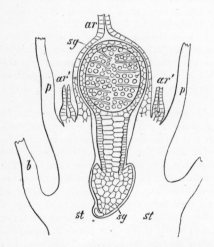

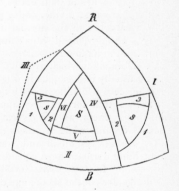

FIG. 104. *Jungermannia bicuspidata.* Longitudinal section of the immature sporogonium *sg*, surrounded by the calyptra *ar* ; *ar'* archegonia in which no fertilisation has been effected, *p* base of the perigynium, *st* stem, *b* leaf. After Hofmeister.

FIG. 105. Diagrammatic representation of the branching of Jungermannieae, the lateral shoots of which appear in place of the under lobe of the upper leaves, apex of the stem seen from above. After Leitgeb.

Jungermannieae is very varied. These plants have without exception a three-sided pyramidal apical cell, one surface of which is turned to the substratum. The apical cell forms three rows of segments, two of which are dorsal and lateral, while the third forms the ventral side of the stem. In the species with two rows of leaves a leaf is produced by each segment of the latero-dorsal rows, in those with three rows of leaves each ventral segment also produces a leaf, which is however smaller and simpler in structure, and is known as an amphigastrium. The insertion of the lateral leaves in the mature state is oblique to the axis of the stem, and of such a kind that the lines of insertion of each pair of leaves form a V-shaped angle. This is however the result of displacement ; the median planes of the lateral leaves next the apex of the axis are perpendicular to the surface of the stem, and their insertions in accordance with the position of the lateral segments are transverse. Before a lateral segment grows out into a papilla to form a leaf, it divides by a longitudinal wall into an upper, the dorsal half, and a lower, the ventral half, and each of them then puts out a leaf-papilla ; hence it arises that the leaves of the Jungermannieae are to a certain extent halved or two-lobed ; this is usually shown in more simple leaves by a more or less deep indentation of the anterior margin, but when the leaves are much divided as in *Trichocolea*, the two halves which were distinguised in the rudimentary state may still be recognised ; the lower lobe of the leaf is often smaller and differently shaped, turned over and hollowed out.

In the branching system we can distinguish between the branches which arise on the sides of the stem and beneath the leaves, and those on the ventral side in the axils of the amphigastria, if there are any, or beside them. The lateral branches arise in a large number of the Jungermannieae from the segment in the place of the lower ventral lobe of the upper leaves. Fig. 105 may serve to illustrate this remarkable arrangement. It is a diagrammatic representation of the apical view of a branching shoot ; *I*, *II . . . VI* are segments of the apical cell *S* of the main shoot, *II* and *V* of the ventral side, *I*, *III*, *IV*, *VI* of the dorsal ; the two segments *I* and *III* are each already divided by a longitudinal wall into a dorsal and a ventral half, and the apical cell *s* of a lateral shoot is already formed in the ventral half by the appearance of the walls 1, 2, 3, while each dorsal half of the segments is developing into the half of an upper leaf ; the other segments which do not form shoots become entire two-lobed leaves. This is the process in a great majority of the Jungermannieae, in *Frullania*, *Madotheca*, *Mastigobryum*, *Lepidozia*, *Jungermannia trichophylla*, and *Trichocolea*. In *Radula*, *Lejeunia* and some others the basal halves of the segments are not applied to the formation of branches in their entire height and before the appearance of further divisions, but the cells first divide, and a part of the free outer surface of the segment forms the lower leaf-lobes in the normal manner, and shoots spring from the basiscopic portion only. The developed shoots are therefore always inserted at the base of a lateral leaf and close to its lower lobe.

The branches which grow on the under, the ventral, side of the stem are peculiar in being usually endogenous in origin, proceeding, according to Leitgeb's statements, from mother-cells which lie beneath the layer of cells that forms the surface of the stem. The branches thus formed may appear in acropetal succession or be adventitious, and in some genera, as *Mastigobryum* and *Calypogeia*, are the only ones that bear the sexual organs, while in others they develope into whip-like forms, flagella, with leaves that are always small and sometimes only rudimentary. They have the power of remaining dormant for a considerable time, and then bursting forth from older parts of the stem. In *Lophocolea bidentata* the branches are almost entirely formed from the ventral halves of the shoots and endogenously, and so too in *Jungermannia bicuspidata*, where some branches are exogenous ; in the latter species the branches bend over and so form an apparently pinnate system, and cells of the ventral segments grow out on older specimens into long tubes at the apices of which buds sometimes form. Adventitious shoots are also sometimes formed on leaves.

b. The **Anthoceroteae** include the genera *Anthoceros*, *Dendroceros* and *Notothylas*. *Anthoceros laevis* and *punctatus*, which grow with us in summer on loamy soil, develope a flat, ribbon-like, leafless thallus, which branches irregularly and forms a circular disk. *Dendroceros* has a strong mid-rib, from which the flat thallus extends on both sides as a single layer of cells with the margin crisped and folded. In *Anthoceros* and *Notothylas* the thallus has more than one layer of cells. The cells of the thallus contain only one chlorophyll-corpuscle, and this incloses a spherical amylum-body and conceals the nucleus. Stomata are formed on the under side of the thallus close behind the growing apex, and the intercellular space beneath is filled with mucilage ; here therefore the stomata would be more fitly called mucilage-slits, since their function is to secrete the mucilage which in other Hepaticae is supplied from club-shaped papillae at the apex. The clefts are formed by the splitting of the cell-wall between any two cells of the thallus ; there is therefore no previous special formation of *guard-cells*, as in Ferns and Phanerogams. Nostoc-colonies are not unfrequently found in the mucilage-cavities, and cause peculiar changes in them ; the organs are attacked by the Alga when quite young, a nostoc-filament forcing its way through the cleft into the mucilage-cavity. This is followed by a rapid process of division in the surrounding cells, and the cleft closes. But the parietal cells of the cavity grow out, in proportion as the *Nostoc* increases, into tubes which come into close contact with the *Nostoc*, and as they multiply and divide they look like a parenchymatous tissue with Nostoc settled in its intercellular spaces. (Compare *Blasia*.) The species of *Anthoceros* are monoecious; the antheridia and archegonia are not placed as a rule in any fixed relative order. The antheridia are always at first in perfectly closed cavities, which in *Dendroceros* rise like bladders above the surface of the thallus, but in our native species of *Anthoceros* and in *Notothylas* are entirely sunk in the thallus. It is not till the chlorophyll-corpuscles in the walls of the antheridia have turned yellow and the spermatozoids are mature that the covering is rent, and the antheridia open at their apex and discharge their contents.

The development of the archegonia is in all important points the same as in the

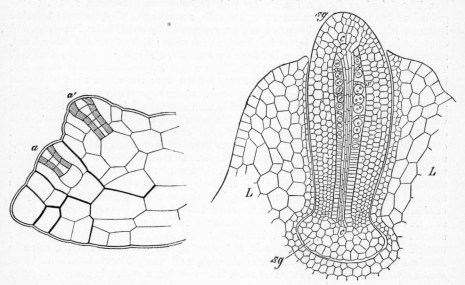

FIG. 106. Longitudinal section through the apex of a thallus of *Anthoceros* with archegonia. After Leitgeb.

FIG. 107. Longitudinal section of a young sporogonium of *Anthoceros laevis*; *L* the involucre. After Hofmeister, magn. 150 times.

rest of the Hepaticae; only the mother-cell remains sunk in the tissue of the thallus, and hence the neck does not project above the thallus even when the archegonium is fully formed (Fig. 106).

The development of the sporogonium has already been described as differing from that of the other Hepaticae. While the embryo becomes a multicellular body broader at its base, the surrounding tissue of the thallus divides repeatedly and grows up into an overarching involucre, which is afterwards pierced through by the elongating sporogonium. Cells which remain sterile and form a connected net-work are separated off from the archesporium. In *Dendroceros* and some foreign species these sterile cells are elaters composed of a row of cells and traversed by a broad brown spiral band. The cells of the foot are prolonged into tubes which penetrate into the adjoining tissue. The sporogonium elongates and forms a narrow capsule which in some European species is from fifteen to twenty millimetres in height; its brown wall opens from above downwards into two valves and its epidermis has stomata. The prolonged intercalary growth at the base of the sporogonium is characteristic of this group. No capsules are ever found in *Anthoceros* which can be properly said to have ceased to grow; in *Notothylas* this growth lasts comparatively but a short time, and its capsules therefore are shorter. In this respect the genus *Notothylas* forms a transition to the Jungermannieae, as well as in the structure of its capsule, which, as was said above, either has not the columella which is characteristic of *Anthoceros* and *Dendroceros*, or one which is only a secondary differentiation inside the spore-chamber.

2. Series of the Marchantiaceae.

The Marchantieae, in the narrower use of the term, and the Riccieae, once looked upon as an independent family, really form one natural group, as Leitgeb has lately shown, the two subdivisions being connected together by intermediate forms supplied by the Corsinieae, that is, by the genera *Corsinia* and *Boschia*.

a. **The Riccieae** form a flat thallus with dichotomous branching, rooted to the ground or floating in water; several apical cells, according to Kny, lie close together in the anterior sinus of the branches, and are segmented by walls inclined upwards and downwards, and multiplied by vertical longitudinal walls; Leitgeb, on the other hand, assumes here as in similar cases, in *Blasia* for example, a single four-sided apical cell. The under side of the thallus is occupied by a single longitudinal row of transverse lamellae (they are wanting in *R. crystallina*) formed from transverse rows of ventral superficial cells. At a later period these ventral scales separate into two longitudinal rows, between which are numerous rhizoids with conical thickenings on their inner walls. In *Boschia* this formation of scales is similar to that of the Marchantieae. The dorsal side of the thallus is formed of a thicker or thinner layer of cells containing chlorophyll, with broader or narrower spaces between them filled with air; this layer may be called with Leitgeb the air-chamber layer. In most species of the genus *Riccia* these chambers run like narrow passages at right angles to the dorsal surface of the thallus, in others, as *R. crystallina* and *R. fluitans*, they form wide spaces. In the first case they are continued through the epidermis and are only partially closed by its cells being swollen into bladders. In the second case a roof is formed by growth of the surface of the epidermal cells in proportion to the successive enlargements of the air-space, as in *R. fluitans*, or where this does not take place, the air-spaces open to the outside along their old breadth, as in *R. crystallina*. The structure is the same in *Riccia natans*, in *Oxymitra, Corsinia, Boschia*, and many Marchantieae, as in *R. fluitans*, with the difference only that there is an opening, a stoma, in the roof of every air-chamber; this is present in a rudimentary form indeed in *Riccia fluitans*, but is often not discernible. The way in which these air-chambers are produced is very peculiar. They are not formed in the tissue by shrinking of the cells from one another, nor by a fissure advancing from without inwards, but they represent depressions in the outer surface caused by certain points in the surface being arched over by the more rapid growth of the neighbouring parts. The cavities thus formed are afterwards covered over by the completion of the growth of the surface in breadth (Fig. 112), but the orifice is as a rule preserved, and represents the stomata of the more highly developed species, the formation of which will be examined more closely when we are describing the Marchantieae.

The sexual organs also, the antheridia and archegonia, are placed in depressions formed in the same way as the air-cavities. Both are at first papillose outgrowths of young epidermal cells, which as they develope become grown over by the surrounding tissue (Fig. 108); this involucre sometimes has a neck which rises high above the sessile antheridium. The archegonia project at the period of fertilisation above the epidermis of the thallus, but are afterwards covered in, and then produce from their oospore the globular sporogonium, which shows those varieties of development in the different genera which have been already pointed out. In *Corsinia* and *Boschia* the archegonia are found not singly but in groups in pit-like depressions of the thallus. The Riccieae have no gemmae, but adventitious shoots appear not unfrequently on the ventral side of the thallus.

b. The **Marchantieae** have a flat ribbon-like thallus which branches dichotomously, has a mid-rib, is always of more than one layer of cells in thickness, and spreads out on the ground.

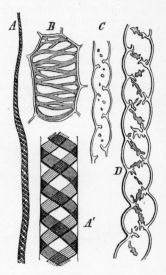

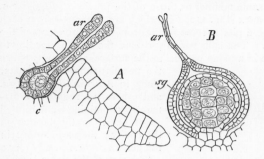

FIG. 10 *Riccia glauca. A* apical region in vertical longitudina section ; *ar* archegonium, *c* oosphere, magn. 500 times. *B* the immature sporogonium *sg* surrounded by the calyptra, which still bears the neck of the archegonium, magn. 300 times. After Hofmeister.

FIG. 109. Cells of *Marchantia polymorpha.*
A piece of an elater with spiral thickening of the inner wall. *A'* a bit of the same more highly magnified. *C* and *D* portions of rhizoids with thickenings which project into the inner cavity. *B* cell of the thallus with broad pits.

The under side has two rows of scales, which however are not due to the splitting of a single original row, as in *Riccia,* and two kinds of rhizoids, simple tubes and tubes with conical thickenings (Fig. 109, *D*). On the dorsal or upper side is a layer of tissue which is traversed by air-chambers and covered over by an epidermis pierced by stomata. Each of these stomata in *Marchantia, Lunularia,* and others is in the middle of a rhomboidal areola (Fig. 97), and the areolae are the

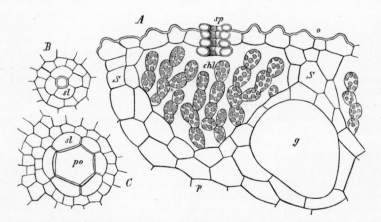

FIG. 110. *Marchantia polymorpha.* Portions of a young receptacle. *A* vertical section ; *o* epidermis, *S* partition-wall between the air-chambers and their chlorophyll-cells *chl, g* a mucilage-cell. *B* and *C* young stoma seen from above, *po* its canal (pore).

portions of the epidermis which form the roofs of the air-cavities ; from the bottom of the cavities, and in many cases from the side-walls and from the roof as well, conferva-like cells grow out containing chlorophyll (Fig. 110, *chl*), while the rest of the tissue is without chlorophyll.

The stomata are in some species bounded by several concentric circles of cells, all lying in the plane of the upper surface of the thallus, which is formed of one layer of cells; this is the case in *Fegatella* (Fig. 112). In *Preissia* and *Marchantia* on the other hand the orifice is a circular canal formed by several tiers of cells (Fig. 110), and a similar construction is found in the stomata on the sexual shoots, and even in species of the Marchantieae which have only simple stomata on their thallus. The air-chambers are formed in much the same manner as those of the previous sub-division. Small pits are formed behind the apex (Fig. 112, *I k*), which are separated from each other at first by one cell only. These pits become much deeper and broader and the adjacent parts grow up over them. The cells which surround the narrow opening to these cavities on the outside divide in a plane parallel to the surface, and thus produce the peculiar canal-like stomata. Then in *Marchantia, Preissia,* and others the segmented filaments containing chlorophyll shoot out from the bottom of the cavity; they are absent in the genera *Sauteria* and *Clevea*.

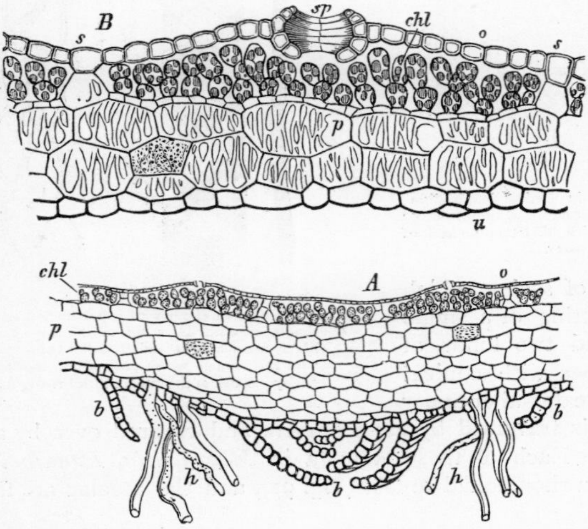

The rest of the tissue is without chlorophyll and consists of long, horizontally elongated cells without interstices (Fig. 111), and often with broad pits on their walls. In *Preissia*[1] are found strings of elongated uniformly thickened cells with very dark coloured walls. The mucilage-organs are peculiar; and are most highly developed in *Fegatella,* where longitudinal rows of cells are transformed into mucilage-canals by the thickening of the cell-walls and their conversion into mucilage, the cell appearing to be filled with a strongly refractive jelly. Single

FIG. 111. Transvers section through the thallus of *Marchantia polymorpha*. *A* middle portion with scales *b* and rhizoids *h* on the under side, magn. 30 times. *B* margin of the thallus more highly magnified; *p* colourless reticulately thickened parenchyma, *o* epidermis of the upper side, *chl* the cells containing chlorophyll, *sp* stoma, *s* partition-walls between the air-chambers, *u* lower epidermis with dark-coloured cell-walls.

cells of this kind are found in the thallus and the sexual shoots of others of the Marchantieae[2].

The sexual organs of the Marchantieae are dioeciously or monoeciously disposed, and there is considerable variety in the construction of the shoots which bear them. In *Clevea hyalina* and *Sauteria alpina* the antheridia appear singly on the dorsal side of ordinary shoots, as in *Riccia.* In *Targionia* the archegonia are formed on the growing apex, which can continue to grow if fertilisation is not effected. The group of archegonia is inclosed by the growth over it of the dorsal and lateral tissue of the thallus. The antheridia and archegonia of many species of *Plagiochasma* and the antheridia of *Fimbriaria* and *Peltolepis* are placed several together one behind another on disc-shaped receptacles on the dorsal side of the thallus. But the male and female receptacles in *Fegatella, Preissia, Marchantia* and *Dumortiera* are composed of an entire branching-system. In the male receptacles of *Marchantia* for instance (Fig.

[1] Goebel, Zur vergl. Anatomie d. Marchantieen (Arb. d. Bot. Instit. in Würzburg, II Bd.).

[2] [Prescher, Die Schleimorgane der Marchantien (Sitz. d. k. Acad. d. Wiss. Wien, 1882).]

113) the apex that is to bear the antheridia divides repeatedly before they begin to be formed, and the whole collection of apices thus formed produces antheridia ; the older

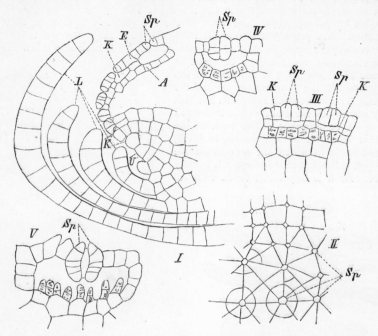

FIG. 112. *I, II Fegatella conica.* *I* Longitudinal section through the apex of a thallus; *L* the scales (lamellae) of the under side of the thallus, *K* the air-chambers formed on the upper side and gradually roofed over during the formation of the epidermis *E.* *II* Surface-view of a portion of the thallus seen from above. *III, IV, V Marchantia polymorpha ;* development of the stomata on a receptacle in longitudinal section ; *Sp* the cells from which the barrel-shaped stomata are formed, and which at first lie close to one another ; the canal leading to the air-chamber is subsequently formed between them. In *V* the cells containing chlorophyll are beginning to shoot out from the floor of the air-chamber. *II* after Leitgeb, the other figures from nature.

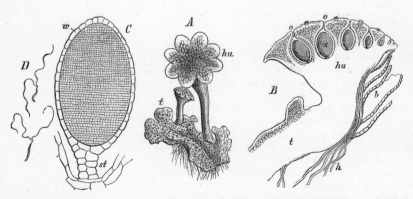

FIG. 113. *Marchantia polymorpha.* *A* a horizontal branch *t* with two ascending male receptacles *hu.* *B* vertical longitudinal section through a male receptacle *hu* which is still developing and the part of the flat shoot from which it springs ; *bb* scales, *h* rhizoids in a ventral channel of the receptacle ; *oo* the openings of the cavities in which the antheridia *a* are placed. *C* a nearly ripe antheridium ; *st* its stalk, *w* the wall. *D* two spermatozoids magn. 800 times.

ones are in the centre of the disk, and groups of them succeed one another from the centre to the circumference where the apices of the shoot are placed, each outer group

[2]

younger than the one next inside it. The antheridia are formed from superficial cells, but they are sunk in the upper side of the receptacle and are arched over by the surrounding tissue. The first archegonia also are formed on the upper side of the cap-like receptacle but are brought round to the under side by the further growth of the receptacle (Figs. 114, 115). The stalk of the receptacle is still quite short when fertilisation takes place, but afterwards elongates, and thus materially facilitates the dispersion of the spores, the stalk of the sporogonium being itself very short. The stalk of the receptacle would appear therefore in this case to do the work of the stalk of the sporogonium in the Jungermannieae and the Mosses. The archegonia appear on the disk which surmounts the stalk and are directed downwards or outwards. The form of the part that bears the archegonia varies much, and the mode in which the archegonia are enveloped in involucres or perigynia is equally various. As it is impossible to describe all

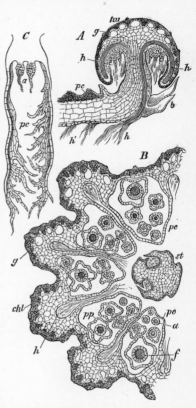

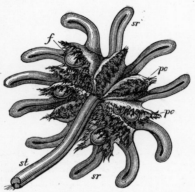

FIG. 114. Female receptacle of *Marchantia poly-morpha* seen laterally from below; *st* stalk with two ventral channels, *sr* the radiating outgrowths from the receptacle, *pc* the envelope between them, *f* sporogonia.

these things in a brief space, *Marchantia polymorpha*, the species most fully provided in this respect, may serve as an example. The explanation of the figures will make the chief points sufficiently clear.

The capsule of the sporogonium of the Marchantieae, which is in most cases shortly stalked, contains elaters, which radiate from the base of the capsule to the circumference (Fig. 100, *IX*); it either opens at the apex by numerous teeth or by four lobes, or the

FIG. 115. *Marchantia polymorpha.* A perpendicular longitudinal section through a female receptacle *hu*; *bb* scales, *h* rhizoids in the channel of the stalk, *g* mucilage-cells between the air-cavities of the upper side. *B* half of the ground-plan of an older receptacle and of its stalk *st*; *chl* the green tissue of the receptacle, *g* large hyaline cells, *pc* the common envelope-leaves (*pc* in Fig. 114), *a* archegonia with their oospores unfertilised, *pp* perianths of fertile archegonia. *C* vertical tangential section through the receptacle; *a* two archegonia, *pc* common envelope of the archegonia (perichaetium).

upper part separates as a lid by a circular fissure. Mention has already been made of the peculiar gemmae and their receptacles.

The branching of the thallus is either dichotomous, as in the thalloid Jungermannieae, or by formation of shoots on the under side; the one or the other form is the more prominent in different genera; *Marchantia, Lunularia*, and *Fegatella* form many bifurcations and scarcely any ventral shoots. In *Targionia* and many species of *Fimbriaria* the latter form of branching prevails; in others, as in *Plagiochasma*, both kinds occur in pretty equal proportions. In *Preissia* the sterile thallus branches dichotomously, but a change takes place when a sexual shoot is formed, the two first bifurcations of a dichotomy being applied to this purpose (in *Marchantia* one of them continues to grow on as a vegetative shoot); then a ventral shoot makes its appearance immediately under the apex, and grows in the direction of the mother-shoot, and in this way the thallus of this genus is formed with its member-like shoots. In *Targionia* and *Sauteria alpina* the regular position of the antheridia is on ventral shoots.

MUSCI [1].

The spore produces a confervoid structure, the protonema, on which the Moss-plant proper arises as a lateral shoot with differentiation of stem and leaf; on this plant the sexual organs are formed, the sporogonium proceeds from the oospore in the archegonium, and the spores are formed in it from a small portion of the inner tissue.

The *protonema* is in the typical Mosses a tubular outgrowth of the endosporium, which has unlimited power of elongation by apical growth and is divided into cells by obliquely transverse walls inclining in different directions; the cells are subject to no intercalary divisions but form branches immediately behind the septa, and these are also divided by transverse walls and have usually a limited power of apical growth; they can in their turn produce branches. The part of the endosporium opposite to the germ-tube may develope into a hyaline rhizoid penetrating into the ground, or it may develope into another germ-tube. The cell-walls of the protonemal filaments are at first colourless, but the primary axes run along the ground or penetrate into it, and then their walls assume a dark colour. The cells that are above the ground form an abundance of chlorophyll-corpuscles; the protonema therefore feeds by carbon-assimilation, and not only attains in many genera a considerable size, covering a surface of from one to several square inches with a turf of closely entangled filaments, but its duration may sometimes be said to be unlimited; in most Mosses it disappears after it has produced the leafy stems as lateral buds; but if these remain very small and are short-lived, as in the *Phascaceae, Pottia, Physcomitrium* and others, the protonema continues in vigorous life after it has produced leafy plants, and even when sporogonia have been formed on them: in such cases we have before us in organic connection at the same time all the three forms of the cycle of development. The Sphagnaceae, Andreaeaceae and Tetraphideae differ from the typical Mosses in the character of their

---

[1] W. P. Schimper, Recherches anat. et physiol. sur les Mousses, Strassburg, 1848.—Lantzius Beninga, Beitr. z. Kenntn. d. Baues d. ausgewachsenen Mooskapsel, insbesondere d. Peristoms (mit prächtigen Abbildungen) (Nova Acta Leopold. 1847).—Hofmeister, Vergl. Unters. 1851; Id. Berichten d. Kön. Sächs. Ges. d. Wiss. 1854;—Id. Entw. d. Stempels d. beblätt. Muscineen (Pringsh. Jahrb. iii).—Unger, Ueber d. anat. Bau d. Moosstammes (Sitz.-Ber. d. Kais. Akad. d. Wiss. Wien, Bd. 43, p. 497).—K. Müller, Deutschlands Moose, Halle, 1853.—Lorentz, Moosstudien, Leipzig, 1864;—Id. Grundlinien zu einer vergl. Anat. d. Laubmoose (Pringsh. Jahrb. f. wiss. Bot. vi. u. Flora 1867).—Leitgeb, Wachsthum d. Stämmchens von *Fontinalis antipyretica* u. von *Sphagnum*, and Entw. d. Antheridien ders. (Sitz.-Ber. d. K. Akad. d. Wiss. Wien, 1868 u. 1869);—Id. Das Sporogon von *Archidium* (Sitz.-Ber. d. Akad. 1879).—J. Kühn, Entwicklungsgesch. d. Andreaeaceen, Leipzig, 1870 (Mittheil. aus d. Gesammtgebiet d. Bot. von Schenk u. Lürssen, Bd. i).—Janczewski, Entw. d. Archegonien (Bot. Zeit. 1872, No. 21 ff.).—Kienitz-Gerloff, Unters. ü. d. Entw. d. Laubmooskapsel (Bot. Zeit. 1878).—[Göbel, Vergl. Entwickgs. d. Pflanzenorgane in Schenck, Handb. d. Bot. III.]

protonema and in the structure of the sporogonium. The spores of *Sphagnum*, at least when they germinate on a firm substratum, produce a flatly expanded tissue, which branches to form a crisped margin and gives rise to leafy stems. In *Andreaea* the contents of the spore divide, according to Kühn's observations, while still within the closed exosporium into four or more cells, thus forming a tissue such as is found in the spores of many Hepaticae, as *Radula* and *Frullania*[1]; ultimately one to three peripheral cells develope into filaments which spread out on the stony substratum. The branches of the protonema may then develope further in three ways; they either undergo longitudinal division in addition to the cross-divisions and so form ribbon-like irregularly branching cell-surfaces, or divisions parallel to the surface also make their appearance and the protonema comes to be of more than one layer of cells, and having thus become a body of cellular tissue grows erect and branches like a tree or shrub; a third form is where the branches of the protonema

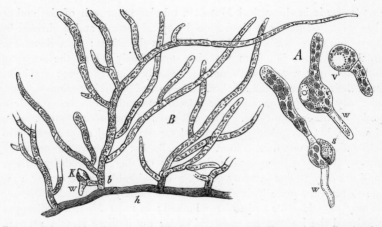

FIG. 116. *Funaria hygrometrica.* *A* germinating spore; *v* vacuole, *w* rhizoid, *s* exosporium. *B* portion of a developed protonema, about three weeks after germination; *h* a prostrate primary shoot with brown wall and obliquely transverse septa, from which proceed the ascending branches with limited growth; at *K* the rudiment of a leafy axis with rhizoid *w*. *A* magn. 550 times, *B* about 90 times.

are leaf-like flat bodies of tissue with simple definite outline. There is some resemblance between these expanded protonemata and the cell-surfaces which form assimilating organs of the protonemata of *Tetraphis* and *Tetradontium*, and which, as is shown in a figure further on, are formed at the end of long slender protonema-filaments. *Oedopodium* too and *Diphyscium* have similar protonemata[2]. Peculiar formations are found also on the felted rhizoids of tufts of *Diphyscium foliosum*, where branches arise on the protonema formed from the rhizoids, which either develope into a cell-surface, or more frequently bear a cell-surface on a stalk which in cross section is seen to be formed of several cells; their apex spreads out into a cell-surface, which is sometimes at length concave above and is placed on a stalk of

---

[1] In true Mosses (*Bartramia, Leucobryum, Mnium, Hypnum*), the first transverse wall of the filament sometimes makes its appearance inside the spore (Kühn).

[2] Bot. Jahresber. 1874, p. 312.

several cells. No young plants have been found on these formations which occur in great numbers; they certainly serve as organs of assimilation to the protonema and take root moreover in an independent manner.

The leaf-buds, which develope into moss-stems, are seldom formed on the extremity of a principal filament of the protonema, but are usually lateral shoots from it. The primary filaments of the protonema and the large rhizoids form oblique transverse septa only in the elongated apical cell, never in its segments; the septa usually lie

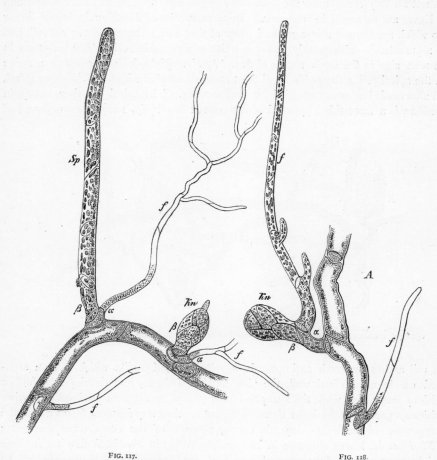

FIG. 117.   FIG. 118.

FIG. 117. Protonema formed from the stem of *Bryum argenteum* (vid. infra); *a* position of acroscopic, *β* of basiscopic cell produced by division of a lateral protuberance, *f* lateral branch with limited growth, *Sp* protonema arising from *β*, *Kn* rudiment of a stem-bud. After Müller (Thurgau).

FIG 118. Protonema formed from the stem of *Barbula ruralis*. Same lettering as in Fig. 117. After Müller (Thurgau).

in three or more directions in no regular succession, apparently without any general principle determining the orientation of the walls. Every segment can put out a protuberance behind its anterior principal septum, and the protuberance is then cut off from the segment by a wall; as it grows, a second wall with a different inclination makes its appearance in it, and thus two cells are formed, one acroscopic which may produce a branch of the protonema, the other basiscopic from which a moss-bud may be formed; one or both of them often developes rhizoid-filaments. The processes of division here mentioned recall those which take place at the growing point of the moss-stem itself, though there is no fundamental similarity between them.

The apical cell of the stem is a three-sided pyramid in every genus except *Fissidens*, where it is two-sided and produces two straight rows of alternating segments; but here too the subterranean shoots grow with a three-sided apical cell, and it is not till they come under the influence of light that the segmentation changes and the leaves are arranged in two rows. In some species of *Fissidens* the lateral shoots also which are formed above ground grow at first with a three-sided apical cell, and the segmentation subsequently passes into that of a two-sided cell. The leaves are in two rows also in the sterile shoots of *Schistotega*[1] which look like the leaf of a Fern; but the apical cell is three-sided and the arrangement of the leaves is therefore spiral, and afterwards becomes two-sided by displacement. The apical cell then, except in *Fissidens*, is a three-sided pyramid with a convex base (Fig. 122); each segment of

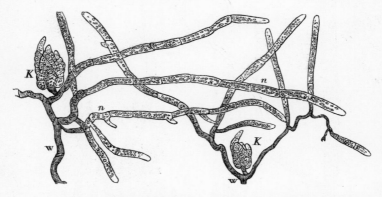

FIG. 119.   Growth of rhizoids from protonema of *Mnium hornum* with leafy buds *k*; *w, w* the rhizoids of an inverted patch, from which the protonema-filaments *n n* are shooting forth, magn. 90 times.

this cell arches outwards and upwards, forming a broad papilla which is then separated off by a periclinal wall, the 'leaf-wall' of Leitgeb, and developes by further divisions into a leaf, while the lower and inner part of the segment produces by further divisions a portion of the inner tissue of the stem. As every segment forms a leaf, the arrangement of the leaves depends on the position of the consecutive segments; in *Fissidens* the leaves alternate in two straight rows; in *Fontinalis* they are in three straight rows with a divergence of one-third, for the segments themselves are so arranged, each new primary wall that is formed being parallel to the last but three, and both belonging to one segment; on the other hand in *Polytrichum, Sphagnum, Andreaea* and others each new primary wall appears in the anodic direction of the leaf-spiral; the primary walls of a segment are not parallel, for the segments themselves, without any torsion of the stem, arise not in three straight rows, but in three lines that wind spirally one above the other round the stem, and the consecutive

[1] Leitgeb, Das Wachsthum von *Schistostega* (Mittheil. des naturw. Vereins zu Gratz, 1874).

segments and their leaves have an angle of divergence which must necessarily be greater than one-third; the phyllotaxis is in fact two-fifths, three-eighths, and so on.

The primary meristem, which passes below the growing point of the stem into permanent tissue, is usually differentiated into an inner and a peripheral mass of tissue, and the limits of the two are as a rule not sharply defined. The peripheral layers, the outermost especially, have their cell-walls usually much thickened and coloured a bright red or reddish-yellow; the cells of the inner fundamental tissue have broader cavities and thinner less highly coloured or colourless walls. The stems of some Mosses have no other differentiation than this, viz. into an outer covering of several layers of cells and a thin-walled fundamental tissue, for example, *Gymnostomum rupestre, Leucobryum glaucum, Hedwigia ciliata, Barbula aloides, Hylocomium splendens* and others, according to Lorentz; in many others, there is besides an axile bundle of very thin-walled and very narrow cells, the central bundle, as in *Grimmia, Funaria, Bartramia, Mnium, Bryum,* and many others; it is only in *Polytrichum, Atrichum,* and *Dawsonia* that the walls of the cells of the central bundle are strongly thickened. Bundles of thin-walled cells sometimes run from the base of the nerves of the leaves obliquely downwards through the tissue of the stem to the central bundle, the leaf-trace bundles of Lorentz; such are found in *Splachnum luteum, Voitia nivalis, Polytrichum,* and others. If we remember that vascular bundles of an extremely simple construction occur even in many Vascular plants, and give due weight to the resemblance between the cambiform cells of true vascular bundles and the tissue of the central bundle and the leaf-trace-bundles in the Mosses, we shall certainly be able to regard these bundles in Mosses as rudimentary vascular bundles of a very simple kind.

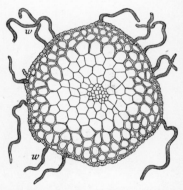

FIG. 120. Transverse section of the stem of *Bryum roseum* with rhizoids *w*, magn. 90 times.

It has been already said that the leaf begins in a broad papillose protuberance of a segment-cell of the stem, and that this protuberance is separated off by a wall; a lower, basilar part of this cell is employed to form outer layers of the tissue of the stem, while the apical part of the papilla is the apical cell of the leaf, and forms two rows of segments by dividing walls which are perpendicular to the surface of the leaf and incline to the right and left. The number of these leaf-segments, in other words the apical growth of the leaf, is limited, and when this growth ceases, the formation of tissue from these segment-cells proceeds basipetally and finally ceases at the base. The whole tissue of the leaf is sometimes, as in *Fontinalis,* a single layer of cells; but very often a nerve is formed running from the base toward the apex, that is to say a bundle of varying breadth, which divides the one-layered lamina into a right and left half, and is itself composed of several layers of cells; its cells are sometimes uniform and elongated, but different forms of tissue may appear in it, especially strands of narrow thin-walled cells, which resemble those of the central bundle of the stem, and are occasionally continued on to it as leaf-trace bundles. The outline of the leaves of Mosses varies from almost circular through broadly lanceolate to acicular;

the leaves are always sessile and with a broad insertion; they usually stand close above and beside each other; it is only on the stolons of many species, on the gemmiferous stalks of *Aulacomnion* and *Tetraphis*, and on the base of many leafy shoots that they are minute and few (cataphyllary leaves); in the neighbourhood of the sexual organs they generally form close rosettes or buds and assume peculiar forms and colours. In *Racopilum*, *Hypopterygium*, and *Cyathophorum* there are two

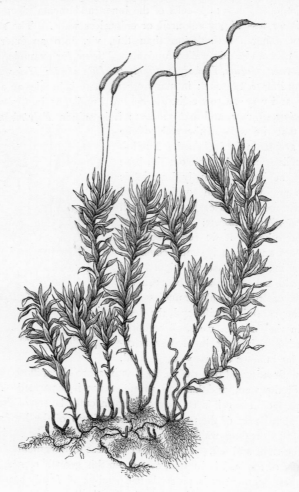

FIG. 121. Catharinea (Atrichum) undulatum with sporogonia. After Schimper.

kinds of leaves; a row of larger leaves on one side of the stem, and a row of smaller leaves on the other. Moss-leaves are not branched, and their margins are entire or toothed, seldom more deeply divided. Peculiar outgrowths occur on the inner (upper) surface of the leaves in many species, such as the articulated hairs with capitate ends of *Barbula aloides* and its allies. The lamina, which in other cases stretches right and left from the median plane, is extended in *Fissidens* in the median plane itself, and springs from an almost sheathing base. The tissue of the leaf, apart from the nerve, is for the most part uniform and composed of cells containing chlorophyll which sometimes have papillose projections on the surface; in the Sphagnaceae and Leucobryaceae it is differentiated into cells containing air, and green cells with watery contents, and these are definitely arranged in the leaf.

The *branching* of the moss-stem appears never to be dichotomous, but it is at the same time probably never axillary though not without relation to the leaves, and even where the branching is copious the lateral shoots are usually much fewer in number than the leaves. In many cases the growth of the lateral branches is distinctly limited, and this leads occasionally to the formation of branch-systems with definite forms and a resemblance to pinnate leaves, as in *Thuidium* and *Hylocomium*. When the primary axis produces sexual organs at its apex, a strong lateral shoot from beneath it often continues the vegetation, and these innovations lead to the formation of sympodia.

A not infrequent form of shoot is the *stolon* which, without leaves or with only small leaves, runs along or beneath the ground and eventually rises into the air and produces erect fully-leaved shoots. The branching is as a rule very various and closely connected with the mode of life. The morphological origin of the lateral branches has been carefully examined and excellently described by Leitgeb in *Fontinalis* and *Sphagnum*. Later researches into the same point in *Hypnum*, *Schistotega*, and *Fissidens* show that his results may be accepted as generally true. It is agreed that the mother-cell, which is at the same time the apical cell, of a branch is formed beneath the leaf and from the same segments as the leaf (Fig. 122); in *Fontinalis* the branch is formed beneath the median plane of the leaf, in *Sphagnum* beneath the kathodic half of the leaf; in consequence of the further development of the mother-shoot the lateral shoot appears later to stand in *Sphagnum* by the margin of an older leaf, and in this way we may explain the earlier statement of Mettenius, that the lateral shoots in *Neckera complanata*, *Hypnum triquetrum*, *Racomitrium canescens* and other species, are placed beside the margins of the leaves. If the shoot arises beneath the median plane of a leaf, the arrangement of the leaves in straight rows and the further growth of the stem may make it seem as though the shoot had originated above the median plane of an older leaf, that is in the axil of a leaf. Leitgeb states that articulated hairs are formed in the genera mentioned above in the axils of the leaves, or perhaps rather on the upper surface at the base of the leaves.

There is a considerable difference between the maximum and minimum of length in the leafy axes and systems of axes in the Mosses; the simple stem of the Phascaceae

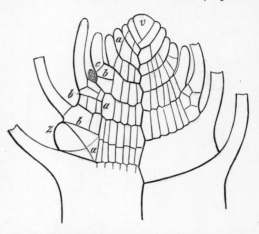

FIG. 122. Longitudinal section through the apical region of a young stem of *Fontinalis antipyretica*; *v* apical cell producing three rows of segments which are indicated by stronger lines. Each cell divides first by a wall *a* (leaf-wall) into an inner and an outer cell; the inner cell produces a portion of the inner tissue of the stem, the outer cell the cortex of the stem and a leaf. After Leitgeb.

and Buxbaumieae and others is scarcely one millimetre in height, the stem of the larger Hypneae and Polytricheae often two, three or more decimetres; it may be even longer, as in *Sphagnum*, if not in one axis yet by innovation and the formation of sympodia. The thickness of the stem does not vary so much: it may be one-tenth of a millimetre in the smallest, and scarcely more than one millimetre in the thickest stems; but its compact tissue, coloured externally, is very firm, often rigid, always very elastic, and capable of long resistance to decay.

The *rhizoids* (root-hairs) play a very important part in the economy of the Mosses. It is only in the Sphagnaceae, which differ in many other points from the rest of the class, that the rhizoids are few and small; in most of the other Mosses they appear in great numbers, at least from the base of the stem, and often clothe it all over with a thick reddish-brown felt. Morphologically there is no sharply defined line of distinction between the rhizoids and the protonema[1]; they originate as tubular outgrowths of the superficial cells of the stem, elongate by apical growth, and are divided by obliquely transverse walls; their wall is hyaline at the growing end and grows into intimate union with particles of matter in the soil; these are afterwards detached, the wall becomes thicker, and assumes the brown colour of the rhizoids that are above ground. The cells contain much protoplasm and some drops of oil, and not unfrequently chlorophyll also (Fig. 123, *B*). The rhizoids in many Mosses branch copiously beneath the soil, forming oftentimes a thick inextricable felt; they can also form a close turf in the same way above ground to serve as a soil for future generations. In *Atrichum* and other Polytrichaceae the thicker rhizoids become twisted together like the strands of a rope; their branches do the same, and only the latest and finest ramifications remain free.

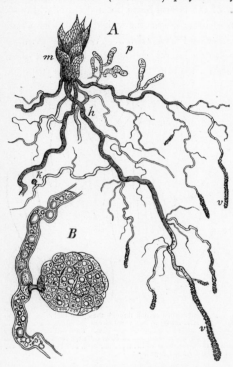

FIG. 123. A young plant of *Barbula m*, with a rhizoid *h*, the growing extremities of which *v v* are covered with particles of soil; a rhizoid running along the surface of the ground is producing branches containing chlorophyll, that is, protonema; a tuber-like bud appears on an underground capillary branch at *k*. *B* the same bud more highly magnified. *A* magn. 20 times, *B* 300 times.

The *vegetative propagation* in the Mosses is more varied and fruitful than in any other portion of the vegetable kingdom. It has this peculiarity, that the formation of a new leafy stem is always preceded by the production of a protonema, even

---

[1] The rhizoids appear to be essentially distinguished from the protonema produced from the spore only by a more sparing formation of chlorophyll, by their brown walls, and by the tendency to grow downwards; the protonema developes some of its branches as rhizoids, and the rhizoids in turn can develope single branches as protonema rich in chlorophyll and growing upwards.

when it proceeds from gemmae. The only exception is in the few cases in which leaf-buds become detached and begin to develope immediately (see too Fig. 124, *A* and *B*).

In describing the different cases, it should be noticed first of all, that both the protonema that springs from the spore and the leafy stems formed on the protonema are capable of propagation in more than one way. The original protonema is an organ of multiplication, inasmuch as its branches bear several, often very many, leafy stems one after another or simultaneously; and sometimes the single cells of the branches of the protonema assume a globular shape and separate from one another; their cell-walls grow thicker and they lie dormant for a time, as in *Funaria hygrometrica*,

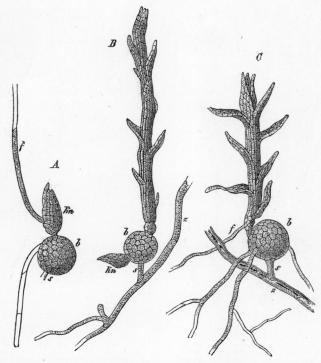

FIG. 124. Small tuberous bodies formed on the protonema produced on the stem *z* of a *Barbula*, which have germinated by the development of single superficial cells into new protonemal filaments; other cells (one in *A*, one in *C* and two in *B*) have become directly the apical cells of a moss-bud (*Kn*, *A*, *B*), and in *C* and *B* have grown already into leafy stems; *s* stalk-cell, *f* lateral branch with limited growth. After Müller (Thurgau).

and probably develope new protonema-filaments at some future period. But a secondary protonema may also be produced from every rhizoid that is kept moist and exposed to the light (Fig. 116 and Fig. 123 *p*); in the case of *Mnium*, *Bryum*, *Barbula* and other species it is sufficient to keep a turf of Moss with its felt of rhizoids turned up and in a moist condition for a few days to see hundreds of new plants formed on it in this way. Many species of *Phascum*, *Funaria*, *Pottia*, which are apparently annual, are virtually perennial by aid of their rhizoids; the plants disappear entirely from the surface of the ground after they have ripened their spores till the following autumn, when the mat of rhizoids again puts out new protonemal filaments, on which new moss-stems arise. Schimper considers the protonemal patches formed by *Polytrichum nanum* and *P. aloides* on banks in lanes, and those of *Schistostega osmundacea* in dark caves to be also growths from rhizoids. .

But rhizoids may produce leaf-buds directly, and in this respect are just like a protonema; if the buds arise on subterranean ramifications of the rhizoids (Fig. 123, *B*), they are small tuber-like bodies of microscopic size filled with reserve food-material, which often remain dormant, till, as happens occasionally, they come to the surface where they then proceed to develope; such buds are found in *Barbula*

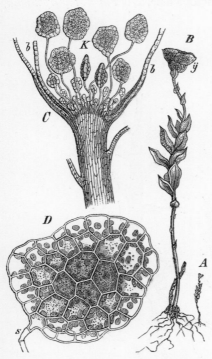

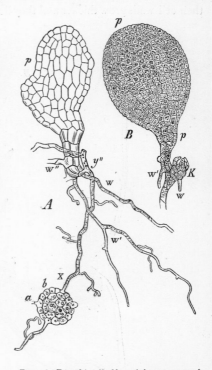

FIG. 125. *Tetraphis pellucida.* *A* a plant of the natural size forming gemmae. *B* the same magnified; *y* the cup in which the gemmae are collected. *C* longitudinal section through the summit of *B*; *b* the leaves which form the cup, *K* the gemmae in various stages of development; the older gemmae are torn from their stalks by the growth of the younger and thrust beyond the edge of the cup. *D* a mature gemma, magn. 550 times, formed of one cell-layer at the margin and several in the centre.

FIG 126. *Tetraphis pellucida.* *A* shows a gemma *b* with the stalk broken off at *a*; a marginal cell of the gemma has grown out into the protonema-filament *x y"*, from which the expansion *p* has been formed as a lateral shoot, and has sent out the rhizoids *w*, *w'*, *w"*. *B* a flat pro-embryo *p*, from the base of which a leaf-bud *K* and root-hairs *w*, *w'* have proceeded; the base of the pro-embryo often puts out a number of new flat pro-embryos before it proceeds to form a leaf-bud. *A* magn. 100 times.

muralis, *Grimmia pulvinata*, *Funaria hygrometrica*, *Trichostomum rigidum*, *Atrichum*. But aerial rhizoids also can produce both a protonema with chlorophyll in their cells and leaf-buds directly; and Schimper adduces the remarkable fact, that annual male plants are produced in this way in the perennial patches of the female plants of *Dicranum undulatum*, and effect their fertilisation.

Even the leaves of many Mosses produce a protonema, simply by their cells growing out into tubes which then become segmented, as happens in *Orthotrichum Lyellii* and *O. obtusifolium*; in *O. phyllanthum* penicillate tufts of club-shaped protonemal growths with short cells are formed on the tips of the leaves; the like occurs in *Grimmia trichophylla, Syrrhopodon,* and *Calymperes.* In *Oncophorus glaucus* a thick felt of tangled protonema-filaments appears on the fertile summits of the plants, prevents their further growth, and eventually produces instead new patches of young plants. In *Buxbaumia,* especially *B. aphylla,* the marginal cells of the leaves form a protonema that grows round them and round the stem. Lastly, leaves, as those of *Funaria hygrometrica,* when cut from the stem and kept moist will put out a protonema.

The cells even of parts of the sporogonium can grow out into a protonema,

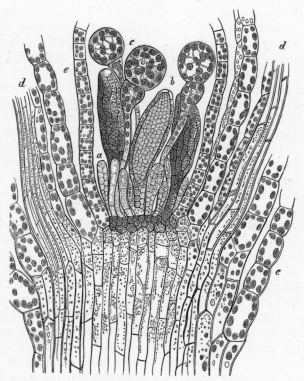

FIG. 127. Longitudinal section of the summit of a very small male plant of *Funaria hygrometrica;* *a* a young, *b* an almost mature antheridium in longitudinal section, *c* paraphyses, *d* leaves divided through the midrib, *e* through the lamina. Magn. 300 times.

as Pringsheim and Stahl have shown[1]. If the seta of detached capsules is placed on moist sand, protonema-filaments will grow from its inner cells and new plants will be formed on the filaments, and the wall of the capsule has equally the power of putting out protonema-filaments from its cells. In *Conomitrium julianum* a young plant often grows from the inner surface of the calyptra (vid. inf.) with the intervention of a short piece of protonema.

---

[1] Pringsheim, Ueber vegetative Sprossung von Moosfrüchten (Monatsbericht d. Akad. d. Wiss. in Berlin, 1876).—Stahl, Ueber künstl. hervorgerufene Protonemabildung an d. Sporog. d. Laubmoose (Bot. Zeit. 1876, p. 689).

Gemmae, which, like those of the Marchantieae, are stalked cellular bodies pointed at both ends or lenticular in shape, occur in *Aulacomnion androgynum*[1] on the summit of a leafless prolongation of the leafy stem (*pseudopodium*), and in *Tetraphis pellucida* enclosed in a delicate cup formed of several leaves, out of which they afterwards fall (Fig. 125, 126). Some species of *Bryum* have gemmae in the axils of the leaves; *Conomitrium julianum* and *Cinclidotus aquaticus* are multiplied, according to Schimper, by leafy branches which become detached from the stems.

The *sexual organs* of the Mosses are usually to be found in numbers at the extremity of a leafy axis, inclosed in an envelope of leaves often of peculiar form, and mixed with *paraphyses*. Such an assemblage of organs terminates the growth of a primary axis (Acrocarpous Mosses) or it appears at the extremity of an axis of the second or third order (Pleurocarpous Mosses), in which case the growth of the primary axis is unlimited. Antheridia and archegonia may be found together in the same group, and then the arrangement is *bisexual*, or one kind only constitutes the group, and in that case the plant which bears them is either *monoecious* or *dioecious*; the male organs are sometimes on smaller plants of shorter duration, as in *Funaria hygrometrica*, *Dicranum undulatum*, and others. Groups which contain both organs, and those with female organs only, resemble one another in outward appearance, while the male groups have a habit of their own. When antheridia and archegonia are both present in the same group, they stand either side by side on the top of the stem in the centre of the envelope (*perichaetium*), or apart from one another in two groups or separated by special leaves of the envelope; in the latter case the antheridia are arranged in a spiral line in the axils of the leaves round the group of archegonia in the centre. The envelope in the female and mixed groups is in the form of an elongated and all but closed bud, formed by several turns of the leaf-spirals; the leaves are like the foliage-leaves and smaller towards the centre, but grow all the more vigorously after fertilisation. The male envelope (*perigonium*) is formed of broader stouter leaves and has three forms; like the female it usually has the form of a bud, but is shorter and thicker, with the leaves often of a red colour and diminishing in size towards the outside; these groups are always lateral. Those on the other hand which take the form of small heads are always terminal on a stouter shoot, and are globular in form with leaves broad and sheathing at the base, thinner and recurved above, growing smaller towards the inside and leaving an open space in the centre of the envelope for the antheridia; they are sometimes also borne on a naked stalk, a prolongation of the stem, as in *Splachnum* and *Tayloria*. Lastly, in the male disk-shaped clusters the leaves of the envelope are quite unlike the foliage-leaves, being broader and shorter, horizontally expanded above, delicate and of a pale green, orange or purple colour, and always smaller as they approach the centre; the antheridia are in their axils (*Mnium, Polytrichum, Pogonatum, Dawsonia*). The paraphyses stand between or beside the sexual organs; in the female inflorescences they are always articulated filaments, in the male either filamentous or spathulate and composed at the upper end of several rows of cells.

The *antheridium* when fully formed is a stalked sac with a wall of one layer

---

[1] [Bower, Note on the gemmae of *Aulacomnion palustre*, Schwaegr. (Journ. Linn. Soc. 1884).]

of cells; the cells contain chlorophyll, but when mature they are coloured yellow or red. In the Sphagnaceae and *Buxbaumia* the antheridia are nearly spherical, in all other Mosses elongated club-shaped. In the Sphagnaceae they open in the same way as in the Hepaticae; in the other subdivisions by a tissue at the apex, through which the spermatozoids issue forth in their cysts as a thick mucilage; they are at first still imbedded in a mucilage, but this dissolves in the water and the spermatozoids slip out of their cysts and swim away.

According to Leitgeb's researches the point of origin of the antheridium is not in all cases the same; in *Sphagnum* the mother-cell of the antheridium originates exactly at the spot where a shoot is usually formed, that is, from the segment of the axis of the antheridial shoot below the kathodic half of the leaf. In *Fontinalis* and indeed in most other Mosses the point of origin varies within the same group of sexual organs; the first antheridium is the direct prolongation of the axis of the shoot and arises from its apical cell; those that follow it are developed from its last normal segments, and agree with the leaves in respec to their origin and position; those formed last come from superficial cells, and are not confined to any definite point. The mother-cell of the antheridium of *Fontinalis* is like an apical cell which forms two alternating rows of segments; in the case of the oldest and terminal antheridium therefore the apical cell of the shoot ceases to form three rows of segments and now only forms two, a proceeding mentioned above as occurring in the shoots of *Fissidens,* and which will be described below in connection with the apical cell of the stem of the embryo of *Salvinia natans.* The segments are first divided by anticlinal and periclinal walls in such a manner that the transverse section, which includes two segments, shows four outer and two inner cells; the former by further division gives rise to the one-layered wall; the latter to the small-celled tissue which produces the spermatozoids. The mode of proceeding is similar in *Andreaea,* where the primary mother-cell of the antheridium makes its appearance as a papilla which is cut off by a transverse wall; the lower cell produces a cushion-like foot; the upper is divided once more by a transverse wall into a lower cell from which proceeds the tissue of the stalk, and an upper which gives rise to the body of the antheridium; the mode of formation is in fact the same as in *Fontinalis.* In *Sphagnum* the long stalk is formed by transverse divisions of the growing papilla which is the rudiment of the antheridium; then the segments divide cross-wise, and the terminal cell swells out and is divided by oblique walls of somewhat irregular position; in this way a mass of cellular tissue is formed, which subsequently consists of a wall of one layer of cells and an inner very small-celled tissue which produces the spermatozoids.

FIG. 128. *Funaria hygrometrica.* *A* antheridium opening; *a* the spermatozoids. *B* a spermatozoid more highly magnified; *b* in the cyst, *c* a free spermatozoid of *Polytrichum.* *A* magn. 350 times, *B* more highly magnified, *c* magn. 800 times.

The *archegonium* when fully formed consists of a thick and rather long stalk, a roundish-ovoid *venter* resting on the stalk, and above it a long slender *neck* usually twisted on its axis. The wall of the venter, which is formed of two layers of cells before fertilisation, is continuous upwards with the wall of the neck, which is of one layer of cells in four to six rows (Fig. 130). The venter and the neck inclose an axile row of cells; the lowermost of these, which is ovoid in shape and lies in the venter, produces the oosphere out of its protoplasm by rejuvenescence; the cells above it are converted into mucilage before fertilisation; the mucilage forces asunder the four uppermost cells of the neck, the lid-cells, and opens the neck-canal which affords the spermatozoids the path to reach the oosphere; Fig. 130 shows the row of canal-cells when disorganisation is beginning and when the lid-cells of the neck are still closed.

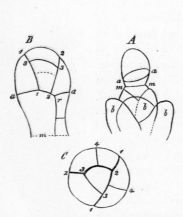

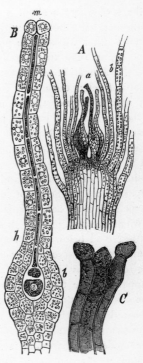

FIG. 129. First stage of development of the archegonium of *Andreaea*, after Kühn. *A* terminal archegonium formed from the apical cell of the shoot. *B* after the formation of the lid-cells. *C* transverse section of the young ventral portion; *bb* in *A* the youngest leaves.

FIG 130. *Funaria hygrometrica.* *A* longitudinal section of the summit of a weak female plant; *a* archegonia, *b* leaves. *B* an archegonium; *b* venter with the central cell, *h* the neck, *m* orifice still closed; the cells of the axile row are beginning to be converted into mucilage (specimen kept three days in glycerine). *C* the orifice of the neck of an archegonium after fertilisation with its cell-walls coloured dark red. *A* magn. 100, *B* 500 times.

With respect to the point of origin of the archegonium, it should be observed that the first archegonium of *Sphagnum* arises from the apical cell of the female shoot, and this is the case too in the typical Mosses. Where there are several archegonia, those that follow the first are formed from the younger segments of the apical cell. In the Mosses as in the Hepaticae the archegonium originates in a superficial cell of the vegetative cone. The cell arches outwards and the projection thus formed is divided by a transverse wall into a lower cell which answers to the stalk in the Hepaticae and into an upper cell, in which two oblique walls inclining in opposite directions are then formed, as in the antheridium. These two oblique cells subsequently give rise to the tissue of the venter and of the stalk, which is much larger here than in the Hepaticae (Fig. 129 *B*, 130 *B*). The upper cell then shows the same divisions as in the Hepaticae; the wall of the venter and the central cell are formed in the same way as in them (p. 150); but there is a striking difference in the further development of the neck. In the Hepaticae the first transverse division of the inner cell produces an upper cell which represents at once the lid of the archegonium; but in the Mosses this cell developes as an apical cell and by successive longitudinal divisions produces tiers of cells, each of which consists of three outer cells enclosing one inner canal-cell, but otherwise behaves in exactly the same way as the single tier of neck-cells in the Hepaticae. A long neck, consisting of six exterior rows of cells and their canal-cells, is thus produced and subsequently becomes twisted, passing below into the wall of the venter formed of two layers of cells, or in *Sphagnum* of four. The central cell, earlier formed here than in the Hepaticae, divides by a transverse wall into an upper cell, the *ventral canal-cell*, and a lower cell, the protoplasm of which contracts and forms the *oosphere* (Fig. 130, *B*). The conversion of the whole of the canal-cells into mucilage and the opening of the neck follow in the same way as in the Hepaticae.

The *sporogonium* (*sporophore, sporophyte*), the product of fertilisation in the oosphere, attains its full development in *Sphagnum* almost entirely within the venter of the archegonium, which grows vigorously as the oospore developes, and is transformed into the *calyptra*; in the rest of the Mosses the calyptra is torn away at its base from the vaginula by the elongation of the sporogonium usually some time before the development of the capsule, and, except in the case of *Archidium* and its allies, is carried up as a cap on the sporogonium; its apex continues for a long time to be surmounted by the neck of the archegonium, the walls of which become a deep reddish brown. The sporogonium in all the Mosses consists of a stalk (*seta*) and the receptacle of the spores (*capsule, theca* or *urn*); in *Sphagnum, Andreaea* and *Archidium* the seta is very short, in almost all others long or very long, and it always has its base sunk in the tissue of the stem, which by luxuriant growth after fertilisation forms a sheath-like wall, the *vaginula*, beneath and beside the archegonium. Archegonia with unfertilised oospheres are often to be seen on its exterior slope, for one only of a group usually, or only the first that has its oosphere fertilised, perfects an embryo. The capsule in all Mosses has its wall composed of several layers of cells with a distinct epidermis, on which stomata are sometimes developed. The whole of the inner tissue is never employed in the production of spores, though it is eventually displaced by the spores in *Archidium*; a large part of the central tissue constitutes the so-called *columella*, and round it the mother-cells of the spores are formed. But the inner structure of the mature capsule, and especially the arrangements for the dispersion of the spores, are so different in the chief divisions of the Mosses, that it is better to study them under the separate divisions, where they will supply characteristic marks for distinguishing the natural groups. The orientation also and further development of the capsule is not the same in the different groups, and the differences are connected on one hand with the growth of the embryo, on the other with the mode of formation and with the form and origin of the archesporium (*vid. infra*).

As regards the succession of cell-divisions in the embryo, *Sphagnum* [1] differs from

---

[1] Besides Schimper's account, see Waldner in Bot. Zeit. 1876, p. 595.

all other Mosses, inasmuch as its embryo has not a two-sided apical cell, but is divided by anticlinal walls which are transverse to the longitudinal axis, and these are few in number. The oospore divides first by a wall at right angles to the axis of the archegonium into a lower and an upper cell; the lower cell undergoes only a few more divisions, the upper developes into the sporogonium; a number of transverse walls with corresponding longitudinal walls are first formed, and this is followed by intercalary growth. The rest of the Mosses which have been examined on this point have, as was said, a different arrangement of the cells in the embryo. After one or more transverse walls have made their appearance in the oospore, an oblique wall is formed in the uppermost cell and then another in the opposite direction, and in this way a two-sided apical cell is produced which gives off a number of segments. These segments are disposed as transverse disks (Figs. 131, 132). The transverse section of a young embryo shows therefore two cells with the form of half cylinders, separated by the segment-wall $s\,s$. Then a second wall appears at right angles to $s\,s$, so that there are now four quadrants of a cylinder (Fig. 131, B), but these are not formed in *Archidium*. Next an anticlinal wall is formed in each quadrant, and to each a periclinal is added (Fig. 131, B). There are now the following cells to be seen in the transverse section of the embryo; four inner cells forming a figure which approximates to a square and eight outer peripheral cells. The archesporium and the columella proceed from the former in the Bryineae and Phascaceae, and the wall from the latter. The square of cells, the fundamental square, may be called the *endothecium*, the peripheral cells the *amphithecium*. It is obvious that the separation into amphithecium and endothecium might have been

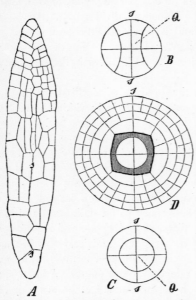

FIG. 131. '*A* embryo of *Ceratoaon purpureus* in optical longitudinal section. *B, C, D* transverse sections through the capsular portion of young sporogonia, *B* and *C* of *Ceratodon purpureus*, *D* of *Funaria hygrometrica*; *Q* the fundamental square, *s* primary wall of the embryo. After Kienitz-Gerloff, *B, C, D* diagrammatically represented.

effected in a more simple manner, namely by the appearance of a periclinal line in each quadrant, which would have separated four inner cells forming the endothecium from four outer, the amphithecium (Fig. 131, *C*); and this in fact does happen in *Funaria hygrometrica* and *Ephemerum*, and we see once more by this case how little weight is to be attached to the succession of cell-divisions; the same result can be obtained by more than one sequence of cell-divisions, and it is the result that we are concerned with more than with the process. A periclinal wall, arising in each quadrant in the endothecium, separates an outer cell-layer, the *archesporium* (Fig. 131, *D*, the shaded part), from the central part, the columella, which suffers further division and becomes a mass of cells, while the archesporium becomes itself the spore-producing tissue without further change, or divides and forms a mass of spore-mother-cells. The amphithecium undergoes other periclinal and radial divisions before the archesporium is differentiated from the endothecium (Fig. 131, *D*) and thus comes to be composed of several layers of cells. An intercellular space is formed in it, which lies between an outer wall of several layers of cells and some cell-layers, usually two in number, next the archesporium (Fig. 142, the longitudinal section); the latter constitute the outer spore-sac, the inner spore-sac being the outermost layer of cells in the columella abutting upon the archesporium (Fig. 144, *B*). The form of the archesporium in the Bryineae and Phascaceae is that of a cask open at both ends, and the columella therefore passes through it; it is otherwise in *Andreaea*, where the archesporium is a curved layer of cells concave downwards, and the columella does not pass through it; the same is the case in *Sphagnum* (Fig. 139). *Archidium*, one of the Phascaceae, shows no differentiation of an archesporium; a few cells of the endothecium, of which neither the number (1–7) nor the position are fixed, become mother-cells of the spores, in each of which four spores are formed by tetrahedral division. This is obviously the lowest form among the Mosses, and its development agrees with the development of the embryo in the Hepaticae; there is here no true separation of the cells of the endothecium into sterile and fertile cells, since under certain circumstances every cell of the endothecium may become a spore-mother-cell. Finally, in *Sphagnum* the archesporium has the same form as in *Andreaea*, but it is formed out of the amphithecium. It still seems doubtful whether the origin from amphithecium or endothecium is an important difference or not; it may however be added to the many other characteristics which separate the Sphagnaceae from their allies. We subjoin a table of the various types of development in the sporogonium of the Mosses according to Leitgeb's views [1].

A. The archesporium is formed from the amphithecium :

1. **Type of Sphagnaceae.** The endothecium forms the columella only, which does not pass through the archesporium, but is covered by it above.

B. The archesporium is formed from the endothecium; all the sporogonia have a two-sided apical cell :

2. **Type of Archidium.** Fertile and sterile cells mingled together in the endothecium. The spore-sac is separated from the wall of the capsule by a bell-shaped intercellular space. There is no columella [2].

3. **Type of the Andreaeaceae.** The endothecium is differentiated into archesporium and columella; the columella does not pass through the archesporium. The innermost layer in the amphithecium becomes the spore-sac, which however is not separated from the rest of the parietal tissue by an intercellular space.

4. **Type of the Bryineae.** Differentiation as in type 3, but the columella passes through the spore-sac, which is separated from the wall of the capsule by an intercellular space in the form of a hollow cylinder.

Such are the changes which take place in the part of the sporogonium which

---

[1] Das Sporogon von *Archidium* (Sitz. d. Wiener Akad. LXXX, Bd. 1. Abthl. Novemberheft 1879, p. 11 of the reprint).

[2] In *Ephemerum* also, one of the Phascaceae, the half-ripe spores lie perfectly free inside the capsule; but the mode of proceeding is different; the columella is formed in exactly the same way as in the Bryineae, but is subsequently displaced by the spore-mother-cells, as they increase in size, and disappears. See N. J. C. Müller, Die Entwicklungsgesch. d. Kapsel von *Ephemerum* (Pringsheim's Jahrb. f. wiss. Bot. VI. p. 237).

forms the capsule.   Recurring briefly to the external form of the embryo, we remark
that it is usually a fusiform body, the lower extremity of which has no growth in
length, but swells in *Sphagnum* and *Archidium*, as it commonly does in the Hepaticae.

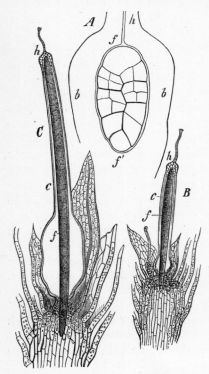

The capsule originates in a globular or ovoid
or, as is often the case, an unsymmetrical
swelling below the apex of the sporogonium
which is now ceasing its growth ; this
swelling does not make its appearance in the
typical Mosses till after the elongation of the
fusiform or cylindrical sporogonium and the
elevation of the calyptra.   Four spores are
produced in each mother-cell ; the preparation for their formation takes place at the
same time all through the same capsule.   The
ripe spores are roundish or tetrahedral with a
delicate finely granulated exosporium, of a
yellowish or brownish or purple colour ; besides protoplasm they contain chlorophyll
and oil ; their diameter in *Archidium*, where
there are only sixteen in a capsule, is about
$\frac{1}{5}$ of a millimetre, in the highly developed
Dawsonia, according to Schimper, scarcely
$\frac{1}{200}$ of a millimetre.   They in many cases
preserve their vitality for a long time if kept
dry ; in the moist state they germinate in a
few days, in *Sphagnum* often not till after
two or three months.

FIG. 132. *Funaria hygrometrica. A* rudiment of the
sporogonium *f f'* in the venter *b b* of the archegonium, in
optical longitudinal section, *h* neck of the archegonium.
B, C more advanced stages in the development of the
sporogonium *f* and of the calyptra *c. A* magn. 500, *B, C,*
about 40 times.

The time necessary for the full development of the sporogonium varies much in the
different species, but in most of them it is
very long as compared with the small size
of the organ in question.   The Pottieae
produce sexual organs in summer and ripen their spores in winter ; those of *Funaria*,
which constantly have sexual organs and have sporogonia at all times of the year in
all states of development, require probably from one to two months to mature their
capsules ; *Phascum cuspidatum* grows in autumn from a perennial underground
protonema and ripens its spores some weeks before winter.   The bog Hypneae,
on the other hand, *H. giganteum, H. cordifolium, H. cuspidatum, H. nitens* and their
allies, form their sexual organs in August and September and ripen their spores in
June of the next year, often taking ten months to perfect their sporogonia ; *Hypnum
cupressiforme* has sexual organs and ripe spores at the same time in autumn, and
therefore takes a year to complete its course, and the same is the case with many
species of *Bryum* and *Philonotis*, and with many *Polytricha* which form their sexual
organs in May and June [1].

---

[1] See Bot. Zeit. 1869, p. 344.

The class of Mosses may be distributed into four groups, not however of equal value :

      1. **Sphagnaceae.**

      2. **Andreaeaceae.**

      3. **Phascaceae.**

      4. **Bryineae,** or true Mosses.

Of the above groups the first has only one genus, the second and third a few genera only, the fourth includes all the remaining very numerous genera. The first two groups have many points of resemblance to the Hepaticae, and this is the case with some genera even of the true Mosses ; there is a certain amount of likeness between the lowest forms of all the groups, but not between the highest ; hence the Mosses form four divergent series, the third and fourth of which may be united into one.

The **Sphagnaceae**[1] contain only one genus, *Sphagnum.* If the spores germinate in water, they produce a branching protonema, on which the leafy buds appear as direct lateral outgrowths (Fig. 133, *C*) ; on a solid substratum the short protonema first forms

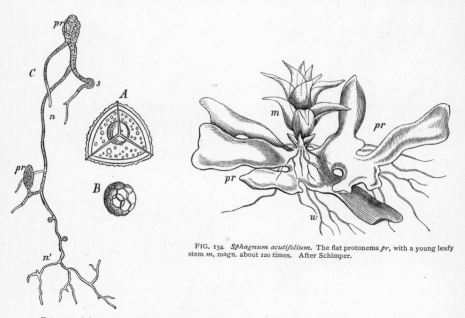

FIG. 134. *Sphagnum acutifolium.* The flat protonema *pr*, with a young leafy stem *m*, magn. about 120 times. After Schimper.

FIG. 133. *Sphagnum acutifolium.* *A* a large spore seen from the apex. *B* a small spore. *C* a protonema *n n'* formed from the spore ; at *pr* the rudiments of young plants. After Schimper, magnified.

a branching flat expansion on which the leaf-buds arise (Fig. 134), as is the case in *Tetraphis.* The leafy stems produce some slender rhizoids only when they are young, and never form a protonema in the copious manner of the true Mosses. The stem in a more advanced stage gives rise to a lateral branch beside every fourth leaf and each branch as soon as formed branches again repeatedly, and in this way tufts of branches are produced arranged regularly and forming a small head at the summit of the stem but further removed from one another lower down. The branches develope in different ways ; one branch, in growth and character like the stem, appears

---

[1] W. P. Schimper, Versuch einer Entwicklungsgesch. d. Torfmoose, Stuttgart, 1858.

beneath its summit every year after the ripening of the fruit and grows beside it, so that the stem gets a false bifurcation every year : as the plant dies away slowly from below upwards these innovations are in time separated from it and become independent plants. But some branches of each tuft turn downwards, become long and slender and sharp-pointed, and lie along the stem forming a closely applied envelope ; others again turn outwards. The leaves, which are sessile on stem and branch with a broad insertion and a divergence of two-fifths, are ligulate or pointed above, and with the exception of the first on the young stem are composed of two kinds of cells with a regular arrangement. The leaf consists necessarily at first of homogeneous tissue, but as it developes the cells of the nerveless lamina are differentiated into large broad cells of somewhat elongate rhombic form, and into narrow tubular cells which run between them and bound them, and form a network among them-

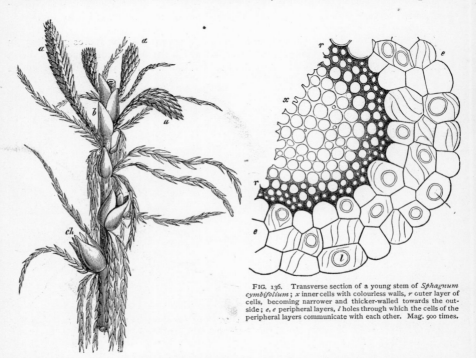

FIG. 136. Transverse section of a young stem of *Sphagnum cymbifolium* ; *x* inner cells with colourless walls, *r* outer layer of cells, becoming narrower and thicker-walled towards the outside ; *e, e* peripheral layers, *l* holes through which the cells of the peripheral layers communicate with each other. Mag. 900 times.

FIG. 135. *Sphagnum acutifolium.* Portion of a stem beneath the summit ; *a* the antheridial branches, *b* leaves of the primary stem, *ch* perichaetial branches with old but still closed sporogonia, magn. 5 or 6 times. After Schimper.

selves ; they have the appearance of being squeezed in between the others. The large cells lose their contents and therefore appear to be colourless, while their walls show narrow spiral bands with irregular and distant coils and large pits with a thickened margin ; the absorption of the enclosed membrane converts these pits into holes, which are usually circular in form. The narrow tubular cells between them retain their contents and produce chlorophyll-corpuscles, and are therefore the nutrient tissue of the leaf, though the whole surface they expose is smaller than that of the colourless tissue (Fig. 138). The axes are composed of three layers of tissue ; the innermost is an axile cylinder of thin-walled colourless parenchymatous cells ; this is surrounded by a layer of thick-walled pitted prosenchymatous cells with firm, perhaps lignified, walls of a brown colour ; lastly, the cortical tissue consists of from one to four layers of very broad thin-walled empty cells, which in *Sphägnum cymbifolium* have spiral threads and round holes like those of the leaves (Fig. 136). These colourless cells both in the leaves and in the cortex of the stem and branches serve as a capillary apparatus to the plant to draw up the water of the bogs in which it lives and convey it to its upper parts; hence it is that plants of *Sphagnum,* which are continually growing taller, are filled with water like sponges up to their summits even when their beds are raised high above the surface of the water.

The archegonia and antheridia are formed chiefly but not exclusively in autumn and winter, and on branches of the tuft before mentioned at the summit of the primary stem, while they still belong to it and are therefore still near the summit. Antheridia and archegonia are always on different branches, and sometimes on different plants, and in the latter case the male and female plants grow in large separate patches. If owing to dry weather the primary stem does not elongate during the development of the

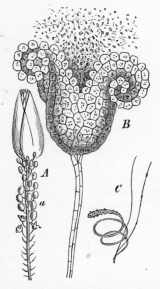

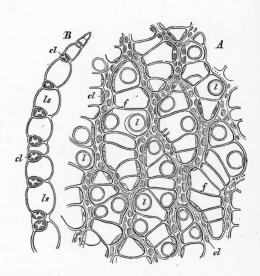

FIG. 137. *Sphagnum acutifolium.* *A* a male branch with some of the leaves removed in order to show the antheridia *a.* *B* an antheridium opened and very highly magnified. *C* a mature motile spermatozoid. After Schimper.

FIG. 138. *Sphagnum acutifolium.* *A* a portion of the surface of a leaf seen from above; *cl* tube-like cells containing chlorophyll, *f* the spiral bands, *l* the holes in the large empty cells. *B* transverse section of a leaf; *cl* the cells containing chlorophyll, *ls* the large empty cells.

sporogonia, the latter are subsequently found still on the terminal tuft; but if there is a sufficient supply of water and consequent growth in length of the stem, the fertile branches are separated from one another and appear lower down on the stem, and the sporogonia and the older antheridial branches are thus moved further from the summit, though they were close to it when the sexual organs were ripe. The branches that bear the antheridia are distinguished externally by their crowded leaves overlapping one another like tiles, and forming beautiful orthostichies or spiral parastichies; their colour is often yellow or a bright red, and especially a dark green, and they are thus easily recognised (Fig. 135, *a, a*). The antheridia are placed beside the leaves on the developed shoot; as they are never terminal but occur one by the side of each leaf in the middle part of the shoot only, the latter may continue to grow at the summit, and pass into an ordinary flagellate branch. The Sphagnaceae resemble many of the Jungermannieae in this position of the antheridia, and still more in their roundish form and long stalk; their mode of opening too recalls the Hepaticae rather than the Mosses (Fig. 137). The archegonia arise on the blunt end of the female branch, the upper leaves of which form a bud-like envelope ; the young perichaetial leaves too are inclosed within this envelope at the period of fertilisation, and afterwards grow to a larger size.   The archegonia are exactly like those of the rest of the Mosses ; the oospheres of several archegonia in a perichaetium are usually fertilised, but only one matures its sporogonium. The sporogonium comes to maturity inside the perichaetium, and it is not till then that the summit of the branch elongates and becomes a long naked stalk, and raises the sporogonium in its calyptra high above the perichaetium ; this organ, which is called the *pseudopodium*, must not be confounded with the seta of other Mosses.   Fig. 139, *B*

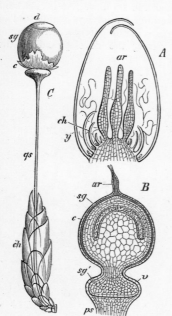

gives a longitudinal section of a nearly mature sporogonium inside the calyptra.   Its lower portion is developed into a thick foot sunk in the top of the pseudopodium, where it forms the *vaginula*. A hemispherical layer of cells beneath the apex of the globular capsule is used to form the spore-mother-cells ; the part of the inner tissue beneath this layer forms a low nearly hemispherical column, which is called the columella, though it differs from the columella of the true Mosses in not reaching to the apex of the capsule.   The spores are formed from the mother-cells in the same way as in the true Mosses ; but in addition to the ordinary large spores there are found other smaller spores in special smaller sporogonia, which owe their origin to further division of the mother-cells, and are probably only deformities (Fig. 133, *B*).   The capsule opens by removal of a lid, the uppermost segment of the sphere, which is sometimes marked by its stronger convexity.   The calyptra, which surrounds the growing sporogonium like a delicate envelope, is ruptured irregularly.

FIG. 139. *Sphagnum acutifolium*. *A* longitudinal section of a bud-like envelope enclosing female sexual organs ; *ar* archegonium, *ch* perichaetial leaves still young, *y* the last leaves of the bud-like envelope. *B* longitudinal section of the sporogonium : *sg* the broad foot of which *sg'* is fixed in the vaginula *v*, while the capsular part is surrounded by the calyptra *c*, *ar* the neck of the archegonium on the calyptra, *ps* the pseudopodium. *C Sphagnum squarrosum* : the ripe sporogonium *sg* with the lid *d*, and the ruptured calyptra *c*, *qs* the elongated pseudopodium growing out from the perichaetium *ch*. After Schimper.

2. The **Andreaeaceae**[1] are small caespitose Mosses with crowded leaves and numerous branches: the shortly-stalked capsule, like that of *Sphagnum*, is raised on a leafless pseudopodium above the perichaetium.   The rather long and pointed capsule carries up the calyptra like a pointed cap, as in the true Mosses, while the short seta remains concealed in the vaginula.   The tissue of the young sporogonium is differentiated into a wall of several layers of cells surrounding the single layer of the spore-mother-cells without any intervening cavity, and a central tissue, the columella ; the spore-producing layer has the shape of a bell with its mouth downwards, as in the Sphagnaceae, and the columella terminates beneath it.   The mature capsule opens not by a lid, but by four lateral longitudinal slits, dividing the capsule into four valves attached at top and bottom, which close in damp weather and open in dry.

3. The **Phascaceae** are little Mosses, whose short stem continues attached to the protonema until the spores are ripe ; they may be regarded as the lowest forms of the next group, the genus *Phascum* being intermediate between the two; the distinguishing mark of the group is that the capsule does not open by a lid, but releases the spores only when disorganised by decay.   While the genera *Phascum* and *Ephemerum*

---

[1] Kühn, Zur Entwicklungsgesch. d. Andreaeaceen, Leipzig, 1876 (Mittheilungen aus d. Gesammtgebiet d. Bot. von Schenk u. Lürssen, I Bd.).

exhibit the same internal differentiation of the capsule as the true Mosses, though in a rather more simple form, the genus *Archidium*, as was stated above, differs considerably from them. The stalk of the sporogonium swells, as in *Sphagnum*, and even recalls the Hepaticae; the roundish capsule bursts the calyptra at the

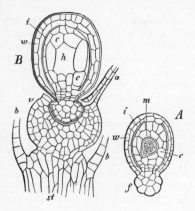

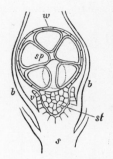

FIG. 140. *Archidium phascoides. A* longitudinal section of the young sporogonium showing the mother-cell *m* of the spores; *f* foot of the sporogonium, *w* wall of the capsule, *i* the intercellular space, *c* the cells round the mother-cell. *B* longitudinal section through the young sporogonium with the calyptra and vaginula; *h* the cavity from which the mother-cell of the spores has fallen, *v* the vaginula, *st* the stem, *b* the leaves, *a* the neck of the archegonium. After Hofmeister, magn. 200 times.

FIG. 141. *Archidium phascoides.* Longitudinal section through a nearly mature sporogonium; *w* wall of the sporogonium, *sp* the spores, *v* the vaginula, *b* leaves of the stem *s*. After Hofmeister, magn. 100 times.

side, and does not carry it up with it as a cap. Other points of difference have been already mentioned.

4. In the **Bryineae** or true Mosses the sporogonium has always a stalk, the *seta*, and

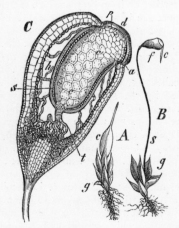

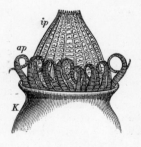

FIG. 142. *Funaria hygrometrica. A* a young leafy stem *g*, with the calyptra *c. B* a plant *g* with the almost mature sporogonium, of which *s* is the seta, *f* the capsular portion, *c* the calyptra. *C* longitudinal section of the capsular portion dividing it into two symmetrical halves; *d* the lid, *a* the annulus, *p* the peristome, *c*, *c'* the columella, *h* air-space, *s* archesporium.

FIG. 143. The mouth of the theca *K* of *Fontinalis antipyretica.* Outer peristome *ap*, inner peristome *ip*. After Schimper, magn. 50 times.

usually a long one; the seta is cylindrical, bluntly pointed at the lower end, and firmly fixed in the vaginula; the capsule opens by throwing off its upper portion as a lid, the *operculum*, which either separates simply and smoothly from the lower part of the capsule, or an annular layer of epidermal cells, the *annulus*, is thrown off by the swelling of its inner walls and the lid is thus separated from the capsule. The margin of the capsule in the majority of species is seen after the removal of the operculum to be occupied by one or two rows of appendages of very regular and delicate structure; the single appendages are known as *teeth* and *cilia*, and together they constitute the *peristome*; where there is no peristome the capsule is said to be *gymnostomous*. The capsule is at first a solid mass of homogeneous tissue; the differentiation of its interior begins with the formation of an intercellular space of annular form, which now separates the wall of the capsule composed of several layers

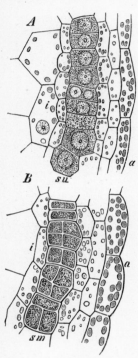

FIG. 144. *Funaria hygrometrica.* Transverse section through the spore-sac; *sm* in *A* the archesporium, *sm* in *B* the mother-cells of the spores not yet isolated, *a* outer, *i* inner side of the spore-sac; magn. 500 times.

of cells from the central tissue, but the tissue of the wall continues to be connected with the tissue of the base and apex of the columella; the intercellular space is traversed by rows of cells stretching from the wall to the inner tissue, which are very like protonemal or algal filaments, but are merely a product of the differentiation of the tissue of the capsule, and, like the inner cell-layers of the wall, contain chlorophyll-corpuscles. The outer layer of the wall constitutes a highly characteristic and strongly cuticularised epidermis. The third or fourth layer of cells of the inner tissue, which is separated therefore from the annular air-cavity by two or three cell-layers forming the *spore-sac*, is the *archesporium*; its cells are at first densely filled with protoplasm in which is a large central nucleus, and are united with the surrounding tissue without interstices like cells in a parenchyma. The spore-mother-cells are the product of the division of the cells of the archesporium, which now separate from one another by the deliquescence of their cell-walls and float free in the fluid which fills the interior of the spore-sac, till by further division they produce the spores. The term outer spore-sac is applied to the layers of cells which divide the large air-cavity from the spore-mother-cells, while the layers which bound them on the side next the axis (Fig. 147, *i*) form the inner spore-sac; the cells of both contain chlorophyll-corpuscles which form starch. The inner large-celled tissue without chlorophyll, which is thus surrounded by the spore-sac, is the *columella*. The spore-sac is ruptured by the removal of the operculum, the columella dries up, and in the Polytrichaceae there remains a layer of cells spreading horizontally over the space covered by the operculum; this layer, which is attached to the points of the teeth and stretched upon them over the mouth of the capsule, is the *epiphragm*.

The origin of the peristome requires to be examined somewhat more in detail. In genera which, like *Gymnostomum*, have no peristome, the parenchyma which fills the inside of the operculum is homogeneous and thin-walled; when the capsule is mature it dries up and shrinks into the bottom of the operculum which essentially is formed only of the epidermis, or it remains attached as a thickening to the summit of the columella and projects above the mouth of the capsule, or it forms a diaphragm covering the mouth of the capsule after the lid has fallen away, as in *Hymenostomum*. *Tetraphis* forms a transition to the genera which have true peristomes; in *Tetraphis* the firm epidermis of the upper conical portion of the capsule falls off as an operculum, while the tissue contained in it, the two outer layers of which are thick-walled, splits cross-wise into four lobes, which are called by systematists a peristome, though their origin and structure are quite different to the origin and structure of the true peristome of other genera. In these, with the exception of the Polytrichaceae, neither the teeth nor the cilia consist of cellular tissue, but only of thickened hardened portions of the walls of a layer of cells which is

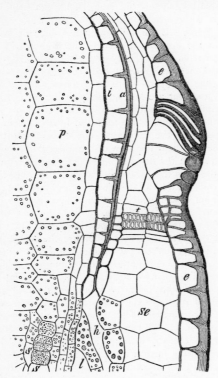

FIG. 145. *Funaria hygrometrica*. Portion of longitudina section of an immature theca. Highly magnified, see the text.

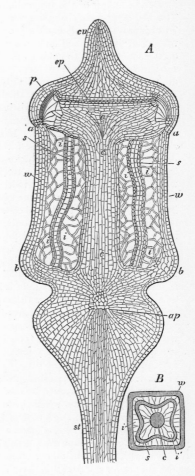

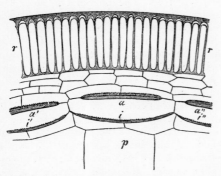

FIG. 146. *Funaria hygrometrica*. Portion of transverse section through the lid (see the text). Highly magnified.

FIG. 147. *Polytrichum piliforme*. *A* Longitu-dinal section of a theca after Lantzius-Beninga. *B* transverse section magn. about 5 times; *w* wall of the theca, *cu* the operculum, *c c* the columella, *p* the peristome, *ep* the epiphragm, *a a* the annulus, *i i* the air-spaces traversed by alga-like cellular filaments, *s* spore-sac containing the primary mother cells, *st* the seta, the upper part of which forms the apophysis *ap*. A magn. 15 times.

separated by a few layers of thin-walled cells from the epidermis which forms the lid; these cells and the thin parts of the layer which supplies the teeth are torn up and dis-appear when the operculum is thrown off, but the thickened portions of the walls remain behind.

An example will make this plain. Fig. 145 represents a portion of a longitudinal section dividing the capsule of *Funaria hygrometrica* into two symmetrical halves ; *e e* is the reddish-brown epidermis strongly thickened on the outside, and corresponds to *a* in Fig. 142, *C* ; at the spot where the epidermis bulges out its cells have a peculiar conformation and constitute the annulus ; *se* is the tissue between the epidermis of the capsule and the air-cavity, the large-celled tissue *p* is the continuation of the columella inside the hollow of the operculum, *s* marks the uppermost cells of the archesporium. The cell-layer which supplies the peristome rises immediately above the air-cavity *h*. The outer walls of this layer *a* are much thickened and of a beautiful red colour, and the thickening is continued for some way along the transverse walls ; the longitudinal walls on the side towards the axis *i* are also coloured, but are less strongly thickened.   Fig. 146 shows a part of a transverse section through the basal portion of the operculum ; *rr* are the epidermal cells immediately under the annulus, which form the lower margin of the operculum, *a* and *i* the thickened parts of the cell-layer concentric with the operculum, which form the peristome.   A section near the apex of the operculum would show not the broad thickening masses *i*, *i'*, *i''* but the middle portion of the inner wall, only more strongly thickened.   If we suppose then that when the capsule is mature the annulus and operculum fall off, that the cells *p* and those between *a* and *e* (Fig. 145) disappear, and that the unthickened portions of cell-wall between *a, a', a''* and *i, i', i''* in Fig. 146 are destroyed, the thick red portions of wall will be all that remains, and these form sixteen pairs of tooth-like lobes pointed at the apex and rising in two concentric circles above the margin of the capsule ; the outer lobes are the teeth, the inner the cilia.   The thickened cells at *t* in Fig. 145 connect the base of the teeth and the margin of the capsule.   The number of the teeth and cilia varies with the number of cells in the layer that forms the peristome as seen in the transverse section, and according as either one or two places are thickened in each of these cells, but it is always a multiple of four, and usually sixteen or thirty-two.   In many cases there is no thickening at *i* and then the peristome is single and formed of the outer row of teeth only ; the thickening at *a* is often much stronger than it is in *Funaria,* and the teeth consequently are thicker. The thickened portions of wall may also unite laterally with one another either wholly or in part ; in that case the parts of the peristome form a membrane either above or below, the teeth appear to be split above, and the *endostome* is composed of a lattice-work of longitudinal or transverse bars instead of cilia (Fig. 143), or there is some similar variation from the ordinary form ; the possible variations are many, but they are not difficult to follow when the principle is clearly perceived.   The inner and the outer faces of the teeth of the peristome are hygroscopic ; hence as the moisture of the air varies they curve inwards or outwards, or they twine round each other, as in *Barbula.*

The Polytrichaceae, which include the largest and most highly developed Mosses, differ in several points from the other groups in respect to the structure of their capsule. The teeth of the peristome are not merely separate pieces of membrane but are formed of bundles of thickened fibre-cells ; these bundles are in shape like a horse-shoe and are placed with the horns of the crescent upwards, the horns of every two bundles uniting to form one of thirty-two or sixty-four teeth.   A layer of cells *ep* (Fig. 147) connects the points of the teeth together and remains, when the operculum has fallen off and the adjacent cells have dried up, as an epiphragm stretched across the mouth of the capsule. The spore-sac in *Polytrichum piliferum* and other species is separated from the columel a by an air-cavity which, like the outer air-cavity, is traversed by conferva-like rows of cells. The seta is in most species swollen beneath the capsule ; this enlargement of the seta, which is known as the *apophysis,* recurs in a somewhat different form in the genus *Splachnum,* where it sometimes appears as a broad flat transverse disk.

THIRD GROUP.

THE VASCULAR CRYPTOGAMS.

UNDER this name[1] are included the Ferns (in the narrower sense including Salviniaceae and Marsileaceae), Ophioglosseae and Marattiaceae, Equisetaceae (in the wider sense of the term), Lycopodiaceae, Psilotaceae, Selaginelleae and Isoeteae. In this group as in the Muscineae the process of development divides into two generations which are very distinctly separated morphologically and physiologically ; first of all the spore gives rise to a *sexual generation* ; from the oospore of its archegonium proceeds a new plant, an *asexual generation* which forms no sexual organs, but numerous sporangia. In the true Ferns and Equisetaceae the spores are all alike ; the Salviniaceae and Marsileaceae (Rhizocarpae) subdivisions of the Ferns, the Selaginelleae also and the Isoeteae, have two kinds of spores, large and small, *macrospores* and *microspores*.

The First or **SEXUAL GENERATION** (*oophore, oophyte*), produced from the spore, is never anything but a thallus ; it never reaches, as in the more highly developed Mosses, to the stage of a differentiation into stem and leaf, but continues small and delicate, and its life comes to an end when the development of the second generation begins, unless it happens to be rendered perennial by adventitious shoots, as in *Gymnogramme leptophylla* ; to outward appearance, therefore, it is merely a forerunner of the after-development of the plant, a kind of transition from the germinating spore to the variously differentiated second generation ; hence the name *prothallium* for this first generation in the Vascular Cryptogams, the generation which produces sexual organs.

In the true Ferns, Equisetaceae and others, the prothallium resembles the thallus of the lowest Hepaticae ; these prothallia in some cases continue to grow for a long time, contain an abundance of chlorophyll, and produce numerous rhizoids ; thus they depend on themselves for their subsistence, and when arrived at sufficient strength they produce antheridia and archegonia usually in large numbers. In the Vascular Cryptogams, which have two kinds of spores and are therefore termed *Heterosporous* Vascular Cryptogams, namely the subdivisions of Ferns above-mentioned, and the Selaginelleae and Isoeteae, the separation of the sexes is previously indicated by the two kinds of spores, for the macrospores are female, and develope a very small

---

[1] The Vascular Cryptogams are also known as Pteridophytes.

prothallium which produces only archegonia and sometimes only a single one. The female prothallium of the Rhizocarpae is a small appendage of the large spore; it is formed inside it, emerges from it afterwards, and is fed by it. In the Selaginelleae and Isoeteae, on the contrary, the prothallium is entirely developed inside the spore, which it fills with its tissue, and only the archegonia come forth to the light through fissures in the outer coat of the spore. The microspores on the other hand are male, their very rudimentary prothallium producing only antheridia.

The *archegonia* of the Vascular Cryptogams, like those of the Muscineae, are bodies of cellular tissue, consisting of a *venter* which contains the *oosphere*, and a *neck* which is usually short and formed of four longitudinal rows of cells; there is this difference between the two groups, that in the Vascular Cryptogams the tissue of the wall of the venter is formed from the tissue of the prothallium itself, and the venter therefore is enclosed in the tissue of the oophyte, the neck only projecting above it. The archegonium originates in a superficial cell of the prothallium, which divides by a tangential (periclinal) wall into an inner and an outer cell; the latter by longitudinal divisions which cross one another and subsequent transverse divisions produces the four rows of cells of the shorter or longer neck; a projection from the inner cell pushes in between the cells of the neck (Fig. 151), and is then divided off and is the *neck-canal-cell*, while from the larger cell below it (Janczewski's central cell) another small portion is cut off to form the *ventral canal-cell*. In this way an axile row of three cells is formed from the original inner cell, and the lowest of the three forms the oosphere; the two neck-cells are converted into mucilage as in the Muscineae. The mucilage thus formed in the neck at length swells considerably, forces open the four apical cells of the neck, and is ejected; thus an open passage is formed leading from the outside to the oosphere, and the ejected mucilage appears to play an important part in the conducting of the swarming spermatozoids to the orifice of the neck. Fertilisation is in all cases brought about by the agency of water, which causes the antheridia and archegonia to open, and serves as a vehicle for the spermatozoids; these have been directly observed in the different classes to make their way to the oosphere and into it, and to coalesce with its protoplasm. The *spermatozoids* are spirally coiled threads usually with numerous delicate cilia on the anterior coils; they are formed in exactly the same way as in the Characeae and the Muscineae, that is, they come chiefly from the nucleus of the mother-cell, which becomes thicker at its circumference and splits into the coiled thread of the spermatozoid. There is left after this process a vesicle of protoplasm containing starch-grains, which adheres to a posterior coil of the spermatozoid and is carried along with it, but is swept off before the spermatozoid enters the archegonium. The mother-cells of the spermatozoids (*spermatocytes*) are formed in *antheridia*, which are roundish bodies rising free from out of the prothallium in the true Ferns and Equisetaceae, but sunk in it in the Ophioglosseae, Marattiaceae and *Lycopodium*; among the heterosporous forms *Salvinia* has a very simple antheridium which emerges from the microspore, while the Marsiliaceae and Selaginelleae produce their antheridia inside the microspore, after a tissue consisting of a few cells, or of one cell only in *Marsilia*, has been formed in it, which we must regard as a rudimentary prothallium.

The second or **SEXUAL GENERATION** (*sporophore, sporophyte*), which produces the spores, proceeds from the oospore in the archegonium. The first divisions of the embryo indicate the rudiments of the first root, the first leaf and the apex of the stem, while a lateral outgrowth of the tissue of the embryo, the so-called *foot*, is formed at the same time at the bottom of the venter of the archegonium, and draws the first nutriment for the embryo from the prothallium. The venter of the archegonium grows vigorously at first in all except perhaps in the Selaginelleae, and still incloses the embryo, but the latter at length emerges from it, leaving the foot for a time still in it to serve as an organ of suction. In this we have an indubitable analogy with the formation of the calyptra in the Muscineae. But while the sporophyte in the Muscineae is never more than a mere appendage of the oophyte and looks to a certain extent like its fruit, the corresponding generation in the Vascular Cryptogams developes into a tall, highly organised, independent plant, which becomes detached from the prothallium and supports itself at an early age. It is this sporophyte which is usually termed absolutely a Fern or an Equisetum, &c., and consists in all cases of a leafy stem, which usually produces a number of true roots, though these may occasionally be wanting, as in many of the Hymenophylleae, in *Psilotum* and in *Salvinia*. In many instances, especially in the true Ferns, Equisetaceae and the fossil Lycopodiaceae, the sporophyte reaches a large size and the term of its duration is unlimited; only a few species are annual, as *Salvinia*, or very small and with the habit of a Moss, as *Azolla* and some Selaginelleae.

The *leaves* are either simple or repeatedly branched as in the Filicineae, but there is not the variety in the forms of the leaves on the same plant, the result of metamorphosis, which is found in the Phanerogams.

The *roots* usually arise in acropetal succession on the stem, or in many Ferns on the petioles, and their branching is either monopodial or dichotomous; they are uniform in character, and the first root never assumes the significance of a tap-root, as happens in many Phanerogams; nor do the lateral roots spring from the pericambium of the primary root, as in Phanerogams, but from the innermost layer of the cortex.

The differentiation of the *systems of tissue* appears for the first time in great perfection in this group of plants; dermal, fundamental and fascicular tissues are always clearly discriminated and their elements assume a great variety of forms. The vascular bundles are closed; their phloem, the sieve-tube portion, usually surrounds the xylem, the wood-portion of each bundle, as a sheath.

The *branching of the stem* is different in the different divisions; it may be monopodial, or decidedly dichotomous, or with a tendency to dichotomy; axillary branching such as that of the Phanerogams probably does not occur.

The *sporangia* usually arise on ordinary or on peculiarly metamorphosed leaves; Schleiden's term *sporophyll* may be adopted for a fertile leaf, a leaf which bears sporangia. In *Selaginella* the sporangia are produced from the growing-point of the stem above the axil of a leaf; in *Psilotum* they are sunk in the extremity of branchlets of a peculiar form. A sporangium either originates in a single superficial cell, as in the Ferns in the narrower use of the term including the Salviniaceae and the Marsiliaceae, or a group of cells takes part in the formation of the sporangium, as in all the other divisions. In both cases the tissue which produces the spores proceeds, in the Vascular Cryptogams as in the Muscineae, from an *archesporium*, which is either a single cell, or a cell-row, or a cell-layer, and makes its appearance at a very early stage in the development of the sporangium.   The mature sporangia are roundish capsules of very simple structure and small size.   A sporangium when half developed consists of three parts : 1. an inner (*sporogenous*) mass of tissue which afterwards becomes the mother-cells of the spores (*sporocytes*) ; 2. one or more layers of tabular cells, the tapetal cells or *tapetum*, which form an investment round the sporogenous cells ; 3. the *wall* of the sporangium formed of one or more cell-layers.

From what has now been said it is plain that the sporangia of the Vascular Cryptogams are physiologically but not morphologically equivalent to the sporogonium of the Mosses ; the latter represents by itself the whole sporophyte of the moss-plant, while the sporangium of the Vascular Cryptogams is a relatively small outgrowth usually of a leaf of the sporophyte which consists of stem, leaf and root.

The way in which the spores are formed in the mother-cells agrees with the corresponding process in the Muscineae ; the mother-cells separate from the previously connected tissue and divide into four spores, a bipartition of the nucleus preceding the division into four in each cell.   The distinction of macrospores and microspores in the Salviniaceae, Marsiliaceae, Selaginelleae, and Isoeteae does not make its appearance till after the division of the mother-cell into four parts, the parent-cells of both kinds of spores being exactly alike up to that time.

It was Hofmeister who in the year 1851 first showed that the sporogonium of the mosses, the moss-fruit as it is usually called, is by its position in the alternation of generations the equivalent of the entire plant with leaves and roots, which bears the spores in the Vascular Cryptogams ; he it was also who showed how the Selaginelleae and Isoeteae are connected with the Coniferae, and these two discoveries have proved to be among the most important and the most fruitful in results that have ever been made in the domain of botanical morphology and classification.

Other enquirers, who will be noticed hereafter, have added so much by their many exhaustive researches to our knowledge of the Vascular Cryptogams that they are at the present time one of the most thoroughly explored groups in the vegetable kingdom.   These investigations into the development of the sexual organs, of the embryo, of the sporangia, of the spores and the germination of the spores have brought to light so great a community of characters, the result of community of descent, that it is now possible to submit the whole to comparative treatment.   But this presupposes a more general knowledge of these plants, and we will therefore give an account of the facts bearing on their relation to other groups when describing the several families [1].

CLASSIFICATION OF THE VASCULAR CRYPTOGAMS.   The connection between the different sections of the Vascular Cryptogams still requires elucidation on many points of detail.   The division of them into Isosporous, or those with only one kind of spore, and Heterosporous, or those with macrospores and microspores, has proved to be artificial, since isosporous and heterosporous forms are found within the same cycle of alliance; in the Ferns, for example, the Polypodiaceae and others are isosporous, the Salviniaceae heterosporous, and in the same way the isosporous Lycopodiaceae are nearly related to the heterosporous Selaginelleae.   The Ferns in the narrower sense, that is, excluding the Marattiaceae and Ophioglosseae, but including

---

[1] Vergleichende Untersuchungen, p. 139.

the Salviniaceae and their allies the Marsiliaceae, stand out as a distinct group. The Ophioglosseae and Marattiaceae are closely related. The Equisetaceae are a rather isolated group, and the remainder of the Vascular Cryptogams may be included in the group of Lycopodineae. Peculiar groups, known only in the fossil state, of which the better known are the Calamites, Annularieae and Asterophyllites, may be classed with the Equisetaceae, under the name Equisetineae; other groups are the Sphenophylleae, Lepidodendreae and Sigillarieae, the first of which are only heterosporous Lycopodiaceae, while the mode of formation of the sporangia, and consequently the systematic position of the Sigillarieae, is not yet certainly known, but they are probably nearest to the Gymnosperms.

As regards the mutual relations of these groups, the Ophioglosseae and Marattiaceae, brought together by Sachs under the name of Stipulatae, are connected by their vegetative structure with the Ferns, but are distinguished from them by the formation of the sporangia, in which they agree with the Equisetaceae and Lycopodiaceae, and thus furnish a transition to the rest of the Vascular Cryptogams. The Vascular Cryptogams may be all brought under two divisions founded on the mode of formation of the sporangia; the first is that of the Leptosporangiatae and includes the forms in which the sporangia proceed from one cell, and the unicellular archesporium is cut off by a peculiar geometrical series of divisions; the second is that of the Eusporangiatae, in which the sporangium is formed from a group of cells, and the archesporium in the simplest case is the terminal cell beneath the epidermis (hypodermal) of an axile row of cells; to this division belong the Ophioglosseae and Marattiaceae (Stipulatae), the Equisetineae and the Lycopodineae [1].

The arrangement given below is essentially the same as that adopted by Sachs in his fourth edition; for the connection between the several groups the reader is referred to what has just been said on the subject of the sporangia. Accordingly the Vascular Cryptogams are distributed in four classes; the Filicineae in the more extensive sense (including the eusporangiate Ferns, namely the Marattiaceae and Ophioglosseae), the Equisetineae, the Sphenophylleae, which are only fossil, and the Lycopodineae.

I. FILICINEAE.

The greater number have spores of one kind only, which produce monoecious prothallia, having the power of independent vegetation; only the Salviniaceae and Marsiliaceae have female macrospores and male microspores, forming rudimentary prothallia which always continue attached to the spores. The sporophyte is an unbranched or sparingly branched stem, with a copious growth of large usually branched leaves and usually numerous roots. The sporangia are formed in large numbers on ordinary or on metamorphosed leaves, and are usually collected together in small groups (*sori*); in the Ophioglosseae they are more or less sunk in the tissue of the sporophyll, and in them and in the Marattiaceae originate in a *group* of epidermal cells, not in a single one as in the other Filicineae. The archesporium is a *single cell*. Accordingly there are two divisions of the Filicineae, the Leptosporangiate and the

---

[1] Goebel, Beitr. zur Entwicklungsgesch. d. Sporangien (Bot. Zeit. 1880, 1881), explains the homologies with regard to the formation of the sporangia between the different groups of the Vascular Cryptogams, and of these with the Phanerogams.

Eusporangiate, the latter with only homosporous, the former with homosporous and heterosporous forms. Stem and root have an apical cell, which in the stem forms two or three rows of segments, in the root always three rows. The vascular bundles are usually very strongly developed, the central xylem, consisting chiefly of tracheides with scalariform thickenings, being usually surrounded with soft phloem.

A. **Leptosporangiate Filicineae**, or Ferns in the more restricted use of the word. The sporangia are formed from a single epidermal cell, and have a peculiarly shaped, usually tetrahedral archesporium.

1. Homosporous Filicineae. The spores are of one kind only, and produce monoecious prothallia which live an independent life. The sporophyte is either an erect unbranched stem, or not erect and then usually more or less dorsiventral and sparingly branched. The leaves, which are exstipulate and when young are rolled inwards (*circinate*), produce on their laminae, which are not at all or very little metamorphosed, very numerous sporangia usually grouped together in sori and covered with *indusia*; the sporangia arise from single cells of the epidermis, contain a central unicellular archesporium, from which usually sixteen spore-mother-cells are formed, and open by means of an *annulus*. Stem and roots have an apical cell; the fundamental tissue tends to form a brown-walled schlerenchyma, which serves chiefly to strengthen the bundle-sheaths.

       Families.   1. Hymenophyllaceae.
                      2. Cyatheaceae.
                      3. Polypodiaceae.
                      4. Gleicheniaceae.
                      5. Schizaeaceae.
                      6. Osmundaceae.

2. Heterosporous Filicineae (Rhizocarpae or Hydropteridae). Female macrospores and male microspores are produced in sporangia of two kinds; the macrospores produce small prothallia which do not separate from the spore, the microspores give rise to the mother-cells of the spermatozoids on very rudimentary prothallia. The sporophyte is a dorsiventral, horizontal, regularly branched stem, with two or more rows of leaves on the dorsal and roots on the ventral face, and with branches on the lateral faces; *Salvinia* only has no roots. The sporangia are formed in sporocarps with one or more compartments, which are metamorphosed leaves or segments of leaves; they originate in single superficial cells of placentas, which bear a sorus in each compartment; the sixteen spore-mother-cells in a sporangium are produced by a central one-celled archesporium, as in the homosporous Ferns. The microspores are many in a sporangium (4×16); the macrosporangium matures only one large spore. The stem grows with a two-sided or three-sided apical cell, the root with a three-sided cell.

       Families.   1. Salviniaceae.
                      2. Marsiliaceae.

The connection between the heterosporous and the homosporous Filicineae has been touched upon above in the description of the former.

B. **Eusporangiate Filicineae.** The sporangia proceed from a group of epidermal cells, and the archesporium is the hypodermal terminal cell of the axile row of cells of the rudimentary sporangium. The antheridia are immersed in the tissue of the prothallium. The species are all homosporous. The sporophyte is a simple, usually unbranched, often tuber-like, erect or obliquely growing stem, with leaves in spirals one close above another; in most Ophioglosseae one only unfolds each year. The leaves are very large in proportion to the stem and usually much branched, and in the Marattiaceae they have commonly at their bases thick fleshy excrescences, which may be compared to the stipules of the higher plants but which are wanting in some species, as in *Danaea*, and in the Ophioglosseae. The sporangia arise on the under side of ordinary foliage leaves, or on sporophylls which form spikes or panicles; they are either sunk in the tissue of the sporophyll, as in *Ophioglossum*, or project above it as spherical capsules that are sometimes amalgamated with one another.

II. EQUISETINEAE.

A. HOMOSPOROUS EQUISETINEAE: Equisetaceae (and Calamites). The spores are of one kind and produce prothallia which live independently and are usually dioecious, the female being larger, the males smaller. The sporophyte is a copiously branched stem, with distinctly articulated internodes and with proportionately small and sheathing whorls of leaves; the branches also are in whorls, and spring from the nodes of the stem in strict acropetal succession; a root which branches monopodially may be given off beneath each branch. The sporangia are formed as pluricellular protuberances on peltate leaves (sporophylls) which form a terminal inflorescence (spike); there are from five to ten sporangia on each leaf; the mother-cells of the spores are produced from a unicellular hypodermal archesporium. Stem and root have a large apical cell which gives off three rows of segments. The vascular bundles of the stem are disposed in a circle; like the bundles of Monocotyledons they contain little xylem. The axile bundle of the root has no pericambium.

B. HETEROSPOROUS EQUISETINEAE (fossil forms only). Macrospores and microspores have been found, but their germination is of course unknown. The sporophyte is a copiously branched stem divided into very distinct internodes, with whorls of linear or lanceolate leaves which are not united into a sheath. The branches are either in whorls like the leaves, or in two rows (*Annularia*). The inflorescences [1] are composed of alternating whorls of fertile and sterile leaves.

    1. Annularieae.
    2. Asterophylliteae.

III. SPHENOPHYLLEAE.

Known only in the fossil state, and heterosporous; the sporangia are seated on the base or in the axil of the leaf, as in Lycopodiaceae. The leaves with frequently bifurcate nerves radiating from a common base are in whorls on the nodes of the stem, in the centre of which is a triarch bundle of tracheids.

IV. LYCOPODINEAE.

The prothallia spring either from spores of one kind and are independent and monoecious, or from spores of two kinds, macrospores and microspores, and then the

---

[1] Whether these really belong to the Annularieae or Asterophylliteae is not certainly ascertained.

female prothallium remains inclosed in the spore till the moment of fertilisation. The sporophyte is a stem which is either simple or repeatedly branched, and has roots; the leaves are always perfectly simple, proportionally small but very numerous, and traversed by one simple vascular bundle. The branching of the stem and roots is monopodial or nearly so, but sometimes distinctly dichotomous. The sporangia appear singly on the upper side of the base of a leaf, or in the axil or on the stem above the axil of a leaf, or they are sunk in the tissue of the extremity of a short branch, as in the Psilotaceae; they are formed from groups of cells. The archesporium is formed as in other Eusporangiatae.

A. **Lycopodiaceae.**

1. Homosporous Lycopodiaceae. The spores are of one kind and produce monoecious prothallia with an independent life. Stem and roots branch dichotomously in planes which cross one another; neither have an apical cell; the leaves have no ligule. Vascular bundle of the stem have several xylem-strands which are separated by phloem and surrounded by it.

To these belong the Lycopodieae, with one genus, and the Phylloglosseae, also composed of one small Australian genus, *Phylloglossum*, distinguished by its peculiar formation of tubers; the sporangia are, as in *Lycopodium*, on the base of bracts, on a spike which is otherwise leafless.

2. Heterosporous Lycopodiaceae; fossil only; *Lepidodendron*.

B. **Psilotaceae.** Only one kind of spores known; the germination not known; the sporangia are sunk in the extremities of short lateral branchlets with two leaves; there are notrue roots, but instead of them subterranean, creeping stems. Two living genera, *Psilotum* and *Tmesipteris*.

C. **Ligulatae.** Spores of two kinds, macrospores and microspores; a female prothallium of some size is produced inside the macrospore, and is only sufficiently exposed through a fissure in the coat of the spore for the archegonia to be laid bare; the microspores also form a rudimentary prothallium which completely fills them, and the mother-cells of the spermatozoids are produced from certain of its cells. The habit of the sporophyte varies much in the two families; the leaves have always a ligule above their base, and below this is the sporangium, which matures either a number of microspores or four or more macrospores.

Families. 1. Selaginelleae.

2. Isoeteae.

(The groups which have been brought together under the name of Ligulatae have scarcely anything in common but the presence of a ligule, and it would be better perhaps to make separate divisions of them.)

I. FILICINEAE.

The character common to all the plants which are here united under the name of the Filicineae, and which distinguishes them from the Equisetineae and Lycopodineae, is the abundance and perfection displayed by their leaves; these are always large in proportion to the stem, and more highly developed in form and structure than the leaves of the other divisions of the Vascular Cryptogams. In the Equisetineae and Lycopodineae the entire external form is determined by the structure and branching of the stem, and the most important physiological duties are committed to it; but in the Filicineae the stem is essentially only the bearer of the leaves and roots, and grows very slowly in length, in many species not even forming distinct internodes; the leaves, on the contrary, are distinguished by vigorous apical growth lasting a long, sometimes an unlimited time. The stem too in the Filicineae shows little tendency to branch; in entire sections it is always simple, and the formation of new buds is not unfrequently effected by the agency of the leaves, in which the tendency to branch is expressed in every variety of pinnation, dichotomous division and formation of lobes. In the Equisetineae and Lycopodineae the stem usually takes part in the formation of the inflorescence; this is always in the Equisetineae and generally in the Lycopodineae a terminal sporangiferous spike which puts an end to the longitudinal growth of the branch on which it is formed; such an arrangement never occurs in the Filicineae; the work of propagation is assigned to the leaves only, the stem takes no part in it at all. The number of sporangia formed on a leaf of the Filicineae corresponds with its size and is usually very large, whereas the small sporophylls of the Equisetineae bear but few sporangia; those of the Lycopodineae only one. The mode of formation of the sporangia on the leaves of the Filicineae varies considerably; in the Ophioglosseae they are sunk in the tissue of the sporophyll; in the Polypodiaceae they are capsules with long stalks. Among the heterosporous forms the Salviniaceae come very near to the Polypodiaceae, Cyatheaceae, and their allies in respect of their 'fructification,' while more complicated processes take place in the Marsiliaceae, where the sporangia are inside capsules of peculiar construction termed spore-fruits or sporocarps.

A. LEPTOSPORANGIATE FILICINEAE (FERNS)[1].

1. HOMOSPOROUS FILICINEAE.

The first or *sexual generation* (*oophore, oophyte*), the prothallium, is a thallus which is rich in chlorophyll and self-supporting; its development offers many striking points of resemblance to that of the thallus of the simpler Hepaticae, and

---

[1] H. v. Mohl, Ueber d. Bau d. Stammes d. Baumfarne (Vermischte Schriften, p. 108).—Hofmeister, Ueber Entwickl. u. Bau d. Vegetationsorgane d. Farne (Abh. d. kön. Sächs. Ges. d. Wiss. 1857, V).—Id., Ueber d. Verzweigung der Farne (Jahrb. f. wiss. Bot. III, 278).—Mettenius, Filices horti bot. Lipsiensis, Leipzig, 1856;—Id., Ueber d. Hymenophyllaceen (Abh. d. kön. Sächs. Ges. d. Wiss. 1864, VII).—Wigand, Bot. Unters., Braunschweig, 1854.—Dippel, Ueber d. Bau d. Fibrovasal-stränge, in dem Ber. deutscher Naturf. u. Aerzte in Giessen, 1865, p. 142.—Rees, Entw. d. Poly-podiaceensporangiums (Jahrb. f. wiss. Bot. V. 5, 1869).—Strasburger, Befruchtung d. Farnkräuter (Jahrb. f. wiss. Bot. VII, p. 390, 1869).—Kny, Ueber Entw. d. Prothalliums u. d. Geschlechtsorgane in d. Sitzungsber. d. Ges. naturf. Freunde in Berlin, 1868 am 21 Januar. u. 17 Nov.;—Id., Ueber Bau u. Entw. d. Farnantheridiums (Monatsber. d. kön. Akad. d. Wiss. Berlin, 1869, Mai);—Id., Beitr. z. Entwicklungsgesch. d. Farnkräuter (Jahrb. f. wiss. Bot. VII, p. 1).—Russow, Vergleichende Unters., Petersburg, 1872.—Janczewski, Ueber d. Archegonien (Bot. Zeit. 1872, p. 418).—Kny, Die Entw. d. Parkeriaceen (Nova Acta Ac. Leop. Car., Bd. 37).—Prantl, Unters. z. Morphol. d. Gefässkryptogamen, Heft 1 u. 2 (Hymenophylleen u. Schizaeaceen).—[Rabenhorst, Kryptog. Fl. Die Gefässkryptog. v. Ch. Luerssen, 1885. Goebel, Vergl. Entwgs. d. Pflanzenorg. in Schenk's Handb. d. Bot. III.] Other treatises are given further on. Sadebeck has recently published an exhaustive account of the Vascular Cryptogams in Schenk's Handbuch d. Botanik, I Bd.

even to that of the protonema in some Mosses. The prothallium produces simple, tubular, unsegmented rhizoids, and ultimately antheridia and archegonia. Its development and duration may occupy a considerable space of time, especially if the oospheres are not fertilised.

If the conditions, especially of moisture and warmth, are favourable, the spores begin to germinate in a few days after they are sown. Most fern-spores retain their vitality a long time; the spores only of the Osmundaceae and Hymenophylleae, which contain chlorophyll as soon as they are fully formed, soon lose the power of germination. Other fern-spores require a longer or shorter period of rest before they germinate. The admission of water causes the contents of the spore to swell and burst the cuticularised exosporium, which is usually provided with ridges, tubercles, spikes or granulations along its edges, if there are any; in bilateral spores the exosporium opens by a longitudinal fissure. In suitable objects, such as the germinating spores of the Gleicheniaceae, it may be seen that when preparing for germination the contents of the spore become invested with a new cellulose-membrane [1], and this proceeding appears to be quite general. Then the newly formed membrane protrudes in the form of a papilla from out of the opening in the wall of the spore, chlorophyll and other substances make their appearance in the protoplasm, and very soon a second small protuberance forms the rudiment of the first rhizoid, which like the first cell of the prothallium is cut off from the contents of the spore by a partition-wall. The Polypodiaceae may be chosen to supply examples of the further development of the prothallium. The papilla which has been described as projecting beyond the wall of the spore first of all developes into a row of cells, the terminal cell in which divides by transverse septa, a proceeding less frequently observed in the other cells of the row. Then the cells towards the end of the row grow broader and the terminal cells also divide longitudinally, and thus the cell-filament becomes a cell-surface of a spathulate form. At its extremity is either a two-sided apical cell, as in *Metzgeria*, or a group of small marginal cells. But the apical cell, when present at first, is not long maintained; a periclinal transverse wall is soon formed in it, and this is followed by a number of longitudinal walls in the cells nearest the apex, so that in this case also the apex comes to be occupied by a number of marginal cells. Soon the prothallium changes its shape and becomes reniform or heart-shaped. The growing point lies in the sinus and is composed of a number of meristematic cells; these cells are plainly distinguished from the rest by their smaller size and the large amount of their protoplasm.

Behind the growing point the tissue of the prothallium is now composed of more than one layer of cells, and a cushion-like mass of tissue forms behind the sinus, on which the archegonia arise, usually in acropetal succession. From this cushion also, but on another part of the under surface, grow numerous rhizoids (unicellular root-hairs), which secure the prothallium to the substratum. The antheridia are not, like the archegonia, confined to the cushion, but may appear on any marginal or other cells of the prothallium. It is not uncommon, especially when the spores have been sown in great profusion, to find prothallia thickly covered with antheridia, but without an archegonium. These prothallia, moreover, have not the meristem

---

[1] Rauwenhoff, Ueber d. ersten Keimungserscheinungen der Kryptogamensporen (Bot. Ztg. 1879, p. 441).

which is found in prothallia that bear archegonia; they are, as Prantl[1] has shown, arrested forms, which in consequence of insufficient nourishment, and especially from want of a due supply of nitrogen, are not fully developed, but produce instead a large number of antheridia. These ' ameristic ' prothallia may be transformed into normal prothallia with archegonia, by supplying them with the necessary food.

This typical course of development is liable to certain variations, the more important of which must now be mentioned. Even in the Polypodiaceae, in *Polypodium vulgare* for example, the formation of a cell-filament is sometimes entirely dispensed with, and a cell-surface proceeds immediately from the germinating spore. This is the rule in *Osmunda*, where a cell-surface is the first product of germination, and, as in the Equisetaceae, a posterior cell produces the first rhizoid; sometimes, however, a short cell-filament is first formed, as in the Polypodiaceae, or even a many-layered cellular body. The rhizoids proceed from marginal cells, and on the under side from surface cells of the prothallium; the apical growth of the prothallium is similar to that of the Polypodiaceae. A mid-rib formed of several layers of cells is characteristic of the prothallium of *Osmunda* (Fig. 148); this is continued from the posterior extremity to the apex, and produces on its under side numerous archegonia in two longitudinal rows; the antheridia, on the other hand, are not on the mid-rib, but on the margin or on the under surface of the prothallium. When an oosphere has been fertilised in an archegonium, the heart-shaped prothallium ceases

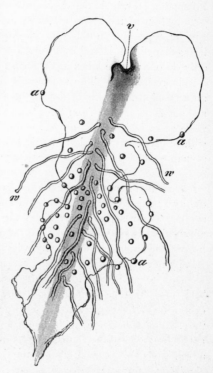

FIG. 148. Old and full-sized prothallium of *Osmunda regalis*, with the midrib shaded; *a* antheridia, *w* rhizoids, *v* the growing-point, in the left depression of which a lateral lobe is being formed (see Bot. Ztg. 1877, p. 705).

to grow, and it disappears as the young plant developes. But if no oosphere is fertilised, the prothallium continues to grow and becomes a ribbon-like body with the aspect of *Pellia* one of the thalloid Hepaticae, and may live during several years attaining a length of more than four centimetres. In this case certain cells in the margin of the terminal sinus grow more vigorously, and lobes are formed in the prothallium, right and left alternately (Fig. 148, left), which may best be compared with the leaves of *Blasia*, and give the prothallium an undulate

---

[1] Beobachtungen über d. Ernährung d. Farnprothallien u. d. Vertheilung d. Sexualorgane (Bot. Zeit. 1881).—The same result ensues in the absence of other substances required for the nutrition of the plant, or when the assimilation of carbon dioxide is impeded. Prothallia of *Osmunda regalis*, grown in the dark, form antheridia only according to Göppert in Sitzungsber. des intern. bot. Congr. zu Petersburg, 1869.

appearance. A few of these prothallia are dichotomously branched, the mid-rib bifurcating and each of the secondary mid-ribs running into one of the two branches of the prothallium. It is highly probable that this branching is brought about in the same way as in the thalloid Hepaticae, in *Pellia* for instance, and a branching which agrees apparently with that of *Metzgeria* has been noticed in *Hemitelia gigantea* [1].

Gymnogramme leptophylla [2] may be adduced here as an example of a species of Polypodiaceae which departs somewhat more widely from the typical forms. The germination of the spore produces at once the rudi ent of a spathulate prothallium. But its apex does not become the apex of a prothallium which is to be ultimately heart-shaped, but lateral outgrowths are formed on both sides of the prothallium or only on one; these lobes again form new lateral branches, and the result is a many-lobed prothallium. The archegonia do not arise as in the rest of the Polypodiaceae on a cushion-like mass of tissue; instead of such a cushion there appears, first of all, a conical outgrowth from the prothallium, which thrusts itself into the ground and there soon puts on the appearance of a small tuber, gradually filling its inner cells with reserve-material, oil, &c., and losing at the same time its green colour. On this structure which is known as the fertile shoot, and on its upper flattened side which is towards the prothallium, the archegonia are produced, and if their oospheres are not fertilised, two new prothallium-lobes grow out from the tuber. Usually the prothallia die away when a fertile shoot is produced, but they are perpetuated by adventitious shoots, which spring either from their margin or from their surface. These flat adventitious shoots often take the form of small tubers that are like the fertile shoot, but are distinguished from it by originating in any part of the surface of the thallus and by never producing archegonia, but only antheridia, as will be readily understood from what has been said above respecting the causes which lead to such variations. The tubers may lie dormant for a time and especially withstand desiccation and other changes, and eventually give rise to a new prothallium; and while the prothallium, the sexual generation, of *Gymnogramme leptophylla* is thus perennial, the asexual generation dies down after forming its spores, and is therefore annual. Marginal adventitious shoots occur also in the prothallia of others of the Polypodiaceae, as in *Aspidium Filix-mas*, *Notochlaena*, &c.; also in *Osmunda*, *Ceratopteris* and other genera. Peculiar gemmae formed of rows of cells have been recently described by Cramer [3] from the prothallia of Ferns, which belong probably to the Hymenophylleae, but may be only prothallia of other Ferns altered by disease.

The development of the prothallium in the Cyatheaceae [4] differs from that in the Polypodiaceae, as already described, only in subordinate points, and the development of the same organ in the Gleicheniaceae [5] agrees in the main with that of the typical prothallia of the Ferns; but like the Osmundaceae they sometimes develope a cell-mass at once instead of a cell-surface. The germination of the Hymenophylleae [6] is

---

[1] Bauke in Beilage zur Bot. Ztg. 1879, Taf. 5 u. 6.

[2] Goebel, Entwicklungsgesch. d. Prothalliums von *Gymnogramme leptophylla* Desv. (Bot. Ztg. 1877).

[3] Ueber d. geschlechtslose Vermehrung d. Farnprothalliums (Denkschr. d. Schweiz.-naturf. Ges. Bd. XXVIII, 1880).

[4] Bauke in Pringsheim's Jahrb. Bd. X.

[5] Rauwenhoff in Bot. Zeit. 1879, p. 441.

[6] Mettenius, Ueber d. Hymenophylleen (Abh. d. K. Sächs. Ges. d. Wiss. VII Bd.).—Janczewski

only imperfectly known. The prothallium of *Hymenophyllum tunbridgense*, according to Janczewski and Rostafinski, differs from the forms described above chiefly in being composed of one layer of cells, and in having therefore no cushion on the under side. The cell-walls are thick and pitted; the rhizoids are all marginal. The antheridia are placed on the under side of the prothallium. The archegonia are in groups on the margin of the prothallium, and their longitudinal axis is at right angles to the surface of the prothallium; some archegonia in a group are directed upwards, some downwards. The embryo forms a root, but the older plant has none. The variations in this case concern chiefly the position of the archegonia. The first stages of germination may be seen in the spores while they are still in the sporangium, or in the cup-shaped indusium. The spore in *Hymenophyllum* divides before the rupture of the exosporium into three cells, one of which developes into the filamentous prothallium, the others into hair-like forms and soon cease to grow. Many of the Hymenophyllaceae form at first a much branched confervoid protonema, on which flat prothallia of from four to six lines in length and from one half to one and a half lines in breadth are produced as lateral shoots. Each cell of the filament can give rise to a branch, which appears behind the anterior transverse wall and is at once cut off by a septum. Some of these branches, like the mother-shoot, have unlimited growth, others end in hair-like processes, a larger number still develope into the flat prothallia just mentioned, but most of them become rhizoids; occasionally the rudiment of a branch may develope into an antheridium or even an archegonium. Round cells, which are probably organs of propagation, appear in *Trichomanes insitum* on flattened marginal cells at the apex of the flat prothallia. Only the marginal cells of these prothallia can develope into rhizoids and new protonema-filaments, and also into new flat shoots. The rhizoids are generally short with brown walls, and form at their extremity lobed disks of attachment or tubular branches.

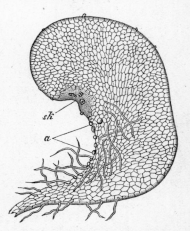

FIG. 149. *Aneimia Phyllitidis.* Prothallium seen from below; *sk* apex of the cushion of tissue on which a few archegonia may be seen, *a* antheridia with rhizoids on the margin and surface of the lower part of the prothallium. After Bauke, magn. 25 times.

In the Schizaeaceae[1] also the formation of the prothallium agrees in the main points with that of the Polypodiaceae. *Aneimia Phyllitidis* may be taken as a suitable example. Fig. 149 shows that the growing point (*sk*) is not at the apex but at the side of the prothallium; and the prothallium is not cordate, there is only one lobe forming the extremity of the prothallium, the other being indicated only by a slight projection. The growing point of the prothallium is sometimes lateral in the Polypodiaceae also.

The *antheridia*, like the rhizoids, are outgrowths of the marginal or of the surface

u. Rostafinski, Note sur le prothalle de *l'Hymenophyllum tunbridgense* (Mém. de la Soc. nat. de Cherbourg, 1875).—Prantl, Unters. ü. d. Gefässkryptogamen, Heft I.

[1] Bauke, Beitr. z. Keimungsgesch. d. Schizaeaceen in Pringsheim's Jahrb. Bd. XI, where other works are cited.—Prantl, in Flora, 1878, p. 12 of the reprint.

cells of the prothallium, and in the Hymenophyllaceae occur also on the protonemal
filaments. The protuberance is usually cut off from the mother-cell by a transverse
wall, and swells out into a globular form either at once or after forming a stalk-cell;
in some cases the spermatozoids can be produced without any further change in this
globular cell, but usually the cell first undergoes divisions[1] which result in giving the
antheridium a wall composed of only one layer of cells with chlorophyll-corpuscles on
their inner surface, and a central cell which by further divisions produces the not very
numerous mother-cells of the spermatozoids. The discharge of the spermatozoids
from the mature antheridium is due to rapid absorption of water by the cells which
form the wall; these swell considerably, and by the pressure which they exercise on
the contents of the antheridium cause its wall to burst at the apex; then the

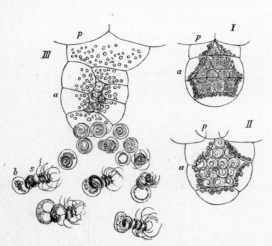

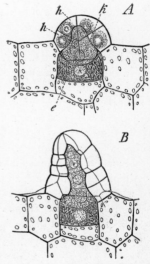

FIG. 150. Antheridium of *Adiantum Capillus-Veneris*, seen in optical
longitudinal section. *I* immature state. *II* the spermatozoids already developed. *III* antheridium burst, the parietal cells being greatly swollen in
the radial direction and most of the spermatozoids escaped; *p* prothallium, *a*
antheridium, *s* spermatozoid, *b* its vesicle containing grains of starch. Magn.
550 times.

FIG. 151. Young archegonia of *Pteris
serrulata* after Strasburger; *e* the oosphere,
h h the neck, *k* the neck-canal-cell. Further
explanation in the text.

spermatocysts issue forth, and each liberates a spermatozoid which is coiled three
or four times in a cork-screw spiral; its finer anterior extremity is beset with
numerous cilia, the thicker posterior end often drags after it a vesicle containing

---

[1] These divisions take place in a very remarkable manner; in *Aneimia hirta* an arched wall
arises in the hemispherical projecting mother-cell of the antheridium, and divides it into an inner
hemispherical cell and an outer cell which covers the other like a bell; the latter then divides by a
circular wall into an upper cell like a lid and a lower cell which is a hollow cylinder; thus the
entire wall is formed of two cells. It is the same in *Ceratopteris*; in other cases, as in *Asplenium
alatum*, a funnel-shaped wall arises in the hemispherical mother-cell of the antheridium, the wider
end of which lies against the arched wall of the mother-cell; the upper part of the cell is cut off by
a horizontal transverse wall to form a lid; two or even three funnel-shaped walls may be formed one
after the other, so that the wall of the antheridium is composed of two or three cells running obliquely round it and lying one above the other and of the lid-cell, as in Fig. 150. The formation of
the wall of the antheridium in *Osmunda* is quite different; it consists below of from two to three
cells, surmounted by several upper cells which have proceeded from the division of the lid-cell
(Kny, as cited on p. 197).

colourless granules, which afterwards drops off and lies where it falls, while the thread hastens away by itself. The spermatozoid in the Ferns, as in the Muscineae, according to the latter researches of Schmitz and others, is derived almost entirely from the nucleus of the mother-cell, the cilia perhaps being formed from the protoplasm. The nucleus becomes thickened at its circumference, and of looser consistence towards its centre ; the body of the spermatozoid is produced by the splitting up of the periphery, the central part supplying the vesicle, which is thus not properly a part of the spermatozoid but only clings to it and swells up strongly by endosmose in water, as Fig. 150 shows.

The *archegonium* proceeds from a superficial cell of the prothallium, which first arches slightly outwards, and is divided into three cells by two walls parallel to the upper surface ; the lowest of these, called by Janczewski the basal cell, (Fig. 151 *A, e*), subsequently divides in the same way as the cells of the surrounding tissue, and thus contributes to the construction of the venter of the archegonium which is entirely sunk in the thallus. The outermost of the three primary cells produces the wall or periphery of the neck of the archegonium (Fig. 151 *A, h h*) by first dividing cross-wise into four cells, from which the four rows of cells forming the wall of the neck are derived by the formation of obliquely transverse walls ; as the neck grows faster and becomes convex on the anterior side, that is on the side towards the apex of the prothallium, the number of the cells in the front rows of the neck is larger, usually six, while that of the cells on the shorter concave posterior side of the neck is usually four. The middle of the three primary cells produces the central cell and the neck-canal-cells, that is, the entire axile row of cells in the archegonium ; during the formation of the periphery of the neck this middle cell becomes pointed at its upper end and forces itself in between the cells of the neck (Fig. 151 *A*); the pointed end is cut off by a transverse wall and now forms the single neck-canal-cell (Fig. 151 *A, k*), which elongates as the neck grows longer, completely fills it, and according to Strasburger shows a tendency to further transverse divisions by the appearance of a few nuclei, but does not form any septa (Fig. 151 *B*), though Janczewski doubts this[1]. The broad central cell now divides into an upper smaller cell, the ventral canal-cell (Fig. 152 *B s*), and into the much larger oosphere (*e*) which is subsequently rounded off. The walls of the canal-cells swell and are converted into mucilage, and the watery mucilage together with the protoplasm of the canal-cells is at length expelled through the opened neck. The spermatozoids collect in great numbers and are caught in the mucilage in front of the archegonium ; many make their way into the canal and often stop it up ; single ones reach the oosphere, enter it and disappear in it; they enter at a clearer spot in the oosphere towards the neck, which is termed the *receptive spot*. (See the oogonia of the Algae [2]).

The second or *asexual generation* (*sporophore, sporophyte*), the Fern, is the product of the oospore formed by fertilisation of the oosphere in an archegonium. The surrounding tissue of the prothallium at first keeps pace with the increase in size of the embryo, which remains for some time enclosed in a projection from the under surface of the prothallium, till the first leaf and the first root burst from it.

---

[1] He is wrong here. Compare *Marattia.*

[2] Strasburger says that the act of fertilisation may be observed with unusual distinctness in *Ceratopteris.* Hofmeister long ago saw the spermatozoids penetrate to the oosphere.

The mode in which the oospore developes into the embryo is essentially the same in all the Vascular Cryptogams that have been carefully observed. The first point to notice is that the primary stem, the primary root and one or two leaves, here as in the Phanerogams called *cotyledons*, are produced independently of each other from the embryo, which is at first round or ovoid and unsegmented. A rather large portion of the embryo is also devoted to forming an organ of suction, the *foot*, which conveys nutrient substances from the prothallium to the embryo. The organs which subsequently appear, the leaves, the roots, &c., are as usual produced at the apex of the stem, but the members of the plant which are first developed on the embryo originate, as has been said, in a different manner. As regards the orientation of the different organs, it has been shown that the neck of the archegonium is turned downwards towards the ground. The rudiments of the apex of the stem and of the foot lie on the side of the embryo which is towards the under side of the prothallium,

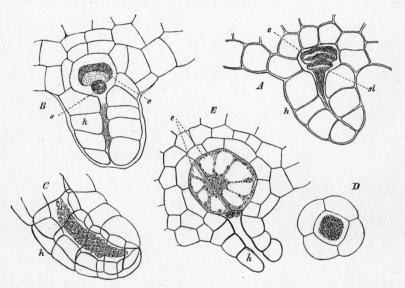

FIG. 152. Archegonium of *Adiantum Capillus-Veneris*, magn. 800 times. *A, B, C, E* in optical longitudinal section, *D* in optical transverse section; *A, B, C* before, *E* after fertilisation has taken place; *h* neck of the archegonium, *sl* canal-cells converted into mucilage, *s* in *B* the ventral canal-cell, *e* the oosphere, *e* in *E* the two-celled embryo. After lying nine days in glycerine.

and are therefore turned upwards; the cotyledon and the rudiment of the root on the side towards the neck of the archegonium, and are therefore directed downwards. The view which has been repeatedly expressed, that external forces, that of gravitation especially, affect the position of the organs in the embryo, has not been found to be correct; their formation is determined only by the position of the embryo in the prothallium and archegonium, and is wholly independent of gravitation[1].

The steps by which the oospore is changed into a mass of cellular tissue

---

[1] Leitgeb, Studien ü. Entwicklung d. Farne (Sitzungsber. d. KK. Akad. d. Wiss., Bd. LXXX). The fact alleged in the text was demonstrated by Leitgeb in a simple manner; he showed that the organs are formed in the embryo in the ordinary position in archegonia on the upper side of pro-thallia, on which the light was thrown from below.

have been clearly ascertained by modern investigations, which correct Hofmeister's earlier observations. The part of the embryo which is towards the underside of the prothallium will in the following description be called the upper part (marked | in Fig. 153), the part towards the neck of the arche-gonium the under part (+ in Fig. 153); the anterior half is the half which is turned towards the growing point of the pro-thallium. The arrangement of the cell walls[1] presents nothing unusual; it agrees with that of other organs with a similar out-line, as is shown by the young gemma of *Marchantia*, which is given in Fig. 153 *B* for the pur-pose of comparison. The first wall is nearly coincident with the axis of the archegonium; it is called the *basal* wall (Fig. 153 *b b*), and divides an anterior half of the embryo, the half which forms the stem, from the posterior half which forms the root; Leitgeb calls the anterior half the *epibasal*, the posterior the *hypobasal* half. Two fresh walls then make their appearance at right angles to the basal wall and to one another, and divide the embryo into octants. The order of appearance of these walls is variable; one called the *transversal* wall (Fig. 153 *t t*) runs parallel to the surface of the pro-thallium, the other, the *median* wall (Fig. 153 *m m*), which is not visible in *A*, being in the plane of the paper, is at right angles to the

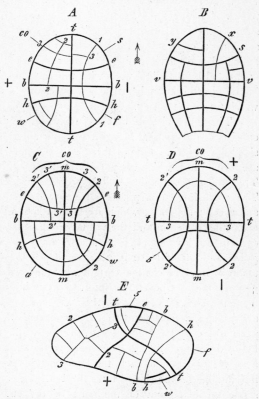

FIG. 153. *A, C, D* Diagrammatic representations of the cell-division in the embryo of the Filicineae, from a model. *B* young gemnae of *Marchantia polymorpha; b* basal, *t* transversal, *m* median wall, *h* hypobasal, *e* epibasal wall, *s* rudiment of the apex of the stem, *w* root, *co* cotyledon, *f* foot. The numbers serve to distinguish the walls in the different figures (the 5 in *D* should be *s*). The arrow indicates the direction of the apex of the prothallium, the mark | the underside of the prothallium, + the neck of the archegonium. *A* is a side view of an upright embryo in a prothallium. *C* is a view of *A* rotated through an angle of 90 degrees, the axis of rotation being the line of intersection of the transversal with the median wall. *D* anterior view of *A* and *C* also rotated through an angle of 90 degrees, the axis of rotation being the line of intersection of the transversal with the basal wall. *E* same view as *A*, but lying down, not upright, and showing an embryo of *Ceratopteris* after Leitgeb.

surface of the prothallium. Of the two anterior upper octants one becomes the grow-ing point of the stem, the other undergoes as a rule no further differentiation; the two anterior lower octants develope into the first leaf, the cotyledon; the two posterior upper octants form the foot, and one of the two posterior and lower ones forms the root, while the other does not usually develope like the rest. Two walls then appear

---

[1] A clear idea of the construction of the embryo may be obtained by marking the walls on an ovoid or round wooden model separable into four or eight pieces, such as any turner can supply. See Goebel, Zur Embryologie d. Archegoniaten (Arb. d. bot. Inst. Würzburg, Bd. II).

in the epibasal and hypobasal halves with the same direction as the basal, the epibasal (Fig. 153 *e*), and the hypobasal wall (Fig. 153 *h*). These walls show in all side views of the embryo as anticlinal walls, in the front and hinder views as periclinal walls. It is the same in Fig. 153 *D*, where the basal wall is in the plane of the paper. The portions separated off by the epibasal and hypobasal walls on both sides of the basal wall are called by more recent writers the epibasal and hypobasal segments; concerning their further divisions we will only say here, that by two anticlinal walls having the same direction as the transversal wall, which are then connected by periclinal walls with the transversal wall, an inner mass of cells which in transverse section has nearly a quadratic form is divided off from an outer tissue which forms the cortex.

The epibasal half of the embryo after the appearance of the epibasal wall consists of the epibasal segment and four anterior cells which have the form of three-sided apical cells. One of these cells is in fact the apical cell of the stem, and walls are formed in it which are parallel to the basal, transversal and median walls in turn. Thus a persistent apical cell is produced, which is in form a three-sided pyramid. The cotyledon which proceeds from two octants on the other hand shows no such apical cell; the leaves which are formed later will be noticed further on.

The cotyledon and the primary root remain small; the latter dwindles away very early in the Hymenophylleae, and in many species of the group no fresh roots are formed, and their place is taken by subterranean shoots. When the cotyledon and the root have reached a certain size, they break through the venter of the archegonium, the root penetrates into the ground, and the cotyledon and the young stem bend upwards. New leaves then arise on the latter. The later-formed leaves are always larger, their form more complicated, and the structure of the stem, as the parts added by longitudinal growth increase in thickness, becomes continually more highly developed: the first portions of the stem like the primary leaf-stalks have only one axile vascular bundle each, the later portions have several, as soon as stem and leaf have attained some size. Thus the Fern goes on increasing in strength, not by subsequent enlargement of the parts of the embryo, but by each succeeding part attaining a greater size and higher development than the preceding, till at length a kind of stationary condition is reached, in which the new organs that are formed are about equal to the preceding ones. The following remarks refer especially to this the fully-developed condition of our plants; but before we proceed to them, we must first mention the peculiar phenomenon which De Bary[1] has minutely investigated, and to which he has given the name of *apogamy* or loss of sexual propagation. There are, that is to say, Ferns in which the sexual generation, the prothallium, produces the asexual generation, the fern-plant, not by the development of an oosphere fertilised in the archegonium, but by the formation of a shoot. This phenomenon is at present known only in *Pteris cretica*[2], *Aspidium Filix-mas* var. *cristatum, Aspidium falcatum,* and *Todea africana*[3]. In *Pteris cretica* the prothallium

---

[1] Ueber apogame Farne u. d. Erscheinung d. Apogamie im Allgemeinen (Bot. Zeit. 1878, p. 449). [Leitgeb, Die Sprossbild. an apogam. Farnprothallien (Ber. Deutsch. Bot. Ges. III, 1885.]

[2] Described for the first time in this species by Farlow in Bot. Zeit. 1874, No. 12, [and in Q. J. M. S. 1874].

[3] On *Todea* see Sadebeck, *loc. cit.* p. 231.

as a rule produces no archegonium; when the prothallium has grown into the cordate form, a prominence appears on its under side not far from the growing point, and this prominence developes into a leaf. The apex of the stem is formed near the base of the leaf and soon gives rise to a second leaf, and as it increases in size assumes the typical character of the fully-developed state. The primary root is formed inside the tissue near the insertion of the primary leaf; the point of origin of this primary root is generally in the base of the leaf, but it may be in the prothallium, if the vascular bundle is prolonged so far. The succeeding roots are formed in the

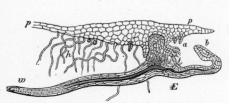

FIG. 154. *Adiantum Capillus Veneris.* Longitudinal section through the prothallium *pp* and the young Fern *E* ; *h* root-hairs, *a* archegonia of the prothallium, *b* the first leaf, *w* the first root of the embryo. Magn. about 10 times.

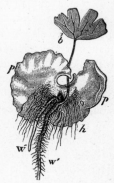

FIG. 155. *Adiantum Capillus Veneris.* The prothallium *pp* seen from below has a young fern-plant attached to it ; *b* the first leaf, *w'* and *w''* the first and second root, *h* root-hairs of the prothallium. Magn. about 30 times.

same way as in the plant produced from an oospore. Thus the formation of the organs in the case of the young plant which is produced as a shoot from the prothallium is similar to their formation in the plant that springs from an embryo, inasmuch as the origin of the organs first formed (the root and leaf) is independent of the primary bud, whereas all succeeding leaves are outgrowths from it. Two leaves also may be formed instead of a single primary leaf, and two primary roots, or two stems by the side of the primary leaf; such occurrences show that these organs arise independently of one another. There are other abnormalities connected with this interesting point, which cannot be mentioned here. Antheridia often in numbers are found on these apogamous prothallia of *Pteris cretica* ; but in much the greater number of them there is no trace of an archegonium; of some hundreds examined by De Bary only seven had one archegonium each, and none of these seven appeared capable of fertilisation. In *Todea africana*, on the contrary, according to Sadebeck archegonia are almost invariably formed on the apogamous prothallia, and De Bary found them comparatively abundant in *Aspidium falcatum*, but these archegonia, though apparently of normal structure, never showed signs of fertilisation, but died off, while young ferns were being produced asexually as shoots from the prothallium. Lastly, no archegonia occur on the apogamous prothallia of *Aspidium Filix-mas* var. *cristatum*. This plant at the same time, as De Bary has pointed out, suggests an explanation of the origin of apogamy; it is a comparatively new garden variety of the common *Aspidium Filix-mas*. The prothallia of the latter have sexual organs with the usual functional power and produce normal embryos. Sexuality, it would seem, has disappeared in the variety *cristatum*, and been replaced by an asexual formation of shoots, and the same may be inferred in the case of all other apogamous Ferns.

Either female sexual organs occur on them in abundance, but are infertile (*Todea*), or they are very rare (*Pteris cretica*), or they are not found at all[1] (*Aspidium Filix-mas* var. *cristatum*). We have already pointed out a similar advance from step to step in the apogamy of the Saprolegnieae, and we shall have to notice analogous phenomena in some of the Phanerogams (see too *Isoetes*)[2].

The full-grown Fern, to the consideration of which we now return, is in many of the Hymenophyllaceae a small and delicate plant not greatly exceeding the dimensions of the large Muscineae. In the other divisions fully developed specimens are usually handsome plants, and many species from the tropics and the southern hemisphere have the habit of a palm, and are known as Tree-ferns. The stem either creeps on or in the ground (*Polypodium, Pteris aquilina*), or climbs on rocks or the stems of other plants, or ascends obliquely, as in *Aspidium Filix-mas* and many others, or rises erect and columnar as in the Tree-ferns. They have usually a very abundant formation of roots; the stem of many Tree-ferns is often quite covered with a thick mass of downward growing roots. The roots arise on the stem in acropetal succession, sometimes close behind the growing apex, as in *Pteris aquilina*. If the internodes remain very short and the stem is covered with leaf-scars, the roots often spring from the leaf-stalks, as in *Aspidium Filix-mas*. In many Hymenophyllaceae without true roots branches from the stem assume the form of roots, as was mentioned above. The leaves in the creeping and climbing forms, and in many of those which grow free and erect, are separated by evident or even long internodes; in thick stems, both ascending and vertical, the internodes are usually not developed, and the leaves are placed so close together that no bit of the surface of the stem, or a very inconsiderable part of it, remains free and uncovered by them[3]. Many stems show in the arrangement of their parts a distinction between a ventral side which is turned to the substratum and a dorsal side; they are in a word dorsiventral. Thus in many Hymenophyllaceae the leaves are on the dorsal side of the stem; the same thing may be seen but less distinctly in some species of *Polypodium, P. vulgare* for example and *P. aureum*, where two rows of leaves stand near each other on the dorsal side, while in *Lygodium* there is only a single dorsal row of leaves present from the first[4].

---

[1] See the description of the phenomena connected with apogamy in the Saprolegnieae and Ascomycetes in preceding portions of this work.

[2] [The converse condition, the direct passage from the Fern (sporophyte) to the prothallium (oophyte), aptly termed by Bower *apospory*, has been observed in *Athyrium Filix-femina* var. *clarissima* by Druery and in *Polystichum angulare* var. *pulcherrimum* by Wollaston. From Bower's description we learn that in the former plant sporangia attached to the pinnae and arrested in their normal development exhibit active vegetative growth of the stalk and of the superficial cells of the capsule resulting in the formation of a flattened parenchymatous structure with chlorophyll-cells and growth by wedge-shaped cells at one or more points of the margin, in fact prothallia. Sexual organs are developed upon the prothallia. In the second plant prothallia bearing sexual organs are formed by simple vegetative outgrowths of the tip of the pinnae without any connection with sori or sporangia. The degrees of apospory observed in these cases may be compared with those of apogamy in the text, and it may be noted in connection with the explanation of the origin of apogamy that the cases of apospory known occur also in garden varieties. See Druery in Journ. Linn. Soc. XXI, 1885; Bower in same vol.; Thiselton Dyer in Nature, No. 791, and Wollaston in Gard. Chron. XXIV, 1885.]

[3] Brongniart concluded from the changes in shape and size of the older leaves that the stems of Tree-ferns grow in length and perhaps in thickness also after the leaves have fallen.

[4] See also what is said below with regard to the branching.

The leaves of the Ferns are generally distinguished by their circinate arrangement in the bud; the mid-rib and the lateral veins are rolled up from behind forwards, and only unroll when the growth is just being completed. The forms of the leaves are among the most perfect in the vegetable kingdom; they show a marvellous variety in the general outline, and the lamina is usually repeatedly lobed, branched and feathered. They are generally very large in proportion to the stem and the slender roots, reaching sometimes extraordinary dimensions; those of *Pteris aquilina, Cibotium* and *Angiopteris* may be from ten to twenty feet in length. They are always stalked and continue to grow at the apex for a long time; the stalk and the lower parts of the lamina are often fully unfolded when the apex is still growing, as in *Nephrolepis,* and this apical growth of the leaf is in many cases interrupted periodically, a point which will be noticed again below; in *Lygodium* the leaf-stalk or the mid-rib may even become like a climbing stem with long-continued growth, on which the pinnae appear as leaves. At the same time the metamorphosis of the leaves is slight and unimportant; the same forms, and these chiefly foliage-leaves, are continually repeated on the same plant; scale-like leaves are found on subterranean stolons in *Struthiopteris germanica* and *Osmunda regalis,* where as in Cycadeae and other plants they alternate with the foliage-leaves and envelope the bud at the apex of the stem in winter

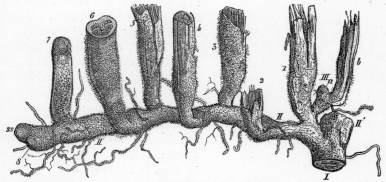

FIG. 156. A portion of the underground stem of *Pteris aquilina* with leaves and bases of leaf-stalks, half the natural size. *I* older portion of the stem, bearing the two bifurcations *II* and *II'*; *ss* the apex of the weaker branch *II*, close to it the youngest leaf-rudiment *s*; *1—7* the leaves of this branch, one of which is developed in each year; *1—5* the leaves of earlier years, which are already dead to a certain distance from the stem, 6 the leaf of the present year with unfolded lamina and with the stalk cut through, 7 the young leaf for the next year with its lamina still quite small and covered up with hairs at the apex of the stem. The leaf-stalk 1 bears a bud *III a* which after developing a leaf that is already dead has now become dormant. The more slender filaments are roots. All the parts shown in the figure are subterranean.

(Prantl). In many cases the fertile leaves, those which bear sporangia, assume special forms; but the great amount of variation in the development of the leaves of the plant, which occurs in the Phanerogams, is not found in the Ferns; yet *Platycerium alcicorne* must not be forgotten, in which the foliage-leaves alternate periodically as broad sheaths closely pressed against the surface on which they grow, and as long ribbon-like erect dichotomously branching leaves, which are however generally sterile in our hot-houses. Of the different forms of hair-structures in the Ferns the most remarkable for their number and flat leaf-like appearance are the *ramenta* (*chaff-scales* or *paleae*), by which the younger leaves are usually covered and concealed.

After these preliminary remarks we may now proceed to the consideration of the growth of the several members.

[2]

The *growing end of the stem* sometimes projects some way beyond the point of origin of the youngest leaves, and then appears naked, as in *Polypodium vulgare, P. sporodocarpum* and other creeping species; the same may be observed in *Pteris aquilina*, where in old plants according to Hofmeister the growing end is often without leaves for the space of several inches; in many Hymenophyllaceae Mettenius informs us that such leafless prolongations of the stem have been taken for roots. In other cases on the contrary, especially in species that grow erect, the longitudinal growth of the stem is much slower and its apex is concealed in a leaf-bud. The apex of the stem is often flat, and sometimes, as in *Pteris*, it is even sunk in a funnel-shaped projection of the older tissue (Fig. 160 *E*). The apex of the stem is always occupied by a distinct apical cell, which either divides by walls alternately inclined, and then resembles when seen from above the transverse section of a biconvex lens, or it is a three-sided pyramid with a convex anterior surface and three oblique lateral surfaces which intersect behind. The bounding lines of the segments, which in the first case are formed in two rows, in the second in three rows or with more complicated divergences, soon disappear in consequence of the numerous cell-divisions and the distortions caused by the growth of the masses of tissue around the apex and that of the leaf-stalks. The apical cell, for example, in *Pteris aquilina* has the shape of a wedge with two sides, and its segments on the horizontal stem form a right and a left series; the edges of the cell are turned upwards and downwards (Fig. 157); the same is the case, according to Hofmeister, in *Niphobolus chinensis* and *N. rupestris*, in *Polypodium aureum* and *P. punctatum*, and in *Platycerium alcicorne*; in *Polypodium vulgare*, according to the same authority, the apical cell is sometimes two-sided, sometimes a three-sided pyramid; the last is its form in *Aspidium Filix-mas* and some others. We may for the present take it to be the rule, that creeping stems with bilateral structure have a two-sided apical cell, and that in erect or ascending stems with rosettes of leaves radiating in every direction the apical cell is a three-sided pyramid[1].

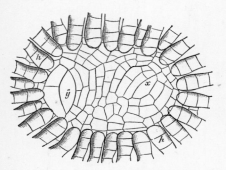

FIG. 157. Apical view of the extremity of the stem of *Pteris aquilina*; *y* the apical cell of the stem, *x* apical cell of the youngest leaf, *hh* hairs covering the apical region which is surrounded by a cushion of tissue.

The details of the genetic relations of the segments of the apical cell of the stem to the formation of the leaves and of the stem itself are not yet clearly ascertained. There is no doubt that each leaf originates in a single segment, and that this segment-cell is applied to the formation of a leaf very soon after it is itself formed; Kny states that a leaf proceeds from every segment in *Ceratopteris*, which agrees therefore in this respect with the Mosses; but this is certainly not the case with most Ferns.

The phyllotaxis sometimes corresponds to the formation in straight rows of the segments of the stem; thus the two rows of leaves in *Pteris aquilina, Niphobolus*

---

[1] [Klein, Vergl. Unters. ü. Organb. u. Wachsth. am Vegetationsp. dorsiventral. Farne (Bot. Ztg. 1884)].

rupestris, and many of the Polypodieae answer to the two rows of segments of the apical cell of the stem; but in the case of a more complicated spiral phyllotaxis with an apical cell which is a three-sided pyramid, as in *Aspidium Filix-mas*, the processes may be similar to those which take place in Mosses with many rows of leaves and a three-sided apical cell, as for instance in *Polytrichum*[1].

The *branching* and the position of the lateral buds are liable to considerable variation in the different species. The lateral buds are either on the dorsal side of

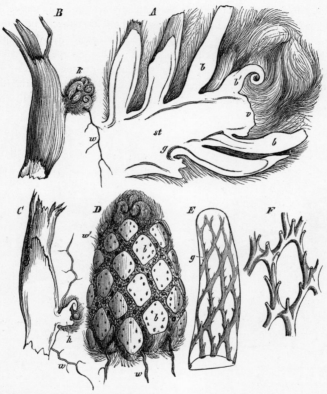

FIG. 158. *Aspidium Filix-mas*. *A* longitudinal section through the extremity of a stem; *v* the apical region of the stem *st*, *bb* the leaf-stalks, *b'* a young still folded leaf, the others being concealed by long paleae, *g* vascular bundles. *B* a leaf-stalk of the same plant broken off and bearing at *k* a bud with several leaves; *w* a root of the bud *k*. *C* a similar leaf-stalk cut through lengthwise, bearing a root at *w* and a bud at *h*. *D* extremity of a stem from which the leaves have been cut off at the base of the stalks, the youngest leaves only of the terminal bud being retained in order to show the arrangement of the leaves; the spaces between the leaf-stalks are filled with numerous roots *w w'*, all of which have sprung from the stalks. *E* extremity of a stem from which the rind has been removed to show the net-work of vascular bundles *g*. *F* a mesh of the net-work slightly magnified showing the basal portions of the bundles which pass out into the leaves.

the bases of the leaves, as in *Aspidium Filix-mas* (Fig. 158), where they appear in rudimentary form at a very early period, or they are placed laterally with respect to them on the stem, and either above or below the insertion of the leaf, seldom in the axil of the leaf, as in higher plants. But on radial stems it is only a very small number of leaves that have lateral buds associated with them (Mettenius asserts that

---

[1] Hofmeister, Allg. Morphol. p. 509, and in Bot. Ztg. 1870, p. 441.

in *Blechnum hastatum* a lateral bud is formed beneath every leaf and becomes a stolon[1]); in Tree-ferns the terminal branching of the stem is reduced to a minimum, either not occurring at all or only in abnormal cases.

The formation of adventitious buds which do not originate in the terminal branching of the stem is connected in the Ferns with the leaves, and in many cases, in *Ceratopteris*, for instance, there is no terminal branching at all, and buds are formed only on the leaves. These buds appear on the stalk or on the lamina of the leaf. Such shoots in *Pteris aquilina* (Fig. 160 *K*) are on the back of the leaf-stalk and near its base; in *Aspidium Filix-mas* (Fig. 158) they appear some way above the insertion of the leaf, usually on one of the lateral edges of the leaf-stalk; in both cases they are formed according to Hofmeister on the young stalk before the development of the lamina and before the differentiation of its tissue; a single superficial cell of the stalk is the mother-cell of the new shoot; as the surrounding tissue grows up round it like a wall, the bud may as in *Pteris* be sunk in a deep depression and there remain dormant for some time; in that case the leaf-stalk continues succulent and filled with

FIG. 159. *Asplenium decussatum*. Middle portion of a leaf; the midrib *st* bears the leaflets *l*, at the base of which the bud *k* has formed and has already put out a root.

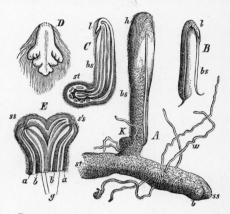

FIG. 160. *Pteris aquilina*. *A* the extremity of a stem *st*, the apex of which is at *ss*; near it at *b* a rudiment of a leaf, *bs* the stalk of a leaf in its second year, at *h* its lamina concealed by hairs, *k* a bud at the back of the leaf-stalk, *w* roots. *B* young leaf in its second year; *bs* its stalk, *l* its small lamina freed from hairs. *C* longitudinal section of a similar leaf with the transverse section of the stem *st* attached; *bs* and *l* as in *B*. *D* the lamina of a leaf in its second year seen from the front, i.e. on the upper side. *E* the horizontal longitudinal section of a bifurcation of the stem; *ss s's* the two apices, *aa* brown epidermal tissue, *bb* brown sclerenchyma, *g* vascular bundles. *A*, *B*, *C* natural size, *D* magn. about 5 times.

nutrient substances for some way above the bud long after the leaf has died away, and in *Aspidium Filix-mas* strong stems with numerous leaves are not unfrequently found connected at their lower end with a leaf-stalk from an older stem. In many cases, as in *Struthiopteris germanica*, these buds from the leaf-stalk develope into long underground stolons furnished with scale-like leaves, which turn upwards in their growth at their free extremity and unfold a circle of foliage-leaves above the ground; in *Nephrolepis undulata* they swell into a tuber at their extremity. Adventitious buds are formed on the lamina of the leaf, especially in many of the Asplenieae[2]; in

---

[1] Mettenius, Ueber Seitenknospen bei Farnen (Abh. d. Kön. Sächs. Ges. d. Wiss. 1860).
[2] On the formation of these buds see Heinricher in Sitz.-Ber. d. Akad. d. Wiss. in Wien, 1878.

Asplenium furcatum, for instance, frequently and in large numbers from the middle of the upper surface of the laciniae, in *Asplenium decussatum* from the base of the pinnae (or ? they are axillary on the mid-rib), (Fig. 159); *Ceratopteris thalictroides* produces buds not unfrequently in all the angles of the divided leaves; they arise at a very early period from superficial cells of the leaf; if the leaf is cut off and laid on the damp ground these buds develope rapidly and grow to strong plants. Long drooping leaves of many Ferns with their extremities lying on the ground put forth roots from them and sometimes new shoots, as in *Chrysodium flagelliferum, Woodwardia,* and others.

The *growth of the leaf* is strictly basifugal and apical, and this is followed by further basifugal development. The stalk is first commenced, and the lamina begins afterwards to show itself at its apex; the lowest parts are first formed, the parts above them in basifugal succession. The excessive slowness of this growth is very remarkable and can only be paralleled in the Ophioglosseae. In older plants of *Pteris aquilina* the leaf is begun fully two years before it unfolds; by the beginning of the second year the stalk, about one inch long and growing from an apical cell which forms oblique walls in alternating directions, is the only portion yet in existence; in the summer of the same year the lamina first arises on the apex of this rod-like stalk, and is then a minute flat body concealed beneath the long hairs; it bends over with its tip downwards and hangs like an apron from the top of the stalk (Fig. 160 *B, C, D*); it continues to grow beneath the ground and in the third spring is raised above the ground by the elongation of the stalk, and has now only to unfold. The whole of the leaves of a rosette of *Aspidium Filix-mas* take two years to form; in their case also the leaf-stalk and the first rudiments of a lamina on the oldest leaves of the young rosette are produced in the first year.

The basifugal growth at the apex of the lamina of the leaves of Ferns is most remarkable, when it goes steadily on for a long time without arriving at a distinct termination, while the lower parts of the lamina have long since been fully developed, as happens in *Nephrolepis*. The periodical interruption to the growth of the lamina at the apex, which has been already mentioned, occurs in many Gleichenieae and Mertensieae, where the development of the leaves comes to a standstill above the first pair of pinnae, and the interruption is repeated at the same place in the several orders of branching when the pinnation is compound; the consequence is that the tip of the lamina appearing like a bud in the fork either remains always undeveloped, or developes in like manner only imperfectly in a succeeding vegetative period; it appears that this intermittent mode of formation of the leaves may be continued during a number of years[1]. According to Mettenius the lamina of the leaf in many of the Hymenophyllaceae is capable of indefinite growth and forms innovations every year; the primary branches also of the lamina of the leaf of *Lygodium* after the formation of each pair of pinnae of the second order remain in a bud-like condition at their extremity, while the mid-rib grows indefinitely and looks like a twining stem.

The branching of the lamina of the leaves of Ferns in the developed state is not unfrequently forked, as in *Platycerium, Schizaea,* and others, but generally the leaf is

---

[1] Braun, Verjungung, 123.

once or repeatedly pinnate. The rudiment of the leaf is formed by the arching outwards of a single cell at the growing point of the stem. The growing point of the

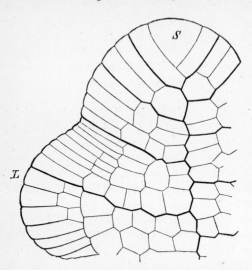

young leaf is either occupied from the first by a group of marginal cells, as in the cotyledon, or at first by a two-sided wedge-shaped apical cell, which forms segments for a time in the plane of the leaf (Fig. 161), and is then replaced by a group of cells, in the same manner as in the prothallia, by the formation of a periclinal and other walls. The branches of the leaf, the pinnae, &c. are next formed; a group of cells below the growing point of the leaf grows more vigorously, and so commences the formation of a pinnate leaf (Fig. 161 at *L*).[1]

FIG. 161. Tip of a leaf of *Ceratopteris Thalictroides*. *S* the apical cell of the leaf, *L* rudiment of a lateral lobe (lacinia) of the leaf which has no apical cell. After Kny.

The root. The stem, as it grows, is as a rule constantly putting forth new roots in acropetal succession, and in the creeping species these roots secure the plant to the surface on which it grows. In *Pteris aquilina* the new roots

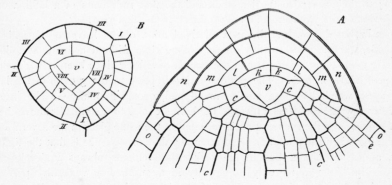

FIG. 162. Apical region of fern-roots. *A* longitudinal section through the extremity of a root of *Pteris hastata*; *v* apical cell, *k* segment of the same reaching to the root-cap, *k, l, m, n* layers of the root-cap, *c* segments of the root. *B* transverse section through the apical cell and the adjoining segments of the root of *Aspidium Filix-femina*. After Nägeli and Leitgeb.

appear from immediately below the apex, and in this species and in *Aspidium Filix-mas* they also grow at a very early period from the adventitious buds of the leaf-stalk. It

---

[1] [Bower, Comp. morph. of the leaf in the Vasc. Crypt. and Gymnosp. (Phil. Trans. 1884), regards the whole leaf in Vascular Cryptogams from apex to base as an axis, the *phyllopodium*, which may be branched or unbranched. In most homosporous Ferns the phyllopodium shows a two-sided apical cell and monopodial branching with not infrequent dichotomy in the higher series of the branching; but in the Hymenophylleae the branching is chiefly, if not exclusively, dichotomous. In Osmundaceae the phyllopodium has a three-sided conical apical cell and the branching is monopodial.]

has been already stated that if the stem of the last-named plant in its full-grown state is entirely covered with the bases of the leaf-stalks, the roots all grow from them and not from the stem; in the Tree-ferns the lower part especially of the erect stem is quite covered with slender roots, and these as they grow downwards form an envelope several inches thick before they enter the ground, and thus give a broad base to the stem which is really much thinner in this part; on the upper portions of the stem also the roots are very numerous. They are very slender in small plants, on larger stems they may be from one to three millimetres in thickness; they are cylindrical in shape, usually covered with a felt of numerous hairs, and are coloured brown or black. The history of the development of the roots of Ferns has been studied by Nägeli and Leitgeb[1] (Fig. 162). The apical cell is a three-sided pyramid with an equilateral base; the segments of the root-cap cut off by curved transverse walls are first divided each into four cells, arranged crosswise in such a manner that the inter-sections in the successive segments alternate at an angle of about 45°; each of the four cells of a segment then divides into two outer and one inner or central cell, so that the segment is now formed of four inner cells placed crosswise and eight outer cells; further divisions may then take place; the cells in the middle of the segment grow more rapidly in the direction of the axis of the root and may divide by trans-verse walls, so that the segment comes to be of two or more layers in the middle. The formation of a segment of the root-cap is usually followed by the formation of three segments of the root before a new segment of the root-cap appears; the root segments lie in three straight longitudinal rows answering to the three-sided apical cell. Each of the triangular tabular segments takes in a third of the circumference of the root and is first divided by a radial longitudinal wall into two unequal halves; a transverse section of the root now shows six cells (sextants), three of which meet in the centre, while the other three do not quite reach the central point. Each of these six cells then divides by a periclinal wall (parallel to the surface), into an inner and an outer cell; the inner belongs to the vascular bundle, which is therefore formed of six cells lying about the centre, while the six outer cells are the rudiments of the cortex.

The roots of the Ferns, like the roots of the Equisetaceae, branch monopodially; the lateral roots are formed in acropetal succession on the outside of the primordial vascular bundle, usually in two rows, seldom in three or four. The mother-cells of the lateral roots belong to the innermost layer of the cortex and are separated by the pericambium from the vascular bundle of the primary root; the roots begin to appear near the apex before the formation of the vessels. There are no adventitious lateral roots, that is, roots arising behind those already formed. The mother-cell of a lateral root first of all forms a three-sided pyramidal apical cell by three oblique divisions, and from this cell the first segment of the root-cap proceeds. If two primordial vascular bundles are formed in the lateral root, they lie right and left of the primary root. The cortex of the primary root is simply broken through, no root-sheath being formed.

The *hair-structures* in the Ferns are very various in form. True root-hairs, simple unsegmented tubes, are found not only on the roots, but also on underground stems and on the bases of leaf-stalks, as in *Pteris aquilina* and the Hymenophyllaceae.

---

[1] Sitzungsber. d. bair. Akad. d. Wiss. 15, Dec. 1865.—[Bower, On the apex of the root in Osmunda and Todea (Q. J. M. Sc. 1885).]

An abundance of usually brownish or dark brown flat pluricellular hairs, which soon become dried up, occurs on aerial creeping stems and on their leaf-stalks; these are the chaff-scales or *paleae* which often quite conceal the buds and may be from one to six centimetres in length (*Polypodium, Cibotium,* &c.). Long stout bristles appear sometimes on the laminae of leaves, as in *Acrostichum crinitum,* and not unfrequently fine delicate pluricellular hairs.

The *sporangia* of Ferns are small roundish capsules with a long stalk in the Polypodiaceae and Cyatheaceae, but sessile in all other Ferns. The wall of the mature capsule is formed of one layer of cells; a row of cells in this layer running straight or obliquely across the capsule or down its length is developed in a peculiar manner and forms the *annulus*; the contraction of the annulus by drying causes the capsule to burst at right angles to the plane of the annulus; in some cases instead of the annulus an apical or lateral group of cells of the wall is developed in a similar manner.

FIG. 163. *Aspidium Filix-mas.* Under side of a pinnule showing eight indusia *i*, twice the natural size.

The sporangia are usually collected in groups, each of which is termed a *sorus*; the sorus contains a small fixed number, or a large indefinite number of sporangia, and between them occur not unfrequently delicate pluricellular hairs, the *paraphyses.* A luxuriant growth from the leaf, the *indusium*, often covers over the entire sorus with a kind of roof, or surrounds it as with a cup, or even incloses it entirely as in a capsule. The indusium is often only an excrescence of the epidermis, but in other cases it is formed by an outgrowth of the tissue of the leaf

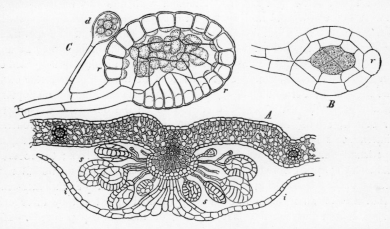

FIG. 164. *Aspidium Filix-mas. A* transverse section of a leaf with a sorus consisting of the sporangia *s* and the indusium *i i*; a small vascular bundle is seen on each side in the mesophyll of the leaf, the cells of the sheaths showing the dark brown thickenings on the inner walls. *B* young sporangium with the annulus perpendicular to the plane of the paper; *r* its uppermost cell; four cells are visible in the interior, formed by division of the central cell. *C* side-view of an almost mature sporangium; *r r* the annulus, *d* the stalked gland peculiar to this species; the young spores appear just formed in the sporangium.

itself, and is then composed of several layers of cells, and may even have stomata. In the Lygodieae each separate sporangium is enveloped in a pocket-shaped formation from the tissue of the leaf, as if in a bract; in this case[1] the indusium grows up

---

[1] Prantl, Untersuch. ü. d. Gefässkryptogamen, Heft II. (Schizaeaceen).

from underneath the young sporangium on the margin of the leaf in the form of an annular wall, which incloses the sporangium in a pocket; the upper side of the wall has the structure of the upper side of the leaf. A false indusium, which is not, like those above described, a new formation from the leaf, is produced by the folding or rolling back of the margin of the leaf over the sorus, as in *Allosurus*, *Cheilanthes*, and many species of *Pteris*.

Sori are not generally formed on all the leaves of the full-grown plant; sometimes groups of fertile leaves alternate at regular periods with groups of sterile leaves, as in *Struthiopteris germanica*; sometimes the sori are distributed uniformly over the whole of the surface of a leaf, in other cases they are confined to certain sections of it. The fertile leaves may be in other respects similar to the sterile, or they may be strikingly different from them; the latter case is often the result of the total or partial absence of the mesophyll between and near the fertile veins; the fertile leaf or the fertile portion of the leaf then looks like a spike or panicle of sporangia, as in *Osmunda* and *Aneimia*. The sporangia are usually formed on the veins of the leaf, and on the under surface or on the margin of the lamina; but in the Acrostichaceae they are derived from the mesophyll, as well as from the veins; in *Olfersia* they cover both surfaces of the leaf by the side of the mid-rib, in *Acrostichum* only the under surface. Where, as is usually the case, the veins alone bear the sporangia, the fertile veins may be similar to the sterile, or the fertile undergo certain changes at the spots where they bear the sori; they may swell up into the form of a cushion, and so form a *receptacle*, or, as it would be better to call it, a *placenta*, for the receptacle in the Ferns is homologous with the placenta in the Phanerogams; or they project beyond the margin of the leaf, as in the Hymeno-phyllaceae. The sorus may be on the extremity

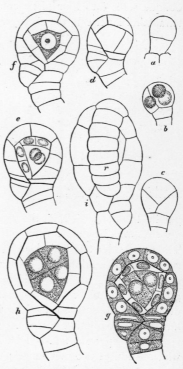

FIG. 165. Development of the sporangium of *Asplenium Trichomanes*; order of succession according to the letters *a—i*. In *i r* is the annulus; the other figures are given in optical longitudinal section and the annulus would be perpendicular to the paper. Magn. 550 times.

of a vein, which then often forms two branches in the angle of which the sorus is placed, or it is on the dorsal surface of the vein behind its extremity, or it runs for some distance along the side of the vein; the fertile veins sometimes run close to the margin of the leaf, or they may be near the mid-rib or in some other part of the lamina[1].

The process in the *development of the sporangium*[2] is essentially the same in all

---

[1] [Čelakovský, Unters. ü. d. Homolog. d. generativ. Prod. d. Fruchtbl. b. d. Phanerog. und Gefässkrypt. in Pringsheim's Jahrb. XIV, 1883.]

[2] Reess, Entwickl. d. Polypod.-Sporang. (Pringsheim's Jahrb. V, 1866).—Russow, Vergl. Unters. Petersbourg, 1872.—Prantl, Untersuch. ü. d. Gefässkrypt. I. and II.

the Ferns which have been examined as that which will now be described for the Polypodiaceae[1]. The sporangium originates in a papilla-like outgrowth of one of the epidermal cells which give rise to the sorus. The papilla is cut off by a transverse wall, and becomes the mother-cell of the sporangium; after further elongation a transverse wall next divides it into a lower cell which produces the stalk and an upper which becomes the capsule of the sporangium. The stalk-cell is transformed by intercalary transverse divisions and longitudinal walls usually into three rows of cells; the nearly hemispherical mother-cell of the capsule is first divided by four successive oblique walls into four plano-convex outer cells which form the outer wall, and a tetrahedral inner cell, the *archesporium*; further divisions perpendicular to the surface then appear in the cells of the outer wall, while the archesporium forms four tabular segments, which lie parallel to the outer cells forming the wall; these inner parietal cells divide in planes at right angles to the surface of the capsule, and may even separate into two layers which together form the *tapetum*. The cells of the wall which are to form the annulus further divide by septa which are perpendicular to the surface of the sporangium and to the median line of the annulus and are

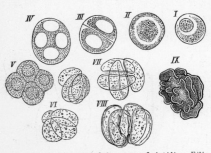

FIG. 166. Development of the spores of *Aspidium Filix-mas*; magn. 550 times. See the text.

parallel to one another, till the proper number of the cells of the annulus is obtained; the cells then become convex outwards and project above the surface of the capsule. Then while the tetrahedral archesporium forms the mother-cells of the spores by successive bipartitions, the cells of the tapetum are dissolved, and the inner space of the sporangium is considerably enlarged by this means and by the surface growth of the outer wall, so that the mass of the spore-mother-cells, the number of which according to Russow is usually sixteen, floats free in the fluid which fills the sporangium (Fig. 164).

Every spore-mother-cell has a distinct nucleus (Fig. 166 *I*)[2], the division of which produces two new nuclei; each divides again, and so four new smaller nuclei are seen (Fig. 166 *IV*); the mother-cell thereupon breaks up into four spore-cells, (*V*), the relative position of which varies, as appears from *VI, VII, VIII*; next the spore is invested with a membrane, which becomes differentiated into an endosporium showing the reaction of cellulose in *Osmunda* and other genera, but not in *Gleichenia* and some others, and a brown cuticularised exosporium with ridges on its surface; the contents of the spore form chlorophyll in the Osmundaceae and Hymenophyllaceae. In various other Polypodiaceae the course of formation of the spores according to Russow runs somewhat differently; the mother-cell divides into four rather thick-walled compartments, the so-called special mother-cells, as in the formation of pollen in the Phanerogams, whereupon the protoplasm of each compartment becomes

---

[1] Sporangia are found in every stage of development in the same sorus.
[2] The figure was drawn when the circumstances connected with the division of the nucleus were not yet known, and its details therefore are not shown in *II, III*, and *IV*.

invested with the permanent wall of the spore, and the wall of the mother-cell and of the compartments is then absorbed. Spores of the form given in Fig. 166 are said to be bilateral, in contradistinction to those which are formed after the four nuclei were arranged tetrahedrally in the mother-cell, and have therefore a rounded tetrahedral form ; the latter only are said to occur in the Hymenophyllaceae, Osmundaceae and Cyatheaceae, in the other families sometimes the one kind, sometimes the other is found. The mode of formation of the walls still requires explanation in some points.

The development of the sporangia in the other Filicineae agrees with the above description in the main points, that the sporangium proceeds from a single epidermal cell, and that it forms a tetrahedral[1] archesporium, which first gives off the tapetal cells and then divides to form the spore-mother-cell. But there are several variations in points connected with the position of the sporangia. For instance, in *Ceratopteris* they are not collected into sori and are not placed on a placenta, but are formed one by one, while the sporophyll is still rolled up, from the superficial cells of the under side of the leaf in acropetal succession, which is however interrupted by intercalations. In the Hymenophyllaceae the placenta is formed by the extremity of a vein which is prolonged beyond the surface of the leaf, and on which the sporangia arise in basipetal succession, as in the Polypodiaceae. The sorus is surrounded by a cup-shaped indusium. In *Aneimia* and *Lygodium* the sporangia are formed singly from cells of the margin of the leaf, and the arrangement of the cells also is somewhat different. The first step in the formation of the sporangium is the arching outwards of a cell of the leaf-margin. An anticlinal wall appears after the formation of the basal (periclinal) wall of this cell, then a wall inclined in the opposite direction to the anticlinal wall, then a wall parallel to the first wall, then a periclinal wall (parallel to the margin of the leaf) which separates off an outer parietal cell and the archesporium ; this has not the form of a tetrahedron, but more nearly that of a quadrant of a cylinder, the difference from the ordinary condition being due to the origin of the sporangium on the margin of the leaf. The annulus in the Schizaeaceae is formed from a group of cells with thickened walls which lies on the apex of the sporangium. The sporangia open by a longitudinal fissure, at right angles therefore to the annulus (in the Polypodiaceae by a transverse fissure). The peculiar formation of the indusium of *Lygodium* has been already mentioned. The sporangia of the Osmundaceae according to Prantl follow the customary course of development, and are collected into sori without indusia.

a. **Histology**[2]. The epidermis of the leaves of Ferns is distinguished by the presence of chlorophyll in its cells, while that substance is usually absent from the epidermal cells of phanerogamous land-plants, and by the peculiar construction of its stomata. Fig. 167 shows that in *Pteris flabellata* a small cell is taken out of an epidermal cell by a wall which is curved in the shape of a watch-glass ; this cell is either itself the mother-cell of the stoma, or the mother cell is cut off from it by a second anticlinal

---

[1] With regard to the Schizaeaceae see below.

[2] De Bary, Vergleich. Anatomie, pp. 181, 289, 355, etc.—[Polonie, Ueber d. Zusammensetz. d. Leitbündel d. Gefässkrypt. (Jahrb. Kön. Gart. Berlin, II, 1883).—Terletzki, Anat. d. Vegetationsorgane von Struthiopteris u. Pteris (Pringsheim's Jahrb. XV, 1884).]

wall. In *Aneimia* on the other hand the stomata are in the middle of an epidermal cell (Fig. 169 *s*). This peculiar position, which occurs also in *Polypodium Lingua*, is

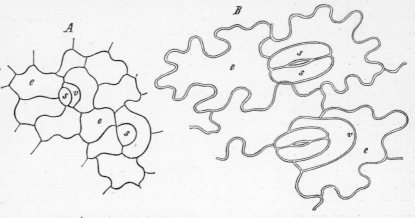

FIG. 167. *Pteris flabellata;* development of the stomata. *A* very young, *B* nearly mature epidermal cells; *s* in *A* mother-cell of the guard-cells, *v* preparatory cell.

due to the circumstance that the wall of the mother-cell of the stoma has the form of a ring narrowing conically inwards, and set at right angles to the surface of the

FIG. 168. Portion of a leaf of *Adiantum* (nat. size) with the nerves spreading fan-like from the base of the leaf, and bifurcating repeatedly.

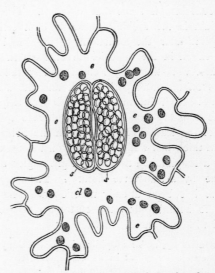

FIG. 169. *Aneimia fraxinifolia.* Surface-view of a stoma lying in the middle of an epidermal cell; *s s* guard-cells of the stoma, *e* epidermis, *cl* chlorophyll-corpuscles.

epidermis, but touching no side wall. Occasionally we find here too an arrangement such as is shown in Fig. 167.

The *fundamental tissue* of the stem and of the leaf-stalk is in many species, such as *Polypodium aureum, P. vulgare, Aspidium Filix-mas,* composed entirely of thin-walled parenchyma ; in other kinds, as *Gleichenia,* species of *Pteris* and in the Tree-ferns, certain portions of the fundamental tissue in the form of strings, ribbons or

threads become differentiated from the rest, and their cells become firm and prosenchymatous with their walls much thickened and of a brown colour. Two such thick
bands of sclerenchyma (Fig. 179 *A*, *pr*) run in the stem of *Pteris aquilina* between the
inner and outer vascular bundles, and slender threads of sclerenchyma appear as dark
points on the transverse section of the colourless parenchyma. In other cases, as in
Polypodium vaccinifolium and the Tree-ferns, dark layers of sclerenchyma, the nature
of which was first correctly conceived by Von Mohl, form thick and very firm sheaths
round the vascular bundles, and are the chief cause of the stiffness of the erect stem.
In stouter stems and leaf-stalks the outer layer also of the fundamental tissue immediately beneath the epidermis is often dark brown and sclerenchymatous and forms a hard
and firm shell, as for instance in *Pteris aquilina* (Fig. 179 *A*, *r*) and in the Tree-ferns.
In order to ensure communication in spite of this solid coat of mail, between the outer
air and the inner parenchyma, which is rich in assimilated material, this hard shell is

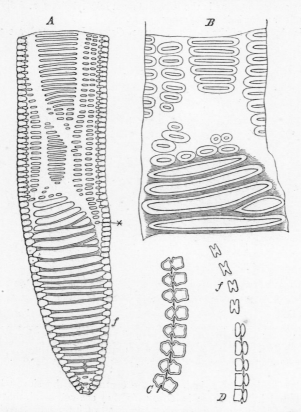

FIG. 170. Rhizome of *Pteris aquilina*. *A* end of a short member of a vessel. The oblique scalariform surface
of the extremity *f*, and a portion of the lateral wall in surface view. *B* a portion of *A* at ×. *C* thin longitudinal section
through part of a lateral wall, where the surfaces of two vessels touch one another. *D* a similar section through the
oblique partition wall *f* and its margin adjoining the lateral wall. At *f* the pits are open. From De Bary. Vergl. Anat.
A magn. 142, *B* and *C* 375 times.

interrupted in *Pteris aquilina* on the two sides of the stem, and there the colourless
parenchyma comes to the outer surface ; in the Tree-ferns, on the other hand, there are
pits in the swollen bases of the leaves, where the sclerenchyma is replaced, according
to Mohl, by a loose and pulverulent tissue.

We may notice here in passing a circumstance which stands alone in histology, that in *Aspidium Filix-mas* according to Schacht rounded stalked glands occur in the fundamental tissue of the stem; Sachs has found them also in the green parenchyma of the leaves and on the stalks of sporangia of the same plant (Fig. 164 *C, d*).

It is only in the Hymenophyllaceae that the lamina of the leaf is formed, as in the Mosses, of a single layer of cells; in all other Ferns it is of several layers, and between the upper and lower epidermis lies the mesophyll, a spongy parenchyma rich in chlorophyll and traversed by the vascular bundles which form the venation of the leaf. The course of the veins is very various; sometimes they run from below upwards and sideways spreading like a fan and branching dichotomously with acute angles, without anastomosing and without forming a stouter mid-rib (Fig. 168); more commonly the undivided lamina or a lacinia of the lobed, divided or pinnate leaf is traversed by an evident though only slightly projecting median vein, from which finer veinlets run branching monopodially or dichotomously to the lateral margins; sometimes these slenderer veins anastomose, as in the leaves of most Dicotyledons, and divide the surface into areolae of characteristic appearance.

The vascular bundles of the stems of Ferns, *Osmunda* excepted, are concentric, that

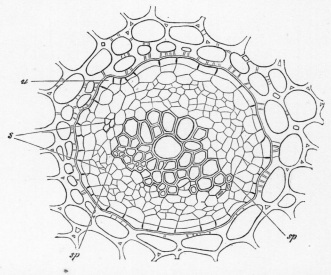

Fig. 171. *Polypodium vulgare.* Transverse section through a weak vascular bundle of the creeping stem (rhizome); *s* the phloem (the sieve-tube structure not clear), *sp* narrow spiral tracheides of the xylem, the larger part of the elements of the bundle being scalariform tracheides; *u* the endodermis (bundle-sheath) evidently formed by tangential division from the same cell-layer as the layer of parenchyma which adjoins it on the inside; on the outside of *u* parenchyma with pitted cell-walls, the pits being shown in the figure only in a few places. From De Bary, Vergl. Anat.

is, the vascular portion, the xylem, is in the centre, and the sieve-tube portion, the phloem, lies round it (Fig. 171); in *Osmunda* they are collateral, that is, the phloem lies beside the xylem and usually somewhat in front of it towards the circumference of the stem. Collateral bundles are found also in the leaves of many Ferns.

In the xylem of the bundle we rarely find true vessels with perforated walls; it usually consists chiefly of long broad scalariform tracheides with bordered pits. True vessels occur in *Pteris aquilina* with septa perforated in a scalariform manner (Fig. 170). At certain points between or more rarely outside these scalariform tracheides are found a few narrow spiral and narrow scalariform tracheides, the primary formations of the xylem (protoxylem), the starting points of the development of the broad tracheides (Fig. 171). Sometimes tracheides occur in the xylem of the vascular bundle; sometimes narrow thin-walled cells, which contain starch in winter, are found lying among them, as in *Pteris aquilina* (Fig. 172). The xylem in the concentric bundles (Fig. 171) is surrounded by the phloem containing parenchymatous cells as well as sieve-tubes. In Fig. 172, which is a transverse section from *Pteris aquilina*, outside the xylem there is first of all a layer of parenchymatous cells containing starch, next the large sieve-tubes (*sp*), then a zone of narrow, thick-walled elements, which are either some peculiar form of cells (bast-fibres of Dippel) or must be reckoned with the sieve-tubes (protophloem of Russow), then another layer of parenchyma containing starch, and lastly the bundle-sheath or endodermis (*sg*) ; the latter cell-layer forms a very distinct boundary line round the vascular bundle, and consists of compressed cells with walls which early become transformed into cork and have usually a brownish colour. This layer and the layer of parenchyma next inside it are the product of a

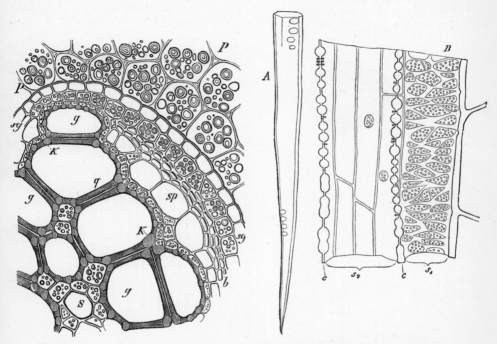

FIG. 172. A fourth part of the transverse section of a vascular bundle in the stem of *Pteris aquilina* with the surrounding parenchyma *PP* containing starch ; *sg* the endodermis, *b* the bast-fibres or protophloem of Russow, *sp* the large sieve-tubes, *qq* the wide vessels thickened in a scalariform manner, *s* a spiral vessel surrounded by cells containing starch, *K* thickened wall of vessel between the pits. Magn. 300 times.

FIG. 173. *Pteris aquilina*. *A* extremity of a sieve-tube isolated by maceration. *B* piece of a longitudinal section ; *s₁* and *s₂* sieve-tubes roughly bisected, *s₁* is bounded on the right by cells of the parenchyma, on the left by *s₂* ; the whole of the smooth-walled posterior side of *s₂* adjoins parenchyma, (the nucleus is shown in two of the cells) ; *cc* transverse section of the walls bearing sieve-pits. From De Bary, Vergl. Anat. *A* magn. 142, *B* 375 times.

single layer of the fundamental tissue which afterwards divides into two. In smaller bundles the sieve-tubes are often not easy to recognise ; in *Pteris aquilina* (Fig. 173) they have long narrow points and sieve-plates on the side walls. It was said above that *Osmunda* has collateral bundles, which are seen in a transverse section to be arranged in a circle and to be separated from one another by parenchymatous tissue. The phloem-regions are on the outside toward the circumference and are connected together into a circular zone.

Through the young plants in all Ferns runs a single axile bundle which is a sympodium of the leaf-trace bundles ; the first bundle, which generally comes to an abrupt termination in the foot of the embryo, runs a short distance through the stem and then bends into the first leaf; from the point where it turns off another bundle begins and bends into the second leaf, and this proceeding is repeated indefinitely. An axile bundle is found also in a number of Ferns with slender stems, as in the Hymenophyllaceae, *Gleichenia, Lygodium,* species of *Schizaea* and others, and also in the heterosporous Filices *Salvinia* and *Azolla.* In the Osmundaceae (Figs. 174–176) the vascular bundles are arranged so as to form a cylinder, and this is inclosed by a sclerosed cortical tissue through which the bundles run obliquely outwards into the leaves, one into each leaf; those which pass into the first leaves of the young plant unite into a single axile bundle in which there is no medullary tissue, and this gradually opens out into the ring of bundles surrounding a pith. A similar process takes place in most Ferns; the original axile bundle of the young plant becomes a cylinder which incloses the pith and is itself inclosed by a parenchymatous rind; there is a gap, the foliar gap, in the tube opposite the point of insertion of every leaf, and from its margin the bundles pass into the leaf; everywhere else the cylinder is closed, or its con-

FIG. 174.

FIG. 175.

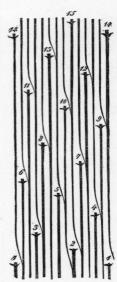

FIG. 176.

FIGS. 174–176. *Osmunda regalis.* FIG. 174. Transverse section of a strong stem, about twice the natural size; *i* lowest leaf-trace-bundle with a root-bundle going off from it through the rind. FIG. 175. Sketch of the vascular bundle-cylinder of the former fig. more highly magnified; 1 lowest leaf trace-bundle cut through exactly where it enters the cylinder with one of the two root-bundles which are attached to it at this point; 1–13 the leaf-trace-bundles of the thirteen successive leaves seen in the transverse section (10 being united abnormally with 2). FIG. 176. Diagrammatic representation of the course of the vascular bundles in the stem when the cylinder is projected in one plane and with a phyllotaxis of $\frac{5}{13}$. The foliar bundles are numbered at their point of exit according to their genetic succession, each with two root-bundles indicated by two short transverse strokes; 2 and 10 show the irregularity indicated in the transverse section. From De Bary, Vergl. Anat.

tinuity is broken by perforations giving it a net-like character. Separate bundles are sometimes found in the pith and in the cortical tissue along with this simple cylinder, or several concentric cylinders (rings) may be formed.

The simplest case is where the originally axile bundle opens out as the stem strengthens into a cylinder, which is usually closed all round except at the insertion of the leaves, and there the parenchyma of the pith communicates with the cortical tissue through the foliar gap, from the margin of which one or more bundles pass into the leaf; examples are to be seen in the species of *Marsilia,* in *Pilularia globulifera,* and others.

Most Ferns with ascending or erect rhizomes or stems differ from the type just described in having the foliar gaps large and the bands of the vascular bundle-cylinder comparatively narrow. To this class belong the many species of the Polypodiaceae, of which *Aspidium Filix-mas* may serve as an example. A like arrangement is found in the Ophioglosseae which will be described further on. E in Fig. 158 shows the network of bundles with the large foliar gaps of an older stem ; each leaf receives several bundles from the edge of its gap. The transverse section in Fig. 177 shows the network of bundles forming a circle, and outside of it in the rind the smaller bundles which pass obliquely upwards into the bases of the leaves. The conditions are more simple in the young plant ; the leaf-trace bundles are here united at first in the stem into a solid axile bundle ; then the stem increases in thickness and the formation of

FIG. 177. *Aspidium Filix-mas.* Transverse section through a strong stem with a phyllotaxis of 8/21. From De Bary, Vergl. Anat.

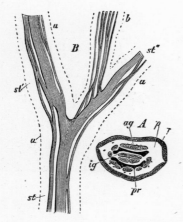

FIG. 179. *Pteris aquilina. A* transverse section of the stem; *r* its brown epidermis with a layer of sclerenchyma beneath it; *p* colourless soft parenchyma of the fundamental tissue, *pr* brown layers of sclerenchyma of the fundamental tissue, *ig* inner vascular bundles (upper and lower bundles), *ag* upper broad middle strand of the outer network. *B* isolated upper middle strand of the outer (cortical) network *st* and its branches *st'* and *st''* ; *b* bundles of the leaf stalk, *aa* outline of the stem. Natural size.

FIG. 178. *Aspidium caria-ceum,* rhizome slightly magnified. *A* system of vascular bundles in the cylinder laid out flat. *B* transverse section. *o* upper bundle, *u* lower bundle, both conspicuous in the transverse section from their greater breadth. After Mettenius.

the reticulated vascular bundle-cylinder begins ; at this stage each leaf receives a single bundle from the lower angle of the foliar gap ; in the second year the leaves receive several bundles from the edge of the foliar gap, and the number may be as high as seven in vigorous full-grown stems. In horizontal stems with two rows of leaves foliar gaps are found placed alternately right and left on the lateral faces of the stem. A transverse section shows a circle of bundles ; one of these bundles runs along the upper or dorsal side and one along the under or ventral side ; they are more developed than the others and are known as the upper and lower bundle.

[2]   Q

Several concentric rings of bundles are found in a number of fern-stems with many rows of leaves, as in *Pteris*, in species of *Saccoloma*, in the Marattiaceae and *Ceratopteris*. *Pteris aquilina* is one of this number. In its underground stem are seen an upper and a lower bundle (the two long central ones at *ig* in Fig. 179), and this vascular bundle-cylinder is strengthened by a cortical system of many accessory bundles (Fig. 179 *ag*). The young plant has an axile crescent-shaped vascular bundle up to the time of the formation of the seventh and ninth leaves, then the stem forks. As the branches increase in thickness the course of the bundles alters. The axile bundle divides into an upper and under one, and thus the upper and lower bundles are formed, and these split up by forking into slenderer branches which soon unite again (Fig. 179 *B, st, st*). When the branches are about six centimetres long and four millimetres thick, weaker branches are given off from the two bundles, and these pursue their course through the cortex near the surface, where they form a net-work with long

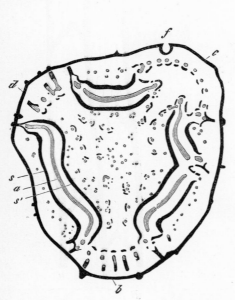

FIG. 180. *Cyathea Imrayana*: transverse section through the fresh stem, nat. size. All the quite black bands and points are sections through sclerenchyma, all the lighter through vascular bundles. In or near the leaf areas, especially *b* and *d*, are root-bundles going to the periphery; *f* small pits of the base of the leaf, *a* vascular bundle of the main tube, *s* outer, *s'* inner plate of its sclerenchymatous sheath. Inside *s'* the pith, outside *s* the cortex, with their small bundles. From De Bary, Vergl. Anat.

FIG. 181. Piece of a fresh stem of *Cyathea Imrayana* with the bases of four leaf stalks after peeling off the outer layers of the cortex, seen from without. The margins of four foliar gaps, the bundles which spring from them and go into the leaves with the rudimentary roots (black) rising on them, and the small bundles which descend in the cortex, are laid bare; the latter and the roots are quite free, the other parts are still covered by some transparent parenchyma, through which they are clearly seen, and which holds all the parts together in their natural position. Natural size. From De Bary, Vergl. Anat.

narrow meshes, the upper middle strand (Fig. 179 *A, ag*) of which is distinguished by its size. The rhizome retains this structure when fully grown; the peripheral net-work of bundles is separated from the cylinder formed by the upper and lower bundles by two stout plates of brown sclerenchyma (Fig. 179 *pr*). Branch-bundles pass from both net-works into the branches and leaves, into the roots only from the outer.

Cyathea Imrayana (Figs. 180 and 181) may serve as an example of the occurrence of bundles in the pith and cortical tissue along with the simple vascular cylinder. Those in the cortex proceed from the bundles which pass into the leaf, those in the pith from the foliar gaps.

Taxonomic summary of the homosporous Ferns. The main divisions are as follows :—

1. HYMENOPHYLLEAE. The sporangia have an oblique or transverse complete annulus and open therefore by a longitudinal fissure; they are formed on a prolongation of the fertile vein, the columella or placenta, which projects beyond the margin of the leaf and is surrounded by a cup-shaped indusium. The mesophyll of the leaf is usually formed of a single layer of cells, and in that case is necessarily without stomata ; stomata are found on the leaf of *Loxosoma*[1], which has more than one layer. The stem is often creeping and usually very slender and furnished with an axile vascular bundle. True roots are not found in all the species; where they are wanting the stem is itself clothed with root-hairs; a large number of species of *Trichomanes* were considered by Mettenius to be without roots, and in these cases the ramifications of the stem assume a deceptive appearance of roots. The axes grow more rapidly than the leaves develope, and it is not uncommon for several internodes to have fully completed their growth while their leaves are still quite small ; these apparently, or perhaps really, leafless shoots often branch repeatedly. The formation of the tissue also has many peculiarities, on which Mettenius should be consulted (Hymenophyllaceae, *l. c.*). The fertile extremity (columella) of the vein, which projects beyond the margin of the leaf, elongates by intercalary growth, and new sporangia are accordingly produced in basipetal succession ; they are arranged on the columella in a spiral line, and are sessile and biconvex, being attached to the columella by one of the convex faces. The annulus which forms a cushion-like protuberance between the two convexities is usually oblique and divides the circumference into two unequal portions ; in *Loxosoma* the sporangia are pear-shaped and distinctly stalked. Paraphyses occur in some species of *Hymenophyllum* only.

2. CYATHEACEAE. The sporangia have a complete, oblique excentric annulus and a short stalk, and are placed on a placenta which is often greatly developed ; they form a sorus which is usually closely packed, and is either naked or surrounded by a cup-shaped indusium which sometimes forms a closed capsule. The Tree-ferns are included in the genera *Cibotium, Balantium, Alsophila, Hemitelia,* and *Cyathea* ; they have tall erect unbranched stems often thickly clothed with roots, which bear on their tops a rosette of large usually compoundly pinnate leaves.

3. POLYPODIACEAE. The sporangia are very numerous on the under side of usually unaltered leaves with a vertical incomplete annulus, and they dehisce transversely. The very numerous species have been arranged by Mettenius in the following subdivisions :—

a. Acrosticheae. The sorus covers the mesophyll and veins of the under surface or of both surfaces of the leaf, or is placed on a thickened placenta running along the vein : there is no indusium (*Acrostichum, Polybotrya*).

b. Polypodieae. The sorus is attached along the course of the veins, or of special anastomoses of the veins, or on the back or on the thickened extremity of a vein ; it is naked or rarely has a lateral indusium (*Polypodium, Adiantum, Pteris*).

c. Asplenieae. Sorus unilateral on the course of the veins, and almost always covered with a lateral indusium, seldom without an indusium, or the apex of the sorus arches over the back of the vein and is covered by an indusium that springs from it, or it occupies special anastomoses of the veins, and is unilateral and covered by an indusium which is free on the side of the vein ; the leaf-stalk is not articulated (*Blechnum, Asplenium, Scolopendrium*).

d. Aspidieae. The sorus is dorsal with an indusium, rarely terminal and without an indusium (*Aspidium, Phegopteris*).

e. Davallieae. The sorus is terminal or where a vein forks with an indusium, or on

---

[1] One species only of this genus is known from New Zealand, and by some botanists is made the type of a distinct family.

an intramarginal anastomosing bend of the veins and covered by a cup-shaped indusium which is free at the outer margin (*Davallia, Nephrolepis*).

4. GLEICHENIACEAE. Sporangia without stalks, usually three or four together in a sorus, without indusium on the dorsal surface of ordinary leaves, with a complete transverse annulus in the centre of the sporangium and longitudinal dehiscence. Stem a slender creeping rhizome ; leaves with peculiar innovation of the lamina.

5. OSMUNDACEAE. In *Osmunda* the sporangia are arranged in panicles and placed on the laciniae of leaves which have no mesophyll ; in *Todea* the fertile leaves resemble the sterile. The sporangia are on short stalks and of an unsymmetrical roundish form ; they have on one side of their apex a group of peculiarly shaped cells, and open by a longitudinal fissure on the other. The short stem, which is very densely covered with roots, gives rise to similar lateral shoots. The structure of the stem which has been described above is remarkable; the course of the vascular bundles resembles that in the Coniferae and Dicotyledons.

6. SCHIZAEACEAE. The laciniae which bear the sporangia are arranged in spikes or panicles, except in *Mohria*, where the sporangia are on the under surface of the leaf near the margin which is turned back over them, the indusium being a con-tinuation of the leaf margin; in *Schizaea* and *Lygodium* the sporangia are in two rows on the under side of very reduced laciniae, and in *Lygodium* each sporangium is covered by a pocket-shaped indusium : in *Aneimia* the two lowest branches of the lamina have no mesophyll and form panicles with long stalks, on the ultimate ramifications of which the sporangia arise in acropetal succession from the marginal cells of the segment of the leaf. In the other Schizaeaceae also the sporangia proceed from mar-ginal cells, and subsequently appear displaced on the under side of the leaf. *Schizaea* has bilateral spores ; in the other genera they are roundish-tetrahedral. The ovoid or pear-shaped sporangia are sessile ; their apex is occupied by a cap-like zone of peculiarly formed cells ; the dehiscence is longitudinal. The stem, except in *Aneimia* and *Mohria*, appears occasionally to remain unbranched, and is very feebly developed; the leaf-stalks have only one vascular bundle ; the leaves of *Lygodium* resemble a climbing stem.

2. HETEROSPOROUS FILICINEAE OR HYDROPTERIDEAE[1].

The heterosporous Filicineae, once grouped together under the highly unsuitable name of Rhizocarpae, fall naturally into two families, one of which, the Salviniaceae, comes very near to the homosporous Ferns, while the other, the Marsiliaceae, exhibits a special type of its own in the formation of its sporocarps. Although the two families therefore are derived from different original stocks among the homosporous

---

[1] Bischoff, Die Rhizokarpeen u. Lycopodiaceen (Nürnberg, 1828).—Hofmeister, Vgl. Unters. 1851, p. 103 ;—Id. Ueber d. Keimung d. *Salvinia natans* (Abh. d. Kön. Sächs. Ges. d. Wiss. 1857, p. 665).—Pringsheim, Zur Morph. d. *Salvinia natans* (Jahrb. f. wiss. Bot. iv. 1863).—Hanstein, Befruchtung u. Entw. d. Gattung *Marsilia* (Jahrb. f. wiss. Bot. iv. 1865) ;—Id. *Pilulariae globuliferae* generatio cum *Marsilia* comparata (Bonn, 1866).—Nägeli u. Leitgeb, Ueber Entstehung u. Wachsthum d. Wurzeln beid. Gefässkryptogamen in Nägeli's Beitr. z. wiss. Bot. iv. 1867.—Millardet, Le prothallium mâle des Cryptogames vasculaires, Strasbourg, 1869.—A. Braun, Ueber *Marsilia* u. *Pilularia* (Monatsber. d. kgl. Akad. d. Wiss. Berlin, 1870 u. 1872).—Russow, Vergl. Unter. Petersburg, 1872.—Strasburger, Ueber *Azolla*, Jena, 1873.—Juranyi, Ueber d. Entw. d. Spo-rangien u. Sporen von *Salvinia natans*, Berlin, 1873.—Arcangeli, Sulla *Pilularia* e la *Salvinia* (Nuovo Giornale Bot. Ital. vol. viii. 1876).—Leitgeb, Zur Embryologie d. Farne (Akad. d. Wiss. zu Wien, 1878).—Prantl, Zur Entwickl. Gesch. d. Prothallium von *Salvinia natans* (Bot. Zeit. 1879, p. 425).—Sadebeck, Keimung von Marsilia-Mikrosporen, *loc. cit.* [Bower, Comp. Morph of the leaf in Vasc. Crypt. and Gymnosp. (Phil. Trans. 1884).]

Ferns, we shall nevertheless describe them together in this place on account of the many points which they have in common in their life-history.

The *first* or *sexual generation* (*oophore, oophyte*) of the heterosporous Ferns is developed from two different kinds of spores; the small spores produce only spermatozoids and are therefore of the male sex; the large spores, which are several hundred times larger than the others, produce a small prothallium which never separates from the spore and forms one or more archegonia; the macrospores may therefore themselves be said to be female.

The microspores produce a very rudimentary prothallium and an antheridium.

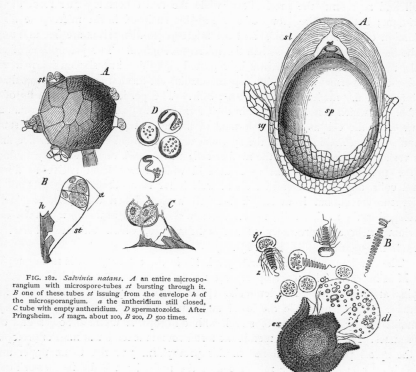

FIG. 182. *Salvinia natans.* *A* an entire microsporangium with microspore-tubes *st* bursting through it. *B* one of these tubes *st* issuing from the envelope *h* of the microsporangium. *a* the antheridium still closed. *C* tube with empty antheridium. *D* spermatozoids. After Pringsheim. *A* magn. about 100, *B* 200, *D* 500 times.

FIG. 183. *Marsilia Salvatrix.* *A* a macrospore *sp* with its mucilaginous envelope *sl* and the apical papilla projecting into its funnel and enclosing a broad yellowish drop; *sg* the ruptured wall of the macrosporangium. *B* a microspore which has burst and discharged the spermatozoids; *ex* the exosporium, *dl* the protruded endosporium containing granules, *zz* the spirally twisted spermatozoids, *yy* their vesicles with grains of starch. The gelatinous envelope of the microspore has disappeared; the exosporium does not show the arrangement of the protuberances which is incorrectly indicated in the figure. *A* magn. about 300, *B* 550 times.

In *Salvinia* they are imbedded in a mass of hardened granular frothy mucilage which fills the entire microsporangium, and are not discharged from the sporangium, but each of them puts out a tube from its endosporium which pierces through the mucilage and the wall of the sporangium, and forms a transverse septum at its curved extremity (Fig. 182 *A* and *B*); the cell thus formed at the extremity of the tube divides by an oblique wall, and the two cells represent the antheridium, while the lower cell (Fig. 182 *st*) must be considered to be the prothallium reduced to a single cell[1].   The protoplasm in each of the two cells of the antheridium contracts and by repeated bipartition divides into four roundish primordial cells (spermatocytes), each of which produces a spermatozoid, a small portion of the contents remaining unused in each cell.   The walls of the antheridial cells split by transverse fissures into valves which open and release the spermatozoids.   The body of the spermatozoid is spirally coiled and lies in (?) a vesicle which according to Pringsheim it does not part with during its time of active movement, but which it certainly loses eventually.

The course of proceeding is exactly the same in the Marsiliaceae (*Marsilia* and *Pilularia*).   There too the microspore divides into three cells, one of which is very small and represents the prothallium, while the two others together form the antheridium; but the entire group of cells remains enclosed in the microspore till the formation of the spermatozoids, and the microspores themselves are free and not as in the Salviniaceae still inclosed in the microsporangium.   The protoplasm of each of the two antheridial cells divides by repeated bipartition into sixteen spermatozoid-mother-cells (spermatocytes).   The spermatozoids are formed as in the Ferns, that is, mainly from the nucleus of the mother-cells.   The portion of the contents of the mother-cell which is not employed in their formation appears when the spermatozoid issues from the cell as a vesicle formed of the unused protoplasm with its starch-granules.   In *Pilularia*, where the spermatozoid is a thread coiled four or five times, this vesicle remains behind in the mother-cell; in *Marsilia* on the contrary it adheres to the posterior coils of the spermatozoid which forms from twelve to thirteen spiral coils, and is often carried about with it for some time during its period of active movement, but is at length brushed away.   When the spermatozoids are developed in the mother-cells, the exosporium is ruptured at the apex and the endosporium swells and protrudes as a hyaline vesicle, which ultimately bursts and releases the spermatozoids (Fig. 183).

The development of the female prothallia in the macrospores is most simple in the Marsiliaceae.   The macrospores are nearly ovoid in form and have a roundish papilla at their apex.   The lenticular space inside the papilla is filled with finely granular protoplasm, while the lower and much larger portion of the macrospore contains chiefly large grains of starch with oil-drops, albuminoid bodies and other substances.   In germination a membrane forms round the lenticular mass of protoplasm in the apical papilla.   Divisions[2] in this protoplasm give rise to an upper and a lower layer of cells, and the middle cell of the upper layer is the mother-cell of the archegonium which developes in the same way as in the homosporous Ferns.   The prothallium contains chlorophyll, which according to Arcangeli is found also in macrospores that have been kept from the light.   The archegonium then makes its appearance completely sunk in the prothallium, which in *Marsilia* therefore appears to form a part of the venter of the archegonium (see Fig. 185).   The reserve-material stored up in the lower, larger portion of the macrospore which does not contribute to the formation of the prothallium is subsequently used by the latter for its support.

That a prothallium is present as a distinct structure and that it is not entirely

---

[1] Even among the homosporous Ferns prothallia bearing antheridia are often found in an imperfect state of development and in the form of a few-celled filament.

[2] According to Arcangeli, *loc. cit.* Hanstein gives a somewhat different account of the process in *Marsilia*.

merged in the formation of the archegonium is shown both by the history of development, and by the fact that, when the oosphere in the single archegonium remains unfertilised, the prothallium continues to develope and becomes a relatively large body which contains chlorophyll, and has root-hairs proceeding from it. The further growth of the prothallium ruptures the epidermal layers of the papilla above, and its dorsal surface emerges into the free space known as the *funnel* beneath the thick outer membranes of the macrospore; subsequently the wall or diaphragm which separates the prothallium from the rest of the macrospore becomes arched convexly outwards and thrusts the prothallium still further out of the macrospore.

In *Salvinia* also a small meniscus-shaped cell is cut off from the rest of the

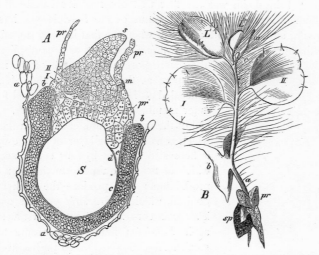

FIG. 184. *Salvinia natans. A* longitudinal section through macrospore, prothallium and embryo in the median line of the prothallium; *a* cell-layer of the sporangium, *b* episporium formed of hardened mucilage, *c* coat of the spore with its continuation *e*, *d* the diaphragm separating the prothallium from the spore-cavity, *pr* prothallium already broken through by the embryo, *m* neck of archegonium, *I, II* the two first leaves of the embryo, *v* the apex of its stem, *s* the scutiform leaf (cotyledon). *B* an older germ-plant with the spore *sp* and the prothallium *pr*; *a* the caudicle, *b* the scutiform leaf, *I, II* first and second single leaves, *LL'* aerial leaves of the first whorl, *w* its submerged leaf. After Pringsheim. *A* magn. about 70. *B* 20 times.

spore, and from this cell the prothallium proceeds[1]. But in *Salvinia* the prothallium attains a much larger size than in the other two genera; it contains a large amount of chlorophyll, and produces several or even many archegonia in definite positions. After it has burst through the membranes of the papilla, it is seen from above as a three-sided body between the three lobes of the exosporium; one of these sides is the anterior side, the two posterior sides meet behind in an angle; a line from this angle to the middle of the anterior side passes along the raised saddle-like back of the prothallium and is called the median line; the anterior side rises higher than the back, and the two angles formed by its junction with the posterior sides grow out subsequently into long wing-like processes which hang down by the side of the macrospore. The first archegonium appears on the median line immediately behind the growing anterior side of the prothallium; then two more archegonia are always

[1] See further in Prantl, Zur Entw.-Gesch. d. Prothall. von *Salvinia natans* (Bot. Ztg. 1879, p. 425).

formed by the side of the first and right and left of it, so that they form a transverse row parallel to the anterior side or apical line. If the oosphere in one of these archegonia is fertilised the work of the prothallium is accomplished; otherwise the prothallium continues to grow on its anterior side and produces from one to three fresh transverse rows of archegonia, and each row may contain from three to seven archegonia. The elongated oosphere in each archegonium lies obliquely in the tissue of the prothallium with its outer, that is the neck-end, looking backwards, and the inner and deeper end towards the anterior extremity of the prothallium; it is in the latter position that the apical cell of the young stem is subsequently found. The development of the archegonium is exactly the same as in the homosporous Ferns; Pringsheim was the first who observed the canal-cell of the neck. The prothallium of *Azolla*[1], the second genus of the Salviniaceae, has usually but one archegonium, and only produces more when the first is not fertilised.

The prothallium in *Marsilia* and *Pilularia* emerges as a hemispherical mass of tissue from the apical papilla of the macrospore after rupture of the membranes of the spore at that spot (Fig. 186, *A, B*), and lies concealed at the bottom of the funnel formed by the outer membranes of the macrospore. The central cell of the archegonium, enclosed in the prothallium which consists of one layer of cells only (Fig. 186), is here also covered by four cells placed crosswise, which at the same time form the apex of the whole prothallium; they produce the neck of the archegonium, which in *Marsilia* projects only a little, in *Pilularia* considerably, by much the same process as in *Salvinia*; here too according to Hanstein a small neck-canal-cell, which pushes itself in between the lid-cells and which behaves as in *Salvinia*, may be distinguished above the central cell, the protoplasm of which contracts. The ventral canal-cell is cut off as a very small portion of protoplasm from the large protoplasmic body of the central cell, which rounds itself off into the oosphere. After fertilisation the layer of tissue surrounding the central cell is doubled, a few chlorophyll-granules are formed in it, and its outer cells

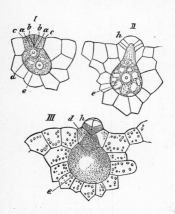

FIG. 185. Development of the archegonia of *Salvinia natans. a, b, c* the divisions in the neck-cells, *d* the neck-canal-cell, *e* oosphere from which the ventral canal-cell, not shown in the figure, is subsequently cut off, *h* neck-cells. As the divisions of the neck-cells by the walls *a, b, c* are formed when the neck is only just protruded above the prothallium, these walls appear to be inclined. In the Ferns the divisions of the neck-cells are not formed till after the protrusion of the neck. After Pringsheim. Magn. 150 times.

develope in *Marsilia Salvatrix* (Fig. 187) into long rhizoids which grow more luxuriantly if no fertilisation takes place. In *Marsilia Salvatrix* the spermatozoids gather in great numbers in the funnel above the prothallium at the time of impregnation, and force their way into the neck of the archegonium.

Development of the second, asexual generation (sporophore, sporophyte). The order of formation of the cells and the mode of development of the organs in the embryo agree exactly with the same processes already described in the homosporous Ferns.

---

[1] Berggren, Om Azollas prothallium och embryo (Lunds Univ.-Arsskrift, T. XVI, reported in Bot. Zeit. 1881, p. 565).

Thus the oospore[1] divides by basal, transversal and median walls into octants, one of which on the side turned towards the prothallium produces the young stem, one turned towards the neck of the archegonium the young root (wanting in *Salvinia* which has no roots), two produce the foot and two the cotyledon. There is a second cotyledon in *Marsilia* formed from the fourth octant of the epibasal half of the embryo which is not employed in the homosporous Ferns to form the organs. *Azolla* too according to Berggren has a second cotyledon, which also proceeds from the fourth octant of the epibasal half, while one of the other three produces the stem and the two others the cotyledon, which in the Salviniaceae is often termed the *scutiform leaf*.

The *subsequent growth* of the genera in this group, though they differ much in general habit, has one point which is the same in all, namely that it is distinctly

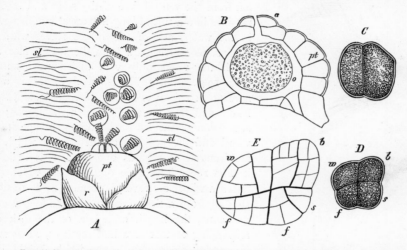

FIG. 186. *Marsilia Salvatrix.* *A* the prothallium *pt* projecting from the ruptured coat *r* of the spore, *sl* layers of mucilage forming the funnel with numerous spermatozoids. *B* vertical section of a prothallium *pt* with the archegonium *a* and the oosphere *o*. *C, D, E* young embryos; *s* apex of the stem, *b* cotyledon, *w* root, *f* foot. *B—E* after Hanstein.

dorsiventral. As in the homosporous so in the heterosporous Filicineae a leaf is not produced from every segment of the apex of the stem, as is the case in the Muscineae and Equisetaceae, but certain segments remain sterile and are employed in forming the internodes. The growth of the leaves is basifugal, as in the homosporous Ferns and Ophioglosseae, and by means of an apical cell which gives off alternating segments in two rows. Before the development enters on an unvarying course, the young plant shows an increase of strength both in the greater size of the leaves and the greater perfection of their form and in a change in their relative positions; but to make this clear, it will be necessary to give a separate consideration

---

[1] The macrospores float in water in such a manner that their longitudinal axis is nearly horizontal. Since the basal wall nearly coincides with the axis of the archegonium, it is also nearly horizontal and divides the embryo into an upper or epibasal half which gives rise to the stem and one or two cotyledons, and a lower half which produces the foot and root. Fig. 187 therefore does not show the true position of the macrospore, which must be supposed to lie horizontally to the left, so that the roots and root-hairs (*wh*) of the prothallium are directed downwards.

to the Salviniaceae on one side, and the Marsiliaceae (*Marsilia* and *Pilularia*) on the other.

The embryo of *Salvinia*, like that of all the Filicineae, has at first, as may be gathered from what has been already said, a three-sided apical cell, but its segmentation soon passes into that of a two-sided cell. Leitgeb says that the segments lie right and left from the very first as in the full-grown stem. The first leaf, the cotyledon or scutiform leaf, is placed medio-dorsally, and is followed by a second and third aerial leaf each standing alone, and the final position of the leaves in a whorl is not established till the formation of the fourth node. Each whorl of leaves consists from that time forwards of a submerged leaf which springs right or left from the ventral face of the stem and at once ramifies into a tuft of long filaments hanging down in the water, and of two others leaves with flat expansions which grow from the dorsal face and touch the water only with their under surface (Fig. 194). These whorls of three leaves alternate and so form two rows of ventral submerged leaves and four rows of dorsal aerial leaves; the succession of the leaves, according to age in the whorl and the position of the whorls which are antidromous as regards one another, is indicated in Fig. 188. The node of the stem, which produces a whorl of leaves, is formed, as Pringsheim showed, from a transverse disk of the long vegetative cone, the length or height of the disk corresponding to that of a half segment, while every internode corresponds to the whole height of a segment. A nodal disk, like every internode, is made up of cells of the right and left row of segments of different ages (Fig. 189). In each whorl the submerged leaf is the oldest, the aerial leaf which is further from it is the next in age, the aerial leaf nearer to it is the youngest. Every leaf is formed from a cell in a definite position; this cell arches outwards (Fig. 189, B, L_1, L_2) and developes into the apical cell of the leaf forming segments on two sides. In *Azolla* too, which has been studied by Strasburger, the apical cell of the stem which floats in a horizontal position but is curved upwards at the apex forms a row of segments lying on the right and on the left, and each segment is divided by a lateral longitudinal wall into a dorsal and a ventral half; each half is divided by a transverse wall into an acroscopic and a basiscopic portion, and each of these four cells is again divided into two cells by a longitudinal wall inclined obliquely upwards or downwards. Thus the stem, apart from later divisions, is composed of eight

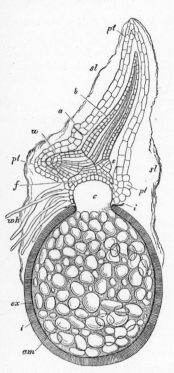

FIG. 187. *Marsilia salvatrix.* Longitudinal section through the spore, prothallium and embryo; *am* starch grains of the spore, *i* inner coat of the spore torn above into lobes, *ex* the episporium with prismatic construction, *c* the space beneath the convex diaphragm, on which the basal layer of the prothallium rests, *pt* the prothallium, *wh* its rhizoids, *a* the archegonium, *f* the foot of the embryo, *w* its root, *s* the apex of the stem, *b* the first leaf (cotyledon) which stretches the prothallium, *sl* the mucilaginous envelope of the spore, which at first forms the funnel above the papilla and still surrounds the prothallium fifty hours after the dissemination of the spores. Magn. about 60 times.

longitudinal rows of cells, which proceed from two rows of segments; the two dorsal rows are sterile and produce neither leaves nor buds; the two rows of leaves are formed from one right and one left row of the dorsal half, and the branches from the two neighbouring rows of cells of the ventral half of the stem, in front of or behind the leaves; lastly, the two lower ventral rows form roots, each of which arises beside (under) a bud and developes by means of a three-sided apical cell. If in the Fig. 188 we suppose the leaves marked L_2 to be the only ones present, we get very nearly the arrangement of the leaves in *Azolla* in which the dorsiventrality is shown by the position of the leaves on the dorsal or upper face, the lateral buds on the lateral faces, and the roots on the ventral face. The roots have this interesting peculiarity, that they after a while cast off the root-cap and so come to be just like the submerged leaves of *Salvinia*[1].

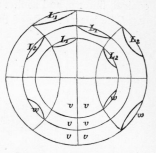

FIG. 188. Diagram of the leaf-arrangement of *Salvinia natans*. The side marked with the letters *vv* is the ventral side. Each pair of aerial leaves and one submerged leaf *w* are inserted at the same height on the young stem. The submerged leaf *w* is formed first, then the aerial leaf L_1, last the aerial leaf L_2, and so on. After Pringsheim.

In *Marsilia* the segmentation of the apical cell in three rows is maintained even in the grown plant; one row of segments comes to be below and ventral, the two other rows form the dorsal face of the stem. The ventral side of the stem gives off

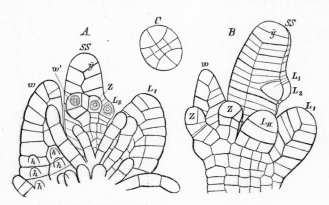

FIG. 189. Summit of the horizontal floating stem of *Salvinia*. *A* inferior or ventral side. *B* left side. *C* transverse section of the elongated vegetative cone; *SS* apical cell of the stem, *y* last division of the apical cell, *w* submerged leaf, *Z* its lateral teeth, L_1, L_2 the aerial leaves, *h h* the hairs. After Pringsheim.

roots in strict acropetal succession, as in *Azolla*; the youngest is found at the apex of the stem: the leaves are formed on the dorsal side of the stem in two alternating rows, since certain dorsal segments are sterile and serve to form internodes. The first leaf of the embryo, which has no lamina and is placed in the median line, is followed in the arrangement in two rows, which is now commencing, by a number of juvenile leaves with short stalks, and with the lamina at first entire, then divided

---

[1] Westermaier u. Ambronn, Eine biolog. Eigenthümlichkeit d. *Azolla caroliniana* (Verh. d. bot. Vereins d. Prov. Brandenb. 1880).

into two, afterwards into four lobes; these are succeeded by normal leaves with a long stalk and a four-lobed lamina which is at first rolled up. *Pilularia* agrees with *Marsilia* in all these points according to Hanstein, only all the leaves are long, conical, filiform, and at first rolled up spirally forwards (Fig. 191).

The lateral shoots of the Salviniaceae and Marsiliaceae are on the sides of the

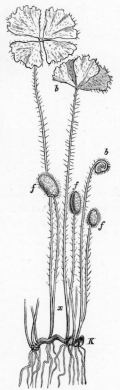

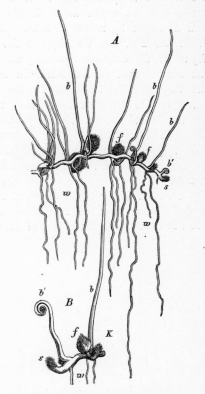

FIG. 190. *Marsilia Salvatrix.* Anterior portion of the stem with leaves, half the nat. size; *k* terminal bud, *b b* leaves, *f f* the sporocarps springing from the leaf-stalks at *x*.

FIG. 191. *Pilularia globulifera. A* the nat. size. *B* the extremity magnified, *s* terminal bud of the stem, *b b'* leaves, *w* roots, *f* sporocarps, *K* lateral bud.

stem, as has been already stated and as is often the case in dorsiventral shoots. In this case a leaf stands over a lateral bud, and the branching therefore is not axillary. The origin of the lateral buds in *Salvinia* has not yet been ascertained, but the analogy of *Azolla* scarcely leaves room for doubt that they proceed from superficial cells of the stem lying below and somewhat in front of or behind the origins of the leaves. Adventitious shoots from leaves, which are so common in the homosporous Ferns, are not known in the heterosporous.

The *growth of the roots* in the Marsiliaceae and their monopodial branching are the same in all the more important points as in the Ferns. It has been already stated that in the Salviniaceae *Salvinia* itself has no roots, but that *Azolla* produces roots near the lateral shoots from the two rows of cells on the ventral face of the stem; while the apical cell of the stem in these plants forms its segments in two rows, that of the root is a three-sided pyramid as in the Ferns and Equisetaceae. A root-sheath, which grows with and covers the root, is formed according to Strasburger from the cells of the stem which lie above the endogenous mother-cell of the roots of *Azolla*; it is especially remarkable that the root in *Azolla* has only a single root-cap-cell; from this cell proceed two layers of tissue, which grow with the root and

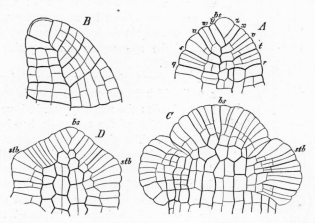

FIG. 192. Development of the leaf of *Marsilia Drummondi*. *A, C, D* seen from within. *B* longitudinal section perpendicular to *A*; *bs* apex of the leaf, *q—s* segments of the apical cell, *stb* the lateral lobes of the lamina in a very young state. After Hanstein.

envelope it completely on every side; in *Azolla caroliniana* the root-cap is eventually thrown off, and the tip of the root is then naked.

The *sporangia* of the heterosporous Ferns are enclosed in peculiar structures which are termed *sporocarps* and have the appearance of capsules. In respect of these structures the Salviniaceae are very near the Ferns, for their sporocarps are only a special development of the indusium. The sporangia are enclosed in unilocular capsules, which are formed two or more together on the segments of leaves (Fig. 194 *A, B*); in *Salvinia* the basal segments of the submerged leaves bear these capsules; in *Azolla* it is the outer descending segments of the deeply bipartite leaf, and always of the first leaf in each shoot, which bears the sporocarps. The leaf-segment first developes into a *placenta* or columella, on which the sporangia arise, while a circular wall, the rudiment of the indusium, rises from beneath out of the base of the placenta, and growing up above its apex ultimately closes over it and forms the wall of the capsule in which the sorus is entirely enclosed. Thus the sporocarp in the Salviniaceae resembles the sorus in the Hymenophyllaceae, with the difference only that there the envelope remains open like a cup, but in the Salviniaceae it closes completely over the sorus as in *Cyathea*. The sporocarp of the Salviniaceae is therefore a sorus, the closed indusium of which is of much more solid construction than in the homosporous Ferns, and consists of two layers of cells, and these in *Azolla* have their walls lignified in the upper part. Each sorus, that is, each sporocarp, produces microsporangia only or macrosporangia only, but both kinds of sporocarps are found on the same plant and indeed on the same leaf; the plant is therefore monoecious. The microsporangia in a sporocarp are many in *Azolla* and in *Salvinia*; several macrosporangia are formed within one indusium in *Salvinia*, one only in *Azolla*. All the spores formed from the sixteen mother-cells in a microsporangium come to maturity, whereas only one of the four times sixteen spores developes in a macrosporangium, so that in *Azolla*, where as was said there is only one macrosporangium in a sporocarp, there is but one macrospore inclosed before maturity in the indusium, and within this by the wall of the sporangium which perhaps eventually disappears.

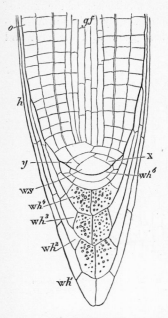

FIG. 193. Longitudinal section of a root of *Marsilia Salvatrix*; *ws* apical cell, *wh1*, *wh2* the first, *wh3*, *wh4* the second, *wh5* the third root cap, each cap consisting of two layers, *xy* the youngest segments of the root, *o* the epidermis, *gf* vascular bundle, *h* the parts of the root-cap which extend farthest back.

The sporangia are capsules with long stalks and a wall which in the mature state is formed of one layer of cells; the macrosporangia have short stalks. The formation of the sporangia has been observed by Juranyi. The placenta has an upper layer of cells which are elongated in the radial direction; each of these cells grows out into a papilla and thus forms the rudiment of a sporangium; the papilla divides by a transverse wall into a lower and an upper cell; the lower cell produces by repeated transverse divisions the long segmented stalk, which in the macrosporangia (not in the microsporangia) consists eventually through longitudinal divisions of several rows of cells. The upper cell after a time swells into a hemispherical form, and produces the body of the sporangium by cell-divisions exactly similar to those which take place in the Polypodiaceae (Fig. 165); in this way a wall of one layer of cells is formed, and inside it is the tetrahedral *archesporium* surrounded by a layer of cells densely filled with protoplasm; the archesporium by repeated bipartitions produces the sixteen mother-cells of the spores (sporocytes), and the surrounding layer developes into two layers of *tapetal* cells. The sixteen spore-mother-cells divide each of them into four young spore-cells tetrahedrally disposed. Up to this point the processes are the same in the microsporangia and in the macrosporangia. All the four times sixteen spores develope in the microsporangia; they separate from one another and lie without any particular arrangement inside the sporangium, while the tapetal cells become disorganised and changed into a frothy mucilage which subsequently hardens and encloses the spores[1]. But in the macrosporangia only one of the newly formed four times sixteen spores developes; this one however increases so greatly in size, as at length almost to fill the cavity of the sporangium, and at the end which is towards the apex of the sporangium there is a large nucleus. During the growth of the macrospore the tapetal cells, and at a later period all the undeveloped spores also, become disorganised and run together into a frothy plasm, which spreads over the wall of the macrospore and forms a specially

---

[1] See the remarks in the Introduction.

thick layer over its apex; this frothy mucilage, which eventually hardens, is the substance which forms the thick envelope, the *episporium* (formerly called the exosporium), round the ripe macrospore (Fig. 184 *A*); it splits as it forms into three lobes above the apex of the spore, and from the space between these lobes the prothallium afterwards protrudes. Strasburger proved some time since the existence of this hardened frothy slime in both kinds of sporangia in *Azolla*, and there it assumes very striking forms; in the microsporangia it looks like a large-celled tissue, and collects into from two to eight portions (*massulae*) quite distinct from one another, each of which encloses a number of microspores; in some species, as *A. filiculoides* and *A. caroliniana*, these massulae have on their surface hair-like

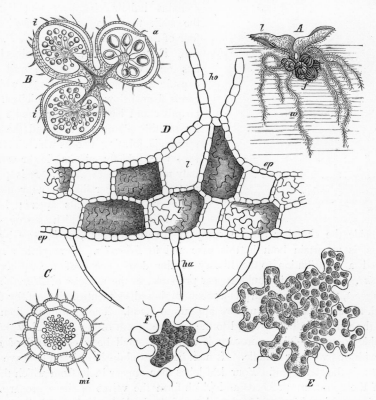

FIG. 194. *Salvinia natans. A* transverse section of the stem, bearing a whorl; *l* aerial leaves, *w* submerged leaf with several teeth, *b* sporocarps on the teeth. *B* longitudinal section through three fertile teeth of a submerged leaf; *a* a sporocarp with macrosporangia, *ii* two similar ones with microsporangia. *C* transverse section of a sporocarp with microsporangia *mi. D* transverse section of the aerial leaf; *hu* hairs of the under side, *ho* hairs of the upper side, *ep* epidermis, *l* air-cavities, the shaded ones showing the vertical walls of the tissue in the background. *E* cells of a lamella of tissue in the leaf. *F* a similar cell after the contents have been contracted in glycerine. *A* natural size, *B* and *C* magn. 10 times.

appendages barbed at their upper end (*glochidia*), by means of which when they have issued from the sporangia and are floating in the water they anchor themselves to the macrospores which are also floating about there. The roundish macrospore of *Azolla*, which does not nearly fill the sporangium, is completely covered with a very thick verrucose layer of hardened frothy mucilage, which projects high above the apex, and there forms three or three times three large masses of the same substance, and runs out besides into a tuft of delicate threads; in these forms the mucilage, which contains air in its pores, serves as a floating apparatus for the macrospore, which by its means carries also with it the upper part of the ruptured sporangium.

The sporocarps of the Marsiliaceae are of much more complicated and firmer structure than those of the preceding family. Those of *Pilularia* are roundish capsules with a short stalk, and their morphology is still obscure. The capsule,

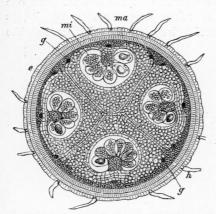

FIG. 195. Transverse section of the sporocarp of *Pilularia globulifera* below the middle, where the macrosporangia and microsporangia are mingled together *ma* and *mi*; *g* the vascular bundles, *h* hairs, *e* the epidermis of the outer surface.

which is surrounded by a thick and hard wall composed of several layers of cells and filled with soft succulent parenchyma, contains hollow chambers reaching from the stalk to the apex; *P. globulifera* has four of these chambers (Fig. 195), *P. minuta* two, *P. americana* three. Each chamber has on the side towards the wall of the capsule a cushion-like placenta, which ascends from below through the length of the chamber and has a vascular bundle behind it; on this placenta are placed the stalked sporangia, forming a sorus which has macrosporangia chiefly at its lower end and only microsporangia above. It is probable that each chamber has in its young state an open passage at its apex[1]; how far the delicate tissue which surrounds the sorus inside the chamber can be compared to an indusium, as is done by many botanists, is uncertain both in this case and in *Marsilia*. Juranyi has recently published a contribution to the history of the development of the sporocarp of *Pilularia*[2]. From this it would appear probable, as the analogy of *Marsilia* would itself suggest, that the sporocarp is a metamorphosed segment of the leaf, by the side of which the sporocarp when mature appears to stand. The sporophyll then would occupy the same position in regard to the sterile segment of the leaf in *Pilularia* as in the Ophioglosseae. The sporocarp is at first a small body composed of cellular tissue, with one vascular bundle. It next becomes club-shaped and concave on the side towards the sterile leaf. Four leaf-lobes then appear in it, from which the main body of the sporocarp proceeds and which form the valves of the sporocarp. The sporangia are formed in cavities, the edges of the leaf-lobes unite, and the sporocarp becomes pear-shaped. The four rows of cells visible in the figure would then be the lines of union of the four leaf-lobes.

The sporocarps of the various species of *Marsilia* are usually somewhat bean-shaped capsules with very hard walls and with stalks of varying length. They are

----

[1] This is really the case according to my observations; the sori therefore are not formed inside closed cavities, as has hitherto been assumed.

[2] Juranyi, Ueber d. Gestaltung d. Frucht bei *Pilularia globulifera* (Report in Bot. Centralblatt, 1880, p. 201). The account in the text is an imperfect one, and further investigation is desirable.

borne on the ventral side of the petiole of ordinary foliage-leaves (Fig. 190), or at the base of the leaves, but always on the petiole ; their stalks may be simple and bear one sporocarp, or be forked and bear several sporocarps, and several usually grow together from the petiole. The stalk runs along the dorsal edge of the capsule (Fig. 200), and gives off lateral veins to the right and left which branch dichotomously and run to the ventral edge. The ripe capsule is symmetrically bilateral and has within it two rows of chambers, each of which reaches from the ventral to the dorsal edge (Fig. 196 _A, B_) ; these chambers open to the air in the young fruit by narrow canals on the ventral side. In each chamber a cushion of placental tissue runs along the outer side, the side towards the wall of the capsule, and bears the macrosporangia along its middle line and the microsporangia on its flanks ; each chamber contains therefore in _Marsilia_ as in _Pilularia_ a sorus of two kinds of sporangia. When the capsule bursts it is clearly seen (Fig. 200) that the soft inner tissue forms a small closed sac round the sorus, as in _Pilularia_.

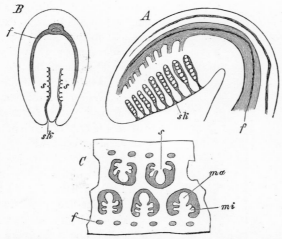

FIG. 196. Very young sporocarp of _Marsilia elata_. _A_ median longitudinal section. _B_ transverse section. _C_ part of a longitudinal section perpendicular to _A_ ; _f f_ vascular bundles, _s s_ the sori, _sk_ canals of the sori ; _ma_ macrosporangia, _mi_ microsporangia. After Russow. (See FIG. 200.)

The mature microsporangia contain sixty-four spores, the macrosporangia only one ripe macrospore.

The formation of the sporangia begins with the appearance of protuberances on certain superficial cells of the placenta that bears the sorus ; then these cells by repeated oblique divisions (otherwise therefore than in the Salviniaceae) form three rows of segments, till at length a convex transverse wall cuts off the three-sided apical cell and converts it into the tetrahedral _archesporium_ (Fig. 197 _I–III_) ; from the archesporium by further divisions parallel to the last four is formed the _tapetum_, which as in the Salviniaceae and the true Ferns surrounds the archesporium. The stalk of the sporangium in the Marsiliaceae is from the first formed of three rows of cells, and by longitudinal divisions it comes to be of several rows. While the body of the young sporangium constantly swells to a larger size, radial divisions appear in the cells of the wall, and radial and tangential in the tapetal cells ; then the archesporium divides by successive bipartitions into sixteen spore-mother-

[2]   R

cells, each of which produces four spores formed and tetrahedrally disposed in the usual manner; during this process the tapetal cells too are gradually disorganised, and a granular protoplasm then fills the space in the sporangium between the isolated mother-cells and the spore-tetrads, and is subsequently used to form the peculiar episporia or gelatinous envelopes of the spores. Up to this point the course of development in the two kinds of sporangia is the same, but beyond this point it differs. In the microsporangia all the spores in the sixteen tetrads

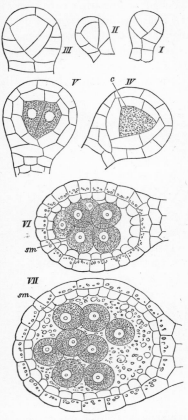

arrive at maturity; each young spore in the mother-cell, which is now divided into four compartments, assumes its permanent membrane, and then the walls of the compartments in the mother-cell are dissolved. In the macrosporangia, on the contrary, one of the young spores in each of the sixteen tetrads grows at first more vigorously than the other three, but ultimately all the tetrads except one waste away, and in this one the preferred cell, the future macrospore, grows very vigorously, while the other three languish. Figs. 198 and 199 show the development of the macrospore of *Pilularia globulifera*, from drawings made by Sachs in 1866; they show the young macrospore (*I, II, III*) still in connection with its three sister-cells, which are invested with the substance of the cell-walls of the four compartments of the mother-cell already converted into mucilage (*I*); the four cells adhere by their spike-like projections, that of the macrospore being the most strongly developed. After a while the macrospore is seen to have increased greatly in size; the sister-cells which have dwindled away hang to it at its side (Fig. 199 *x*); its firm membrane has become brown, and is invested with a covering of mucilage (Fig. 198 *IV, b*), which often appears to be folded. It subsequently forms a papilla above the apex, which shrivels when the

FIG. 197. Development of the sporangium of *Pilularia globulifera*, all the figures being in optical longitudinal section; *c* archesporium, *sm* spore-mother-cells. Magn. 550 times.

spore is ripe (Fig. 199 *b'*). Later a layer of a white substance of marked prismatic structure is formed on the mucilaginous covering (Fig. 199 *c*), and this is afterwards overlaid by a still thicker covering of a less evidently organised substance. Both envelopes leave the apex uncovered, and thus form the *funnel*, through which the spermatozoids enter (Fig. 186). The macrospores of *Marsilia* have a similar episporium, but its development is not satisfactorily explained in the descriptions which we at present possess[1].

---

[1] Russow, *loc. cit.* p. 228.

The ejection of the macrospores and microspores from the very firm capsules is attended by some remarkable circumstances, a knowledge of which we owe especially to Hanstein. The ripe sporocarps of *Pilularia globulifera* lie on or in moist soil; they open at the apex by four valves and discharge a tough hyaline mucilage, which evidently proceeds from the tissue between the chambers, and forms a round drop on the surface of the ground which grows larger and larger for some days. The macrospores and microspores issue from the capsule in this drop of mucilage to germinate in it, and it does not liquefy till after fertilisation has taken place. After fertilisation the fertilised macrospores remain lying on the damp ground, to which the prothallia are secured by their rhizoids, till the first root of the embryo penetrates into the ground. Fig 200 gives the most important of the corresponding processes in *Marsilia*

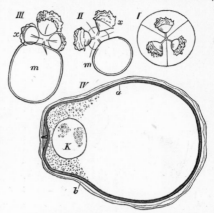

FIG. 198. Development of the macrospore of *Pilularia globulifera*; *x* the abortive sister-cells, *m* the macrospore, *K* its nucleus, *a* its inner, *b* its outer coat. Magn. 550 times.

salvatrix. If the wall of the capsule which is of stony hardness is injured a little at the ventral margin and the sporocarp placed in water, the water finds its way in and makes the tissue that forms the chambers swell up, till the capsule opens at the dorsal edge by two valves. Fig. 200 *B* shows that a hyaline cushion which fitted into the angle

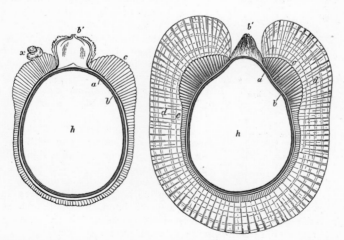

FIG. 199. Further development of the macrospore of *Pilularia globulifera*; *h* cavity of the spore, *x* remains of sister-cell, *a* inner and first, *b* second, *c* third, *d* fourth coat. Magn. 80 times.

formed by the two valves along the ventral margin has swollen up and protrudes from the capsule, and brings out with it the chambers which do not swell so much; as the cushion enlarges, the chambers become detached at the dorsal end, and are then drawn entirely out of the capsule; generally the ring at last parts at one end and elongates, and it now bears the chambers in two lateral longitudinal rows as small closed pouches, which are now some distance from one another, though they were closely packed together inside the capsule. These proceedings occupy a few hours, till at length the spores of both kinds are set free, and with a suitable temperature fertilisation is accomplished in from twelve to eighteen hours after the sporocarp is placed in water.

a. **Histology.** The formation of the tissues in the heterosporous Ferns agrees in the most important morphological points with that of the homosporous (*vid. supra*).

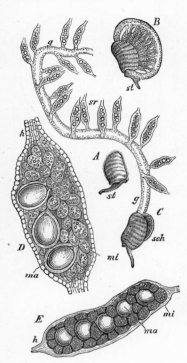

FIG. 200. *Marsilia salvatrix. A* a sporocarp in natural size; *st* the upper part of its stalk. *B* a sporocarp which has burst in water and allowed the gelatinous ring to protrude. In *C* the gelatinous ring *g* is ruptured and stretched out; *sr* the compartments of the sorus, *sch* shell of the sporocarp. *D* a compartment of an unripe sporocarp with its sorus. *E* a similar one from a ripe sporocarp; *mi* microsporangium, *ma* macrosporangium. *B* after Hanstein.

The epidermis shows some peculiarities, especially in the matter of the stomata; the fundamental tissue has the large intercellular spaces that are common in water and bog plants; the formation of sclerenchyma in the leaves and in the walls of the capsule in the Marsiliaceae is described by Braun and Russow. The vascular bundles especially in the Marsiliaceae are very similar in composition to those of the true Ferns; there is a central xylem surrounded by phloem, and round the phloem is a bundle-sheath of a single layer of cells with wavy lateral walls. A single bundle traverses each root and leaf-petiole; this bundle divides in the lamina of the leaf in *Marsilia* and produces a dichotomous venation; the vascular bundles in the stem of the Marsiliaceae, as seen in transverse section, form a cylinder filled in with fundamental tissue [1].

b. **Classification.** The account already given in the text has made it plain, that the heterosporous Ferns fall naturally into two very distinct families: the Salviniaceae, which are closely allied to the homosporous Ferns, and the Marsiliaceae, which have not much in common with the homosporous Ferns, with similar formation of sporangia; but the insertion of the sporocarp on the sterile portion of the leaf recalls a similar relation of the sporophyll to the sterile portion of the leaf in the Ophioglosseae.

Family 1. SALVINIACEAE. Plant floating horizontally on the water; stem with an apical cell forming two rows of segments, right and left; sori male or female, one in each unilocular sporocarp; spores invested by frothy hardened mucilage (massulae, episporia); the microspores in *Salvinia* form a prothallium, which though very simple emerges from the spore; the prothallium of the macrospore is a vigorous growth, and bears several archegonia; *Salvinia* is rootless, *Azolla* has roots.

Family 2. MARSILIACEAE. Plant creeping on wet ground or sometimes floating; stem with a three-sided apical cell, which forms two latero-dorsal rows of segments, and one ventral; each sorus comprises macrospores and microspores, and two to many sori are enclosed in a plurilocular sporocarp. Spores invested by hardened mucilage forming episporia which show radial prismatic structure, and have to some extent the power of swelling. Microspores and macrospores remain for a long

---

[1] See above on the histology of the homosporous Ferns.

time shut up in the sporangia, and pass the winter there. The prothallium of the macrospore is much reduced, almost to a single archegonium ; the prothallium of the microspore is reduced to one cell, as in the Salviniaceae. The fertile portion of the leaf, the portion which forms the sporocarp, is a shoot from the petiole of the sterile leaf.

B. EUSPORANGIATE FILICINEAE[1].

The two families which compose this group are especially distinguished from their allies by the mode in which they form their sporangia, though they also agree together in other important points. The germination is thoroughly known only in the Marattiaceae; the prothallia of the Ophioglosseae are known only as small underground tubers without chlorophyll; those of the Marattiaceae form a large green thallus resembling the prothallium of other homosporous Ferns. In both families the antheridia are sunk in the tissue of the prothallium (a peculiarity which they share with the rest of the homosporous Eusporangiatae, for in *Equisetum* also the disposition of the antheridia is similar), and the neck of the archegonium also scarcely reaches above the surface of the prothallium. It is highly probable that a green prothallium is first formed in the Ophioglosseae as well as in the allied family, and that this gives rise to the small tuber which buries itself in the ground; at least, the analogy of *Gymnogramme leptophylla* points to this. The stem of the second, or asexual generation, the sporophyte, is remarkable in both families for its extremely small longitudinal growth, by the consequent absence of internodes and branching, by the entire concealment of the surface by the insertions of the leaves, and by the formation of roots in acropetal succession close behind the apex. Both families are distinguished from the true Ferns by the absence or imperfect formation of bundle-sheaths, and of sclerenchyma with brown walls in the fundamental tissue of the stem and leaves, the Ophioglossaceae being the furthest removed from them by their peculiar mode of vegetation, and by the secondary growth in thickness of the stem, insignificant it is true, which has been ascertained in Botrychium.

1. OPHIOGLOSSEAE[2].

The *prothallium* (*oophore, oophyte*) is known only in *Ophioglossum pedunculosum* and *Botrychium*. In both cases it is an underground body formed of parenchymatous tissue and without chlorophyll, which in the former species, according to Mettenius[3], takes the form of a small round tuber, from which is developed a cylindrical vermiform shoot growing erect under ground by an apical cell, and rarely puting forth a few branches; when the apex appears above the ground and assumes a green colour, it becomes lobed and ceases to grow. The tissue of this prothallium is differentiated

---

[1] Called by Sachs the group of Stipulatae ; but this name can hardly be maintained now that we know that there are no stipules in the Ophioglosseae, and that they are sometimes wanting in the Marattiaceae.

[2] Mettenius, Filices horti bot. Lipsiensis, Leipzig, 1856, p. 119.—Hofmeister, Abhandl. d. Kgl. Sächs. Ges. d. Wiss. 1857, p. 657.—Russow, Vergl. Unters. Petersburg, 1872, p. 117.—Holle, Ueber d. Vegetationsorgane d. Ophioglosseen (Bot. Ztg. 1875).—Goebel, Beitr. z. vergl. Entwicklungs-gesch. d. Sporangien, in Bot. Ztg. 1880 (*Botrychium*) und 1881 (*Ophioglossum*).—[Prantl. Beitr. z. Syst. d. Ophiogl. (Jahrb. Kön. Bot. Gart. Berlin, III, 1884).]

[3] A fresh examination of this species is much to be desired.

into an axile bundle of more elongated and a rind of shorter parenchymatous cells, and the upper surface is clothed with rhizoids ; it is from two lines to two inches long and from a half to one and a half line broad. The prothallium of *Botrychium Lunaria* is, according to Hofmeister, an ovoid firm mass of cellular tissue, the greatest diameter of which is not more than a half line and often much less (Fig. 201), light brown on the outside and yellowish white within, and furnished on every side with scattered rhizoids of no great length. These prothallia are monoecious, and each produces a number of antheridia and archegonia pretty equally distributed over its entire surface; there are none on the primary tuber in *O. pedunculosum*; in *Botrychium* the upper side which is towards the surface of the ground chiefly bears antheridia. The *antheridia* are cavities in the tissue of the prothallium, covered on the outside with a few layers of cells and only slightly projecting in *Ophioglossum*. In this genus the mother-cells of the spermatozoids are formed by repeated divisions from one or two cells of the inner tissue, which lie beneath one or two external layers [1]. The mother-cells form a roundish mass of tissue which slightly raises the covering layers, and, as in *Botrychium*, produce the spermatozoids, which are of similar form to those of the Polypodiaceae, but larger, and escape through a narrow orifice in the roof of the antheridium. The *archegonia* appear to follow the course of development observed in the other Vascular Cryptogams, and the statements of Mettenius agree entirely with what is known respecting the formation of the archegonia in the rest of the Filicineae. The venter of the archegonium is wholly sunk in the prothallium, and only the neck, which is usually very short, projects above the surface.

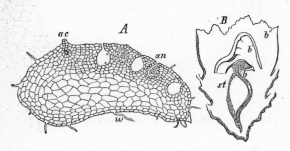

FIG. 201. *Botrychium Lunaria. A* prothallium in longitudinal section; *ac* archegonium, *an* antheridium, *w* rhizoids. *B* longitudinal section of the lower portion of a young plant dug up in September; *st* stem, *b*, *b'*, *b''* leaves. After Hofmeister; *A* magn. 50, *B* 20 times.

The *asexual generation (sporophore, sporophyte)*. The manner in which the oospore developes into the embryo is not known, but it probably agrees with that of the other Filicineae ; we gather from the statements of Hofmeister and Mettenius that the orientation only of the organs in it is different.

The mode of growth in the developed plant is in some respects remarkable. The stem, which in *Ophioglossum* and *Botrychium* is buried deep in the ground, appears never to branch in *Ophioglossum*, while several cases of branching have been described by Roeper and Holle in *Botrychium*. Even the comparatively thick roots of *Ophioglossum* do not branch, but many of them give rise to adventitious buds which develope into new plants [2]. The roots of *Botrychium* on the contrary do not produce adventitious buds, and they not unfrequently form a number of lateral branches.

---

[1] As in *Marattia* (*vid. infra*).

[2] The Ophioglosseae become perennial as well as multiply by means of these adventitious shoots.

The flat apex of the stem, which is walled round by the insertions of the leaves and buried in their sheaths, has a three-sided apical cell both in *Ophioglossum* and *Botrychium*. The leaves have a sheathing base, and in *Botrychium*, as Fig. 203 shows, each younger leaf is completely enclosed in the one which is next above it in age. In *Ophioglossum* the general conditions at the apex of the stem are more complicated, because the rudimentary leaves are enclosed in a sheath of tissue, which proceeds not from the base of the older leaves but from the surface of the stem, and

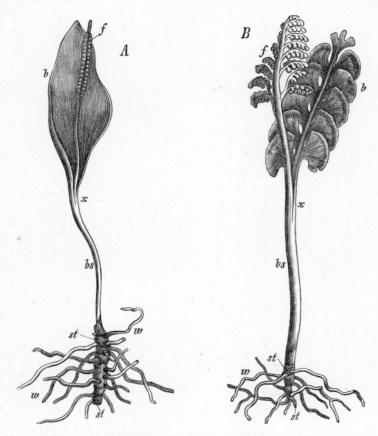

FIG. 202. *A Ophioglossum vulgatum. B Botrychium Lunaria.* *w* roots, *st* stem, *bs* leaf-stalk, *x* point of branching of the leaf, where the sterile lamina *b* separates from the fertile lamina *f.* Natural size.

each leaf is thus shut in in a kind of chamber; but an opening is left free at the top of each chamber, so that the apex of the stem is in contact with the outer air through a narrow canal. Both in *Ophioglossum* and *Botrychium* a root is formed normally beneath each leaf. The root, like the stem, has a three-sided apical-cell [1].

As soon as the plant has reached a certain age, each leaf produces a sporangiferous branch springing from the axile side of the leaf. In *Ophioglossum* both

---

[1] See the account of the growth of the root in the true Ferns given above.

the outer sterile branch and the sporangiferous branch of the leaf are usually un-branched (Fig. 202 *A*); in the Brazilian species, *Ophioglossum palmatum*, the lamina is dichotomously lobed, and several sporangiferous lobes arise from either side of the margin of the lamina where it passes into the stalk. In *Botrychium* both branches are again branched in parallel planes (Fig. 202 *B*). The earlier idea of a cohesion of the two stalks of a fertile and a sterile leaf is at once disproved by the history of development

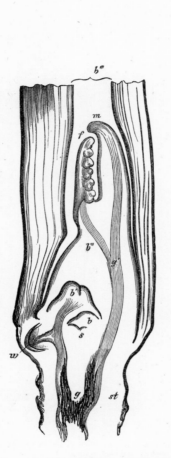

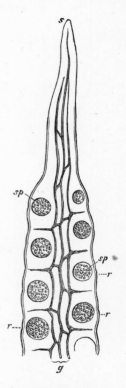

FIG. 204. Longitudinal sec-tion of the upper part of the fertile lamina of *Ophioglossum vulgatum*; *s* its free apex, *sp* the sporangial cavities, *r* the spot where they open trans-versely, *g* the vascular bundles. Magn. about 10 times.

FIG. 203. Longitudinal section through the lower portion of a developed plant of *Botrychium Lunaria*; *st* stem, *g*, *g'* vascular bundles, *w* a young root, *s* apex of the stem, *b*, *b'*, *b''*, *b'''* the four leaves already formed, *b'''* the one unfolded in the present year; *b'* shows the first indication of the branching of the leaf, in *b''* this is already considerably advanced; *m* is the median line of the sterile lamina, which has its lobes already formed to the right and left but not visible in this figure, *f* is the fertile lamina with the young branches, on which the sporangia will be formed. Magn. about 10 times.

(Fig. 203), which shows, as Hofmeister pointed out, that the sporangiferous branch proceeds from the inner side of the leaf. The fertile branch of the leaf either separates when fully developed from the sterile green branch at the base of the lamina, or it springs from the middle of the lamina, as in *O. pendulum*, or the two branches of the leaf appear to be separated as deep down as the insertion, as in *O. Bergianum*, or finally the sporangiferous branch proceeds from the middle of the leaf-stalk, as in *Botrychium rutaefolium* and *dissectum*.

The structure of the *sporangia* in the Ophioglosseae agrees in the main with that of the same organs in the Marattiaceae. The sporangium in *Botrychium* is a roundish capsule opening by a transverse fissure; the spot in the wall where this fissure afterwards appears is recognisable at an early stage by the presence of smaller cells with more delicate walls. The wall of the sporangium is formed of several layers of cells, the outermost of which passes below into the epidermis of the sporophyll. The young sporangia of *Botrychium Lunaria* are clusters of cells, forming hemispherical protuberances; they take the place of pinnules of the fertile portion of the leaf (sporophyll), but appear subsequently to have been moved to its upper (inner) side. The terminal cell of the axile row beneath the epidermis is the *archesporium*, which acts as mother-cell of the sporogenous tissue (see Fig. 208). The sporogenous cells are here, as in all sporangia, surrounded by layers of tabular cells, the *tapetal cells*, which are not employed to form the spores, but are eventually disorganised.

In *Ophioglossum* the mature sporangia form curved cavities in the tissue of the fertile portion of the leaf and on its lateral faces, but somewhat nearer to one margin. A longitudinal section through the immature sporangiferous branch of *O. vulgatum* (Fig. 204) shows that the outer layer of the wall of the sporangia is continuous with the epidermis of the entire fertile branch of the leaf, and is furnished with stomata[1]; at the spots where the lateral transverse fissure appears in each sporangium these epidermal cells are radially elongated, and the whole layer lies in an indentation which is at first scarcely perceptible. The spherical cavities which contain the mass of spores are deep in the tissue of the organ and are entirely surrounded by its parenchyma; some layers of this parenchyma are also present on the outer side where the transverse fissure afterwards arises; the middle part of the parenchyma is traversed by vascular bundles which anastomose and form long meshes, and send off a bundle in a transverse direction between every two sporangial cavities.

A similar arrangement will be found in *Botrychium*, if we compare the separate lobes of the sporangiferous branches with the sporangiferous branch in the Ophioglosseae; the sporangia in both cases are in two rows and alternate, but in *Botrychium* they are rounder and more prominent because the tissue of the branch is less developed between each pair of sporangia. Each mother-cell produces four spores, dividing, after indication of bipartition, into four segments tetrahedrally disposed and surrounded each by a delicate membrane, the special mother-cells; the protoplasm in each of them becomes invested with a new and firmer cell-wall, the true coat of the spore, and then the walls of the segments are dissolved and the spores are set at liberty. In specimens preserved in spirit the young spores of both genera still hanging together in fours are seen imbedded in a colourless, granular, coagulated jelly, which evidently is the same as the fluid in which the spores of the rest of the Vascular Cryptogams float in the living plant before they are mature. The spores are tetrahedral, and in *Botrychium* are furnished when still young with knob-like prominences on the cuticularised exosporium.

---

[1] This is not the case in the early condition of the sporangia. On the history of their development see Bot. Ztg. 1881.

Histology. Of the *forms of tissue* in the Ophioglosseae the predominant one is the parenchyma of the fundamental tissue, which in the leaf-stalk especially consists of long, almost cylindrical, thin-walled, succulent cells, with straight transverse walls and large intercellular spaces; these spaces are very large in the lamina of the leaf in *Ophioglossum vulgatum*, and the tissue is spongy. The epidermal tissue in *O. vulgatum* and *Botrychium Lunaria* has no hypodermal layers; a well developed epidermis with numerous stomata on both sides of the leaf lies immediately upon the outer layers of the fundamental tissue; layers of cork are formed at the periphery of the stem, which is completely covered by the scars of the leaves. The vascular bundles in the stem of *O. vulgatum*, on which the leaves are arranged spirally with a divergence of 2/5, form, according to Hofmeister, a hollow cylindrical network in which each of the meshes corresponds to a leaf. The slender bundles, in number from five to eight, which run through the petiole, unite at its base into a single strand, which descends as the leaf-trace in the stem to nearly as far as the point of entrance of the leaf-trace which is the fifth below it in point of age, and which runs down the stem in the same straight line; when it has reached this point it joins on to the outside cylindrical network (Holle). In many cases the whole of the tissue which fills the meshes of the network is changed into scalariform vessels, which form a closed hollow cylinder over considerable lengths of the stem; sometimes the change takes place on one side of the stem only. The leaf-stalk is traversed by from five to eight slender bundles arranged in a circle on the transverse section, the fundamental tissue forming wider lacunae between them; on the axile side of each of these bundles is a strong bundle of narrow vessels with reticulately thickened walls, and on their peripheral side is a broad bundle of soft bast (phloem); these bundles therefore are collateral, as is usually the case also in the bundles of the skeleton of the stem. The slender bundles branch repeatedly in the lamina of the sterile part of the leaf and anastomose, forming a network with many meshes; they lie in the mesophyll which contains chlorophyll and do not form projecting veins. The four vascular bundles which traverse the leaf-petiole of *Botrychium Lunaria* are concentric. Each of them consists of a broad axile band of scalariform or reticulate tracheides surrounded by a thick formation of phloem, which shows an inner layer of narrow cambiform cells, while the outside is formed of thick-walled, soft, bast-like prosenchyma, as in *Pteris* and other Ferns. The bundles form repeated bifurcations in the lobes of the sterile lamina, and run through the middle of the mesophyll without forming projecting veins. The fundamental tissue forms no bundle-sheath round the vascular bundles of the leaves in *Ophioglossum*; in *Botrychium* the sheath is only slightly different from the surrounding parenchyma, being distinguished only by the undulation of the longitudinal band in the middle of the radial side-walls of the cells. Russow states that the vascular bundle-system in the stem of *Botrychium* manifests a slight subsequent growth in thickness [1].

It was stated above on the authority of Holle that a root arises normally beneath each leaf; the leaf-trace after passing down the central cylinder bends out into the root.

Habit and Mode of Life. The number of leaves which make their appearance each year is small and constant in each species; thus *Ophioglossum vulgatum* and *Botrychium Lunaria* unfold a single leaf only each year, *B. rutaefolium* two, a sterile and a fertile one, *O. pedunculosum* from two to four, as Mettenius informs us. The development of the leaves is extraordinarily slow; in *Botrychium* each leaf requires four years, the first three of which it spends under the ground; the two branches, the sterile and the fertile laminae, are commenced in the second year, and are further developed in the third, but do not appear above the ground till the fourth (Fig. 202); this recalls the slow growth of the leaves of *Pteris aquilina*; the case is the same with *Ophioglossum vulgatum*; in both genera the sporangia are commenced a full year before they reach maturity.

---

[1] This is not difficult to verify in older specimens.

Vegetative propagation is effected in *Ophioglossum* by adventitious buds on the roots ; *O. pedunculosum* is monocarpic, since it dies down as a rule after it has formed fertile leaves, but it maintains its existence by means of root-buds according to Hofmeister. Most species, reckoning from the base of the stem to the tip of the leaf, are only from five to six inches high ; some may be a foot in height ; *Botrychium lanuginosum*, an Indian species, is said by Milde to grow to the height of three feet ; its leaf is tripinnate or quadripinnate, and the stalk contains from ten to eleven vascular bundles.

2. MARATTIACEAE [1].

The formation of the *prothallium* in the Marattiaceae agrees in its main features with that of leptosporangiate homosporous Ferns, and resembles especially that of the Osmundaceae. A cell-surface or a body of cellular tissue is the first product of the germinating spore, and ultimately a deep-green heart-shaped prothallium is formed with a hemispherical projecting cushion of tissue on its under side. The *antheridia* are sunk in the tissue as in *Ophioglossum* and as a rule in all eusporangiate Ferns, and are placed on the upper and the under side, but especially on the cushion on the under side of the prothallium. A superficial cell divides by a transverse wall into an upper cell, the lid-cell, and a lower which is the central cell of the antheridium. The latter divides into a large number of mother-cells of spermatozoids (*spermatocytes*) ; the lid-cell also is divided by walls at right angles to the surface of the prothallium. Tabular cells to form the parietal layer are cut off from the cells surrounding the central cell of the antheridium. The central and youngest of the lid-cells is broken through when the antheridium is mature, and allows the escape of the spermatozoids. The antheridia appear when the prothallia are some months old.

The *archegonia* are on the cushion on the under side of the prothallium as in the other homosporous Ferns. Their development agrees with that of the rest of the Ferns, but they are so deeply sunk in the prothallium that the neck scarcely projects above its surface. The canal cell of the neck divides, according to Jonkman's figures, by a transverse septum ; indications of this proceeding, that is, of the division of the nucleus of the canal cell, but without the appearance of a cell-wall, have been observed by Strasburger in other Ferns (see Fig. 151 of *Pteris serrulata*).

The second or *asexual generation* (*sporophore, sporophyte*). The development of the embryo is unknown, but it may be assumed to be in conformity with the rest of the Ferns, with which the Marattiaceae agree also in habit. The stem is usually erect, short, thick and tuber-like ; the leaves that spring from it are large, on long stalks, crowded together and spirally arranged, with pinnatifid or sometimes palmatifid laminae ; the resemblance to the true ferns is greatly increased by the circinate folding of the leaves in the bud, which unroll slowly from below upwards.

The *stem* of *Marattia* and *Angiopteris* reproduces on a larger scale the mode of development of the stem of the Ophioglosseae ; it grows erect without reaching any

---

[1] De Vriese et Harting, Monographie des Marattiacées, Leide et Düsseldorf, 1853.—Lürssen's researches are given in his Handb. d. system. Bot. 1 Bd. Leipzig, 1879.—Russow, Vgl. Unters. 1872, p. 105.—Tschistiakoff, Matériaux pour servir à l'histoire de la cellule végétale (Ann. d. sc nat. 5° sér. T. XIX).—Holle, Ueber d. Vegetationsorgane d. Maratt. (Bot. Ztg. 1875, p. 215).— Goebel, Beitr. z. vergl. Entwicklungsgesch. d. Sporangien (Bot. Ztg. 1881).—De Bary, Vergl. Anatomie, Leipzig, 1877.—Jonkman, Ueber d. Entwicklungsgesch. d. Prothall. d. Maratt. (Bot. Ztg. 1878, p. 129);—Id. Die Geslochtsgeneratie der Maratt. mit 4 Tafeln (Holländ).

great height; it is tuber-like in form and is partly buried in the ground, and is so covered with leaves that no part of the surface is free.   In some species this tuberous stem remains comparatively small, in the large Marattiae and in *Angiopteris evecta* it may be of considerable circumference and from one to two feet high.   The stem of *Kaulfussia assamica* is, according to De Vriese, an underground creeping dorsiventral rhizome, with leaves on the upper and roots on the under side; that of *Danaea trifoliata*, as we learn from Holle, is rather long and branched, and the leaves so far differ from the leaves of other species that they have no stipules at the base of the petiole.   The stem of the Marattiaceae, *Danaea* excepted, like that of the Ophioglosseae

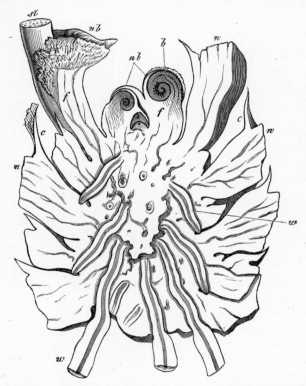

FIG. 205.   Vertical longitudinal section of the stem of a young plant of *Angiopteris evecta*; *b* the youngest leaves still quite covered up by the stipules *nb*, *st* stalk of an unfolded leaf with its stipula *nb*, *n* everywhere the leaf-scars on the basal portions *ff*, from which the leaf-stalks have separated, *cc* the commissures of the stipules in longitudinal section, *ww* the roots.   Natural size.

and Isoeteae, appears never to branch.   The lower and older region of the stem is covered with the basal portions of the older petioles bearing the stipules, and from these portions the upper parts of the petioles, provided at this point with large cushion-like swellings (pulvini), have fallen away, leaving behind them a broad smooth flat scar girt with the stipule (Fig. 205 *n*); the upper part of the stem bears a large rosette of living leaves, in the centre of which is the bud composed of rather numerous young leaves of all ages (*b*, *nb*).   The leaves in the bud are circinately rolled up, and are completely enveloped by the stipules till the elongation of the petiole and the unrolling of the lamina begins; each pair of stipules belonging to a petiole forms an anterior and a posterior chamber, separated from one another by a longitudinal wall, the commissure, as is seen in Fig. 206; the leaf to which the stipule belongs lies rolled up in the posterior chamber, and the two posterior wings of the stipule unite over it; the chamber formed by the anterior wings encloses all the younger leaves. These peculiar stipules continue fresh and succulent, and adventitious buds may even be produced from them, not only during the lifetime of the unfolded leaves, but after they have fallen.

The *roots*, as Fig. 205 shows, arise close beneath the growing point of the stem, one at least, it would appear, at the base of each young leaf[1]; from hence they grow obliquely downwards through the succulent parenchyma of the stem and of the older basal portions of the leaves, and at length emerge much lower down between them or out of a leaf-scar. The roots are less numerous, thicker, of more delicate consistence and of a lighter colour than in most of the true Ferns; in these points they agree with the roots of the Ophioglosseae. Beneath the ground they branch copiously and, like those of other Ferns, monopodially.

The *leaves*, which in the smaller species are from one to two, in the largest (*Angiopteris*) from five to ten feet in length, have a long and very strong petiole grooved on the inside, and a compound lamina which is pinnate or bipinnate, or in *Kaulfussia* palmate. The primary petiole has an enlargement at the point where it unites with its base, the secondary petioles also where they join the primary, and the leaflets where they join the rhachis have a similar swelling, as in the Leguminosae.

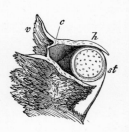

FIG. 206. Base of a leaf-stalk *st* with the stipules cut through obliquely; *v* the anterior, *h* the posterior wing; the two stipules are united by a commissure *c* where the anterior and posterior wings meet. Natural size.

The Marattiaceae are distinguished from the glabrous Ophioglosseae by a growth of hairs, which however is scanty as compared with that of the true Ferns.

The *sporangia* of the Marattiaceae are formed in large numbers on the under side of ordinary foliage-leaves which undergo no metamorphosis. They are placed, as in most of the true Ferns, on the veins of the leaves, and usually form two rows of sori, which cover the veins running from the mid-rib to the margin of the leaflet either along their whole length, as in *Danaea*, or towards the margin only as in *Angiopteris* and *Marattia*; in *Kaulfussia* they are on delicate anastomosing veins between the mid-rib and the lateral vein. The sorus is attached to a cushion-like outgrowth of the tissue of the vein, the placenta. In *Angiopteris* only the individual sporangia of a sorus are free, not having grown together into a compound structure; they are ovoid in shape and without stalks, and they open when ripe by a longitudinal fissure on the inside (Fig. 207 *A*); if we imagine the sporangia in each longitudinal row in a sorus united together, and the two rows adhering to one another by their inner surfaces or fused together, we shall have such a structure as we find in *Marattia* (Fig. 207 *B*, *C*). That we are not dealing in this case with a sporangium with several compartments in two rows, but with a sorus formed of two rows of sporangia united together by their sides, is shown both by the history of development and by comparison

---

[1] According to Holle there is one root to each leaf in *Marattia*, two in *Angiopteris*.

with *Angiopteris*. Each sporangium in *Marattia* and in *Angiopteris* opens by a
longitudinal fissure on its inner side. In *Kaulfussia* the eight to twenty sporangia in
a sorus are arranged in a circle, and have grown together so as to form a plurilocular
structure; they, too, open by a longitudinal slit on the inner side. In *Danaea* the
united sporangia are in two long rows which cover the entire length of the vein that
bears them, and each compartment or sporangium opens by a hole at its apex.
Round the sorus are usually some flat lobed hairs forming a kind of indusium, which
in *Danaea* looks like a cup in which the long sorus lies.

The history of the development of the sporangia is in essential points the
same in *Angiopteris* and *Marattia*. The placenta is a cushion-like protuberance
from epidermal cells above a vascular bundle. In *Angiopteris* two rows of papillae
appear separate from one another on the placenta, each of which proceeds from
a group of cells on the surface of the placenta. Each papilla developes into one
of the free sporangia of the sorus. The hypodermal terminal cell of the central

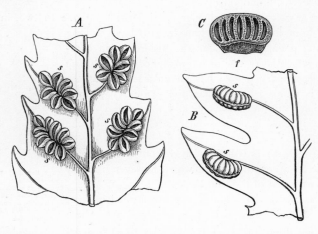

FIG. 207. *A* under side of the upper portion of a leaflet of *Angiopteris caudata* with the sori *s s*. *B* teeth of the margin
of a leaf of *Marattia* with the sori *s s*. *C* half of a sorus of *Marattia* with open sporangia (compartments).

row of cells (Fig. 208, where it is divided already by a longitudinal wall) is the
archesporium; the tapetal cells come from the surrounding tissue. Each of the
sporangia which are united together laterally in *Marattia* has its own archesporium,
which originates exactly as in *Angiopteris*; this proves that in *Marattia*, as in
Angiopteris, we have two rows of distinct sporangia which have grown together by
their lateral faces.

The spores are formed from their mother-cells in the usual manner; bilateral
bean-shaped spores and spheroid-tetrahedral spores occur in the same species, but
there is no difference in their mode of germination.

The wall of the mature sporangium is formed of several layers of cells; the cells
of the outermost layer have thick dark-coloured walls, especially at the apex of
the sporangium; this structural arrangement recalls the rudimentary annulus of the
sporangium of *Osmunda*. The cells in the parietal layers have thinner walls in the
place where the sporangium dehisces than elsewhere, as is the case also in *Botrychium*

and *Ophioglossum*. In *Danaea* each sporangium opens when ripe by a hole at its apex.

Histology. A peculiar feature in the epidermis is seen in the extraordinarily large stomata with wide orifices in the leaves of *Kaulfussia*; these are formed in the usual manner but are afterwards distinguished by the unusual size of the apertures, and by the guard-cells which form a narrow ring and are surrounded by two or three layers of epidermal cells also arranged in a ring. (Lürssen.)

In the parenchyma of the fundamental tissue of the leaves, Lürssen found outgrowths on the walls of the cells bounding the intercellular spaces; these outgrowths project into the spaces, and where these are small they take the form of bosses or conical projections, but in larger ones they become long slender filaments which are quite solid and consist of cuticularised substance; large intercellular spaces are quite filled with a web of these filaments; Lürssen found them in *Kaulfussia, Danaea, Angiopteris*, and *Marattia*. Layers and bundles of sclerenchyma are found in the fundamental tissue of the leaves, but, except in *Danaea*, they have not the hardness and dark colour of the sclerenchyma of the Ferns; these tissues become collenchymatic in the thickenings at the joints. Long chains of tubular cells containing tannin traverse all parts of the fundamental tissue, and gum-passages are scattered about in the thin-walled parenchyma. There is

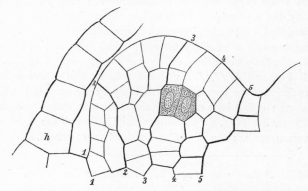

FIG. 208. *Angiopteris evecta.* Longitudinal section through a young sporangium. The shaded archesporium has divided by a longitudinal wall. The young sporangium still shows in the longitudinal section the 5 cell-rows (1–5) from which it proceeded; *h* a hair.

no sclerenchyma in the stem of *Angiopteris*, as we know from Sachs' researches; the general mass of the fundamental tissue is formed of a wide-celled thin-walled parenchyma, in which a large number of cells containing tannin and a red cell-sap, and large gum-passages, are distributed; the contents of the latter cover a piece of the stem, which is allowed to lie in water, with a thick layer of gelatinous mucilage.

The vascular bundles both of stem and leaves resemble those of Ferns. A central xylem, composed of broad tracheides with scalariform thickenings, is surrounded by a layer of phloem; the bundles in the leaf of *Angiopteris* are mostly flattened, those of the stem circular in transverse section. The bundle-sheath of one layer of cells with sinuous longitudinal walls, so common elsewhere especially in the Ferns, is wanting in the Marattiaceae both in leaf and stem, while it is present in the roots, where it is formed of large cells[1].

---

[1] Harting has described the roots which pass through the parenchyma of the stem (Fig. 205 *w*) as vascular bundles of the stem, and figured them on Table VII, Figs. 3 and 4, in his monograph of *Marattia*; he did not examine the structure of the true vascular bundles. It is necessary to point out this mistake, because Russow, relying on Harting, gives a bundle-sheath to the bundles of the stem; but this sheath belongs only to the roots passing through the stem.

The growing point of the stem is slightly convex and has, according to Holle, a long one-sided apical cell; a similar cell is found also in the smaller roots. According to Schwendener[1], a median section of a root of *Marattia* shows two apical cells lying right and left of the median plane. From both these cells segments are cut off by periclinal walls on the one hand for the root-cap, and on the other for the body of the root; longitudinal divisions also take place from time to time. A transverse section of the rounded apex shows that altogether four such apical cells are grouped round the centre[2].

II. EQUISETINEAE.

A. HOMOSPOROUS EQUISETINEAE : EQUISETACEAE (HORSE-TAILS)[3].

Sexual generation or *prothallium* (*oophore, oophyte*). The spores of the Equisetaceae, which retain their vitality only a few days, if sown in water or on moist ground as soon as they are ripe show in a few hours the first preparations for germination; in a few days' time the prothallium will have developed into a flat pluricellular body, but its further growth will be slow. The spore, which contains a nucleus and chlorophyll-corpuscles, increases in size as germination begins; it becomes pear-shaped and bursts the exosporium, and divides into two cells, the smaller of which has almost wholly colourless cell-contents and soon developes into a long hyaline rhizoid (Fig. 209 *I, II, III w*); the anterior and larger cell receives the chlorophyll-corpuscles of the spore, which multiply by division, and it then produces by further divisions the first lobe of the prothallium, which continues to grow at the apex and soon branches (*III, IV*). The multiplication of the cells thus resulting appears to be very irregular; the very first divisions vary; sometimes the first wall in

---

[1] Ueber Scheitelwachsthum mit mehreren Scheitelzellen (Sitzber. d. Ges. naturf. Freunde in Berlin, 1879).

[2] [See Bower, Morph. of the leaf in Vasc. Crypt. and Gymnosp. (Phil. Trans. 1884) for the development of the leaf.]

[3] On the Calamites, *vid. infra.* G. W. Bischoff, Die kryptogamischen Gewächse, Nürnberg, 1828.—Hofmeister, Vergl. Unters. 1851;—Id. Ueber d. Keimung d. Equiseten (Abh. d. Kgl. Sächs. Ges. d. Wiss. 1855, IV. 168);—Id. Ueber Sporenentwicklung d. Equiseten (Jahrb. f. wiss. Bot. III. 283).—Thuret in Ann. d. Sc. nat. 1851, XVI, 31.—Sanio, Ueber Epidermis u. Spaltoffn. d. Equis. (Linnaea, Bd. 29, Heft 4).—C. Cramer, Längenwachsthum u. Gewebebildung bei *Equis. arvense* u. *sylvaticum* (Pflanzenphys. Unters. von Nägeli u. Cramer, III, 1855).—Duval-Jouve, Histoire naturelle de *Equisetum*, Paris, 1864.—H. Schacht, Die Spermatozoiden im Pflanzenreich, Braunschweig, 1864.—Rees, Entwicklungsgesch. d. Stammspitze von *Equiset.* (Jahrb. f. wiss. Bot. 1867, VI. 209).— Milde, Monographia Equisetorum in Nova Acta Acad. Leop. Carol. xxxv, 1867.—Nägeli u. Leitgeb, Entstehung u. Wachsthum d. Wurzeln. (Beitr. z. Wiss. Bot. von Nägeli, Heft iv, München, 1867).— Pfitzer, Ueber d. Schutzscheide (Jahrb. f. wiss. Bot. VI. 297).—Russow, Vergl. Unters. über d. Leit-bündelkryptog., Petersburg, 1872, p. 41.—Janczewski, Ueber d. Archegonien (Bot. Ztg. 1872, p. 420).—Van Tieghem, Ueber Wurzeln (Ann. d. sc. nat. 5 sér. T. XIII).—Janczewski, Recherches sur le développement d. bourgeons dans les Prêles (Mém. d. l. soc. nat. d. sc. nat. de Cherbourg. T. XX. 1876).—Famintzin, Ueber Knospenbildung bei Equiset. (Bulletin de l'Acad. d. Sc. de Péters-bourg, p. xxii, 1876).—Sadebeck, Ueber Keimung u. Embryobildung in Schenk, Handb. d. Bot. 1 Bd. pp. 174, 183, 221.—Goebel, Beitr. z. vergl. Entwickl.-Gesch. d. Sporangien (Bot. Ztg. 1880-1).— On Spermatozoids, see Strasburger in d. Jen. Zeitschr. Bd. X. p. 401 ff., and Zellbildung u. Zelltheilung, III Ed. p. 96; also Sadebeck, Die Entw. d. Keimes d. Schachtelhalme (Pringsheim's Jahrb. Bd. XI, und Encykl. d. Nat. Wiss. Bd. I).

the cell which contains chlorophyll is slightly inclined to the longitudinal axis of the young plant (being sometimes dichotomous in *E. Telmateja*), and the two cells thus formed develope into separate tubes; in other cases this cell developes into a longer tube, the apical portion of which is cut off by a transverse wall, as happens sometimes in *E. arvense*.

Cell-surfaces are formed as growth continues; branches arise as outgrowths from lateral cells and develope in a similar manner; and as the cells multiply, the chlorophyll-corpuscles which they contain are also constantly being multiplied by division. The young prothallia are usually ribbon-like and narrow, and formed of one layer of cells in *E. Telmateja*; the older prothallia in other species and in *E. Telmateja* also are irregularly lobed; one of the lobes sooner or later outstrips the others and becomes thicker and fleshy, being formed of several layers of cells, and puts out rhizoids on its under side.

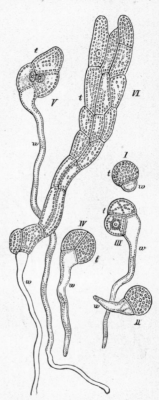

The prothallia of the Equisetaceae are for the most part dioecious; the male are always smaller, a few millimetres long, and according to Hofmeister produce archegonia only exceptionally and on late shoots. The female are much larger, reaching a half inch in length; Hofmeister compares them to the thallus of *Anthoceros punctatus*, Duval-Jouve to a curly endive-leaf. Sadebeck avers that antheridia may appear at a later period on the lobes of female prothallia. It is probable that in this as in other cases the male prothallia are those which have been insufficiently fed; at least the observation of Hofmeister just mentioned, that they can afterwards produce archegonia as well as antheridia, points to this conclusion (see p. 198). These statements refer chiefly to *E. arvense*, *E. limosum*, and *E. palustre*; according to Duval-Jouve the prothallia of *E. Telmateja* and *E. sylvaticum* are broader and less branched, those of *E. ramosissimum* and *E. variegatum* are more slender and elongated.

FIG. 209. First stages in the development of the prothallium of *Equisetum Telmateja*; *w* the first rhizoid, *t* rudiment of the thallus; the numbers from *I* to *VI* indicate successive stages of development. Magn. about 200 times.

The *antheridia* appear at the extremity or on the margin of the larger lobe of the male prothallium. The apical cells of the layer which envelopes the antheridium contains little or no chlorophyll, and like the same cells in the Hepaticae they separate from one another when they come in contact with water, and release the spermatozoids which are still inclosed in cysts and may be from one hundred to one hundred and fifty in number. The spermatozoid is larger than in other Cryptogams and forms two or three coils, and the posterior and thicker coil carries an appendage with it on its inner side,—a vesicle such as is seen in the spermatozoids of the Ferns, containing granules of starch and cell-sap (compare Filices and Isoeteae). The mother-cells of the spermatozoids (spermatocytes) are formed by division of a central cell of the young antheridium.

The *archegonia* are formed from single superficial cells of the meristematic anterior margin of the fleshy lobes of the female prothallium; as the thallus beneath them continues to grow, they come, as in *Pellia*, to be on its upper surface. The direction of the archegonium is therefore the opposite to that of the homosporous Ferns; the neck points upwards; but the development agrees perfectly with that of the archegonium in the Filicineae, except that the neck-canal-cell does not extend

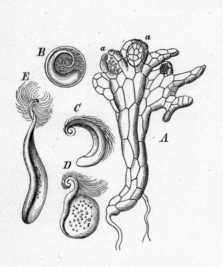

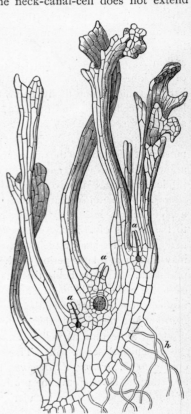

FIG. 210. *A* male prothallium with the first antheridia *a* of *Equisetum arvense*, after Hofmeister. *B—E* spermatozoids of *Equisetum Telmateja*, after Schacht. *A* magn. 200 times.

FIG. 211. Vertical section of a lobe of a strong female prothallium of *Equisetum arvense*; at *a, a, a* two abortive and one fertile archegonium, *h* rhizoids. Magn. about 600 times.

the whole length of the neck. The four long upper cells of the neck bend radially outwards in a half circle, like a four-armed anchor, when the canal opens.

Development of the *asexual generation* (*sporophore, sporophyte*) which forms the spores. The succession of the divisions and the formation of the organs in the embryo is the same, according to Sadebeck, as in the Filicineae. The first wall, the *basal* wall, is nearly transverse to the axis of the archegonium; then follows the division into octants by the formation of the *transversal* and *median* walls at right angles to the basal wall. Of the four quadrants in the upper or *epibasal* half, one gives rise to the rudimentary stem with a three-sided pyramidal apical cell, two others produce one *cotyledon*, and the fourth the second cotyledon; these cotyledons, how-ever, do not develope as separate leaves, for they unite as they grow at a very early period with the first leaf which proceeds from the apex of the stem, to form an annular wall. The root and the foot are formed from the *hypobasal* half of the embryo, just as in the Filicineae.

The first leafy shoot grows upwards and forms from ten to fifteen internodes with foliar sheaths, each with three teeth; it soon produces at its base a new and stronger shoot having sheaths with four teeth (*E. arvense, E. pratense, E. variegatum,* Hofmeister), and this again gives rise to new generations of shoots constantly developing thicker stems and sheaths with more numerous teeth; sometimes the third or one of the succeeding shoots strikes downwards into the ground and forms the first persistent rhizome, which then produces fresh underground rhizomes and ascending leafy shoots from year to year.

To facilitate the understanding of the growth of the stem and leaves, we must first examine their structure in the fully developed state. Every shoot consists of a series of segments of the axis or inter-nodes, which are usually hollow and closed at their base by a thin transverse septum or *diaphragm*; each of these internodes passes upwards into a foliar sheath which em-braces the next internode, and the sheath divides at its upper margin into three or four or usually more teeth. A vascular bundle runs downwards in a straight line from each tooth into the internode as far as the node at its base, and parallel with the rest of the bundles of the internode; at its lower end each bundle splits into two short diverging arms, by means of which it

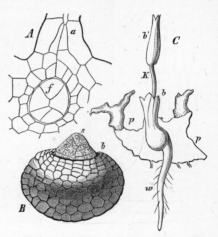

FIG. 212. Development of the embryo of *Equisetum arvense*, according to Hofmeister. *A* archegonium cut through vertically with the embryo. *B* older embryo isolated; *b* annular leaf-cushion formed by union of the two cotyledons and the first leaf of the stem, *s* apex of the first shoot. *C* vertical section of a lobe of the prothallium *pp* with a young plant; *w* the first root, *b*, *b'* the leaf-sheaths. *A* and *B* magn. 200, *C* 20 times.

unites with the two adjacent bundles of the next internode below, where they descend into it from their sheath-teeth; in this way the stem-segments or internodes with their foliar sheaths alternate, and as in every segment the arrangement of the bundles, foliar teeth, projecting longitudinal ridges and furrows, is repeated with exact regu-larity in the transverse section, the formations in one segment always coincide with the intervals between the homologous formations in the next segment above and below. If, for example, the internode shows a longitudinal ridge projecting on its surface, a similar ridge runs down from the tip of each foliar tooth parallel with the other as far as the base of the internode; between every two teeth begins a furrow or channel, which also continues on to the base of the internode. The projecting ridges are on the same radii as the vascular bundles, which contain each an air-space, the carinal canal; the depressions or furrows lie on the same radii as the lacunae of the cortical tissue (vallecular canals), though these are sometimes wanting, and alternate with the vascular bundles. The branches and roots spring exclusively from inside the base of the leaf-sheath, and as this is a whorl, the branches and roots are therefore also arranged in whorls. The branches have the appearance as if of endogenous origin, being formed on the inside of the basal tissue of the leaf-sheath on a radius of the stem which falls between the vascular bundles, and therefore also between the teeth of the sheath; a root may be formed between each branch, and they both break through the base of the leaf-sheath. All the segments of the stem agree in these points, whether they are developed as underground rhizomes, as tubers, as ascending stems, as leafy branches, or as sporangiferous shoots.

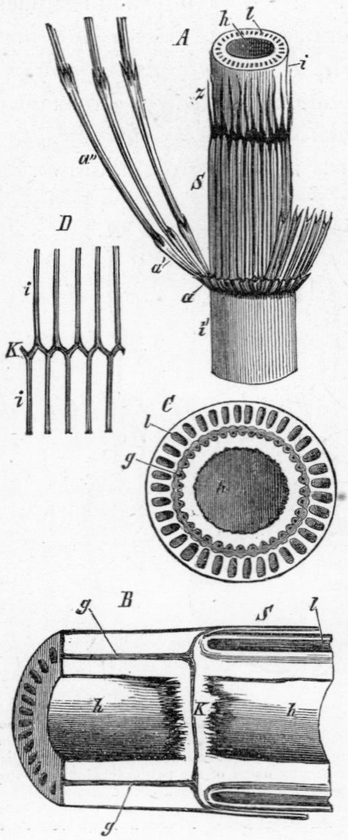

The end of the stem enclosed in a number of young foliar sheaths culminates in a large apical cell, the upper wall of which is strongly convex, while its inferior and lateral bounding lines are almost plane; consequently the apical cell has the form of a three-sided pyramid, the upturned base of which is an almost equilateral spherical triangle. The segments are cut off by walls which are parallel with the oblique sides of the apical cell, that is, with the youngest primary walls of the segments; the segments, which are arranged with a spiral divergence of one-third, lie in three straight rows. Each segment is in form a three-sided tabular cell with an upper and under triangular primary wall, a right and a left quadrangular lateral wall, and a curved quadrangular outer wall. Each segment divides first by an anticlinal wall parallel with the primary walls into two equal tabular cells lying on one another and half the height of the original segment; then usually each half-segment is again halved by a nearly radial vertical wall, the sextant wall. The segment now consists of four cells, two of which lie one above the other and extend to the centre, but the two others do not, because the vertical wall (sextant wall) is not exactly radial, but joins on at its inner end to one of the lateral walls of the segment (the anodal wall) (Fig. 214 E). Then follow divisions, but not in fixed order, in the four cells of each segment parallel

FIG. 213. *Equisetum Telmateja. A* piece of an erect stem; *i, i'* internodes, *h* its central cavity, *l* lacunae of the cortex, *S* leaf-sheath, *z* its apex, *a, a', a''* the lower internodes of slender leaf-shoots. *B* longitudinal section of a rhizome; *k* transverse diaphragm between the cavities *h h, g* vascular bundle, *l* cortical lacunae, *S* leaf-sheath. *C* transverse section of a rhizome; *g* and *l* as above. *D* union of vascular bundles of an upper and a lower internode *i, i'; K* the node. *A* natural size, *B* and *C* about twice the nat. size.

with the primary and lateral walls, and soon after periclinal divisions appear by which the segment is divided into inner and outer cells, and these are then subjected to further divisions; the inner cells form the pith, which is soon destroyed by the elongation of the stem as far as the diaphragm at the base of each internode; the outer cells produce the leaves and the whole of the tissue of the hollow internodes. It has been already stated that the segments as first formed are disposed in a spiral line with a divergence of one-third, and since each segment without exception produces, as in the Mosses, a leaf or a portion of a leaf-sheath, the leaves of the Equisetaceae must also

be inserted in a spiral line running round the stem; this is actually the case sometimes in plants of abnormal growth; but in ordinary cases, owing to a small
displacement at a very early period, the three segments, which form a cycle on the
stem, arrange themselves so as to form a transverse disk of the stem, their outer
surfaces combining into an annular zone. Thus by unequal growth of the segments
in the longitudinal direction each cycle in the spiral formed by the segments gives rise

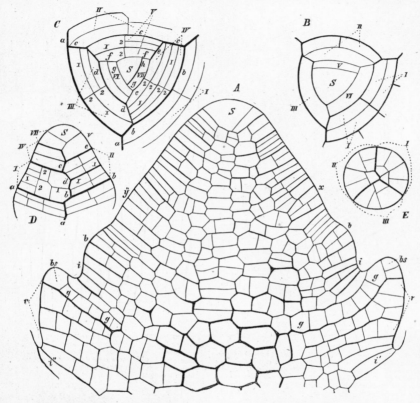

FIG. 214. *A* longitudinal section of the extremity of the stem of an underground bud of *Equisetum Telmateja*;
S apical cell; *xy̆* first indication of an annular cushion for the formation of leaves, *bb* an older cushion of the same kind,
bs, bs the apical cells of a leaf-cushion already considerably advanced, *rr* rudiment of the cortical tissue of the internodes,
qq cell-rows from which the tissue of the leaf and its vascular bundle are formed, *ii* the lower cell-layers of the segments,
which take no part in the formation of the leaves. *B* horizontal projection of the apical view of a stem of *Equisetum
Telmateja*; *S* apical cell, *I—V* the successive segments, the older ones further divided (*VI* should be *IV*). *C* horizontal
projection of the apical view of *E. arvense*. *D* optical longitudinal section of the extremity of a very weakly stem.
E transverse section of the extremity of a stem after the appearance of the vertical and first tangential walls. The Roman
ciphers indicate the segments, the Arabian the walls formed in them in the order of their succession, the letters the
principal walls of the segments. *C, D,* and *E* after Cramer. *A* natural size.

to a whorl, which strictly speaking is not a true whorl because it is due to subsequent
displacement[1]. Each whorl of segments now produces a leaf-sheath and the internode beneath it. While the three segments are being adjusted to form a transverse
disk of the stem, they undergo the divisions above described, which convert each of
them into a cellular body containing from four to six layers of cells. As soon as a
transverse zone is formed, the leaves begin to develope by the growth of the outer

---

[1] See what was said above on the development of the leaves in germinating plants.

cells of the segments, which form an annular cushion; one of the upper cell-layers of the segment projects most strongly outwards, forming the apex (the circular apical line) of the cushion (Figs. 214 *A bs*, 215 *b'*), and its cells which lie most outside divide by

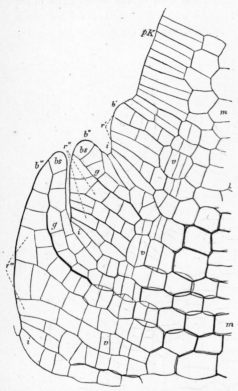

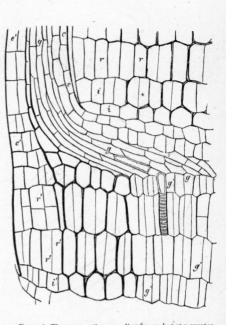

FIG. 215. *Equisetum Telmateja.* Left half of a radial longitudinal section beneath the apex of an underground bud in September; *vK* lower part of the vegetative cone, *b', b'', b'''* leaves, *bs bs* their apical cells, *r' r'' r'''* cortical tissue of the corresponding internodes, *m m* pith, *v v v* thickening-ring, *g g* cell-layer from which the vascular bundle of the tip of the leaf is formed, *i i i* apical cell of a branch.

FIG. 216. The same as the preceding figure, but at a greater distance beneath the apex, and showing the more advanced differentiation of leaf-sheath and internode; *r r* cortex of the upper, *r' r' r'* cortex of the lower internode, *e e* the inner, *e' e'* the outer epidermis of the leaf-sheath, *g g* the limb of the vascular bundle belonging to the leaf, *g' g' g'* the descending limb belonging to the internode; the first annular vessel is formed where the two limbs meet.

walls inclined alternately to and from the axis of the stem, while the circular apical line is constantly raised, and thus the annular cushion developes into a sheath which envelopes the end of the stem. This layer of cells, the outermost cells of which form the apical line of the annular cushion, forms a meristem in the interior of the sheath, in which the vascular bundles of the sheath originate. The lower layers of cells of the whorl of segments do not grow much outwards and upwards; they divide by vertical, and subsequently and more vigorously by transverse walls, and so produce the tissue

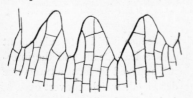

FIG. 217. Exterior view of three teeth of a young leaf-sheath of *Equisetum Telmateja.*

of the internodes, which passes continuously into the tissue of the leaf; an inner layer of this tissue forming a hollow cylinder (Fig. 215 *v, v*) is distinguished by its many longitudinal divisions; it forms a ring of meristem (a thickening ring in Sanio's sense), in which the vertical descending vascular bundles of the internode are formed; these bundles are the prolongation of the bundles of the teeth of the foliar sheath, which they meet at an obtuse angle (Fig. 216 g,g'), and then coalesce with them to form curved common bundles. The layers of cells outside this ring of meristem which

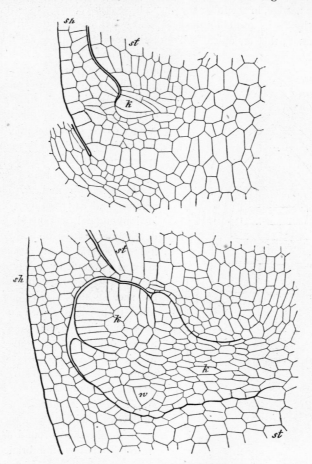

FIG. 218. *Equisetum arvense.* Longitudinal section through the growing point of the stem; *sh* leaf-sheath, *st* stem, *k* rudiment of a bud. In the upper portion of the figure the apical cell of the bud has already formed some segments, two of which are shown; in the lower portion the lateral bud is considerably developed and is overarched by the leaf-sheath and the tissue of the stem *st*; at *w* is the rudiment of the root of the lateral bud. After Janczewski.

forms the bundles produce the cortex of the internode, in which air-conducting intercellular passages soon appear. The rudiments of the leaf-teeth (the teeth of the foliar sheath) make their appearance at an early stage as protuberances at several equidistant points on the apical line of the annular cushion, which forms a leaf-sheath; each of these protuberances ends in one or two apical cells (Fig. 217 [1]).

[1] On the original number and subsequent increase of the teeth of the sheath and on other points see Hofmeister and Rees as cited on page 286.

The position of the lateral buds is peculiar, and gave occasion to the view that the *branching* of the Equisetaceae is endogenous from interior cells of the stem. The branches are placed vertically beneath the angle between every two leaf-teeth, and therefore alternate with them. The young branches originate in a single super-ficial cell of the growing point of the stem, which is always opposite a depression, never opposite a ridge, in the foliar sheath. The first three divisions of the mother-cell, was observed by Sachs and confirmed by Janczewski, are inclined in three directions in such a manner, that an apical cell with the form of a three-sided pyramid is at once produced, and the first three divisions are therefore the first three segments of the cell. But soon the young bud is sur-rounded by the luxuriantly growing tissue of the sheath, and as this unites with the surface of the stem above the bud, the latter is completely enclosed by tissue and has the appearance of being endogenous in origin (Fig. 218). Lateral buds from the rhizome of *E. Telmateja* and *E. arvense* in late autumn and early spring will usually show in longitudinal section all stages in the development of the buds. After they have formed several foliar cushions and their apex is covered by a compact envelope of leaves, they break through the base of the sheath; they may remain dormant for some time, as is shown by the fact that buds burst into activity when underground nodes of ascending stems are exposed to the light. It may be assumed that as many buds as leaf-teeth are originally formed, and on the erect leafy stems of *E. Telmateja*, *E. arvense* and others they all develope, and produce the many slender green foliage-shoots found in these species. In other species the branching is more scanty; some like *E. hiemale* usually have no aerial lateral shoots, except when the terminal bud of the stem is injured,

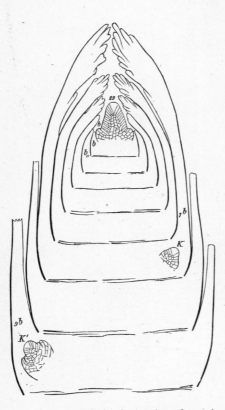

FIG. 219. Longitudinal section through an underground bud of *Equisetum arvense*; *ss* apical cell of the stem, *b* to *gb* the leaves, *k*, *k'* two buds; the transverse lines in the stem show the position of the diaphragms.

in which case the next node below puts out a shoot. Branches do not usually appear on rhizomes in complete whorls, but only two or three together; but these are more vigorous and develope either new rhizomes or ascending stems. Since in the cases first described the buds are produced like the leaves in strict acropetal succession, we may assume that, where the shoots develope only at a late period and under the influence of accidental circumstances, the buds have up to that time remained dormant in the interior.

The *roots* are formed in whorls, one immediately beneath each bud, but they also like the buds are not always developed; they are produced sometimes even on aerial nodes in moisture and darkness, and from lateral buds on the nodes (compare Fig. 220). The apical cell of the root is seen in the lower part of the lateral buds, and in *E. arvense* these are the only adventitious roots that are produced. The buds on the underground parts of stems usually disappear when they have produced a root. In the lower part of the stem, the rhizome, of *E. limosum* are found buds which develope from one to six roots, the *rhizogenous buds* of Janczewski; with them are a few others which become vigorous branches or stems. In these rhizogenous buds the growing point of the branch is arrested in its development.

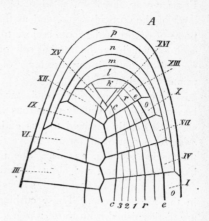

The mode of growth of the roots is in its earliest stages essentially the same as in the roots of Ferns, as is represented diagrammatically in Fig. 220[1]. The cortical tissue is differentiated into an inner and an outer layer; the former gives rise to air-conducting intercellular spaces, which like the cells themselves are at first disposed in radial and concentric rows, and afterwards unite by rupture of the cells into a large air-space surrounding the vascular bundle. In the formation of the vascular bundle of the root, three only of the six primary cells which compose the rudiment of the bundle as seen in transverse section, the three, namely, which extend to the centre, are each at first divided by a tangential (periclinal) wall, so that the rudiment of the bundle now consists of three inner and six outer cells; the six outer cells produce a cambial tissue, in which the formation of vessels begins from two or three points, and proceeds inwards; at length one of the three inner cells produces a wide central vessel; phloem forms in the circumference of the bundle. While in the other Vascular Cryptogams the innermost layer of the cortical tissue becomes the bundle-sheath, the radial walls of the cells showing the characteristic folding, in the roots of the Equisetaceae it is the layer next outside the innermost layer which has this peculiarity;

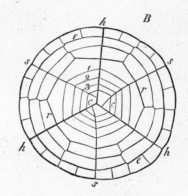

FIG. 220. Diagram of the succession of cell-division in the tip of the root of *Equisetum hiemale*; the diagram serves also in the main for the Ferns and for *Marsilia*. *A* longitudinal section. *B* transverse section at the lower end of *A*; *h, h, h* the primary walls, *s, s, s* the sextant walls of the segments indicated in *A* by the figures *I* to *XVI*, *k, l, m, n, q* the layers of the root-cap omitting all further divisions; *c, c* denotes the walls in the substance of the root which separate the primordial vascular bundle from the cortex, *e* the boundary-wall between the epidermis *o* and the cortex, *r r* the boundary-wall between the outer and inner cortex; 1, 2, 3 the successive periclinal walls, by which the inner cortex is divided into several layers, the radial divisions being omitted. After Nägeli and Leitgeb.

---

[1] The curvature and junction of the walls is not quite correctly given in the figure, as will be seen by comparison with Fig. 193.

the innermost layer which is next the axile bundle takes the place to some extent of the pericambium which is wanting in the roots of the Equisetaceae. At the same time this layer is distinguished from the pericambium of the roots of other Cryptogams by the circumstance that the lateral roots originate in it ; in the Equisetaceae, therefore, as in all Cryptogams, the lateral roots spring from the inner layer of the cortical tissue, and as there is no pericambium in the Equisetaceae, the point of origin of the roots is close to the outer vessels of the axile bundle. The cells, each of which is the mother-cell of a lateral root, are formed in strict acropetal succession in the innermost layer of the cortical tissue on the outer margin of the primary vessels.

The *sporangia* of the Equisetaceae are outgrowths of peculiarly metamorphosed leaves formed in usually numerous whorls on the summit of ordinary shoots, or of shoots specially destined to this end. An imperfectly developed foliar sheath, the *annulus*, is first of all formed above the last foliar sheath of the vegetative portion of the fertile axis (Fig. 221 *a*). The annulus is sometimes more, sometimes less leaf-like in appearance, and above it and below the apex of the growing shoot annular cushions appear in acropetal succession, as in the ordinary formation of the leaves in the Equisetaceae. These cushions do not project much above the surface, and are distinguished from those which give rise to toothed foliar sheaths by the circumstance, that all the rows of cells in the portion of the axis where they arise are employed to form them, whereas in the case of the toothed foliar sheaths the lower rows of cells help to build up the cortex of the stem. These hemispherical projections are the rudiments of the *sporophylls* (*sporangiophores*), and on each of them a large number of protuberances arise, answering to the teeth of ordinary foliar sheaths ; in this way several whorls of hemispherical projections are formed, lying close one above the other, which grow more rapidly on their outer side, and press against each other and so become polygonal and usually six-sided, while the basal portion of each protuberance remains more slender and forms the stalk of the six-sided peltate disk. The outer surface of the disks is tangential to the axis of the sporangiferous spike; on the inner side which is towards the axis from five to ten sporangia are produced on each disk. The sporangium in an early stage of development looks like a small blunt pluricellular wart, and developes exactly in the same way as the sporangium of the Marattiaceae. The mother-cells of the spores are developed from a hypodermal *archesporium*, while of three outer layers of cells which surround it at first, only the outermost remains at the last as the wall of the sporangium. The spore-mother-cells, adhering to one another in groups of four or eight, float free in a fluid which fills the cavity of the sporangium and has granules distributed in it.

The *spores* are formed by division into four parts (repeated bipartition) of their mother-cells, and are tetrahedrally arranged. The ripe sporangium opens by a longitudinal fissure on the side towards the stalk of the peltate disk. The very thin-walled cells of the wall previously form spiral thickening ridges on the dorsal side of the sporangium and annular thickening ridges on the ventral side, and these ridges are formed in *E. limosum*, according to Duval-Jouve, very rapidly just before the dehiscence of the sporangium. The spores of the Equisetaceae have the peculiarity of forming several coats. Each spore forms at first an outer coat which is not cuticularised and is capable of swelling, and this when subsequently split up into two spiral bands forms the so-called *elaters*; soon after a second coat and then a third make their appearance. The three lie at first close one on the other like layers (shells) of one coat. But if the spore is placed in water the outer coat swells and rises up from off the others (Fig. 222 *B*). Even when the spore is quite fresh and is just placed in distilled water the three coats can be readily distinguished (Fig. 222 *A*), for the outer (1) is colourless, the second (2) is a light blue, the third (3) is yellowish, (*E. limosum*). As the spore develops the outer coat separates like a loose garment from the body of the spore (*C d, e*), and then appear the first signs of the formation of elaters. An optical longitudinal section shows that the spiral thickening bands of

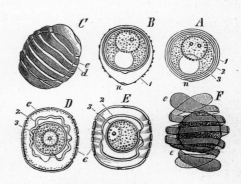

FIG. 222. Development of the spores of *Equisetum limosum*, magn. 800 times. *A* unripe spore with three coats just placed in water. *B* the same after lying two or three minutes in water, the outer coat having become detached ; a large vacuole appears close to the nucleus. *C* beginning of the formation of elaters on the outer coat *e*=1 in Figs. *A* and *B*. *D, E* the same stage of development in optical section after lying twelve hours in glycerine ; *e* the coat which forms the elaters, 2 and 3 the inner coats separated from one another. *F* the outer coat split into spirally-twisted elaters, which are coloured a beautiful blue by Schultze's solution.

FIG. 221. *Equisetum Telmateja. A* the upper part of a fertile stem with the lower half of the sporangiferous spike ; *b* the leaf-sheath, *a* the annulus, *x* the stalks of the peltate scales which have been cut off, *y* transverse section of the axis of the spike. *B* peltate scales (sporophylls) in different positions and slightly magnified ; *st* the stalk, *s* the peltate scale, *sg* the sporangia. *A* natural size, *B* slightly magnified.

this coat are only separated by very narrow and thin portions of membrane (*D, E*). These thin strips at length disappear, and the thicker parts separate from one another, if the environment is dry, as two spiral bands. These two bands form a four-armed cross when unrolled, and are narrower in the centre where they are attached to the second coat; it is this point of attachment probably which is seen in the unripe spore as an umbilical thickening (*n, A, B*). An outer very thin cuticularised layer may be distinguished on the developed elaters, which are more than usually hygroscopic, rolling themselves round the spore when the air is damp and unrolling again as the air becomes drier ; if alternation of these conditions is rapidly brought about, as by breathing lightly on the spores under the microscope, the latter are set in lively motion by the movements of the elaters. The office of the elaters is to cause a number of spores to remain attached to one another at the period of dispersion, so that they leave the sporangium in small groups[1]; if they become wetted, as they may on slightly moistened ground, the union between them becomes still closer, since the elaters which are only partially rolled up hold them all the tighter together. As the prothallia are generally unisexual, it is evidently advantageous to the plant that the elaters should cause several spores to germinate in the immediate neighbourhood of one another. If spores, in which the outer coat is not yet split up to form the elaters but shows the preliminary differentiation, are allowed to lie for some time in glycerine, each spore surrounded by its third (inner) coat shrinks considerably, and the second cuticularised coat separates from the inner in folds. The third (inner) coat is differentiated into an outer granular cuticularised *exosporium*, and an inner layer of cellulose, the *endosporium*.

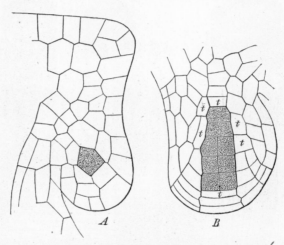

FIG. 223. *A* longitudinal section through a portion of a sporophyll (sporangiophore) of *Equisetum palustre*; a sporangium is being formed, the archesporium shaded. *B* an older sporangium in axile longitudinal section, *t, t, t* tapetal cells. The mass of sporogenous cells formed from the archesporium consists at first of a few cells only.

There is little to be said in this place on the subject of the *classification* of the Equisetaceae ; all existing forms in this family are near enough to each other to be included in one genus, *Equisetum*, and to this genus the numerous fossil species may also be united.

In *habit* as in morphological character the Equisetaceae are very distinct from almost all other plants. They are perennial by means of underground creeping rhizomes ; these send up shoots every year which rise erect above the surface of the ground and there last usually during one period of vegetation, more rarely for several years. The sporangiferous spikes appear at the summit of these vegetative assimilating axes or on special fertile shoots, which when without chlorophyll and unbranched die down after

---

[1] This was demonstrated by De Bary in Bot. Ztg. 1884, p. 782. The name 'elater' is therefore quite unsuitable. With regard to the origin of the membrane which produces the elaters, opposing views have been published ; that taken in the text is founded on the researches of Sachs ; see also Russow, Vergl. Unters. p. 149.

the dispersion of the spores, as in *E. Telmateja* and *E. arvense*, or, as in *E. sylvaticum* and *E. pratense*, throw off the fertile head and continue to live as vegetative shoots. The fertile axes are developed from the underground internodes of ascending vegetative axes; during the summer in which the latter are unfolded above ground the fertile shoots remain in the bud state beneath the ground, but they form their sporangia in this state, either so completely that in the next spring they have only to elongate their stems and disperse their spores, as is the case in *E. arvense*, *E. pratense*, *E. Telmateja* and others, or the spikes do not complete their development till after the elongation of the axes which bear them in the spring (*E. limosum*). The outward appearance of the aerial shoots depends chiefly on the number and length of their whorled and usually very slender lateral branches, which in some species, as *E. trachyodon*, *E. ramosissimum*, *E. hiemale*, *E. variegatum*, are as a rule entirely wanting, in others, as *E. palustre* and *E. limosum*, are somewhat scanty, in others again, as *E. arvense*, *E. Telmateja*, and *E. sylvaticum*, are developed in great abundance. The height of these leafy stems is in our native species usually from one to three feet; in *E. Telmateja* the ascending axis of the sterile shoot, which is without chlorophyll and colourless, reaches a height of from four to five feet with a thickness of about half an inch, while the slender leafy branches are scarcely half a line in thickness. The tallest stems are those of *E. giganteum* from South America; these may be as much as twenty-six feet high, but are only about the thickness of a thumb and are kept in an upright position by the neighbouring plants; the Calamites must have been as tall, and sometimes a foot thick. The rhizomes generally run at a depth of from two to four feet beneath the surface and spread over spaces of from ten to fifty feet in diameter, but they are sometimes found at much greater depths; they prefer wet gravelly or loamy soil; their thickness varies from one or two lines to half an inch or more. The surface of the internodes in the rhizome of many species (*E. Telmateja*, *E. sylvaticum*, etc.) is covered with a felt of brown root-hairs; a similar covering is found on the foliar sheaths of even the underground parts of ascending stems, and in this point there is a resemblance to the Ferns; in other species, as *E. palustre* and *E. limosum*, the surface is smooth and shining or in others again dull. The ridges and furrows characteristic of the aerial stems are generally less developed on the underground stems, which are sometimes perfectly smooth. The internodes of the rhizomes are not always hollow, but the lacunae of the vascular bundles (carinal canals) and those of the cortical parenchyma (vallecular canals) are always present, for they serve to convey the needful air, which is not to be obtained in the usually compact soil, from the surface to the organs underground. The branches of the leafy stem, like the fructifications, are also formed either wholly or to a great extent in the underground bud in the course of the preceding year, so that only the elongation of the internodes of the ascending axis and the unfolding of the slender lateral branches remain to take place in the spring; the process may be easily observed in *E. Telmateja*. It follows that all the more important cell-formations and the processes which result in the morphological differentiation of the plant are accomplished underground; the unfolding in the air has for its chief objects the dispersion of the spores and assimilation by means of the chlorophyll in the cortical tissue of the leafy shoots when exposed to the light. The rapid elongation of the erect stems in spring is chiefly due to simple increase in length of the cells of the internodal tissue already formed, but permanent intercalary growth of the internodes sometimes occurs at their base inside the sheaths, where the tissues often continue for a long time in the young state; in this way the internodes in *E. hiemale* which are still short and of a lighter colour grow out of their sheaths when the winter is over, and the shorter they were before the winter, the more do they afterwards increase in length.

Special organs for vegetative propagation, such as are known in the Mosses, are not found in the Equisetaceae any more than in the Ferns; but instead of these every piece of rhizome and the underground nodes of ascending stems are adapted for the production of new plants. In some species underground shoots swell out into tubers of the size of a hazel-nut, which are ovoid in form in *E. arvense*, pear-shaped in *E. Telmateja*; Duval-Jouve states that these tuberous stems occur also in *E. palustre, E. sylvaticum*, and *E. littorale*, but have not yet been observed in *E. pratense, E. limosum, E. ramosissimum, E. hiemale*, or *E. variegatum*; they are due to considerable increase in thickness of an internode, and have a bud at their extremity, which may produce a succession of tuber-like internodes like a string of beads or may develope as a simple rhizome; sometimes an internode in the middle of a rhizome developes into a tuber. The parenchyma of these tubers is filled with starch and other food-material, and may, it would seem, remain dormant for a long time, and then under favourable conditions give rise to new stems.

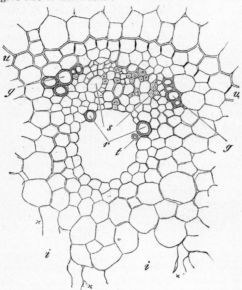

FIG. 224. Part of a transverse section through a full-grown internode of *Equisetum palustre*; *u* endodermis, *i* axile air-canal, at *x* remains of the walls of shrivelled pith-cells, in the middle a vascular bundle without distinct sheath surrounded by parenchyma. At the interior margin of the vascular portion is a wide intercellular passage in which the letters *s*, *r*, *t* are inscribed; *t* a ring, still adhering to the membrane, from the wall of a primary tracheide, the greater part of which is destroyed, *r* persistent annular tracheides, *g* groups of the last formed annular and reticulated tracheides which are also persistent, distinguished from the surrounding parts by the shading of the walls, *s* the sieve-tube portion (phloem) in which the broad lumina belong to the sieve-tubes, the narrower and sometimes granularly dotted to the cambiform cells. The doubly-contoured bands on the outer edge of the phloem, inside the cell-layer following *u*, indicate the collapsed protophloem. From De Bary, Vergl. Anatomie.

Of the *forms of tissue* in the Equisetaceae the dermal system and the fundamental tissue are the two which show the greatest variety of structure; the vascular bundles, which are so stout in the Ferns and so highly organised especially in their xylem, are less favoured in the Equisetaceae; there they are slender and their xylem is very slightly lignified, as is the case also in many water and marsh plants; the firmness of their structure is chiefly due to the dermal system with its highly developed epidermis and to the hypodermal bundles of fibres. The following remarks refer chiefly to the internodes; the lower and middle portions of the leaf-sheaths are much alike in structure, while the tissues are different and more simple in the teeth.

The *cells of the epidermis* are usually elongated in the direction of the axis, and disposed in longitudinal rows in which the adjoining cells have tranverse or slightly oblique walls, and the walls between two cells are often undulated. The epidermis in underground internodes is almost always free from stomata and is composed of cells which have thick or thin, usually brown walls, and in many species, as *E. Telmateja* and *E. arvense*, develope into delicate root-hairs. The epidermis of the deciduous fertile stems in the above species and in the sterile erect colourless stem of *E. Telmateja* is like that of the rhizomes, and has no stomata. In all other aerial internodes with chlorophyll in their tissues, in the leaf-sheaths and in the outer surface of the peltate disks, the epidermis forms numerous stomata, all lying in the furrows never on the ridges, and arranged in single longitudinal rows or in several lying close to one another. The epidermal cells are longer on the ridges, shorter in the furrows between the stomata. The outer walls of all cells, even those of the stomata, are strongly silicified; their surfaces often show protuberances of various forms, granules or bosses, rosettes, rings, lobes, transverse bands, teeth or spikes, which are still more strongly silicified; prominences of this kind on the guard-cells of the stomata (Fig. 225) usually take the form of ridges running at right angles to the orifice. The guard-cells are usually partially overlapped by the subsidiary epidermal cells. The stoma when fully developed appears to be formed of two pairs of guard-cells lying one over the other; these four cells, according to Strasburger, proceed from a single epidermal cell and lie at first side by side in a transverse row; eventually the two inner cells, the true guard-cells, are pressed inwards by the two outer cells which grow more vigorously, and are overlapped by them. Beneath the epidermis both of the rhizomes and upright stems, as well as of the leafy shoots (with the exception of the deciduous fertile stems), strands or layers of firm thick-walled cells, hypodermal tissue, are commonly found in the Equisetaceae; they form in the rhizomes a continuous stratum of many layers of brown-walled sclerenchyma; in the aerial internodes they are colourless and most strongly developed in the projecting ridges.

The *fundamental tissue* of the internodes consists chiefly of a colourless thin-walled parenchyma, which is found only in the rhizomes, the deciduous fertile stems and the colourless sterile stems of *E. Telmateja*; the green colour of the other shoots is due to

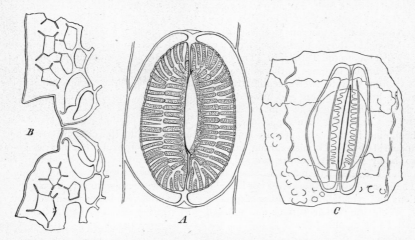

FIG. 225. Stem of *Equisetum hiemale*, and a stoma with its environment. *A* view of the inner surface; the pair of guard-cells girthed at the side by the edge of the superposed pair of subsidiary cells. *B* transverse section of the stem passing through the middle of a stoma, which lies in a depression of the surface; the narrow orifice is bounded by the two flat guard-cells and the subsidiary cells which surround them; the cells of the epidermis and of the sclerenchyma beneath it have numerous pit-canals. *C* silicious residuum of a small piece of epidermis with a stoma after maceration in Schulze's mixture and subsequent ignition, seen from the outside. The curvilinear figures are the outlines of the prominences of the outer surface. From De Bary, Vergl. Anatomie.

a 1–3 layered stratum of parenchyma containing chlorophyll, in which the cells lie transversely. This green tissue lies chiefly beneath the furrows, being associated with the stomata on their upper surface; it is ribbon-like in outline as seen in a transverse section and concave outwardly, and preponderates in the slender leafy branches, where the ridges sometimes give a stellate form to the transverse section, as in *E. arvense*. The lacunae (vallecular canals) which lie on the same radii as the furrows are formed in the fundamental tissue by the separation of the cells from one another, sometimes by their rupture; they are sometimes wanting in the slender leafy branches.

A transverse section of an internode shows the *vascular bundles* arranged in a circle, as in the Dicotyledons, each on the same radius with a ridge on the surface and between the cortical lacunae or nearer the axis. In the axis of the sporangiferous spikes, where there are no diaphragms, their course is the same, and they bend outwards into the stalks of the peltate disks, one into each, as they do into the foliar teeth. The bundles in a shoot are all parallel with one another; each bundle is formed by the coalescence of two arms, one of which belongs to the leaf-sheath and is formed in the median line of a tooth of the sheath from below upwards, while the other is formed in the internode itself from above downwards; the formation of vessels begins in both at the angle where the two arms meet, and advances in opposite directions; the lower extremity of each bundle joins by two lateral commissures with the two next bundles, which alternate with it, of the next internode below; thus the Equisetaceae have only 'common' bundles. The vascular bundles seen in transverse section resemble the bundles in the Monocotyledons and especially in the grasses; the annular, spiral and reticulated vessels which are first formed and belong to the axile side of the bundle, and the thin-walled cells between them, are subsequently destroyed and in their place is a canal (lacuna) which runs through the length of the bundle on its axile side; right and left of this canal towards the outside, are a few not very broad reticulately thickened vessels; radially outside these and in front of the canal is the phloem, consisting of a few broad sieve-tubes and narrow cambiform cells, and towards the circumference of some narrow thick-walled bast-like cells. In some cases the separate bundles are surrounded by bundle-sheaths, as in *E. limosum*, but it is more usual to find a common plerome-sheath of one layer of cells running round the whole circle of bundles on the outside, as in most Phanerogams.

Appendix. Numerous species[1] of *fossil plants*, which appear from their structure to belong to the Equisetaceae, have been found in very various formations from the Lower Trias to the Tertiaries. They occur sometimes in vast quantities, as *Equisetum arenaceum* for instance in the sandstones of the Upper Trias. The stems are stated to vary from four to twelve centimetres in diameter, the sporangiferous spikes to be two and a-half centimetres and upwards in diameter, while the stems are supposed to have reached a height of from eight to ten metres.

The CALAMITES[2] are Equisetaceae which appear in the older geological formations, beginning in the carboniferous limestone, culminating in the coal-measures and disappearing in the Permian formation. The spikes of sporangia are either not known, or so badly preserved (*Calamostachys*) that their structure cannot be determined; it remains doubtful therefore whether they were homosporous or heterosporous forms. The stems had neither leaves nor leaf-sheaths, or else these were very transitory formations and soon fell off; in other respects the structure of the stems resembles that of the Equisetaceae; their surface was marked with ridges, and they had a central hollow divided by diaphragms.

B. HETEROSPOROUS EQUISETINEAE.

These are all fossil species forming the group of the Annularieae, with which it is probable that the 'Asterophyllites' should be associated.

1. ANNULARIEAE[3]. The stem of the Annularieae was as much as eighty centimetres in diameter, with feebly developed dermal and vascular systems. There were dia-

---

[1] Twenty, according to Renault's computation in his Cours de botanique fossile, II. Bd. 1882.

[2] Excluding *Calamodendron, Arthropitys, Calamites gigas*, etc., the connection of which with the Calamites is at present at least doubtful.—[The views of Prof. Williamson and other British Palaeophytologists regarding the structure and affinities of the Calamites are quoted at some length by Vines on p. 40 of the second edition of the English translation of Sachs' Lehrbuch, and references to literature are there given. The valuable monographs of Prof. Williamson 'On the Organisation of the Plants of the Coal-measures' which have appeared in the Phil. Trans. at intervals from 1871 to the present time should be also consulted.]

[3] Renault, *loc. cit.* p. 126 ff.—Compare Schenk, Ueber Fruchtstände fossiler Equiseten (Bot. Ztg. 1876). The short description given in the text from Renault may serve at least to draw attention to these interesting types, in which there is much that is yet uncertain. We cannot enter further here into disputed or doubtful points. [See Prof. Williamson in Phil. Trans. 1874.]

phragms at the nodes as in the Equisetaceae ; the internodes, which were from five to six centimetres in length, were hollow. The leaves were a characteristic feature of the group, not being united into a sheath as in the Equisetaceae, but disposed separately in whorls at the nodes, lanceolate and with a mid-rib. The structure of the stem, so far as it can be determined, was the same as in *Equisetum.* The branches were in two rows on the stem ; only the two opposite leaves in each whorl bore each a shoot in its axil.

The sporangiferous spikes, known as *Bruckmannia,* and assigned to *Annularia,* differed considerably from those of existing Equisetaceae, and especially in the circumstance that sterile leaves alternated in them with fertile (sporophylls) [1]. The sporophylls bore four sporangia ; in the lower part of the spikes the sporangia contained macrospores which were twelve to fifteen times larger than the microspores found in the upper sporangia.

2. Similar sporangiferous spikes appear in the group of the Equisetineae known as ASTEROPHYLLITES, but our knowledge of them is very defective, especially in all points connected with the spores. These plants had jointed stems and branches, and at the nodes whorls of linear erect leaves with a mid-rib. The branches also were in whorls. The sporangiophores, in form like the sporophylls of the Equisetaceae and agreeing with those of the Annularieae, were placed between and a little above the sterile leaves (bracts) of the spikes, while the sporangiophores of *Annularia* were inserted at about the middle of the internode between two sterile whorls. The number of the sporangiophores also was only about half the number of the sterile leaves, but the sporangiophores do not appear to have been axillary but to have been placed between two sterile leaves, and were most probably here as elsewhere only modified leaves.

III. SPHENOPHYLLEAE [2].

This interesting group of fossil species is not closely allied to any existing forms, and has consequently been associated with very different families. They are herbaceous plants, with simple or branched, and furrowed stems ; but the furrows do not as in the Equisetaceae alternate with one another on successive internodes. Sessile cuneiform leaves without a mid-rib, but traversed by bifurcating veins of uniform size, are inserted in whorls on greatly enlarged nodes. The sporangiferous spikes are cylindrical, the bracts and sporangia in whorls. The Sphenophylleae have little in common with the Annularieae and Asterophyllites except the verticillate arrangement of their leaves, and they differ from them especially in the structure of the stem. The diameter of the stem is from one and a half to fifteen millimetres ; in the centre of the stem is a three-cornered mass of tracheides or vessels, in which pitted, scalariform and spiral elements succeed one another from within outwards. The leaf-traces, which in *Sphenophyllum quadrifidum* consist of two bundles, connect with the corners of the central mass at the nodes, and each bundle bifurcates in the cortex ; (Renault conceives that the central mass is composed of three vascular bundles, each with two groups of tracheae lying at the corners, the central tracheides being formed subsequently, as they are in the roots). The central mass is surrounded by a tissue of peculiar structure, which we must not describe here. Macrosporangia and microsporangia are together on the same spike ; the sporangia are placed upon the base of the leaves, as in *Lycopodium,* the macrosporangia apparently nearer the axil of the leaf than the microsporangia, or in the axil itself.

---

[1] The relative position of the sterile to the fertile leaves appears to me not sufficiently ascertained to admit of further discussion here. It may be remarked that the number of sterile leaves in a whorl is double the number of the fertile in the succeeding whorl. See also p. 195, note.

[2] Renault, Botanique fossile, II. 1882.

IV. LYCOPODINEAE.

Under the name Lycopodineae are included the Lycopodieae, *Phylloglossum*, *Psilotum*, the Selaginelleae and Isoeteae. The Lycopodineae agree on the whole with the Ophioglosseae, Marattiaceae, and Equisetaceae especially in the mode of development of their sporangia. In habit they are distinguished at once from the Filicineae by the circumstance that in the latter the critical point as regards the morphological characteristics is in the leaves, whereas in the Lycopodineae the leaves are precisely the organs which are most simply formed, and are unimportant in size, with the exception of *Isoetes*, though they are usually many in number. A feature common to most of the Lycopodineae is the frequent dichotomous branching of the stem and root, though examples of genuine monopodial branching are not wanting. The position of the sporangia varies; in *Lycopodium* and *Phylloglossum* there is a single sporangium on the upper side at the base of the leaf; the position is the same in *Isoetes* but the sporangium is multilocular. In *Selaginella* the sporangia are formed singly from the surface of the stem above the leaf; in *Psilotum* they occur several together and sunk in the extremities of short lateral branchlets.

A. LYCOPODIACEAE[1].

1. HOMOSPOROUS LYCOPODIACEAE (LYCOPODIUM AND PHYLLOGLOSSUM).

The *prothallium* or *sexual generation* (*oophore, oophyte*). The circumstances attending the germination of *Lycopodium* and *Phylloglossum* are up to the present time unknown[2], though many have attempted their cultivation. De Bary is the only

---

[1] Bischoff, Die kryptogamischen Gewächse, Nürnberg, 1828.—Spring, Monographie de la famille des Lycop. (Mém. de l'Acad. roy. belgique, 1842 and 1849).—Cramer, Ueber *Lycop. Selago*, in Nägeli u. Cramer, Pfl.-phys. Unters. Heft 3, 1855.—De Bary, Ueber d. Keimung d. Lyc. in Ber. d. naturf. Ges. zu Freib. in Br. 1858, Heft 4.—Nägeli u. Leitgeb, Ueber d. Wurzeln, in Nägeli's Beitr. z. wiss. Bot. Heft 4, 1867.—Payer, Bot. cryptogamique, Paris, 1868.—Hegelmaier in Bot. Ztg. 1872, No. 45, and 1874, p. 513.—Russow, Vergl. Unters. Petersburg, 1872, p. 128.—Mettenius, Ueber *Phylloglossum* (Bot. Ztg. 1867).—Juranyi, Ueber *Psilotum* (Bot. Ztg. 1871, p. 180).—Fankhauser in Bot. Ztg. 1873, No 1.—Strasburger in Bot. Ztg. 1873, No. 6.—Bruchmann, Ueber Anlage u. Verzweigung d. Wurzeln von *Lycopodium* u. *Isoetes* (Jen. Zeitschr. f. Naturwissenschaft, viii, p. 522).—Goebel, Beitr. etc. II (Bot. Ztg. 1880 and 1881).—[Treub, Etudes sur les Lycopodiacées (Ann. d. Jard. Bot. d. Buitenzorg, iv, 1884.—Bruchmann, Das Prothallium v. *Lycopodium* (Bot. Centralbl. xxi, 1885).—Thiselton Dyer in Nature, 1885.—Bower, on the Development and Morphology of *Phylloglossum Drummondii*, Part I, Vegetative Organs (Proc. Roy. Soc. xxxviii, 1885). See also the literature mentioned by Solms as quoted on p. 282.

[2] [Bruchmann found in the Thuringer Wald, in Aug. 1884, three prothallia of *Lycopodium annotinum*, and he described them in Bot. Centralblatt, xxi, 1885. They were rather younger than those discovered by Fankhauser, and enabled Bruchmann to confirm and slightly extend Fankhauser's observations. But the most important contribution to our knowledge of the life-history of the group is that of Treub in the Ann. d. Jard. Bot. d. Buitenzorg, iv, 1884, a contribution which modifies considerably the statements in the text. Treub has succeeded in cultivating at Buitenzorg the spores of *Lycopodium cernuum* and has also found prothallia growing naturally. He describes and figures the mature prothallium as a cylindrical body about $\frac{1}{12}$ of an inch long, growing vertically, yellowish below and bright green towards its summit where it is surrounded by a tuft of lobes, its base clothed with rhizoids among which is a tubercle (primary tubercle) representing the pluricellular product of the apical cell formed by division of the germ-tube (the first stages in germination are like those described by De Bary in *L. inundatum*). Round the summit of the

observer who has succeeded in seeing the first stages in the development of the prothallium of *Lycopodium inundatum*. The exosporium opened by three valves and the endosporium protruded in the form of a spherical vesicle; the germ-tube divided by a transverse wall into an inner basal cell, which suffered no further change, and an outer, which developed as an apical cell and formed two rows of segments. Each segment divided by a tangential (periclinal) wall into an inner and an outer cell, so that the young prothallium had now an axile row of four short cells and round them two rows of lateral cells and the basal and apical cells; no further stage of development was obtained. It was not till fifteen years after this, namely in 1872, that Fankhauser found fully developed prothallia of *Lycopodium annotinum* among some mosses in Switzerland, one of them being still connected with the young plant of the second generation (Fig. 226). These prothallia, which had grown in the dark, were yellowish-white masses of tissue with cushion-like lobes and a few small rhizoids; they had a number of antheridia entirely sunk in the tissue of the upper surface, forming ovoid cavities covered over by a single layer of the cells of the prothallium (compare *Marattia*), and containing a large number of the mother-cells of spermatozoids; the form of the spermatozoids themselves was not clearly made out. As these prothallia bore no archegonia but had young plants growing from them, it follows that *Lycopodium* has but one kind of spores, which agrees perfectly with the results of direct observation, and that the prothallia are monoecious; by this latter character the Lycopodiaceae are at once clearly distinguished from the Selaginelleae and Isoeteae, and also by the large size of the prothallium which lives entirely outside the spore. It is probable that the other genera with spores of one kind only, *Phylloglossum, Psilotum,* and *Tmesipteris,* have similar prothallia. The

FIG. 226. *Lycopodium annotinum; p* the prothallium, *l* the young plant, *w* the root of the plant, nat. size. After Fankhauser.

cylindrical portion and beneath the crown of lobes antheridia and archegonia seem sunk in the monoecious prothallium. The antheridia resemble those described by Fankhauser in *L. annotinum,* and are like those in Marattiaceae and Ophioglossaceae. They arise from a single peripheral cell, which divides into an outer lid-cell (subsequently divided by vertical walls into three cells) and an inner cell within which the spermatozoids are formed. The form of the spermatozoids is not certainly ascertained; probably they have only two cilia as in *Selaginella.* The archegonia have very short necks of three tiers of cells; no basal cell is formed in their production and there is no special wall-layer round the oosphere. At an early period the product of the division of the oospore consists of a massive foot connecting with the prothallium, a cylindrical mass of tissue, in the anterior end of which a cotyledon is differentiated, whilst the posterior portion, rounded at the end and there usually provided with a few hairs, shows no differentiation into members and is termed by Treub the 'embryonic tubercle.' There is no primary root; subsequently a root is developed laterally and internally on the embryonic tubercle. Treub calls attention to the resemblance between the young sporophyte and the young oophyte. In the cells of the primary tubercle of the oophyte endophytic Fungus-hyphae are found so commonly that Treub is tempted to suggest a possible commensalism, and it may be noted that Bruchmann found bodies like swarm-spores of Chytridieae in the prothallia which he examined.]

prothallium of Lycopodium evidently bears several archegonia, for Fankhauser found on it other plants in less advanced stages of development as well as the one which was more fully grown. From the point of attachment of the plants to the pro-thallium it may be gathered that the archegonia are formed on the upper surface at the bottom of the depressions between the lobes.

The *second* or *asexual generation* (*sporophore, sporophyte*). It follows from what has been said above that nothing is known as to the formation of the embryo. The young plants found by Fankhauser were however sunk in the tissue of the prothallium by means of a swollen knob about the size of a pin's head, which evidently answers to the foot of the Ferns and is a lateral formation at the base of the stem and of the first root.

The habit of the full-grown plant is remarkably different in the different genera. There are species of *Lycopodium* with erect stem and branches, as *L. Selago*; in such cases the roots which arise in the lower region of the stem often grow downwards in its tissues and only issue in a tuft at its base as in *L. Phlegmaria, L. alvifolium,* and others. In many species on the other hand the primary stems and the strongest branches creep on the ground, sending roots into the ground at various points, and only certain leafy shoots, the forked branches especially which bear the sporangiferous spikes, grow upwards; such forms as these show a tendency to dorsiventrality, especially in the structure of the axile vascular bundle. All the species are thickly clothed with small, often narrow elongated leaves. The variety of habit depends chiefly on the more or less vigorous development of the individual branches of the bifurcating shoots. The sporangia are found at the base of ordinary foliage leaves in *L. Selago,* but more commonly on leaves of a different shape and colour which form the terminal spikes of special fertile shoots often of peculiar formation.

Phylloglossum, a small Australian plant a few centimetres high which sends up its stem from a small tuber, is very unlike *Lycopodium*; the stem produces a rosette of a few long leaves and one or more lateral roots at its base, continues upwards as a slender scape, and ends in a spike of sporangia with small leaves. The plant is reproduced by adventitious shoots consisting of a tuber with a leafless rudimentary bud, and in this respect resembles our own Ophrydeae[1].

---

[1] [Bower (On the Development and Morphology of *Phylloglossum Drummondii,* Part I, Vege-tative Organs in Proc. Roy. Soc. vol. xxxviii. p. 445, a summary of the paper which will shortly appear in the Philosophical Transactions), has recently investigated the morphology of this interesting genus. Tubers sent from Australia were successfully grown at Kew, and Bower gives a summary of the results of his examination of them in the following words:—'The mode of development depends to a certain extent upon the size of the tuber: where the tuber is small only vegetative organs are formed, where it is relatively large the plant may form sporangia. Taking first the simpler case, it is found that outgrowths appear on the broad apex of the tuber, which is before germination a simple, smooth and rounded cone; these outgrowths are leaves; their number may vary from one to six or seven. They are arranged in an irregular whorl, of which the members on one side take precedence of the rest in time of appearance; they constitute in fact a " successive whorl." From the first they are rounded at the apex and have no single apical cell. The apex of the axis, which has a central position at first, becomes gradually depressed and is overarched by the surrounding tissue; it developes directly into the apex of the new tuber, which is accordingly of exogenous origin and represents in this simpler case the actual apex of the parent plant. By a peculiar localisation of growth this apex becomes inverted, and by a process of development very similar to that of the axillary shoot in certain orchids (e.g. *Herminium Monorchis*), it projects

The history of the development of the vegetative organs is only perfectly known in our native Lycopodiaceae. There is no apical cell at the growing end of shoot, leaf or root in *Lycopodium*. The growing point of the shoot is occupied by a small-celled primary meristem, in which no differentiation into dermatogen and periblem can be perceived, and the rudiment of the vascular bundle formed of elongated cells comes nearly up to the apex of the shoot. In *L. Selago* the apex is flat, in *L. complanatum, L. clavatum, L. annotinum, L. alpinum,* and others it is convex and rises above the youngest leaves. The leaves and the rudiments of new shoots (bifurcations and brood-buds) are formed, as in the Phanerogams, not from single cells of the growing point, but from groups of cells which embrace both the outermost and the deeper-lying layers of the tissue of the vegetative apex.

The *branching* of the stem is partly monopodial, partly dichotomous, and there are not a few cases where it is uncertain which of the two schemes more properly applies. The branching of the vegetative shoots of *Lycopodium clavatum, L. annotinum,* and *L. inundatum* is monopodial. In *L. clavatum*, for instance, the rudiment of the branch appears as a protuberance beneath the growing point of the primary axis, and the protuberance is considerably smaller than the point itself. The branching in this case has no relation to the leaves; the rudiments of the branches are much larger than the rudiments of the leaves, so that they are not placed in the axils of the leaves, but above a number of them. On the axis of the spike of *L. alpinum* there is a bifurcation; the vegetative cone broadens out into two new growing points which are formed right and left of it, and then ceases to grow itself; while the two lateral shoots develope as the prongs of the fork, the apex of the mother-shoot is suppressed. A similar process takes place in the branching of *L. Selago* according to Cramer, and in the vegetative shoots of *L. complanatum* and *L. Chamaecyparissus,* two heterophyllous species. Cramer states that in *L. Selago* two new growing points of equal strength appear side by side on the level surface of the apex, and develope in a forked manner.

Lycopodium complanatum and *L. Chamaecyparissus,* which like the Selaginelleae have their leaves in four rows, branch only in a plane which coincides with the plane of the larger lateral leaves. The other species, in which the leaves are inserted spirally or

---

laterally from the parent plant. Meanwhile an outgrowth appears on the opposite side of the axis from that on which the tuber projects, and below the insertion of the oldest leaf: this is the first root. It has been clearly proved by both external observation and by study of sections, that the root in *Phylloglossum* is of *exogenous origin*. Among other known examples of this anomalous mode of root development it is interesting to note the root of the embryo of *Isoetes*. In those cases where the tuber is relatively large, sporangia are formed; these are, as is already known, borne upon an elongated axis, which is the direct product of the apex of the tuber. A different origin is necessary in this case for the tuber, and it has been found that the tuber originates in such plants in an adventitious manner, as a depression at the base of the sporangium-bearing axis or peduncle; the details of its development are otherwise similar in this case to that above described.' A comparison of both external form and as far as possible of internal structure between *Phylloglossum* and the young plants of *Lycopodium cernuum*, recently described by Treub (see note on page 275), shows many points of striking similarity; and Bower is led to the conclusion 'that provided the oophore generation of *Phylloglossum* (which has never yet been observed) corresponds in its more important points to that of *Lycopodium*, we may regard *Phylloglossum* as a form which retains and repeats in its sporophore generation the more prominent characteristics of the embryo as seen in *Lycopodium cernuum*; it is a permanently embryonic form of a Lycopodiaceous plant.']

in whorls of many members, have a radial disposition of their branches. The gemmae common in *L. Selago* are according to Hegelmaier branches of a peculiar kind.

These gemmae, which have a few leaves and a rudimentary root and eventually become detached, are formed on the shoot in place of a leaf. In other species Strasburger found adventitious buds at the base of the stem, as in *L. aloïfolium, L. reflexum* and others. As the leaves stand from the first close above and beside one another so as to cover the surface of the stem, there are not only no internodes in the Lycopodiaceae any more than in *Ophioglossum, Marattia, Aspidium* and *Isoetes*, but the outer layer of the cortex of the stem is genetically connected with the tissue of the bases of the leaves; it is not till intercalary growth supervenes at a later time that the leaves move farther apart, and a line of demarcation often very distinct arises between the base of the leaf and the stem.

The *rudiments of the leaves* in the Lycopodieae appear on the vegetative cone as pluricellular protuberances of considerable breadth; growth is at first at the apex, but this in most cases soon ends in a hair-like prolongation, while intercalary growth begins and proceeds towards the base. The size and shape of the leaves varies much from one species to another; but they are always simple, unbranched, without a stalk and sessile with a narrow base; they are sometimes closely applied to the stem up to the free point, like the leaves of *Thuja*, but more commonly they are free along their whole length, and acicular or narrow; there is a mid-rib only and no lateral veins as in all the Lycopodineae.

The *phyllotaxis* is sometimes verticillate, sometimes spiral, or both on the same plant. The whorls may consist of decussate pairs, or be of three, four, or many members, and in creeping stems are usually inserted on a transverse zone which is oblique to the axis of the stem. The number of members in the whorls varies in the same shoot. According to Hegelmaier the whorls are true whorls, that is, the leaves arise simultaneously at the same level on the growing point, but the spiral arrangements are also spiral from the first, and the divergences undergo no subsequent displacements of any importance. The small and at the same time highly variable divergences of the leaves are remarkable, as Braun has observed; he found in *L. clavatum* with spiral arrangement the divergences $\frac{2}{9}$, $\frac{2}{11}$, $\frac{2}{13}$, $\frac{2}{15}$, $\frac{2}{17}$, and whorls of from four to eight members; in *annotinum* the divergences $\frac{2}{7}$, $\frac{2}{9}$, and whorls of from four to five members; in *L. inundatum* a divergence of $\frac{2}{9}$ and whorls of five members, and so on[1].

The *roots* in the primary stems of the creeping or climbing Lycopodiaceae arise singly, and when they penetrate into the ground they bifurcate in crossing planes.

It has already been mentioned that in erect stems, as in *L. Selago, L. Phlegmaria,* and *L. aloïfolium*, all the roots emerge in a tuft from the base of the enlarged tuberous stem; but these roots have their origin much higher up the stem, according to Strasburger as much as five centimetres above the base of the stem and even above the first bifurcation; they come, it will be understood, from the periphery of the axile vascular mass, but are peculiar in growing downwards inside the fundamental tissue of the stem, and occasionally even dichotomise in it (see *Angiopteris,* p. 253).

The *sporangia* of the genus *Lycopodium* are formed singly on the base of the leaves. They are considerably larger than in the Ferns, as is the case in all the

---

[1] Bot. Ztg. 1872, p. 815.

Lycopodineae, and have a short broad stalk; the capsule is more or less reniform, having the broader diameter in the direction transverse to the median plane of the leaf, and opens by a slit which runs in this direction over the apex and divides them into two valves which remain united at the base. The rather small spores are between round and tetrahedral in form, very numerous, of uniform size and shape, and with a variety of markings on the exosporium. The sporangia originate in a group of superficial cells of the base of the leaf, and appear at first as flat prominences which

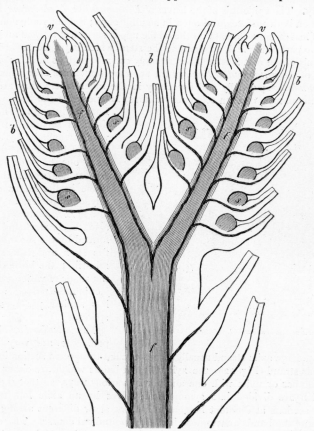

FIG. 227. A forked sporangiferous branch of *Lycopodium Chamaecyparissus* in longitudinal section, slightly magnified; *f f* the axile vascular body, *b b* leaves, *s s* young sporangia.

occupy the breadth of the leaf. An axile longitudinal section through a young sporangium shows here also a hypodermal *archesporium-cell*, but with so great a breadth of the sporangial protuberance it may be questioned whether the archesporium is not really a row of cells. The wall of the sporangium is at first composed of one layer of cells, which however subsequently splits, and this process is repeated in the inner of the two layers thus formed; the innermost of the three resulting layers of cells forms the layer of *tapetal cells*, which becomes separated from the adjacent cells at the lower part of the sporogenous tissue, but not at the part where this abuts upon the wall of the sporangium. The spore-mother-cells become isolated and invested with thick walls, and divide into four compartments ('special mother-cells') within which each of the four protoplasmic bodies becomes invested with its permanent cell-wall; when the cell-wall has acquired its bosses, spikes, and the like markings, the walls of the compartments of the mother-cells dissolve.

Histology. The epidermis of the leaves of *L. annotinum, L. clavatum,* and *L. Selago* has stomata on both surfaces, and often in small groups; the heterophyllous species have four rows of leaves have stomata on the whole upper surface of the leaf and on the under surface of the part of the leaf, adhering to the stem, which is turned towards the ground. The epidermis of the root is sometimes strongly cuticularised, as in *L. clavatum.*

The cells of the *fundamental tissue* of the stem are sometimes everywhere thin-walled, as in *L. inundatum;* usually and especially in the inner layers they are thick-walled and prosenchymatous, or even sclerenchymatous, but never of the brown colour of the Ferns (Fig. 228). The fundamental tissue is separated from the axile vascular cylinder by a strongly developed bundle-sheath composed of from one to three layers of cells. Air-cavities occur in the fundamental tissue in the leaves of the heterophyllous species, and in the stem also in *L. inundatum;* in this species also Hegelmaier found gum-passages formed by the separation of cells in the stem and leaves (one in the mid-rib); the bordering cells have the shape of varicose hairs and project into the passage; *L. annotinum* has similar passages only in the spikes.

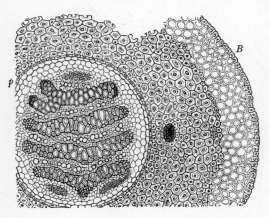

FIG. 228. Transverse section of a stem of *Lycopodium Chamaecyparissus.*

The *vascular bundles* of the Lycopodiaceae are very characteristic, and form one large axile strand usually with a circular transverse section in the stem and root. In this strand (Fig. 228) the xylem lies in bands which are either quite separate from one another or unite with one another in various ways, so that the xylem forms figures which are divided into symmetrical halves by an axile longitudinal section. Transverse sections at different heights in a shoot show different arrangements of the xylem, because the bands anastomose in their longitudinal course. These xylem-bands consist, as in the Ferns, of tracheides pointed at both ends and increasing in breadth from without inwards, the narrow ones with roundish pits, the broader with pits that have the form of fissures. Very narrow spiral tracheides occur at the outer edges only of the xylem-bands. The concavity of the bands in creeping and oblique stems is always directed upwards. The bands are inclosed in narrow-celled phloem, in which are rows of broader elements between the xylem-bands; these elements may be regarded as representing sieve-tubes, though according to Hegelmaier they have no sieve-plates. Between the peripheral corners of the xylem-bands are bast-like fibrous elements, the 'protophloem-elements;' thus we have an arrangement which reminds us in many respects of that in the axile cylinder of the roots. The peripheral phloem inside the bundle-sheath is surrounded by some layers of broader cells, which Hegelmaier terms phloem-sheaths, and which may certainly answer to the layer in the Ferns which is so named. The axile cylinder in the stem of the Lycopodiaceae may be considered to be formed by the coalescence of a number of vascular bundles (as polyarch), and this view is supported by its resemblance to the axile cylinder of the roots. The leaves have each a slender bundle of very simple construction, which runs very obliquely from the base of the leaf through the cortex of the stem, and attaches itself lower down to an edge of the xylem of the axile cylinder of the stem.

The axile vascular strand is cauline, and may be followed up to close beneath the apex, where it is a bundle of elongated cells (the initial bundle) ; the rows of spiral cells of the xylem-bands are first formed, with which the similar formations in the leaf-bundles become connected (Fig. 227) long before the tracheides begin to be developed.

2. HETEROSPOROUS LYCOPODIACEAE[1].

The term heterosporous Lycopodiaceae may be used to designate the species of *Lepidodendron* which are characteristic of the coal-measures and which disappear in the Permian formation. These were dichotomously branching tree-like plants, sometimes thirty metres in height and thickly covered with lanceolate leaves which have left behind them peculiar rhomboidal scars. These scars are made up of the 'leaf-cushion' and the small leaf-scar properly so called. There is still much uncertainty with regard to the structure of the stem. Renault states that a section of a branch of *Lepidodendron Rhadumnense* shows a uniform central vascular cylinder consisting of tracheides with transverse striation, which are broadest towards the middle of the cylinder. The leaf-traces formed each of a single bundle unite with this cylinder, outside which is an endodermis, and beyond this a strongly developed cortical tissue. The diameter of the stem in this species was about five centimetres ; the central vascular cylinder ('cylindre ligneux') of the stem is hollow, owing perhaps to rupture of the enclosed tissue, and consists of scalariform tracheides ; the leaf-traces are distinguishable at the periphery of the cylinder. There is no certain indication of secondary growth in thickness, though the condition of things may have been similar to that which will be described below in *Isoetes*. The connection of fossil stems capable of great increase in thickness, such as the Sigillarieae and *Calamodendron*, with the Vascular Cryptogams is at present questioned. The cortical tissue also is much more largely developed in the stem than the vascular mass, and contains layers of sclerenchymatous fibres. The sporangiferous spikes of *Lepidodendron*, of which we have fortunately some remains in a silicified state, were on the ends of branches ; they are elliptical or rather elongated bodies known by the name of *Lepidostrobus*, and are thickly covered with sporophylls, the lower portion of each of which is set at right angles to the axis and bears a large microsporangium or macrosporangium. The microsporangia are said to have been about two centimetres long. Both kinds of sporangia were placed on the upper side of the base of the leaf. The spherical macrospores were eight-tenths of a millimetre in diameter ; the length of the chief axis in the tetrahedral microspores is given as one-tenth of a millimetre. The two kinds of sporangia are on the same or on different spikes, but the latter condition may be the result of the imperfect state in which we have them.

---

[1] Renault, Cours de Bot. fossile, II Bd. The attempts to connect the Lepidodendreae with the other heterosporous Lycopodineae (Selaginelleae and Isoeteae) have been less successful. These plants have more resemblance to the homosporous Lycopodiaceae, with which we unite them ; heterospory may very well have appeared several times in the same cycle of affinity. [Prof. Williamson contributes a note of his views on the structure and affinity of these forms to the second edition of the English translation of Sachs' Lehrbuch ; see also his Monographs in the Phil. Trans. from 1871 to the present date.]

B. THE PSILOTACEAE[1].

The family of the Psilotaceae contains two genera, *Psilotum* and *Tmesipteris*, small shrubs with straggling branches, of which *Tmesipteris* belongs to Australia, *Psilotum* to Madagascar, the Moluccas and the Sandwich islands. The slender stem of *Psilotum* with its numerous long thin branches, which are all dichotomously developed, rises above the ground in the form of a straggling shrub, and as it has no roots, supplies their place with a system of branches from the stem; the leaves are few and developed only as small acute scales even on the aerial parts of the plant. The sporangia appear three or four together on quite short and small lateral shoots from the long branches, and do not form compact spikes.

The stem of *Psilotum* is slender and many-angled, and bifurcates repeatedly; its subterranean shoots possess a three-sided apical cell, which according to Nägeli and Leitgeb forms three rows of segments; these are spirally disposed on account of the advance of the primary walls in the anodic direction, as in many Mosses. The leaves, which are small and distant from one another and are even destitute of a vascular bundle, show in their position on the angles of the stem no direct connection with its dichotomies; *Psilotum triquetrum* is entirely without roots, but produces a number of underground shoots which fulfil the duties of roots and are extremely like them in appearance. The shoots from the rhizome which approach nearer to the surface of the ground have very minute subulate whitish leaves which may be seen with the aid of a lens; the shoots which lie deeper and are like roots are blunter at the extremity and show no sign of a leaf even under the lens; the anatomical structure of the former is the same as in the true stems of the plant; but in the latter the vascular bundles are collected into an axile group, as in true roots. The shoots in which the rudiments of leaves can be discerned can turn upwards, become green and develope into ordinary foliage-shoots; the root-like shoots, which are naturally more slender, may also turn upwards and become thicker and assume the appearance of ordinary superficial rhizome-shoots. In this respect therefore they differ at once from true roots, and still more in the absence of a root-cap; they terminate in an apical cell which forms oblique segments inclining alternately in different directions. But the most important point is that these shoots actually have rudiments of leaves which consist of a few cells, and do not burst forth above the surface but remain concealed in the tissue. They are most easily recognised in a longitudinal section, and may be seen to consist of an apical cell and from two to five cells with the arrangement characteristic of leaves. Similar few-celled rudiments of leaves occur also on ordinary rhizome-shoots, but there they develope further, especially if the extremity of the shoot comes above the ground. The root-like shoots branch in the same way as the ordinary shoots.

Whether *Tmesipteris* has similar underground shoots, or true roots, appears not to be known; the plant has not been studied in the living state, and herbarium specimens which I have seen show only portions of the shoots. The leaves which appear to grow erect are considerably larger than in *Psilotum* and are traversed by

---

[1] [Solms, Der Aufbau d. Stockes v. *Psilotum triquetrum* u. dessen Entw. aus d. Brutknospe (Ann. d. Jard. Bot. d. Buitenzorg, IV, 1884), gives an account in detail of the morphology of *Psilotum* and adds a list of the literature of the group, giving under each work quoted an indication of its scope.]

a vascular bundle. Branching appears to be rare, at all events much rarer than in *Psilotum*.

The position of the sporangia is peculiar. They are sunk in the apex of short branches bearing two leaves, and in *Psilotum* apparently they form a single sporangium with three (two to four) compartments, in *Tmesipteris* one of two compartments. The small spikes of sporangia are formed at the growing point of the primary shoot in the same way as the branches. Then two distinct rudiments of leaves arise beneath the summit of the young sporangiferous spike. By more rapid growth of the tissue of the sporangiferous shoot at the point of insertion of the leaves they are carried up on a common base, and then appear to form a single two-cleft leaf. The sporangia are sunk in the expanded summit of the branchlet and their development agrees with that of the sporangia of the other Eusporangiatae; they form in *Psilotum* usually three, sometimes two or four compartments separated by longitudinal walls (composed of a few layers of cells) and an axile mass of tissue; the compartments are strongly protuberant outwards. A vascular bundle is formed in the fertile branch and terminates beneath the sporangia. The portion of the branch beneath the sporangia is usually very short, and has therefore been sometimes incorrectly described as the ' stalk' of the trilocular sporangium which arises on the base of the two-cleft leaf. That this view is incorrect is shown by the history of development and by the fact that the fertile branches are sometimes more than a centimetre in length and have all the characters of the sterile branches (Goebel, *loc. cit.*). Upon the ripe sporangia is an indentation running lengthwise, where they subsequently open by a longitudinal fissure. In *Tmesipteris* the sporangiferous spikes have as a rule only two sporangia, one of which is turned towards the primary axis, the other away from it.

Psilotum has a cauline bundle [1], which is circular in the transverse section in the aerial branches and is separated by an endodermis from the surrounding parenchyma; the vascular portion is composed of from three to eight groups of vessels; in the centre of the bundle are threads of sclerenchyma, and between the groups of vessels is parenchymatous tissue, in which, especially towards the circumference, groups of a few narrower sieve-tubes with thicker walls lie scattered here and there.

C. THE LIGULATAE [2].

The two last groups of the Lycopodineae, the Selaginelleae and Isoeteae, together make up the Ligulatae. Both have two kinds of spores, large female macrospores and small male microspores.

---

[1] De Bary, Vergl. Anatomie, p. 362.

[2] Hofmeister, Vergl. Untersuch. 1851 ;—Id. Entw. von *Isoetes lacustris* (Abhandl. d. Kön. Sächs Ges. d. Wiss. iv, 1858).—Nägeli u. Leitgeb, Ueber Entstehung u. Wachsth. d. Wurzeln in Nägeli's Beitr. z. wiss. Bot. iv, 1867.—A. Braun, Ueber *Isoetes* (Monatsber. d. Berliner Akad. 1863).—Milde, Filices Europae et Atlantidis, Leipzig, 1867.—Millardet, Le prothallium mâle des crypt. vasc. Strasburg, 1869.—Pfeffer, Entw. d. Keims der Gattung *Selaginella* in Hanstein's bot. Abhandl. iv, 1871.—Janczewski in Bot. Ztg. 1872, p. 441.—Tschistiakoff, Ueber Sporenentw. von *Isoetes* (Nuovo giornale Bot. Ital. 1873, p. 207).—Russow, Vergl. Unters. Petersburg, 1872, p. 134 ff.—Goebel, Beitr. z. vergl. Entw.-Gesch. d. Sporangien (Bot. Ztg. 1880 u. 1881).—De Bary, Vergl. Anat. *Isoetes*, pp. 291, 361, 641.—Bruckmann, Ueber Anlage u. Wachs. d. Wurzeln von *Lycopodium* und *Isoetes* (Jen. Zeitschr. f. Naturw. viii, 522).—Kienitz-Gerloff, Entw. d. Embryos von *Isoetes lacustris* (Bot. Ztg. 1881).—Treub, Recherches sur les organes de la vegetation du *Selaginella Martensii* (Musée bot. de Leide II).—Hegelmaier, Zur Kenntn. einiger Lycopodinen (Bot. Ztg. 1874).—[Belajeff, Antheridien u. Spermatozoiden d. heterosporen Lycopodiaceen (Bot. Ztg. 1885).]

The microspore of both groups, like those of the heterosporous Ferns, produce an antheridium and a unicellular rudimentary prothallium.

The *sexual generation* (*oophore, oophyte*). The microspore of *Isoetes lacustris* lies dormant during the winter and then divides into a very small sterile cell, and a large cell which encloses the whole of the rest of the cell-contents (Fig. 229 *A–C*); the smaller cell, invested with a firm wall of cellulose (*v*), undergoes no further changes of importance; the larger cell, the mother-cell of the antheridium, on the contrary divides into four naked primordial cells; each of the two ventral cells of the four produces two, together therefore four mother-cells of spermatozoids, while the other two cells are displaced and absorbed. In the Selaginelleae also a small sterile cell is first

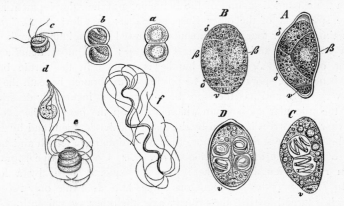

FIG. 229. Germination of microspores of *Isoetes lacustris*. *A* and *C* microspores seen from the right side. *B* and *D* from the ventral side. *A* and *B* show the formation of the antheridium; δδ its dorsal, ββ its ventral cells. *C* and *D* show the formation of the spermatozoids, δ and β have disappeared; *v* is everywhere the vegetative cell, the prothallium of Millardet. The development of the spermatozoids is indicated by the letters *a* to *f*. *A—D* and *a—d* magn. 580 times, *e* and *f* 700 times. After Millardet.

separated off by a firm wall some time before the spores fall out of the sporangium, and the other and larger cell, the mother-cell of the antheridium, divides into from six to eight primordial cells (Fig. 231 *A–D*). According to Millardet only two inner cells produce the mother-cells of the spermatozoids, and these multiply and displace the others and fill the cavity of the spore; on the other hand, Pfeffer finds in *Selaginella Martensii* and *S. caulescens* that all the primordial cells first formed in the antheridium divide again and at length give rise to spermatozoids[1]. The spermatozoids in *Isoetes*

---

[1] [Belajeff gives a somewhat different account of the development of the antheridium and spermatozoids. In *Isoetes* the mother-cell of the antheridium is divided by two successive anticlinal walls into a basal, apical and middle lateral cell; this latter then divides by a vertical wall at right angles to the plane of the previous anticlinals. A periclinal wall in each of the daughter-cells so formed produces two central cells, which are therefore surrounded by four peripheral cells. Each central cell then divides by a transverse wall, and the four daughter-cells are spermatocytes and float in the mucilage resulting from the disorganisation of the outer antheridial cells. These spermatozoids have many cilia attached to the delicate anterior end. In *Selaginella* the mother-cell of the antheridium is first divided into halves by a wall nearly parallel with the axis of the microspore. In each half three successive anticlinal walls appear, separating a basal and apical cell from two intermediate ones. In both of the intermediate cells a periclinal wall separates an inner from an outer cell, and thus the whole antheridium consists of four central cells surrounded by eight peripheral cells (*S. Krausiana* and *S. Poulteri*); in one only, that next the basal cell, of the intermediate cells in each half is a periclinal wall formed, and there are therefore only two central cells (*S. cuspidata, S. laetevirens,*

are long and slender, becoming attenuated and splitting into a pencil of long slender cilia at both ends; those of *Selaginella* are shorter, thick at the posterior extremity but tapering gradually at the anterior, and there divided into two long delicate cilia; the spermatozoids when fully developed are coiled up into a longer or shorter spiral. The mode of formation in the mother-cells is the same in both genera and agrees with that of the Ferns. The spiral body of the sperma-tozoid is obtained by the splitting up of the protoplasm of the thickened periphery of the nucleus of the mother-cell, proceeding from the anterior to the posterior ex-tremity; the spermatozoid when formed lies coiled round a central vacuole, which invested with a delicate mem-brane often remains hanging to the posterior extremity of the spermatozoid after it has escaped from the mother-cell, and is carried about with it. The spermatozoids of *Isoetes* continue only about five minutes in movement, those of *Selaginella* from half to three quarters of an hour. About three weeks elapse from the beginning of germination to the complete development of the sperma-tozoids in *Isoetes*, and the same time is required in *Selaginella*, reckoning from the dispersion of the spores.

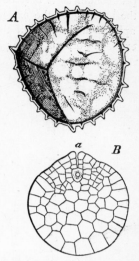

FIG. 230. *Isoetes lacustris. A* macro-spore two weeks after being placed in glycerine and become transparent. *B* lon-gitudinal section of the prothallium after four weeks in glycerine; *a* archegonium. *A* magn. 60, *B* 40 times.

The macrospores produce the female prothallium, which is an endogenous formation in a still higher degree than it is in the heterosporous Ferns; in this respect and in the mode of its development it shows a still greater resemblance to the prothallium in the macrospores (the embryo-sac) of the Gymnosperms and even of the Angiosperms. A few weeks after the macrospores of *Isoetes* are set free from the decaying macrosporangium their interior begins to fill with cell-tissue, the cells of which are at first all naked and without a cell-wall; it is not till the endosporium is quite filled with them that they are seen to be bounded by firm walls (Fig. 230). Meanwhile the endosporium becomes thicker and is dif-ferentiated into layers, and assumes a finely granular appearance; these phenomena, as Hofmeister has pointed out, are all seen in the embryo-sac of the Coniferae. Then through the swelling of the spherical prothallium the three coherent edges of the exosporium separate longitudinally and produce a three-rayed aperture, where the prothallium is now covered only by the endosporium; this too 'peels off' and softens, and finally allows the underlying portion of the prothallium to become ex-posed to the air. On its apex appears the first archegonium; if its oosphere is not fertilised several others may be formed by its side. While the macrospores of the Selaginelleae are still lying in the sporangium, their apical region is occupied by a small-celled meniscus-shaped tissue, formed probably during the maturing of the spores by the breaking up of a quantity of protoplasm collected there. It is this tissue which subsequently produces the archegonium, and is therefore the true

S. fulcrata, S. stolonifera, S. Martensii, S. viticulosa, S. inaequalifolia, S. caulescens). Many divisions in the central cells produce a complex of spermatocytes, which by the breaking down of the inner walls of the peripheral cells floats in a quantity of mucilage within the outer antheridial wall.]

prothallium; but some weeks after the dispersion of the spores free cell-formation begins beneath this earlier tissue in the cavity of the spore, which results in the filling up of the entire cavity and the production of a large-celled tissue, a secondary prothallium as it may be termed[1]. The formation of the archegonia begins before the bursting of the exosporium, which ensues as in *Isoetes*. The first archegonium appears at the apex of the prothallium; others arise in centrifugal succession on the exposed portions of the prothallium, whether fertilisation is effected in the first or not[2].

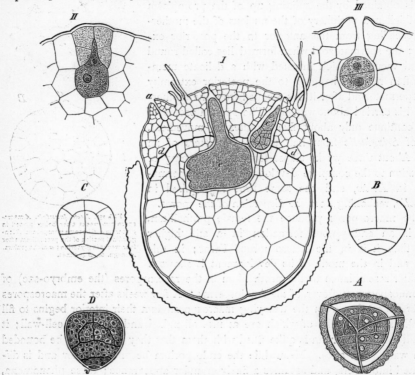

FIG. 231. Germination of *Selaginella*. *I—III S. Martensii*, *A—D S. caulescens*. *I* longitudinal section of a macro-spore filled with the prothallium, in which two embryos *e, e'* have begun to form; *d* the diaphragm. *II* a young archego-nium still closed. *III* an archegonium with the oosphere fertilised and once divided. *A* a microspore showing the divisions of the endosporium. *B, C* different views of these divisions. *D* the mother-cells of the spermatozoids in the matured antheridium. After Pfeffer.

In both genera the formation of the archegonium begins with the division of a superficial cell of the prothallium parallel with the surface; the outer of the two new cells divides by cross division into four cells, and each of these divides by obliquely

---

[1] Pfeffer compared this tissue with the endosperm of the Angiosperms and gave it that name; but since the homology of the two formations must be doubtful as long as the processes in the macrospore of the Selaginelleae are not better known than they now are, a more definite term is prefer-able. It is probable that the contents of the macrospore divide into two primordial cells, one of which moves to the apex of the macrospore and there produces the primary prothallium, while the other remains at first at the base of the macrospore, and subsequently produces the secondary prothallium.

[2] [Pfeffer, Locomotor. Richtungsbew. d. chem. Reize (Ber. Deut. Bot. Ges. 1883), states that in *Selaginella erythropus* the spermatozoids are attracted by malic acid, and that, as in the case of the Filices, the presence of this substance in the mucilage of the archegonium is influential in bringing about fertilisation.]

transverse divisions into cells that lie one above the other; thus the neck is formed, consisting in *Selaginella* of four rows of cells with two cells in each row, in *Isoetes* of as many rows of four cells each. The lower of the first two cells, the inner cell, thrusts a narrow prolongation in between the neck-cells, and this becomes separated off as the canal-cell of the neck (Fig. 229 *II*); the lower and larger portion, the central-cell of Janczewski, parts, as that observer states, with another small portion of its protoplasm which answers to the ventral canal-cell of other Archegoniatae, and then becomes the oosphere; the two canal-cells are converted into mucilage and ejected through the opened neck in order to admit the spermatozoids to the oosphere.

The *spore-producing generation* (*sporophore, sporophyte*). Formation of the embryo. In *Isoetes* as in the Filicineae the embryo is divided into octants by three walls at right angles to one another; the orientation also of the cotyledon, root and foot is the same as in them, except that while the cotyledon as usual proceeds from two octants, according to Kienitz-Gerloff the root requires not one octant, as is usually the case, but two for its formation, and the foot four. There is nothing left therefore for the apex of the stem, which does not seem very likely; I am inclined to think that the stem proceeds from the same octant in *Isoetes* as in the Filicineae, but that it is easily overlooked, because like the other organs in *Isoetes* it has no apical cell and developes a leaf at a very early period; the point requires further examination. *Selaginella*, in which Pfeffer has investigated the development of the embryo, also varies in some points from the Ferns and Equisetaceae. The basal wall is at right angles to the axis of the archegonium. The upper or hypobasal half of the oospore by considerable elongation produces the *suspensor*, a structure which does not appear in any other Vascular Cryptogam[1] but which occurs in almost all Spermaphytes (Phanerogams) and thus brings *Selaginella* more closely to them. The suspensor seldom remains a single cell; one or more divisions usually appear in its lower part (Fig. 232 *A, B* . . .). The embryo itself arises from the lower or epibasal half of the oospore. By the elongation of the suspensor with compression and absorption of the adjacent cells the mother-cell of the embryo is thrust downwards first into the primary and then into the secondary prothallium, where the embryo is further developed, as in the Gymnosperms. The transversal wall (Fig. 232 *II*) is now formed in the mother-cell of the embryo at right angles to the basal wall (Fig. 232 *I*). According to Pfeffer's account no median wall is formed[2], the succeeding walls being all at right angles to the transversal wall (Fig. 232 *II*). On one side of these walls the mother-cell of the stem (Fig. 232 *s*) is cut out by the wall *III*, while the lower part of the same half gives one cotyledon (Fig. 232 *b*), the other cotyledon proceeding from the other half, which also gives rise to the foot. The rudimentary stem has a two-sided apical cell, which gives off segments alternately right and left. An inner portion of tissue soon becomes marked off as the initial strand of the axile bundle, and a portion at the periphery as dermatogen and periblem. The expansion of the foot forces the stem-segment over to the other side, so that the apex comes to be horizontal and subsequently even to be turned upwards (Fig. 231 *I*); and finally when the

---

[1] [See Vines in Q. J. M. Sc. 1878.]

[2] It is quite possible however that a median wall is formed, for the question was approached from a different point of view at the time of Pfeffer's researches; at all events a fresh investigation would be desirable.

embryo begins to elongate, the bud with its first leaves, the cotyledons, grows erect out of the apical part of the spore. The formation of the first root, a lateral root, begins rather late between the foot and the suspensor; the apical cell of this root originates in an inner cell of the tissue of the older segment, and the first layer of its root-cap is formed by the splitting of the dermatogen which covers it into two layers; the later layers of the root-cap are formed from the apical cell of the root itself.

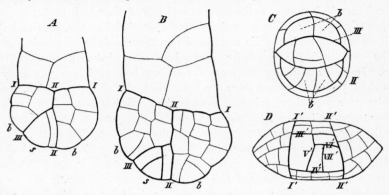

FIG. 232. Formation of the embryo of *Selaginella Martensii*. *A*, *B* lower portion of the suspensor with the apical cell *s* of the young stem; *b b* the first leaves. *C* apical view of the preceding. *D* the apex only seen from above, and forming two new apical cells right and left. *I* basal, *II* transversal wall; *I'*, *II'*, *III'*, *IV'*, *V'*, *VI'*, *VII'* the longitudinal walls by which two new apical cells are formed. After Pfeffer.

It has been already mentioned that in *Pteris* the plane of the apical cell of the growing stem forms an angle of about ninety degrees with that of the embryo. Something of the same kind takes place in *Selaginella*, where the apical cell which lies between the first two leaf-rudiments is divided by walls so disposed as to form a four-sided wedge-shaped apical cell (Fig. 232 *C, D*), from which segments arise in decussate pairs. In the fifth or sixth segment a second four-sided apical cell is formed by a curved wall which is convex towards the first apical cell, so that a vertical plane passing through these two apical cells intersects at right angles the common median plane of the first leaves and that of the original two-sided apical cell. Each of the two four-sided apical cells then developes into a branch of an apparent bifurcation, but neither grows on in the direction of the hypocotyledonary axis; the branching therefore comes immediately over the first leaves or cotyledons. The four-sided apical cells of the two shoots are however soon transformed into two-sided apical cells producing two rows of segments.

The rudiments of all the organs are formed and the first branching takes place before the embryo issues from the spore.

External differentiation. The *stem* is distinguished in *Isoetes* by the unusually small amount of its growth in length, which is accompanied in this, as in the similar cases of the Ophioglosseae, Marattiaceae and many Filices, with an absence of branching; no internodes are formed, and the leaves with their broad insertions are arranged in a compact rosette and leave no portion of the surface of the stem uncovered. The upper part of the stem which is occupied by the leaves has the shape of a shallow funnel, sinking in towards the middle where the apex is (Fig. 233). The considerable and permanent growth in thickness, which distinguishes the stem of *Isoetes* from that of all other Cryptogams, is due to an interior layer of meristem, which surrounds the central vascular group and is continually producing new layers of parenchyma on the outside; this formation takes place especially in two or three directions on the transverse section, and gives rise to two or three projecting masses of tissue which die off slowly on the outside, and between which lie as many deep furrows meeting on the under side of the stem; from these furrows numerous roots arise in rows in acropetal succession.

In the Selaginelleae the stem remains thin, but increases rapidly in length forming distinct internodes, and displays copious monopodial branching, which from the vigorous growth of the lateral shoots often appears to be dichotomous. The extremity of the stem rises as a slender cone above the youngest leaves. The systems of shoots with their many branches are developed bilaterally in one plane in such a manner that they frequently have a definite outline and resemble a multi-pinnate leaf. As the leaves of *Selaginella* are small, the general habit is determined chiefly by the systems of branches; the primary shoots are creeping rhizomes, or they ascend obliquely, or climb erect, or are the primary stems of small tree-like or shrub-like plants. But in all these cases the branches are all in one plane and spring from the sides of the primary axis; and the dorsiventrality so strikingly displayed in the position of the branches and leaves is present from the first in the growing point of the shoot.

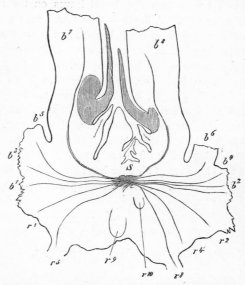

FIG. 233. *Isoetes lacustris.* Longitudinal section at right angles to the bifurcation of the stem, 10 months old; *S* stem, *b1* to *b8* leaves, *r1* to *r10* roots; the ligule of the two developed leaves is shaded. Magn. 30 times.

The *leaves* are always simple and unbranched, and traversed by a single vascular bundle; they terminate above in a simple point, in the Selaginelleae not unfrequently in a delicate awn. The largest leaves occur in *Isoetes*, where they may be from four to sixty centimetres long. In this genus they are divided into a basal portion, the *sheath*, and into an upper portion, the *lamina*. The sheath does not entirely embrace the stem, but rising from a very broad insertion ends in a long point above and is therefore nearly triangular in form; it is convex behind, concave in front, and on that side has a large depression, the *fovea*, in which the sporangium is fixed; the margin of this depression rises into a thin membranous outgrowth which in many species lays itself over and covers the sporangium, and is termed the *velum* (*indusium*). Above the fovea and separated from it by the 'saddle' is a smaller depression, the *foveola*, the lower margin of which forms a lip, the *labium*, while from its cavity rises a membranous structure, the *ligule*, which is acuminate above from a cordate base and projects beyond the foveola (Fig. 241 *L*). The lamina into which the sheath passes above contains chlorophyll and is thick and narrow, almost circular in

[2]   U

outline, but flattened in front and traversed by four broad air-canals which are segmented by transverse plates. This is the form of the fertile leaves of all the Isoeteae, and a rosette of such leaves is formed every year; but between every two circles of these leaves there appears a circle of imperfect leaves, which in *I. lacustris* have nothing but a small lamina, while in terrestrial species the lamina is so reduced in size that the leaves are only scale-like and cataphyllary.

The leaves of the Selaginelleae are never more than a few millimetres in length; from a narrow insertion they are generally broadly cordate and acuminate above, but may be ovate or lanceolate. In most species the sterile leaves are of two sizes; those on the under or shaded side of the obliquely ascending stem, the ventral leaves, are much larger than the dorsal leaves on the upper or illuminated side of the stem (Fig. 235 A). A ligule is also found on the upper side of the leaf above the base; the sporangium stands below the ligule on the fertile leaves, which form a quadrangular terminal spike, and are of uniform size and usually of a somewhat different shape to the sterile foliage-leaves.

The *phyllotaxis*. The rosettes in *Isoetes* are arranged in spirals with the divergences $\frac{3}{8}$, $\frac{5}{13}$, $\frac{8}{21}$, $\frac{13}{34}$; the divergences become more complicated as the number of the leaves formed each year increases. In the Selaginelleae with dorsal and ventral leaves in four rows one dorsal and one ventral leaf form together a pair, the median line of which however does not intersect that of the adjacent pair at a right angle but obliquely; this is often easily perceptible on older shoots of *S. Kraussiana*.

The *apex of the stem* has no apical cell in *Isoetes*, but is occupied by a group of meristem-cells. The different species of *Selaginella* vary much in this respect and afford much instruction. *S. spinulosa*, *S. arborescens*, and some others have the vegetative cone of the Lycopodiaceae, that is they have no apical cell; *S. serpens*, *S. Martensii*, *S. hortensis*, etc. have the two-sided apical cell described above (Fig. 234 *A*); in *S. Wallichii* Strasburger found the apex of the growing stem occupied by two apical cells of equal size and with the shape of an elongated pointed wedge with four surfaces. But Treub found that the arrangement of the cells at the apex varies not only in different species but in the same species. For instance the apical cell of *S. Martensii*

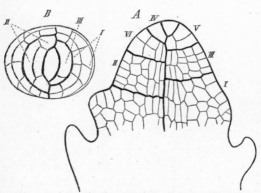

FIG. 234. Apex of the stem of *Selaginella Martensii*. *A* longitudinal section of the extremity of the stem with the rudiments of the youngest leaves. *B* apex of the stem seen from above. The segments are indicated by thicker lines, the segments themselves are marked with Roman numerals.

may be two-sided, or a three-sided pyramidal cell.

It follows from what has been said that the lateral branches are never placed in the axil of a leaf, but above one of the ventral leaves. They do not proceed from a single cell, but from a group of cells which bulges out beneath the apex of the primary shoot. At first the shoot thus formed has no apical cell; such a cell is formed in *S. Martensii*, but it has at first the shape of a four-sided wedge such as is seen in the embryo (Fig. 232); it is not till later that we find a two-sided cell at the apex, as in the primary axis. The branching in this species, as in all the Selaginelleae which have been examined, is not dichotomous but lateral monopodial. The rudiments of the leaves too are formed as in the genus *Lycopodium*, two or more outer cells of the growing point of the stem arching outwards and giving rise to the surface of the leaf.

The *roots*. The species of the genus *Selaginella* have all true roots; but in some species, as *S. Martensii* and *S. Kraussiana*, they are formed on a structure which has the external appearance of a root but has no root-cap, and which Nägeli calls the *rhizophore*. In *S. Kraussiana* the rhizophores spring from the dorsal side of the stem close to the base of a branch, bend round and then grow downwards; it is unusual for two of these organs to be formed near each other. *S. Martensii* on the other hand forms the rudiments of two rhizophores at every place where a branch is formed, one on the dorsal and one on the ventral side, the plane of which crosses the plane of branching; but usually the one only on the ventral side developes, the other remaining as a small prominence. The rhizophores arise very near the growing point, and later than the lateral branches near which they are placed; their mode of formation is the same as that of the branches. After growth has ceased at the apex, the rhizophore which is still very short swells into a round shape, the walls of its cells thicken, and the rudiments of true roots are at once formed inside the swollen part; the young roots however do not break through till the rhizophore has elongated sufficiently by intercalary growth for its swollen extremity to bury itself in the ground, where its cells become disorganised and deliquesce into a homogeneous mucilage, through which the true roots grow out into the ground. Pfeffer has shown in the case of *S. Martensii*, *S. inaequalifolia*, and *S. laevigata* that the rhizophores may be transformed into true leafy shoots, which show some abnormalities of structure in the first leaves, but afterwards develope like normal shoots and even form sporangiferous spikes.

There are no rhizophores in *S. cuspidata*; in this species roots grow directly from the points nearest to the ground where the stem branches, and like the rhizophores of *S. Martensii* branch before they reach the ground; these roots also begin to be formed very early near the growing point of the stem. Both these roots which come immediately from the stem and those formed from rhizophores branch monopodially, and the successive planes of branching cross one another. The branches appear very quickly one after another, and may be seen crowded together at the extremity of the parent-root; the apical cell is tetrahedral (a three-sided pyramid), as in the roots of Ferns and the Equisetaceae; it soon ceases to give off segments, and consequently the elongation of the branches is due almost entirely to intercalary growth. The roots which emerge from the furrows in the stem of *Isoetes* bifurcate three or four times in planes which cross at a right angle, and they have no apical cell; the arrangement of the cells in the growing point agrees with that in the roots of many Spermaphytes (Phanerogams).

The *sporangia* of the Ligulatae are large in comparison with the size of the leaves, and have short thick stalks. Each sporophyll bears one sporangium, which is always placed below the ligule on the leaf in *Isoetes*, or above the leaf and on the stem in *Selaginella*.

In *Selaginella* the sporangia are shortly stalked roundish capsules. The macrosporangia contain usually four, more rarely two or eight macrospores. In the division of the Articulatae only the lowest sporangium on a spike is a macrosporangium, in the others there are several macrosporangia. The sporangia differ from those of *Lycopodium* in their origin and in their separation into microsporangia and macrosporangia, but agree with them almost entirely in their development (Fig. 236). The sporangium is formed from a group of superficial cells at the growing point of the stem lying immediately above the cells, from which the leaf beneath each sporangium is produced. The *archesporium* is formed in exactly the same way as in *Lycopodium* (Fig. 236). The sporogenous group of cells which is formed from the archesporium is surrounded by a layer of *tapetal cells* which are elongated in the radial direction (Fig. 237). Up to this point the process is the same in both

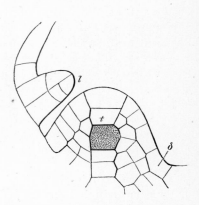

FIG. 236. *Selaginella*. Longitudinal section through a young sporangium and a part of the leaf beneath it with the ligule *l*, *t* primary tapetal cell. The archesporium is dotted.

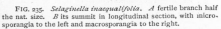

FIG. 235. *Selaginella inaequalifolia*. *A* fertile branch half the nat. size. *B* its summit in longitudinal section, with microsporangia to the left and macrosporangia to the right.

kinds of sporangia. The sporogenous cells soon become isolated and rounded off, and in the microsporangia each of them divides after previous indication of bipartition (Fig. 237 *E, e, f*) into four spores disposed tetrahedrally, and this disposition is retained till the spores are mature (Fig. 237 *E, g, h*). In the macrosporangia on the other hand one of the mother-cells grows more vigorously than the rest, divides and produces four macrospores, while the other mother-cells remain undivided but still maintain themselves for some time, at least in *inaequalifolia*, by the side of the vigorously growing macrospores. The macrospores remain, till they are released from the sporangium, in the position assigned them by the division of the mother-cell at the four corners of a tetrahedron. It is not uncommon to find weakly macrospores in otherwise normal spikes of sporangia. The three layers of cells

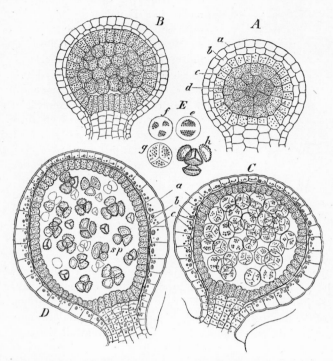

FIG. 237. Sporangia and development of the spores of *Selaginella inaequalifolia*. The order of succession is according to the letters *A—D*. *A* and *B* represent stages in all sporangia. *C* and *D* represent stages in the micro-sporangia. *E* development of the spores; *e—h* marks the succession, *h* four nearly ripe spores. In *A*, *C*, and *D a* and *b* are the two-layered wall of the sporangium, *e* the tapetal cells, *d* the mass of sporogenous cells. *A* and *B* magn. 500, *C* and *D* 200 times.

which form the wall of the sporangium remain intact till the spores are ripe, while the tapetal cells are destroyed during their formation, as happens in the Ferns.

The sporangia of *Isoetes* are formed in the fovea of the leaf-sheath and are attached by a narrow base (Fig. 241). In this case they are undoubtedly the product of the leaf. The outer leaves of the fertile rosette produce only macrosporangia, the inner only microsporangia, and the former contain a large number of macrospores. Both kinds of sporangia are imperfectly divided into compartments by threads of tissue (*trabeculae*) that stretch across from the ventral to the dorsal side; they do not open, but the spores are set free by the decay of the wall.

In *Isoetes* as in *Selaginella* the course of development is the same up to a certain point in both kinds of sporangia, but that point is sooner reached in *Isoetes*. The sporangia originate in a group of cells at the base of the leaf, but are much larger than in *Selaginella*. The *archesporium* is a hypodermal layer of cells. In the micro-sporangia the cells of the archesporium elongate and divide by transverse walls. In this condition no difference is yet to be seen between the sterile rows of cells (the trabeculae), and the fertile. But soon the cells of single rows lose their abundant protoplasm and grow less rapidly, and their division results in the formation only of elongated tabular cells. These are the trabeculae (Figs. 239, 240, 241, *Tr*). On the

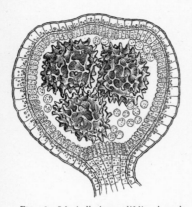

other hand the cells of the sporogenous rows retain their abundance of protoplasm, and from them are produced large masses of cells, the mother-cells of the microspores. The trabeculae meanwhile have become larger masses of tissue, which are clearly distinguished from the sporogenous tissue by the small amount of protoplasm in their cells, and by the intercellular spaces containing air which lie between these. Here too the sporogenous cells are surrounded by *tapetal cells* which are in great part subsequently dissolved, as in the Ferns. The microspores are formed by division of the mother-cell into four parts.

FIG. 238. *Selaginella inaequalifolia.* A nearly mature macrosporangium, in which the fourth spore lies behind and is not shown, magn. 1000 times.

The macrosporangia follow the same course of development as the microsporangia only as far as the formation of the archesporium, and the trabeculae are formed in the same way in both. The fertile cells of the archesporium form by transverse division on the side towards the wall of the sporangium a few cells which remain sterile; each fertile archesporial cell produces only one sporogenous cell, which by the process just described is sunk in the tissue of the sporangium. Hence the mother-cells of the macrospores are isolated, and they each produce four macrospores. The mother-cell of the macrospores is distinguished from all the other cells by its

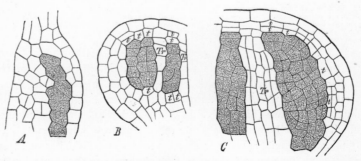

FIG. 239. *Isoetes lacustris,* development of microsporangia. *A* portion of a longitudinal section with the cells of archesporium shaded; the vascular bundle of the sporophyll would adjoin on the left. *B* and *C* portions of transverse sections, in which the groups of sporogenous cells formed from the archesporium are likewise shaded dark; *t* tapetal cells, *Tr* trabeculae.

superior size and by the protoplasm which it contains. It is at first polygonal, but afterwards becomes round and then begins to exercise a destructive influence on the neighbouring cells, especially the tapetal cells. These cells separate from one another, assume a spherical form and are ultimately dissolved, so that the mother-cell comes to lie in a cavity, and there divides into four daughter-cells, the macrospores.

Strasburger's[1] account of the division in *I. Duriaei* is, that the protoplasm of the spore-mother-cell first divides into two and then into four parts, and this is followed by the division of the nucleus of the mother-cell into four daughter-nuclei, one of which goes to each macrospore.

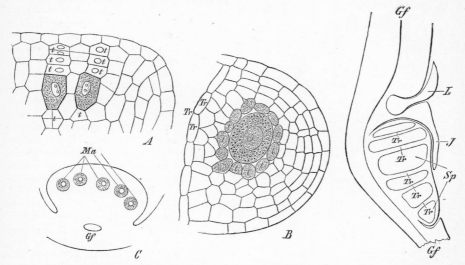

FIG. 240. *Isoetes lacustris*, macrosporangia in different states of development in transverse section. *A* young state. *B* older state, the macrospore-mother-cell having rounded itself off; *t t* tapetal cells, *Tr* trabeculae. *C* complete transverse section of a macrosporangium in the same stage of development as *B*. *Ma* the individual macrospore-mother-cells lying in the tissue (separated by the trabeculae). In Fig. *A* the sterile cells (primary tapetal cells) cut off from the archesporium above the spore-mother-cells are also indicated by *t t*.

FIG. 241. Longitudinal section through the lower sporangiferous portion of a leaf of *Isoetes lacustris*. *L* the ligule, *J* the indusium (velum), *sp* the sporangium (microsporangium), *Tr* the trabeculae, *Gf* vascular bundles of the sporophyll.

The development of the macrospores of *Isoetes* exhibits most significant homologies with the macrospores (embryo-sacs) of the Gymnosperms and Angiosperms, as will be shown more fully further on.

In many specimens of *Isoetes* from one locality, Lake Longemer in the Vosges, a formation of vegetative shoots takes the place of the formation of sporangia[2]. A shoot is formed at the position on the leaf where a sporangium is usually found, and this shoot separates from the mother-plant and developes into a new plant. In these plants the sexual generation is lost, and we have a case of apogamy as in the prothallia of Ferns described above. The apogamy moreover presents itself in Isoetes in various gradations; it is sometimes complete and hereditary, in other cases some leaves bear sporangia, others shoots. These apogamous plants appear to grow in deep water.

Histology. In the Selaginelleae, to which the following remarks chiefly refer, the *epidermis* of the stem consists of long prosenchymatous cells without stomata; the lateral walls of the epidermal cells of the leaves are often delicately sinuous or they have a variety of other forms; like the same cells in the Ferns, they contain chlorophyll, which appears in them and in the fundamental tissue of the leaves in a few

---

[1] Zellbildung u. Zelltheilung, III Ed. p. 167.
[2] Goebel, Ueber Sprossbildung auf Isoëtesblättern (Bot. Ztg. 1879, No. 1).

unusually large granules (Fig. 242). The leaves generally have stomata only on the under side, the small leaves of *S. pubescens* have them on both sides. In some species,

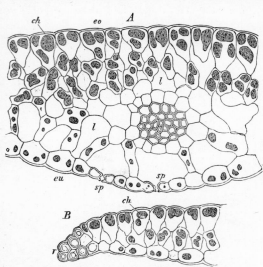

as *S. Martensii* and *S. stenophylla*, epidermal cells may be observed with their walls so thickened that the lumen is occluded (Russow). In most species the epidermis is different on the two sides of the leaf, in a few (*S. Galeotii*, *S. Kraussiana*) it is the same on both sides. The *fundamental tissue* of the stem consists as in *Lycopodium* of elongated cells with oblique transverse walls or with a distinctly prosenchymatous arrangement of the cells; but in contrast to most Lycopodiaceae these cells have thin walls and wide lumina, thicker walls and narrower lumina occurring only in the hypodermal layers (Fig. 243). It would appear that the cells of the fundamental tissue and with them of the other tissues also are capable of long continued growth in length and circumference; the distance be-

FIG. 242. Transverse sections through the leaf of *Selaginella inaequalifolia*. *A* in the middle. *B* at the margin. *ch* the chlorophyll-corpuscles, *eu* under epidermis, *eo* upper epidermis, *l* air-conducting intercellular spaces, *sp* stomata.

tween the leaves in older stems and the considerable thickness of such stems both point in this direction, and it would be worth while to investigate the matter thoroughly in the Selaginelleae, the Lycopodiaceae, and in many Ferns. One marked peculiarity in the Selaginelleae, as

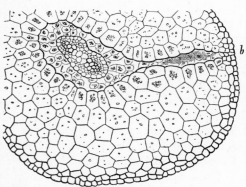

in the stems of the Mosses, is that the fundamental tissue, owing probably to the prosenchymatous arrangement of the cells, forms none of the usual small intercellular spaces, but their place is supplied by a large air-space which surrounds every vascular bundle in the stem and is only interrupted by transverse cellular filaments, like flying buttresses to support the bundles (Figs. 243, 244); if the cells in these filaments are of rounded form, the bundle is surrounded by a loose spongy parenchyma, as in Fig. 243, which is clearly distinguishable from the

FIG. 243. Transverse section of the stem of *Selaginella denticulata*; the xylem of the central bundle not yet completely lignified; *b* air-cavity surrounding a bundle which bends out into a leaf.

compact fundamental tissue without interstices. The fundamental tissue of the leaf is a loose spongy parenchyma containing chlorophyll, and in slender species with thin leaves is developed only round the single bundle which traverses the leaf, while at the thin margins of the leaves the upper and lower epidermis simply lie on one another (Fig. 242).

The *vascular bundles*, one or more of which traverse the stem, are cauline, as in the Lycopodiaceae; they may be traced up to the rudimentary condition in the extremity of the stem close beneath the apical cell and above the youngest leaves ; the single leaf-trace-bundles become connected with the cauline bundles only at a later period, as is the case also in the Lycopodiaceae. The vascular bundles of the stem are similar in structure to those of the true Ferns. They are for the most part ribbon-like in form ; a central xylem, composed chiefly of tracheides thickened in a scalariform manner, is entirely surrounded by thin-walled phloem (Figs. 243, 245) ; the primary elements of the xylem,

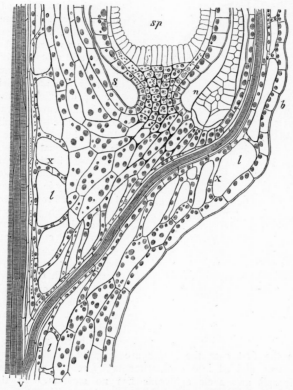

FIG. 244. *Selaginella inaequalifolia.* Longitudinal section through the right side of the axis or a spike *S* ; *b* the base of the leaf, *n* the ligule, *sp* the sporangium, *V* point of union of the bundles of the stem and leaf, *l* air-conducting intercellular spaces with cell-rows *X* lying across them.

very narrow tracheides (Fig. 243), are formed at the extremities of the bundle, and the development and lignification of the broader tracheides proceeds from them to the centre (Fig. 243). The layer of phloem surrounding the xylem is itself surrounded by two or three layers of parenchyma, which Russow compares with the phloem-sheath of the Ferns, and which must at all events be regarded as a bundle-sheath belonging to the fundamental tissue and enclosing the bundle inside the air-space mentioned above. There is no bounding layer with undulated lateral walls (endodermis) in stem or leaves. The vascular bundles in the leaves are slender and of simple construction ; the xylem enclosed in a scanty phloem is composed of spirally or reticulately thickened tracheides.

The short and simple stem of the *Isoeteae* is two- or three-lobed, the lobes being separated from one another by the longitudinal furrows from which the roots proceed. This tuber-like stem has no pith but an axile bundle formed by the union of the inner ends of the leaf-trace-bundles, one of which comes from each leaf. This axile bundle is composed on the transverse section of a roundish polygonal mass of short fusiform reticulated and spiral tracheides with thin-walled parenchymatous cells irregularly distributed among them; the vascular portion thus constituted is surrounded by a mantle of tabular cells which have broad pits but no sieve-pores; still they may be supposed to represent the phloem. The axile bundle extends to close beneath the meristem of the flat apex of the stem, and developes further in proportion as new leaves appear. It arises, as Hofmeister and Sachs perceived, from the sympodial union of the leaf-trace-bundles on the one side and of the bundles which pass into the roots on the other[1]. The entire axile bundle is surrounded, except at the apex and the points where the bundles from the leaves and roots join it, by a cambium-layer of narrow tabular cells, which by their growth and division in the centripetal direction, towards the bundle, and in the centrifugal, towards the cortex, give rise to a number of new cells. But the increase in the number of cells is very unequal in the two directions; it is large in the centrifugal direction, and consequently the cortex increases considerably in thickness and its outer layers turn brown and die off, and are replaced each year by cells formed by the cambium. The secondary cortex thus formed consists entirely of parenchyma. The axile bundle on the other hand adds but few layers to its thickness through the activity of the cambium, and it only rarely happens that any of the cells of these layers become tracheides. The structure of the leaves varies, according as the plants live beneath the water, in marshes or on

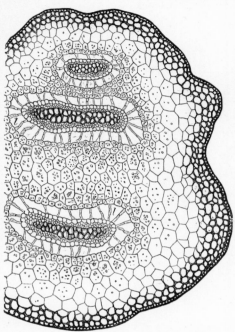

FIG. 245. *Selaginella inaequalifolia.* Transverse section of the stem, magn. 150 times.

dry land. In the first case the leaves are long and conical, and are traversed by four air-spaces divided into compartments by septa; a weak vascular bundle occupies their axis and their epidermis has no stomata. In the second case the general structure is the same, but they have stomata and hypodermal fibrous strands. In the third case the epidermis is furnished with stomata, and the basal portion of the dead leaves form a compact black coat of mail round the stem. The fundamental tissue, which is not separated by a bundle-sheath from the single bundle that traverses the leaf, forms according to Russow beneath the epidermis strands of colourless sclerenchyma, as in *Isoetes Hystrix,* and a dark brown-walled sclerenchyma which is the chief constituent of the sheathing portion of the leaf. The structure of the vascular bundle which traverses the leaf is said by Russow to be collateral, as in the Ophioglosseae and Equisetaceae; the xylem is not surrounded by the phloem, but the two simply lie side by side; consequently Russow considers the layers of transparent tissue lying next to the central xylem of the stem to be also phloem.

---

[1] The class of the Lycopodineae therefore shows two extremes; the one in *Psilotum,* where the leaves are few and small and there are no vascular bundles in the leaves but the elongated stem forms a bundle of its own, the other in *Isoetes,* where the short stem produces no vascular bundles but the large leaves produce one each.

FOURTH GROUP.

THE SEED-PLANTS.

(SPERMAPHYTES OR PHANEROGAMS.)

THE characteristic feature in the Phanerogams is, that the alternation of generations in them is concealed in the formation of the seed, which in the primary state at least consists of three parts, the seed-coat, the endosperm[1], and the embryo which is the product of fertilisation in the oosphere. A seed is formed when the ripe macrospore is not released from the macrosporangium, but remains enclosed in it and there produces prothallium, archegonium, and embryo. The seed therefore is simply a macrosporangium modified in a peculiar manner, which separates from the asexual generation and encloses the macrospore with the prothallium and embryo[2].

We have seen the **SEXUAL GENERATION**, the **PROTHALLIUM**, which is formed directly from the spore, losing more and more the character of an independent plant in the Vascular Cryptogams. In homosporous Ferns, Ophioglosseae and Equisetaceae, it vegetates often for a long time independently of the spore; in hetero-sporous Ferns and Lycopodineae it is formed inside the spore; in the former the female prothallium is thrust forth from the cavity of the macrospore, but continues to be connected with it, but in the Isoeteae it fills the interior of the macrospore as a mass of tissue, which only bursts the coat of the spore to make the archegonia accessible to the spermatozoids. In the Cycadeae and Coniferae this retrogressive metamorphosis goes a step further; the prothallium, here termed the *endosperm*, always remains enclosed in the macrospore, the *embryo-sac*, where, as in the Vascular Cryp-togams, it produces archegonia, formerly known by the quite superfluous name of

---

[1] The ripe seeds of many Dicotyledons have no endosperm, because it has been consumed and displaced by the rapidly growing embryo before the seed is matured; this takes place in other seeds after maturity in germination, that is, during the unfolding of the embryo. More rarely the formation of endosperm is from the first rudimentary.

[2] Macrosporangia and microsporangia, macrospores and microspores have a special terminology in seed-plants, which is now in many cases obsolete and which will be considered further on; but the structures thus named are throughout the same as the sporangia and spores in the Vascular Cryptogams.

corpuscula [1]. The processes in the macrospore or embryo-sac of the Monocotyledons and Dicotyledons are not so easy to understand. In their case three cells are formed at each of the two extremities of the embryo-sac; one of the two groups of cells is known as the *egg-apparatus*, and may be regarded as three archegonia reduced each to one cell (a similar reduction is found among the Gymnosperms in the gnetaceous genus *Welwitschia*), while the other three cells are called the *antipodal cells* and are to be considered as a rudimentary prothallium. Here too a tissue, the endosperm, is formed in and fills the embryo-sac after fertilisation, but the cells of the rudimentary prothallium do not take part in its formation; this commences with the division of the nucleus of the embryo-sac, which is still present along with the six cells. We must not therefore consider the endosperm of the Angiosperms as equivalent to the endosperm of the Gymnosperms, which, as has been said, is simply the tissue of the prothallium in the macrospore, whereas the endosperm of the Angiosperms, as compared with the Vascular Cryptogams, is probably to be regarded as a new formation.

The macrosporangium of the Seed-plants is termed the *ovule*. The arche-sporium is formed in it exactly in the way described above, for instance in the case of *Isoetes*, but the sporogenous tissue is usually much reduced, being limited to a few cells; in the Cycadeae and in some Coniferae it developes into a tolerably large mass of cells; and the macrospore is not produced by the division of a mother-cell into four parts, but from a group of a few cells formed by division of the archesporium, one of which by its growth displaces the others and becomes the macrospore. The macrosporangium of the Seed-plants is also distinguished from that of the Vascular Cryptogams by being usually enclosed in one or two envelopes, the *integuments*, which project above its apex and from which the seed-coat is afterwards chiefly formed. These integuments differ from the envelopes (indusia) of the macrosporangia in the Vascular Cryptogams in being formations from the base of the young macro-sporangium itself, and not luxuriant outgrowths of the leaves which bear the sporangia, as in the Ferns and Isoeteae. It is only in the microsporangia of certain of the Coniferae, namely, the Cupressineae, that we find formations of the nature of an indusium. The part of the macrosporangium which is enclosed by the integuments is termed the *nucellus*.

The microspores of the Seed-plants bear the name of *pollen-grains*. They too, like the microspores of the Vascular Cryptogams, produce a rudimentary male prothallium, which in the Angiosperms is usually represented by only one cell, and this cell is not even separated off by a firm cellulose-membrane [2].

The pollen-grains, like all microspores, contain the male or fertilising principle, which passing into the oosphere stimulates it to the formation of the embryo; but there is a great difference in the way in which the transmission of the fertilising substance is effected. In the Vascular Cryptogams this substance is a motile

---

[1] [As Vines points out (Sachs, Lehrb., Engl. transl., 2nd ed. p. 499), archegonium and corpus-culum are not exactly synonymous, since the latter, properly speaking, is only equivalent to central cell of the archegonium.

[2] Strasburger (Neue Unters. uber d. Befruchtunsgvorgang b. d. Phanerog. 1884) dissents from the view that the cell or cells so cut off are homologous with the prothallium in the Vascular Cryptogams.]

spermatozoid, which with the help of water is able to make its way through the open neck of the archegonium to the oosphere; in the Seed-plants, where the oosphere is enclosed in the embryo-sac and nucellus, in the Angiosperms in an ovary also, such a mode of transmitting the fertilising substance would be ineffectual; the pollen-grains are themselves therefore conveyed to the vicinity of the oosphere by external agencies, by the wind, by mechanical contrivances in the flowers, most often by insects; there each grain germinates like a spore and sends out the pollen-tube, which growing through the tissue of the female sporophyll at length reaches the embryo-sac and transmits the fertilising matter to the oosphere. How the transmission is effected though the closed wall of the pollen-tube is unknown; but the phenomena of fertilisation within the oosphere, as at present known, are the same as the analogous processes in the Vascular Cryptogams.

The microsporangia also of the Seed-plants have a name of their own and are termed *pollen-sacs*. Their structure and origin and the formation of the microspores or pollen-grains by division of the spore-mother-cells (pollen-mother-cells, sporocytes) into four parts agrees in the minutest particulars with the details given above in the case of the sporangia of the Vascular Cryptogams. On the other hand the sporophyll or axis, which bears the microsporangia and is termed the *stamen*, is often of peculiar construction; yet the sporophylls of the Cycadeae and Coniferae are in shape and position just like those of many Vascular Cryptogams, and are more or less modified foliage-leaves which usually bear the microsporangia or pollen-sacs on their under surface.

The important point which results from these considerations is that the seed-bearing plant with its pollen-grains and embryo-sacs is the equivalent of the spore-producing generation (sporophore, sporophyte) of the heterosporous Vascular Cryptogams. But as in the Vascular Cryptogams the sexual differentiation appears first in homosporous Ferns and Equisetaceae in the prothallium alone, and then in the heterosporous Filicineae and Lycopodineae at an earlier stage, namely, in the spores, so in the Seed-plants it is carried still further back, and is manifested not only in the formation of the macrospore or embryo-sac and microspore or pollen-grain, but also in the difference between macrosporangium or ovule and microsporangium or pollen-sac, and even before this in the distinction between male and female flowers and between male and female plants (dioecism).

The oospore of the Seed-plants does not as a rule develope directly into the embryo, but a pro-embryo is formed, which by growth first of all in the direction of the base of the embryo-sac and by division produces the *suspensor* which we have already seen in the Selaginelleae, and the embryo is developed subsequently from a usually roundish mass of tissue at the apex of the suspensor. The embryo has usually advanced so far in its development before the seed is fully ripe, that the first leaves, the primary stem-axis, and the first root can be easily distinguished; it is only in parasitic plants which have no chlorophyll and in saprophytes that the embryo continues in a rudimentary condition without perceptible external differentiation till the time that the seeds are dispersed; in Phanerogams containing chlorophyll it is often of very considerable size and the external differentiation of its parts very far advanced, as for instance in *Pinus, Zea, Aesculus, Quercus, Fagus, Phaseolus*, and others. Apart from the curvatures which often occur in the embryo, the apex of its primary stem is at first always directed towards the base of the embryo-sac, that is towards the base of the nucellus; the first or primary root coincides with the backward prolongation of the primary stem, and is directed towards the apex or micropylar end of the embryo-sac; it is of distinctly endogenous origin, its first rudiment at the posterior extremity of the embryo being covered by the nearest cells of the suspensor.

The apical cell of the growing point, which is easily recognised in many Algae, in the Characeae, Muscineae, Ferns and Equisetaceae as the primary mother-cell of the tissue, is replaced in the Lycopodiaceae, as we have seen, by a small-celled protomeristem. In the Phanerogams also the apex of the shoots, leaves and roots shows no apical cell except for a brief period in the development of some embryos in the Coniferae, but consists of a large number of usually very small cells rich in protoplasm and with large nuclei, and with an arrangement in layers such as we find even in the growing points of Vascular Cryptogams which have apical cells. But in the latter the periclinal cell-walls, that is, the walls which run in the same direction with the circumference, do not go quite up to the apex ; there is a gap always there in the cell-system and this gap is occupied by the apical cell. It is usually the layering due to the periclinal walls which is most evident. An outer simple layer, the *dermatogen*, is seen in the Angiosperms to be the immediate continuation of the epidermis of the older parts, and extends without interruption over the apex of the growing point ; beneath it lies a second tissue, the *periblem*, consisting usually of a few layers of cells which is also continuous over the apex and passes behind into the cortex ; beneath this again is an interior third mass of tissue, the *plerome*, which ends beneath the apex in a single cell in *Hippuris* and others, or in a group of cells, and from which proceeds either an axile strand of vascular bundles (the stems and roots of aquatic plants), or the descending limbs of the vascular bundles. Hence the root-cap is not formed, as in Cryptogams, from transverse segments of an apical cell, but in Gymnosperms by repeated division in the direction of the apex and luxuriant growth of the layers of the periblem of the root, in Angiosperms partly by a similar division and growth in the dermatogen, partly in another way into which we must not enter further here [1]. The first rudiments also of lateral formations, leaves, shoots and roots, cannot be referred to a single cell in the Phanerogams in the same sense as in the Cryptogams; they are seen first as protuberances consisting of a few or more small cells; the protuberance, which is to become a shoot or leaf, shows from its first appearance an inner mass of tissue which is in connection with the periblem of the parent-structure, and is covered with a continuation of the young epidermis.

The normal branching at the growing end of the shoots, leaves and roots is with few exceptions monopodial ; the generating axis as it grows produces lateral members (shoots, lateral branchings of leaves, lateral roots) beneath its apex; but many inflorescences are formed by dichotomous branching, as in *Valeriana*.

The monopodial branching of the axes of shoots is in radial organs usually axillary, that is, the new shoots appear above the median line of very young, but not always the youngest, leaves in the angle which they form with the parent-shoot. In the Gymnosperms it is not usual for the axil of every leaf to produce a shoot; in the Cycadeae for instance, as in many Filicineae, the branching of the stem is sometimes

---

[1] De Bary, Vergl. Anatomie, pp. 9–14, among other authorities, may be consulted on this point.

of the very smallest amount; in the Angiosperms on the contrary it is the rule that the axil of every vegetative leaf, that is, of every leaf which does not form part of a flower, produces a lateral shoot and sometimes more than one beside and above one another, though the buds when formed often remain inactive or develope only in later years. Besides the cases of probable dichotomy mentioned above, it is only in the Angiosperms that we meet with instances of real or apparent extra-axillary branching, and these will be noticed again under that division.

The Phanerogams are distinguished from the Vascular Cryptogams by an unusually varied and far-reaching metamorphosis of morphologically similar members, and this difference is correlated with an endless variety in the mode of life, a strict division of labour in respect to the physiological functions of these plants, and also with a greater differentiation of tissues than is to be found even in the Ferns. In these respects, as in others, the Gymnosperms occupy an intermediate position between the Vascular Cryptogams and the other Phanerogams.

The remarks which have now been made have given a general view both of the differences between Vascular Cryptogams and Phanerogams and also of their points of agreement and their mutual affinity. But to make the descriptions which will be given below of the characteristics of the different classes of Phanerogams more easy to understand, it will be well first of all to make some further mention of certain peculiar features in them, which were only briefly touched upon above, and to endeavour to settle the nomenclature which is to some extent antiquated and in many cases unsuitable to modern views.

The *flower* in the widest sense of the word is formed from the *sporophylls*, and from the axis that bears them; if the leaves on the same axis immediately beneath the sporophylls are different from the other leaves of the plant in position, form, colour or structure, and have a functional connection with fertilisation and its consequences, they are considered as forming part of the flower and are termed the *floral envelope* or *perianth*. The single flower contains only one axis with its sporophylls and perianth-leaves, and thus differs from the *inflorescence* which is a system of axes with several flowers[1]. The whole body of male sporophylls in a flower has been named by Röper the *androecium*, that of the female the *gynaeceum*. If a flower has both kinds of sporophylls, it is said to be *bisexual* or *hermaphrodite*; if the flowers of a plant contain only male or only female sporophylls, they are *unisexual* and are called *diclinous*; if the diclinous flowers are found on the same plant, the plant is said to be *monoecious*, if on different individuals only, the species is *dioecious*. Usually growth ceases at the apex of the flowering axis as soon as the formation of the sporophylls begins, and sometimes even sooner; the apex of the axis is then concealed and often lies deep down in the centre of the flower; in abnormal cases, but normally in *Cycas*, apical growth begins afresh in the flowering axis, and leaves are again produced and sometimes even a new flower; in this way *prolification* of the flower takes place. The sporophylls and perianth-leaves are usually placed close together, forming rosettes or arranged in whorls or spirals; the portion of the axis which bears them remains very short and usually no internodes can be distinguished in it, and sometimes it becomes club-shaped or forms a flat expansion or is hollowed out. This part of the flowering axis is termed the *torus*; in the Coniferae and Cycadeae, and in some Angiosperms also, it may be so elongated that the sporophylls appear to be arranged

---

[1] This and all similar definitions may still leave it difficult to distinguish in some cases between a flower and an inflorescence; the Euphorbiaceae, for instance, have given rise to controversy on this point.

loosely along an axis, as in a catkin. The axis is often elongated and slenderer below the torus, and is either naked or furnished with one or two small leaflets or *bracteoles*; this part of the axis is the flower-stalk or *peduncle*; if it is very short the flower is said to be sessile. As a rule no shoots are formed in the axils of the floral leaves, even though the plant produces shoots in the axils of all the other leaves; yet abnormal cases of axillary branching inside the flower are not altogether uncommon.

The *male spores* (*microspores* or *pollen-grains*) are produced in microsporangia, which may be generally termed *pollen-sacs*; these are at first bodies of solid tissue, in which, as in other sporangia, a hypodermal *archesporium* is differentiated, while the surrounding layers of tissue become the wall of the pollen-sac. It has been already stated, that the mother-cells of the pollen-grains cease to form a connected tissue and become isolated, though this is not always the case, and then form the pollen-grains by division into four parts; a more detailed account of these processes will be found in the description of the separate classes, but something must be said here respecting the morphology of the pollen-sac. The pollen-sacs of the Phanerogams, like the sporangia of most Vascular Cryptogams, are commonly the product of leaves (sporophylls); but in the Phanerogams these leaves usually undergo a striking metamorphosis, and remain as a rule much smaller than the other leaves; a leaf which bears pollen-sacs may be termed a staminal leaf or *stamen* (*androphyll*). Modern research has discovered cases in which the pollen-sacs spring from the elongated floral axis itself, as in *Naias* according to Magnus, in *Casuarina* according to Kaufmann, and in *Typha* according to Rohrbach. In the Cycadeae the pollen-sacs are found singly or in groups (*sori*) on the under side of relatively large staminal leaves, and often in large numbers, like the sporangia on the leaves of Ferns. In the Coniferae the staminal leaves already cease to look like ordinary leaves; they continue small and form several or only two comparatively large pollen-sacs on the under side of the lamina which in most cases may still be distinguished. In the Angiosperms the staminal leaf is usually reduced to a delicate stalk-like supporter, which is often of some length and is termed the *filament*; it bears at its upper extremity, or beneath it on both sides, two pairs of pollen-sacs which are together reckoned as one whole under the name of *anther*; the anther therefore consists usually of two longitudinal lobes, which are at once connected and separated by a part of the filament called the *connective*. The two pollen-sacs of each anther-lobe are united longitudinally to one another, and the two lobes are also not unfrequently combined into a single whole. In this case the pollen-sacs appear as compartments of the anther, which is then said to be quadrilocular as distinguished from bilocular anthers, of much less frequent occurrence, in which each lobe consists of a single pollen-sac.

The *embryo-sac*, the *macrospore*, is formed in the manner indicated above in the central tissue of the macrosporangium (ovule) named the *nucellus*. The nucellus, usually ovoid in shape, is composed of small-celled tissue, and is almost always enclosed in one or two envelopes each formed of a few layers of cells; these envelopes, the *integuments*, grow up round the young nucellus from its base, and becoming narrower at its apex and extending often some way above it form there a canal-like passage, the *micropyle*, through which the pollen-tube forces its way in order to reach the apex of the nucellus and ultimately the apex of the embryo-sac. In many cases the nucellus surrounded by its integuments is borne on a stalk, the *funiculus*; this is sometimes wanting and then the ovule is sessile. The funiculus is with rare exceptions, as in the Orchideae, traversed by a vascular bundle which usually terminates at the base of the nucellus, as happens also in the sporangia of *Botrychium*. The outward form of the ovule when ready for fertilisation varies much; there may be outgrowths of several kinds on the funiculus and integuments, but of special importance is the direction of the nucellus and its integuments with respect to the funiculus. The ovule is *straight* or *orthotropous* when the nucellus appears as a prolongation of the funiculus in the same straight line, and its apex forms the apex of the entire ovule; but it is much more often *inverted* or *anatropous*, that is, the apex of the nucellus, and therefore also the micropyle which projects above it, is turned towards the base of the funiculus, the ovule being bent sharply round at the base of the nucellus, while the funiculus runs along the whole length of the ovule and unites with the integuments or at least with the outer one ; where it is thus in union with them it is termed the *raphe*; in this case the nucellus is straight. A much rarer form of ovule is the *curved* or *campylotropous*, in which the nucellus itself together with its integuments is bent round, and has its apex and therefore also the micropyle turned towards its base ; here there is no union with the funiculus. These are however only the most striking forms and they are connected together by intermediate ones. The spot from which the ovules grow is named the *placenta*, and belongs to the floral axis, or more usually to the sporophylls (carpels) themselves. The placentas in many cases show no particular phenomena of growth, but they not unfrequently form projections which assume the appearance of special organs and at length separate from the surrounding parts. While after fertilisation the endosperm and the embryo are developing in the embryo-sac, the former usually increases greatly in size, and takes the place of the surrounding layers of tissue of the nucellus and sometimes even those of the inner integument ; the tissue of the integuments which is not thus displaced, or more commonly particular layers of it, then becomes the *seed-coat*. If any portion of the tissue of the nucellus, filled with food-material, remains till the seed is mature, it is distinguished as *perisperm*; its nutrient contents, though lying outside the embryo-sac, are consumed by the embryo as it unfolds, and the perisperm therefore may perform the functions of the endosperm. The seeds of the Cannaceae and Piperaceae contain perisperm. Sometimes, as the ovule developes into a seed, a new envelope grows up round it from below, which covers the stout testa usually with a soft mantle, and is termed an *aril*; of this kind is the soft red envelope on the hard-shelled seed of *Taxus baccata*, and the 'mace' of the nutmeg which is the seed of *Myristica fragrans*.

We found considerable variety in position and origin in the sporangia of the Vascular Cryptogams ; in the majority of cases they grow from the surface or margin of the sporophyll, or in its axil, or from a stem-structure ; there is a similar variety in the point of origin of the ovule in the Phanerogams. In a few cases the orthotropous ovule is the prolongation or termination of the flowering axis itself, so that the nucellus actually is in the place of its vegetative cone, as in Taxus and the Polygonaceae ; more commonly the ovule is a lateral shoot from beneath the apex of the floral axis, as in the Primulaceae and Compositae ; but the most common case is where the ovules spring from undoubted leaves, the *carpels* or sporophylls, and usually from their margin, like pinnae from the leaf, of which a very striking example is to be seen in *Cycas* ; it is less usual for the ovule to be formed on the upper (inner) side of the carpel, as in *Butomus, Akebia, Nymphaea,* and others. Sometimes the ovule is in the axil of the carpellary leaf, as in the Cupressineae and Ranunculaceae. Relying on these circumstances of position of the ovule botanists have assigned to it different morphological values, as stem-structure, leaf-structure, emergence, etc.; or they have sought to show by rather forced arguments that the ovule is everywhere a part of the leaf. The whole discussion starts from the assumption that the sporangia or ovules must be referred to vegetative organs or result from the metamorphosis of such organs ; but such an assumption is quite incorrect; sporangia are distinct organs, as much as stems or leaves, and we have a clear insight into the morphological nature of the ovule, and one that requires no further explanation, when we know that it is simply a somewhat modified macrosporangium. The perception of this truth which was first obtained from Hofmeister's investigations and has been confirmed by all later researches, but especially by those of Strasburger and Warming, is not assisted but hindered and obscured by dwelling on the malformations to which ovules are very liable, while the relations described above have been ascertained by the history of development.

The *carpels* are the floral leaves which have the closest genetic and functional relationship with the ovules ; they either produce and bear the ovules or are intended to form a case for them, the *ovary*, and to provide the apparatus, the stigma, for the reception of the pollen. This great variety in the morphological significance of the carpels is clearly seen by comparing the genera *Cycas* and *Juniperus* ; in *Cycas* the carpels are like the ordinary leaves of the plant, and the ovules which are entirely free and exposed are formed on their margins ; in *Juniperus* the ovules are formed in the axils of the floral leaves, which swell up after fertilisation and envelope the seeds in a pulpy substance, the berry-like fruit of the plant. In the Primulaceae the ovules spring from the elongated floral axis itself, and are enclosed at the time they are formed in a case, the ovary, which is composed of the carpels and bears the stigma on a stalk-like prolongation at its upper end. In most other Dicotyledons and Monocotyledons the ovules are placed on the incurved margins of the carpels which have united to form an ovary, and in this case therefore both produce and contain the ovules. With these very considerable morphological differences the carpels agree physiologically in being always excited to further development by fertilisation and during the formation of the seed, and in participating to some extent in its fortunes.

Pollination and fertilisation. In the interaction of the pollen and the oosphere previously formed in the embryo-sac of the Phanerogams there are two points of chief importance which must be carefully distinguished from one another, *pollination* and *fertilisation*. Pollination is the conveying of the pollen from the anthers to the stigma in Angiosperms, or to the nucellus in Gymnosperms ; there the pollen is detained by a viscid substance, often also by hairs, and impelled to the emission of the pollen-tube. In the Gymnosperms this tube at once pierces through the tissue of the nucellus, but in the Angiosperms it grows downwards through the tissue of the stigma and through the style, which is often of considerable length, till it reaches the ovule, when it makes its way through the micropyle to the embryo-sac ; it is not till it is in contact with the embryo-sac, and in the Gymnosperms has penetrated still farther, that the fertilisation of the oosphere is effected [1]. Between the two processes of pollination and fertilisation a long period of time, sometimes months, may elapse, but in many cases only days or hours.

Pollination is rarely brought about by the wind only (*anemophilous* flowers) ; where this is the case large quantities of pollen are produced, in order to secure the desired result, as in many Coniferae ; in a few cases only is the pollen thrown on to the stigma by the bursting of the anthers, as in some Urticaceae ; insects are the means usually employed to effect pollination (*entomophilous* flowers). For this purpose special and often highly complicated arrangements are devised to allure the insects, and induce them to visit the flowers ; and means are at the same time employed to ensure that the pollen of one flower shall as far as possible be always conveyed to the stigma of another flower, even in the case of hermaphrodites. It is with a view to these objects that the parts of the flower assume definite forms and positions, which we will not go further into at present, but only observe that insects are attracted to the flowers chiefly by means of the nectar which is secreted in them ; this usually sweet juice is in most cases produced deep down between the leaves of the flower, and the shape or the parts of the flower is usually so contrived that the insect in searching for the nectar must put its body in certain positions, and in doing so brushes pollen from the anthers, which it afterwards deposits on the stigma of another flower. The variety in the forms of flowers is chiefly due to these conditions, though the plan on which they are all constructed is a comparatively simple one. The organs which secrete the nectar, the *nectaries*, are therefore of special importance to the life of most Phanerogams, but at the same time they are usually very inconspicuous, and in spite of

---

[1] [Strasburger, Neue Unters. ü. d. Befruchtungsvorg. b. d. Phanerog. 1884, has shown that the growth of the pollen-tube through the tissue of the style is comparable with the growth of the hyphae of a parasitic Fungus, in some cases penetrating the cells of the stigmatic surface. See also his Botanische Practicum.]

their great physiological importance are not attached to any particular member of the flower, for almost every single part of it may serve as a nectary; this fact is highly characteristic of the relation between morphology and physiology, and the word nectary expresses not a morphological but a purely physiological conception. The nectary is often only a small spot at the base of the carpels, as in *Nicotiana*, or of the stamens, as in *Rheum*, or of the leaves of the perianth, as in *Fritillaria*, which forms the nectar without assuming a more distinct form; sometimes it is a glandular protuberance on the floral axis between the insertions of the stamens and perianth-leaves, as in the Cruciferae and Fumariaceae; some member, as a floral leaf, is often changed into a hollow receptacle for secreting and preserving the nectar, such as the hollow spur in *Viola*, or all the leaves of the inner floral envelope may form hollow pitcher-like nectaries, as in *Helleborus*, or some may assume the strangest forms, as the petals of *Aconitum*.

Pollination is often followed, even before fertilisation, by striking changes in the parts of the flower, especially in the gynaeceum, and most frequently when the parts concerned are of a delicate character; thus the stigmas, styles and petals wither, while the ovary enlarges, as in *Gagea, Puschkinia*, and other species; the most striking result of pollination is seen in many Orchidaceae, where the ovules are not formed till after it has taken place.

But changes still more energetic and varied are produced when the pollen-tube reaches the embryo-sac, that is, by fertilisation; the oospore developes into the embryo; the endosperm, already formed in the Gymnosperms and constituting the prothallium, now begins to be formed in the Angiosperms; the ovules with the ovaries increase in size, and their tissues are differentiated and become lignified, or pulpy, or dry, etc.; the enlargement of the ovary which is often enormous, in *Cocos, Cucurbita* and other plants several thousand times in volume, is a striking proof that the consequences of fertilisation extend to the rest of the plant in so far as it supplies nutrient material. Great changes in form, structure and size take place after fertilisation as a rule only in the carpels, placentas and seeds, but they occur sometimes in other parts as well; for example, it is the torus which forms the swollen pulpy mass which is known as the strawberry, and which has on its surface the small and true fruits; in the mulberry it is the perianth-leaves which swell up and form the juicy envelopes of the fruit; in *Taxus* it is a cup-shaped outgrowth from the axis beneath the ovule which surrounds the naked seed with a red fleshy envelope (the aril). Popular usage includes all parts, which experience a striking change in consequence of fertilisation, under the name of *fruit*, especially when they separate as a whole from the parent plant; the strawberry, and the yew with its aril, the fig and the mulberry are all alike fruit. But botanical phraseology confines the notion expressed by the word fruit within narrower limits, though these are not very sharply defined. In as strict accordance as possible with botanical usage the whole of the gynaeceum which ripens in consequence of fertilisation may be termed the fruit; if the gynaeceum consists of coherent carpels or an inferior ovary, it produces a single entire fruit; if the carpels are distinct, they each form a mericarp or fruitlet; at the same time this limitation of the conception is often inconvenient, and it would seem to be better to define it differently in different sections of the system.

It must be borne in mind that the fruit taken morphologically is not any new thing on the plant; all parts of the fruit that can be determined morphologically were formed and so determined before fertilisation; the change caused by fertilisation in the parts of the gynaeceum is purely physiological. It is only in the ovule that anything morphologically new is produced, namely, the endosperm and the embryo.

Inflorescence. If a shoot which has hitherto produced numerous foliage-leaves, and especially a strong primary shoot, ends in a flower, the flower is said to be *terminal*; but if a lateral shoot at once developes a flower, forming one or a few bracteoles at most beneath it, the flower is said to be *lateral*. Sometimes the primary axis produced from the embryo ends with a flower ; more often it grows on or ceases to grow without forming a flower, and only lateral shoots of the first or second or some higher order terminate in flowers ; in the first case the plant as regards the formation of flowers may be said to be monaxial, in the other cases biaxial or triaxial. If a plant produces only terminal flowers, or if the lateral flowers spring from the axils of single large foliage-leaves, they appear scattered and solitary. If on the other hand the branches which bear the flowers are close together, and the leaves within this branch-system are smaller than the rest and different in shape and colour, or altogether wanting, then we have an *inflorescence* in the narrower meaning of the word, which is generally clearly distinguished from the vegetative portion of the plant which bears it, and not unfrequently assumes peculiar forms requiring a special nomenclature. The latter case is rare among Gymnosperms, whereas the formation of inflorescences of pecu-liar shape and with a great abundance of flowers is characteristic of the more highly differentiated section of Angiosperms ; hence it seems desirable to defer a more detailed account of the classification and naming of inflorescences till we reach those plants.

As regards the *histology* of the Phanerogams one thing only need be mentioned here. In both Gymnosperms and Angiosperms the vascular bundles have the marked peculiarity, that each bundle that bends outwards into a leaf is only the upper limb of a bundle passing downwards in the stem ; in other words, the bundles are common bundles and each has an ascending portion which bends outwards into a leaf and a descending portion which traverses the stem ; the latter is called the leaf-trace-bundle, after Hanstein. In the simplest cases, as in most Conifers, only one bundle bends out into each leaf; but if the insertion of the leaf is broad or the leaf itself is large and strongly developed, several or even many bundles may pass from the stem into the leaf, where they branch if the leaf is broad ; there are therefore leaf-traces with one or with more bundles. The leaf-trace-bundles are generally thicker at the spot where they pass from the stem into the leaf, that is to say at the bend, than in the lower part of their course ; each leaf-trace-bundle may either run downwards through one internode or through several ; an internode which has several leaves above it has in it the lower portions of bundles, which bend out above into leaves of different height on the stem and of different age. The descending leaf-trace-bundle is never free at its lower end, but attaches itself laterally to the middle or upper part of a lower and older bundle ; it sometimes happens that the bundle splits below into two limbs which anastomose with the lower bundles, or the slender extremities of the bundles coming down from above thrust themselves between the upper parts of the leaf-traces of older leaves, or each bundle bends to the right or left and ultimately attaches itself to a lower bundle. In this way the leaf-traces which were originally isolated become united in the stem into a connected system, which when sufficiently developed gives the impression of having been produced by branching, while it is really due to the subsequent coalescence of separate portions.

But other bundles may be formed in the stems of Phanerogams besides the leaf-trace-bundles or descending limbs of the common bundles ; a net-work is often formed by bundles running horizontally in the nodes of the stem, as in the Gramineae, or girdle-like anastomoses also in the nodes, as in the Rubiaceae and *Sambucus*. Again, longitudinal bundles may be differentiated in the stem which have nothing to do with the leaves, and these cauline bundles may originate in different ways ; they may appear at an early period in the protomeristem of the stem immediately after and inside the leaf-traces in the medullary tissue, as in the Begonieae, Piperaceae, Cycadeae, or they are formed much later outside the leaf-trace-bundles in the periphery of the stem as it continues to grow in thickness, as in the Menispermeae and Dracaenas.

The subsequent history of the leaf-trace-bundles of the Monocotyledons on the one hand, and of the Gymnosperms and Dicotyledons on the other, is different ; in the former they are closed, in the latter a layer of active cambium remains behind, which in stems that are increasing rapidly in thickness and forming wood soon gives rise to a perfect ring by bridging over the primary medullary rays, and then constantly produces new layers of phloem on the outside and new xylem on the inside. In the primary roots also and stronger lateral roots of Gymnosperms and Dicotyledons the subsequent formation of a closed cambium-ring causes an increase in thickness, which, like that of the stem, is not a characteristic of the Cryptogams, and frequently leads to the formation of strong and persistent root-systems, often functionally replaced in the Monocotyledons by rhizomes, tubers, and bulbs. Finally this long-continued growth in thickness is connected with active and copious formation of cork, which usually passes into the production of *bark*, a process foreign both to Vascular Cryptogams and Monocotyledons. But these also are subjects which will be better discussed in detail when we are describing the characters of the several divisions of the Phanerogams.

CLASSIFICATION OF SEED-PLANTS OR PHANEROGAMS. The Phanerogams are distinguished from the Vascular Cryptogams (Pteridophytes) by the formation of the seed, which is the product of the macrosporangium or ovule. The ovule produces the embryo-sac in the nucellus which is its most essential part, and in the embryo-sac are formed the endosperm and the oosphere; the oosphere is fertilised by the contents of the pollen-tube, an outgrowth from the pollen-grain, and after fertilisation a pro-embryo is developed which differentiates into suspensor and embryo. The phanerogamous plant with stem, leaves, roots and hairs answers to the spore-producing generation (sporophore or sporophyte) of the Vascular Cryptogams; the embryo-sac is the macrospore, the pollen-grain the microspore; the endosperm, at least in the Gymnosperms, is the female prothallium (oophore or oophyte), and the seed unites in itself at least for a time the two generations, the prothallium or endosperm and the young plant of the second generation, the embryo.

I. PHANEROGAMS WITHOUT AN OVARY (GYMNOSPERMAE).

The ovules before fertilisation are not enclosed in an ovary formed by the cohesion of carpels; the prothallium or endosperm is produced before fertilisation and forms archegonia; the pollen-grains undergo divisions of their contents before the formation of the pollen-tube, such as take place in the microspores of the Selaginelleae.

Gymnospermae. The formation of leaves in the embryo begins with a whorl of two or several members.

A. CYCADEAE. Branching of the stem rare or altogether suppressed; leaves large, branched.

B. CONIFERAE. Axillary branching copious, but not from all leaf-axils; leaves small, not branched.

C. GNETACEAE. Mode of growth very various; flowers in many respects like those of Angiosperms.

II. PHANEROGAMS WITH OVARIES (ANGIOSPERMAE).

The ovules are produced inside an ovary formed of cohering carpels or of one carpel with coherent margins, and having at its summit the stigma on which the pollen-grains germinate. The endosperm is formed after fertilisation at the same time as the embryo; both sometimes remain in a rudimentary condition. The pollen-grain also suffers division of its contents. Branching usually axillary and from the axils of all the foliage-leaves.

A. **Monocotyledons.** The first leaves of the embryo are alternate. Endosperm usually large, embryo small [1].

B. **Dicotyledons.** The first leaves of the embryo are in a whorl of two members. Endosperm often rudimentary, often consumed by the embryo before the ripening of the seed.

I. GYMNOSPERMAE.

The class of Gymnosperms, composed of the orders Cycadeae, Coniferae, and Gnetaceae, includes plants of strikingly different habit, but which are seen to be connected with one another by their morphological characters, by peculiarities in the formation of their tissues, and especially by their sexual reproduction. They occupy at the same time an intermediate position between Vascular Cryptogams and Angiosperms, approaching most nearly to the Dicotyledons, especially in anatomical structure.

The *pollen-grains* shew their character as microspores by their division before pollination into two or more cells, one or some of which form a very rudimentary prothallium [2], while another and that the largest cell developes the pollen-tube, when the pollen-grain has reached the nucellus of the ovule. The pollen-sacs or microsporangia are always outgrowths from the under side of formations, the stamens, which are undoubtedly of the nature of leaves; they are formed in larger or smaller numbers or in pairs on each staminal leaf, and do not unite together as they grow.

The *ovule*, which is almost always orthotropous and usually provided with one integument only, is either the metamorphosed extremity of the floral axis itself, or is a lateral shoot from below its apex, or springs from the axil of a leaf or from peculiar placental structures, or lastly is formed on the upper side or on the margins of carpellary leaves. These leaves never cohere in the Gymnosperms into a true ovary before fertilisation, but nevertheless often grow considerably during the ripening of the seeds, and close together and conceal the seeds until they are ripe, when they open again to let them fall out; at the same time it is no rare thing for the seeds to remain entirely naked from first to last. The embryo-sac is formed in the small-celled nucellus from the originally hypodermal archesporium at some distance beneath the apex and near the base, and continues till the time of fertilisation to be surrounded by a thick layer of the tissue of the nucellus. The rudiments of several embryo-sacs sometimes appear in a nucellus, but one only is fully developed.

---

[1] [In a considerable number of Monocotyledons, as in Dicotyledons, the small amount of endosperm formed is consumed by the embryo before the ripening of the seed.

[2] See Strasburger, Neue Unters. ü. d. Befruchtunsvorg. b. d. Phanerog. He is disposed to regard the whole pollen-grain as the homologue of an antheridium, and the formation of the small cells (the prothallium of the text) as a physiological process, viz. the separation of substance not essential in the sexual process. He holds the same view with regard to the microspores in the Ligulatae (see page 284).]

The embryo-sac is marked by its thick wall, which sometimes, as in the Cycadeae, is furnished with a cuticularised outer layer corresponding to the exosporium. The prothallium or endosperm is formed in the embryo-sac some time before fertilisation by the formation of free cells, which soon however unite to form a connected tissue and multiply by division; the prothallium therefore is endogenous as in the Selaginelleae, and archegonia are formed on it in larger or smaller numbers. According to Strasburger each archegonium originates in a cell of the prothallium lying at the apex of the embryo-sac, which increases considerably in size and produces by division the neck and central cell of the archegonium; a small upper portion of the large central cell is separated off to be the canal-cell, as in the Vascular Cryptogams, while the other and larger part becomes the oosphere. When the pollen-tube has grown through the tissue of the nucellus and reached the archegonium, and the oosphere has received the fertilising substance from it, the embryo is formed in the oospore, the whole of which is employed for the purpose, as in *Gingko*, or only the lower portion of it[1]. The cells of the suspensor are at first small, but the middle or upper ones grow out into long tubes, which pushing the lower ones before them break through the lower part of the archegonium and make their way into a softened part of the prothallium. Sometimes adjoining tubes of the suspensor separate from one another, and each produces at its apex a small-celled rudiment of an embryo; from this cause and because the oospheres in several archegonia are often fertilised in one prothallium, the immature seed may contain several rudimentary embryos (polyembryony), but one embryo only as a rule is developed and the others dwindle away.

During the development of the embryo the prothallium becomes filled with food-material and increases considerably in size, and the embryo-sac which encloses it grows with it and at length entirely supplants the surrounding tissue of the nucellus; the integument or an inner layer of it is developed into a hard seed-coat, and in naked seeds the outer tissue not unfrequently becomes fleshy and pulpy and gives the seed the appearance of a plum-like fruit, as in *Cycas* and *Gingko*; sometimes the effects of fertilisation extend to the carpels and other parts of the flower, which grow vigorously and form fleshy or woody envelopes round the seeds, or cushions underneath them.

The ripe *seed* is always filled with endosperm (prothallium) in which the embryo lies, distinctly differentiated into stem, leaves and root, and filling an axile cavity in the endosperm; it is always straight, with the tip of the root towards the micropylar end and the points of the leaves towards the base of the seed. The first leaves produced by the stem of the embryo are in a whorl consisting generally of two opposite members, but not unfrequently of three, four, six, nine, or even more. When the embryo unfolds in germination, the tip of the root first protrudes through the bursting seed-coat; by the elongation of the cotyledons or first leaves the bud formed between them at the apex of the stem is thrust forth, but the cotyledons

---

[1] The Gymnosperms afford the only examples in the vegetable kingdom of a phenomenon which is widely spread in the animal kingdom, namely, the formation of the embryo from a part only of the oosphere (meroblastic formation), though we cannot distinguish in them between the ' formative and nutritive yolk.'

themselves continue in the endosperm till the food which it contains has been transferred to the embryo; occasionally they are drawn out by the elongation of the stem and brought above the surface of the ground, and there unfold as the first foliage-leaves. In the Coniferae they become green inside the seed in perfect darkness; the formation of chlorophyll therefore takes place in this case, as in the Ferns, without the co-operation of light; it is not known whether this is the case also in the Cycadeae and Gnetaceae. The young plant when set free from the seed consists of an erect stem, which passes without any distinct line of demarcation into the strong primary tap-root; this grows vertically downwards and sends off numerous secondary roots in acropetal succession, ultimately forming in most cases an extensive root-system. The young stem grows vertically upwards, and its growth is usually unlimited and much more vigorous than that of all the lateral branches, though there may be many of them, as in the Coniferae; in the remarkable Gnetaceous species, *Welwitschia*, growth ceases at the apex of the stem at a very early period, and there is no production even of new leafy shoots; this is usually the case also in the Cycadeae.

There is no apical cell at the extremity of the shoots or at the points of the roots in Gymnosperms; they resemble in this respect the rest of the Phanerogams, but they differ from them in this that the primary meristem of the growing point of a shoot either shows no differentiation, as in the Cycadeae and Abietineae, or only an indistinct differentiation into dermatogen, or young epidermis, and periblem, or young cortex. The well-defined axile fascicular portion (plerome-strand) is covered at the apex of the root by a continuation of the cortical tissue (periblem), the layers of which become thickened over the apex and split, and thus form the root-cap.

Terminal *flowers* occur on the primary stem only in the Cycadeae, and not always in them; they appear in the other families on small lateral shoots, usually of a high order. The flowers are always unisexual, the plants themselves monoecious or dioecious. The male flower consists of a slender and usually much elongated axis, on which the stamens, which are generally numerous, are disposed spirally or in whorls. The female flowers are extremely different in outward appearance and for the most part very unlike those of Angiosperms; the Gnetaceae only have a kind of perianth of more delicate leaves; there is none in the Cycadeae and Coniferae or it is represented by scales. But the peculiar feature in the female flowers, apart from the absence of an ovary, is the elongation of the floral axis, on which the leaves are not arranged in concentric circles, as in Angiosperms, but in distinctly ascending spirals, or in alternating whorls where they are numerous; in *Podocarpus* and *Gingko*, where only a few ovules are produced on a flowering axis which is either naked or furnished with only small leaves, the last trace of any resemblance in habit to the flowers of Angiosperms usually ceases. As our guide in this matter we have only to keep to the definition, that a flower is an axis bearing sporophylls, in order to be clear at all times as to what should be called a flower in the Gymnosperms[1].

---

[1] It would be well perhaps to use the expression 'flower' only in the Gnetaceae and in Angiosperms, for a sporangiferous spike of *Selaginella* might be called a flower as much as the male inflorescence of *Pinus*; both are in fact simply sporangiferous spikes or axes bearing sporophylls, whereas in Angiosperms, at least in typical cases, further modifications occur.—On the histology of the Gymnosperms see the supplementary remarks on the whole class.

A. CYCADEAE[1].

The Cycadeae form the group of Gymnosperms which comes nearest in habit and in other respects to the Vascular Cryptogams and especially to the Ferns, and among the Ferns they show the greatest affinity to the Marattiaceae; like them they played an important part in former epochs of the world's history, and with the Coniferae were once the chief representatives of the Phanerogams.

Leaves. The whole surface of the stem is covered with large leaves arranged spirally, and no internodes can be distinguished. At the summit is a crown of leaves more or fewer in number, as in many Ferns. The leaves are of two kinds; large, stalked, pinnate or pinnatifid foliage-leaves alternate periodically with dry, sessile, leathery scale-leaves, covered with brown hairs and of comparatively small size, which usually much exceed the foliage-leaves in number within the several periods. This alternation of scale-leaves and foliage-leaves, which is not uncommon in the Coniferae and in Angiosperms, is found in the Ferns only in the genus *Osmunda*[2]. The scale-leaves are in this case, as in most others[3], transformed rudiments of foliage-leaves, in which the broad part of the leaf has been arrested in its growth, while the base has attained to considerable development. Every year or every second year a rosette of large foliage-leaves is formed, and among them is the terminal bud of the stem enveloped in scales, under the protection of which the new crown of foliage-leaves slowly developes. This alternation begins in *Cycas* and other genera at the time of germination, since the cotyledons which are like the foliage-leaves are followed by a number of scale-leaves which envelope the bud; the bud produces as a rule only a pinnate though as yet small foliage-leaf, and this is followed by scale-leaves. In *Zamia* on the contrary the formation of scale-leaves precedes that of foliage-leaves. In both cases as the plant grows stronger, foliage-leaves are being constantly produced in greater size and numbers, to form, when the older leaves have died off, the crown of leaves of the time being, while the scale-leaves which stand above enclose at the same time the bud of the stem. The basal portions of the older leaves together with old scale-leaves form a peculiar kind of scale-armour on the stems of some species of *Cycas*, *Encephalartos*, *Ceratozamia*, and other genera. The foliage-leaves are so fully formed within the bud, that when they burst it they have only to unfold, and this takes but a short time, while one to two years elapse before the next rosette unfolds. The arrangement of the leaves in the bud also recalls to some extent that of the Ferns; the pinnae of *Cycas* are circinate, the leaf as a whole is stretched straight out; in *Zamia* and *Ceratozamia* the leaf in general with its apex is more or less bent or loosely rolled

---

[1] Miquel, Monographia Cycadearum, 1842.—Karsten, Organographische Betracht. ü. *Zamia muricata*, Berlin, 1857.—Mohl, Bau d. Cycadeenstammes (Verm. Schr. p. 195).—Mettenius, Beitr. z. Anat. d. Cycadeen (Abhandl. d. Kgl. Sächs. Ges. d. Wiss. VII, 1861).—De Bary, Vgl. Anat. *vid. inf.*—Kraus, Ueber d. Bau d. Cycadeenfiedern (Jahrb. f. wiss. Bot. Bd. IV).—De Bary in Bot. Ztg. 1870, p. 574.—Juranyi, Bau u. Entw. d. Pollens bei *Ceratozamia* (Jahrb. f. wiss. Bot. Bd. VIII, p. 382).—Braun, Ueber d. Gymnospermie d. Cycadeen (Mon. Ber. d. Berl. Ak. 1875.—Warming, Untersogelser og Betragtninger over Cycaderne (Kön. Danske Videnskabes Selsk. obersigter, 1877);—Id. Bidrag til Cycadernes Naturhistorie, overs. over d. Kgl. D. Vidensk. Selsk. Forh. 1879.—Treub, Recherches sur les Cycadées (Annales. du jardin Bot. de Buitenzorg, II, 1881 [and IV, 1884]).—[Goroschankīn, Zur Kenntn. d. Corpuscula b. d. Gymnosp. (Bot. Ztg. 1883).]

[2] According to Prantl, but not in all specimens.

[3] Göbel, Beitr. z. Morphol. u. Physiol. d. Blattes (Bot. Ztg. 1880, p. 753). [See note on next page.]

inwards, while the pinnae are straight. The leaf is pinnate, in the genus *Bowenia* bi-pinnate. The usually sessile pinnae are marked as regards their venation by the absence of anastomoses, the frequence of dichotomy and the uniformity in size of the veins, except in *Bowenia*; these characters are of importance in determining fossil remains [1].

The *stem* when young is like a tuber in form, and in some species it retains this character to a later time. It seldom attains any great height (*Cycas*), and is usually unbranched, as are the similarly growing stems of *Aspidium Filix-mas*, the Ophioglosseae, *Isoetes*, and some others, where also the apex of the stem which elongates very slowly has a considerable breadth. The stem of the Cycadeae has still greater likeness to that of the Tree-ferns, which without forming internodes is thickly beset with leaf-scars and branches from the leaf-stalks; and like it the cycas-stem also enlarges considerably close beneath the apex at an early stage of its growth, and subsequently increases very little in thickness. The anatomical structure will be briefly noticed further on.

On the other hand the Cycadeae are distinguished from all Vascular Cryptogams by the presence of a *tap-root*. Secondary roots appear above the ground and branch dichotomously. *Anabaena*, one of the Nostocaceae, is often found in the intercellular spaces of the roots, where its presence causes tubular protuberances in the adjacent cells [2], but is not the cause of the forked branching, such as is produced for instance in the roots of the Coniferae by the mycelia of Fungi.

The disposition of the *flowers* of the Cycadeae is always dioecious, the plants themselves are therefore male or female; both kinds of flower appear on the summit of the stem, either singly, as in *Cycas*, as the terminal flower of the stem, or in pairs or more together, as in *Zamia muricata* and *Macrozamia spiralis*, perhaps as metamorphosed bifurcations of the stem. The flower consists of a stout conical elongated axis which in its lower part is sometimes a naked stalk, but elsewhere is furnished with numerous crowded leaves arranged spirally and bearing macrosporangia or microsporangia. The flowers of Cycas are therefore not essentially distinct from the sporangiferous spikes of many Vascular Cryptogams.

The female flower in *Cycas* is a rosette of foliage-leaves of the stem slightly metamorphosed; the apex of the stem produces above them first scale-leaves, then fresh foliage-leaves, then scale-leaves and leaves bearing sporangia, as sterile and fertile leaves alternate in some Ferns, *Struthiopteris* for example. The stem therefore grows through the female flower [3]. It is true that the special leaves that bear the macrosporangia are much smaller than ordinary foliage-leaves, but their form and structure are essentially the same. The lower pinnae are replaced by macrosporangia (ovules)

---

[1] [Bower, Comp. Morph. of the leaf in Vasc. Crypt. and Gymnosp. (Phil. Trans. 1884), treating the whole leaf as a branch-system shows that the rounded apex of the phyllopodium (i. e. the main axis of the leaf exclusive of pinnae) is covered with a definite dermatogen-layer; its growth is never very distinctly apical, more so in *Cycas* and perhaps in *Dioon* than in other genera; it is winged throughout; its branching is monopodial, the order of succession with few exceptions being basipetal. This view of the leaf as a phyllopodium is quite at variance with that advanced in the text, which assumes a lower portion of a leaf, a leaf-base, which in the scale-leaves is alone developed, distinct from an upper portion.]

[2] Reinke in Bot. Ztg. 1879, p. 473.

[3] It is true that this expression 'growing through' does not mean the same thing exactly as in Angiosperms.

which reach the considerable size of a mature medium-sized plum before fertilisation; the ripe seed, the altered macrosporangium now containing the macrospore, has the size and appearance of a middle-sized apple hanging naked on the carpel. The numerous leaves of the male flowers that bear the microsporangia, the staminal leaves, are much smaller, seven or eight centimetres in length and not divided, becoming broader above from a narrower base and pointed; on their under side are sori of many microsporangia; the whole flower is from thirty to forty centimetres in length.

The male and female flowers of the other genera of the Cycadeae are not unlike fir-cones in outward appearance; on a short naked stalk rises like a spindle the comparatively slender floral axis bearing numerous closely crowded leaves with macrosporangia or microsporangia (Fig. 247), and ending above in a naked apex which has ceased to grow (Fig. 247 *D*). The staminal leaves are small indeed in comparison with the foliage-leaves of the same plants, and yet they are about the largest and most massive to be found in Seed-plants; in *Macrozamia*, as in *Cycas*, they are from six to eight centimetres long and may be three centimetres broad; they are narrow at the point of insertion, expand into a kind of lamina, and are simply acuminate, as in *Macrozamia*, or divide into two hooked points, as in *Ceratozamia*; or again the lower part is slender like a stalk and bears a shield-like expansion (*Zamia*). The staminal leaves of the Cycadeae are also distinguished from those of most other Seed-plants by their persistence; they become lignified and often very hard. The numerous microsporangia (pollen-sacs) on the

FIG. 246. A fertile leaf (carpel) of *Cycas revoluta* about half the natural size; *f* the lobes of the carpel which resembles a foliage leaf, *sk* ovules in the place of the lower pinnae, *sk'* a more highly developed ovule.

under side of the staminal leaves are usually collected together into small groups of two to five sporangia each, resembling the sorus of the Ferns; these in their turn form larger groups on the right and left side of the leaf. The pollen-sacs are round or ellipsoidal, usually about one millimetre in diameter, and are attached to the under side of the staminal leaf by a narrow base, which in *Zamia spiralis* according to Karsten becomes a stalk; they open by a longitudinal fissure.

The development of the microsporangia and of the leaves that bear them is most fully known in *Zamia muricata* [1], but even here there are points not yet cleared up. A lobe is formed on the right and left side at the base of the young staminal leaf, and on these lateral expansions, which are to be regarded perhaps as rudimentary pinnae, the placentas appear in the form of hemispherical protuberances, six on each lobe. Two microsporangia or pollen-sacs are formed on each placental protuberance essentially in the same way as in the Marattiaceae, and here as in them there is without doubt a unicellular *archesporium*. In a later stage of their development the microsporangia consist of a wall of several layers of cells and an inner group of larger cells filled with dense protoplasm, the pollen-mother-cells, which are invested by a double layer of narrow thin-walled *tapetal cells*. The pollen-mother-cells divide first into two and then into four daughter-cells, as in most Monocotyledons. The micro-spores or pollen-grains of *Ceratozamia* when released from the sporangium are unicellular and spherical (Fig 248); but as they increase in size their contents which are enclosed in an exine and an intine divide into two cells, a large and a small one, each with a nucleus. The small cell lying on one side in contact with the intine of the grain bulges out on the other side and grows in the form of a papilla into the large cell; then the smaller cell divides transversely, parallel, that is, to the first division of the grain, and a second division sometimes follows; in this way a two-celled or three-celled body is produced resting on the intine and projecting into the cavity of the larger cell, as in the Abietineae, from which however *Ceratozamia* differs, because the large cell produced in it by the first division of the pollen-grain developes into the pollen-tube as in the Cupressineae, while the group of small cells, the rudimentary prothallium, remains inactive. In *Cycas Rumphii, Encephalartos,* and *Zamia,* according to De Bary, the pollen-grain divides in the same way into a large and a small cell, and the latter divides again, and here also it is the large cell which developes into the pollen-tube. The spot where the protuberant intine breaks through the exine is diametrically opposite to the small cellular body, the prothallium of the grain; at this spot the exine is thinner and

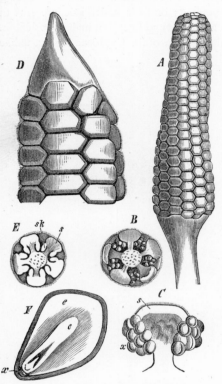

FIG. 247. *Zamia muricata.* *A* a male flower of the natural size. *B* transverse section of the same. *C* a stamen with the pollen-sacs *x x* and the peltate scale *s* to which they are attached seen from beneath. *D* the upper part of a female flower of the natural size. *E* transverse section of *D*; *s* the peltate scale which bears the ovules *sk*. *F* ripe seed in longitudinal section; *e* the prothallium (endosperm), *c* the cotyledons, at *x* the rolled up suspensor. After Karsten.

---

[1] Treub, Recherches sur les Cycadées (Annales du jardin Bot. de Buitenzorg, Vol. II, pp. 52, 53).

infolded deeply in the dry pollen-grain, which therefore looks kidney-shaped in a transverse section; but it resumes its spherical form with the absorption of water which precedes the development of the pollen-tube.

The carpellary leaves are closely crowded on the axis of the female flower in spirals or in apparent whorls. Those of *Cycas* have been already described; in *Zamia, Encephalartos, Macrozamia*, and *Ceratozamia* the carpels are much smaller and bear each of them only two macrosporangia or ovules, one right and one left, on the upper peltate portion which is supported on a slender basal part or stalk. The macro-sporangium (ovule) is always orthotropous and consists of a large nucellus and a thick and solid integument, the inner tissue of which is traversed by numerous vascular bundles. The micropyle is a slender tube formed by the drawing together and elongation of the margin of the integument. The group of cells which produces the spores is at the base of the nucellus; and we may presume from analogy that these cells proceeded from a *hypodermal archesporium* which was probably unicellular; but, as in *Selaginella*, only one cell of the sporogenous group is further developed. This cell soon becomes distinguished from the rest by its size and divides into three cells, the lowest of which usually becomes the macrospore or embryo-sac, and supplants the other two. The cell-wall of the macrospore thickens and splits into two layers, the outermost of which is cuticularised, just like the membrane of a macrospore which is to be released from the sporangium.

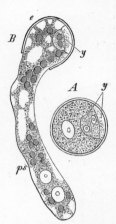

FIG. 248. *Ceratozamia longifolia. A* pollen-grain before germination with the three-celled body *y. B* pollen-grain germinating; *e* the exine, *ps* the pollen-tube formed from the intine, *y* the inclosed cellular body. After Juranyi.

The development of the macrosporangia is not so well known in the Cycadeae as in the Coniferae, though Treub[1] has recently published some important facts in the history of the macrosporangium of *Ceratozamia longifolia*. The rudiments of the sporogenous cells are visible as a group of cells sunk in the tissue of a lateral lobe of the carpellary leaf before any external differentiation of the macrosporangium has taken place, in other words, the macrosporangium in its early stages resembles that of plants like *Ophioglossum*. The nucellus is produced by the luxuriant growth of the cells which lie above the young sporogenous group, and which in a sporangium of *Ophioglossum* become simply the wall of the sporangium, and the integument grows up like a circular wall round the nucellus. If then we compare the history of the development of the macrosporangium of the Cycadeae with that of the sporangia of the Vascular Cryptogams, it appears that the nucellus is essentially only a luxuriant growth of the outer wall of the macrosporangium[2], while the integument is a new formation; the macrospores are not formed by division of a mother-cell into four daughter-cells as in heterosporous Vascular Cryptogams.

The macrospore as it grows exercises a destructive effect on the surrounding cells, like the macrospore of *Isoetes* for example, and becomes filled, as in *Isoetes*, with

---

[1] Rech. sur les Cycadées (Ann. d. jard. Bot. de Buitenzorg, II, 1881, p. 12 of the reprint.
[2] Göbel, Bot. Ztg. 1881.

the tissue of the *prothallium*, which then produces *archegonia* beneath the apex of the macrospore. The presence of a ventral canal-cell seems to be still doubtful [1]; the number of cells in the canal of the neck is limited to two, and these often form lobe-like outgrowths. A cavity is formed beneath the micropyle by absorption of a portion of the tissue of the macrosporangium known as the pollen-chamber (the 'chambre pollinique' of Brongniart), and in which the pollen or microspore lies after it has passed through the micropyle. The embryo in many of the Cycadeae as in many Coniferae is not formed till after the dispersion of the seed, and the mode of formation is in both cases imperfectly known; in each archegonium is produced a suspensor as in Selaginella. As in many heterosporous Vascular Cryptogams, such as *Salvinia* and *Pilularia*, the prothallium of the Cycadeae has the power of independent further development, if no fertilisation takes place; it bursts through the tissue that surrounds it and grows green in the light. Only one of the rudimentary embryos developes, but the suspensors of the others may still be recognised as coils of long threads in the ripe seeds. Pollination appears to be effected by the wind; the micropyle secretes a fluid in which the pollen-grains are caught, and are then drawn down into the cavity beneath the micropyle, from whence they no doubt send their tubes as far as the archegonia. There is no fixed number of cotyledons; *Ceratozamia* has only one, *Cycas* and *Zamia* two which lie with their inner faces flat on one another and cohere towards their apex; the tendency to branch which is shown by the later foliage-leaves appears sometimes in the larger cotyledons by the formation of a rudimentary lamina with indication of pinnae, as in *Zamia* (Fig. 249 *B'*). The seed germinates in damp ground but not till after the lapse of some time; the seed-coat bursts at the posterior extremity and releases the primary root which at first grows vigorously downwards, and afterwards sometimes enlarges like the root of the turnip, or developes a system of thick filamentous roots. According to Fig. 249 *C* taken from Schacht and the more recent statements of Reinke the branching of the primary root is monopodial, but Miquel speaks repeatedly of dichotomous divisions in the more slender roots of older plants of *Cycas*

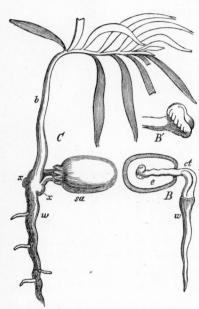

FIG. 249. *B, B', C* germination of *Zamia spiralis* reduced. *B* commencement of germination; *ct* the cotyledons which cohere at *e* above their elongated base, one of them with indication of a pinnate lamina *B'* at its apex, *w* the primary root. *C* germ-plant six months old; *sa* denotes the seed, *w* the primary root, *b* the first pinnate leaf, *x, x* the rudiments of the lateral roots which subsequently grow upwards.

---

[1] Treub, in Ann. d. jard. Bot. de Buitenzorg III, 1884, gives an account of the embryogeny in *Cycas circinalis*. There is no ventral canal-cell; an ovoid pro-embryonic mass of tissue enclosing a central cavity is formed from the oospore, and the pluricellular suspensor with the embryo at its extremity is developed from its lower end. The development of the embryo proceeds as in other Gymnosperms.]

glauca and *Encephalartos.* According to Reinke and Strasburger, only the secondary roots which come up to the surface of the ground branch dichotomously. By the elongation of the cotyledons which remain in the endosperm and absorb the food stored in it, their basal portions and the primary bud, the *plumule*, which lies between them are thrust out of the seed. Both the portion of the axis which bears the cotyledons and that which developes immediately above it continue very short, while a considerable increase in circumference is produced immediately below the apex by extensive development of parenchymatous tissue; thus the stem assumes the shape of a roundish tuber which it also maintains in many species.

B. CONIFERAE[1].

Germination. The endosperm surrounds the embryo in the form of a thick-walled sac open at the root-end; the embryo is straight in the central cavity of the endosperm; its axis is continuous behind with the rudiment of the primary root, and bears at its anterior extremity a whorl of two or more cotyledons, between which it terminates in a roundish apex (Fig. 250 *I*); the Taxineae, most of the Cupressineae and Araucarieae have two opposite cotyledons; but whorls of three or nine also occur in the Cupressineae, and whorls of four in the Araucarieae, while the Abietineae seldom have only two cotyledons, more commonly four, or even as many as fifteen.

When a seed lies in damp ground the endosperm swells and bursts the seed-coat at the root-end of the embryo, which is thrust forth by the elongation of the axis and developes a strong descending tap-root; lateral roots then grow rapidly in acropetal succession one after another from the primary root and afterwards branch, and in this way the foundation is laid for the usually strong and persistent system of roots in the Coniferae. When the root has issued from the seed the cotyledons also elongate and push out their basal portions and the extremity of the axis that lies between them, but remain themselves in the endosperm till this is exhausted; in *Araucaria* (sub-genus *Colymbea*) and in *Gingko* the hypocotyledonary portion of the axis continues short and the cotyledons remain in the seed, but in most of the Coniferae it ultimately becomes much elongated, turns sharply upwards, and breaking through the surface of the soil draws the cotyledons with it; as soon as these have reached the light, the hypocotyledonary portion of the axis straightens itself, the whorl of cotyledons expands, and its leaves which have already become green beneath the ground perform the part of the first foliage-leaves of the young plant, which has in the meantime formed a bud with fresh leaves at the apex of its axis (Fig. 250).

Growth and external differentiation. The terminal bud of the young stem grows more vigorously than any one of the lateral shoots of later formation, and thus produces the primary stem as the direct prolongation of the axis of the embryo; the stem

---

[1] On the formation of the flowers see Rob. Brown, Misc. Bot. Works (Ray Soc.), i. p. 567.— H. V. Mohl, Verm. Schr., p. 55.—Eichler, Ueber d. weiblichen Blüthen d. Coniferen (Monatsber. d. K. Ak. d. Wiss. Nov. 1881).—Hofmeister, Vergl. Untersuch. 1851.—Strasburger, Die Conif. u. d. Gnetac. Jena, 1872;—Id. Die Angiosp. u. d. Gymnosp. Jena, 1879.—[Goroschankin, Zur Kenntn. d. Corpuscula b. d. Gymnosp. (Bot. Ztg. 1885).] Strasburger's works quoted above contain also a very complete account of the literature of the subject.

is never terminated by a flower but grows on indefinitely at the apex, while it increases proportionately in thickness through the activity of a cambium-ring, and thus developes into a slender cone often reaching a height of from one to two hundred feet or more, and a diameter at the base of from two to twenty feet. The primary axis thus largely developed gives off lateral axes of the first order, often periodically in terminal rosettes (false whorls) or more irregularly distributed, and these branch in their turn in a similar manner; as a rule every parent-axis grows more vigorously than its lateral axes, and therefore as long as the primary axis continues to grow with its accustomed strength the collective form of the branch-system is that of a raceme with a conical or pyramidal outline. It is the branching, almost entirely suppressed in the Cycadeae, which gives the Coniferae their peculiar character and beauty, the more so because the leaves with few exceptions are small and inconspicuous, a sort of clothing for the branches in the general impression made by the plants. The branching is always axillary, but the Coniferae unlike the Angiosperms are far from forming buds in all the leaf-axils; in the Araucarieae and some species of *Taxus*, *Abies* and others it is only or chiefly the last leaves of a year's growth that form branches, which then develope vigorously; in *Juniperus communis* there are buds in the axils of most leaves, but few of them develope; in *Pinus sylvestris* and its allies shoots are formed only in the axils of the scale-leaves, which are borne throughout on the primary stem and the persistent woody branches, and these shoots continue very short (spurs) and produce each two, three or more foliage-leaves

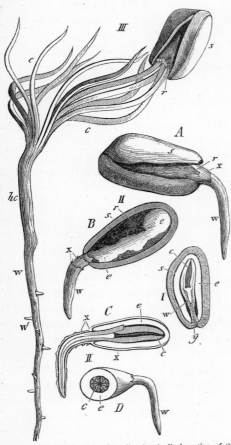

FIG. 250. *Pinus picea*. *I* median longitudinal section of the seed with the micropylar extremity at *y*. *II* commencement of germination and protrusion of the root. *III* conclusion of germination after absorption of the endosperm (the seed was not deep enough in the soil, and was therefore carried up by the cotyledons on the elongation of the stem). *A* shows the ruptured seed-coat *s*. *B* shows the endosperm *e* after removal of one half of the coat. *C* is a longitudinal section of the endosperm and embryo. *D* is a transverse section of the same at the commencement of germination. *c* denotes thecotyledons, *w* the primary root, *x* the embryo-sac forced outwards by the root (ruptured at *x* in *B*), *hc* hypocotyledonary portion of the axis, *w'* secondary root, *r* red membrane inside the hard seed-coat.

(tufts of needles), from the axils of which no lateral shoots arise; in *Larix*, *Cedrus*, and *Gingko* buds are formed in the axils of many but not nearly all the foliage-leaves, and some of them elongate rapidly and serve for the development of the main branch-system, while others (the spurs) remain short and form every year a new rosette of leaves without lateral buds; even in *Thuja* and *Cupressus*, which are marked by their copious branching, the number of the small leaves is much greater than that of the axillary shoots. Many of the Coniferae show great regularity in the position of the developing branches of the first and succeeding orders, and these at the same time increase the regularity of the whole by preserving their relative size. Branches of the first order are often formed on the erect and dominant primary stem in false whorls of several members, one at the close of each period of vegetation, and the same thing is often repeated on the branches themselves, as in *Pinus sylvestris* and *Araucaria brasiliensis*, and especially on *Phyllocladus trichomanoides* and many other species; but the horizontal branches of the first order more often show a tendency to bilateral branching, as in *Abies pectinata*, and sometimes smaller branches appear between these stronger ones which form the main frame-work of the tree, as in *Abies excelsa*. Sometimes the position and growth of the branches is more irregular; the farthest removed from the typical form of growth are the Cupressineae, especially *Cupressus*, *Thuja* and *Libocedrus*, in which the inclination to bilateral branching which appears in the primary stem is still more pronounced on the lateral shoots[1]; branch-systems of three or more orders of shoots are developed in one plane and in such a manner that each system has a definite general outline and looks more or less like a many times pinnate leaf; in *Taxodium* the foliage-leaves are in two rows on slender branches a few inches long, which in *Taxodium distichum* fall off in autumn with the leaves and are thus still more like pinnate leaves; lastly, *Phyllocladus* has only small colourless scale-leaves on all its verticillate shoots, but from their axils beneath the terminal buds whorls of shoots arise with limited growth, which develope bilateral shoots in the form of flat lobed foliage-leaves. These indications, though slight in themselves, may serve to draw attention to the nature of the branching in the Coniferae, which is moreover not difficult of observation.

The *leaves* of any one plant, putting aside the floral leaves, are either all foliage-leaves containing chlorophyll, as in *Araucaria, Juniperus, Thuja,* and others, or all colourless or brownish scale-leaves, as in *Phyllocladus*, where the foliage-leaves are replaced by leaf-like shoots (phylloclades); or lastly scale-leaves and foliage-leaves often occur together and on the same shoots, as in *Abies*, where the scales serve only to envelope the buds, or the two kinds are distributed on different axes, as in the true Pines, where the persistent woody shoots have only membranous scales with short sterile non-persistent leafy shoots in their axils. The seedlings in the Pines have simple acicular foliage-leaves even on the primary axis, but the normal arrangement of the leaves just mentioned is very early established. The foliage-leaves of the Coniferae are for the most part small, of more simple form and rarely divided; they are smallest and most numerous in the Cupressineae, where they thickly clothe the axes of the branches, as in *Thuja, Cupressus*, etc.; they are larger, more distinct from the axis, narrow and comparatively thick and usually prismatic and angular (acicular) in the majority of the Abietineae, in *Taxus* and *Juniperus*; intermediate forms between these needles and the expanded leaves of the Thujeae are to be found in *Araucaria excelsa* and some other

---

[1] The tendency to bilateral development appears also on the horizontal lateral shoots of many species of *Abies* and *Pinus*, in which the spirally-arranged leaves lean over to the right and left and so form two comb-like rows. In *Abies pectinata* this occurs chiefly on shaded branches (on specimens grown in the shade or otherwise), while on those which are more strongly illuminated the leaves are not placed at right angles to the direction in which the light falls on them, but are more or less radially directed.

species. The leaves of the Podocarpeae and of *Dammara* are broader and flat, and the broad flat stalked leaves of *Gingko* are even two-lobed with a deep indentation at the apex as if from dichotomous division.   It is not unfrequently the case, especially in the Cupressineae, that the foliage-leaves of the elongated primary axis are different in form from those of the same axis at a greater height and from those of the lateral shoots; the former, in *Thuja* for example, *Juniperus virginiana* or *Cupressus* and others, stand out clear from the branch and are acicular and of a fair size, the latter are very small and closely applied to the axis; these earlier leaves sometimes make their appearance on single branches of full-grown plants.   The axis of the shoot inside the bud is so densely clothed with the bases of the leaves, that no free portion of the axis can be seen between them; and when the bud unfolds and the axis elongates considerably, still the bases of the leaves usually grow to such an extent in length and breadth, that they spread over the surface of the elongated shoot and conceal it beneath a green covering, in the areolate markings on which it is easy to distinguish the parts which belong to the separate leaves; this is very distinctly the case in the Araucarieae, and in many species of *Pinus*, but is not uncommon in other genera; in *Thuja, Cupressus, Libocedrus*, and some others, the axis of the shoots is in like manner entirely concealed by these leaf-cushions, while the free portions of the leaf are very small and are often only short projecting points or prominences. The phyllotaxis in the Abietineae, Taxineae, Araucarieae, Podocarpeae, and other groups is spiral; the Cupressineae form whorls which have usually from three to five members immediately above the cotyledons, but a smaller number at a greater height on the primary axis, while the lateral axes generally begin at once with decussate pairs of leaves, which in the bilateral shoots of *Callitris* and *Libocedrus* are alternately larger and smaller; in *Juniperus* and *Frenela* the whorls of the lateral axes as well have from three to five members and are alternate; the pairs of leaves in *Dammara* intersect each other at an acute angle.   The foliage-leaves of most Coniferae are very persistent and may be many years old, their bases increasing in size for a long time with the increase in the circumference of the axis ; the leaves are deciduous in *Larix* and *Gingko*, in *Taxodium distichum* the axes that bear the leaves fall with them in the autumn.

The *flowers* of the Coniferae are always unisexual, and the plants are either monoecious, as in the Abietineae and *Thuja*, or dioecious, as in *Taxus*, the Araucarieae and *Juniperus communis*; the male flowers are usually much more numerous than the female.   The flowers are never terminal on the primary stem, and differ in this respect from those of the Cycadeae ; even the larger woody branches seldom have terminal flowers, as in *Abies excelsa* where they are female ; the flowers are usually either terminal on small leafy shoots of the last order, or spring from the axils of the leaves of stronger shoots.   In *Thuja*, for example, male and female flowers appear on the end of small short leafy members of bilateral shoot-systems, in *Taxus* and *Juniperus* in the axils of foliage-leaves of larger shoots ; in *Abies pectinata* both are formed on the under side of shoots of a higher order at the summit of older trees and in the axils of foliage-leaves, the female singly, the male in numbers ; the male flowers of *Pinus sylvestris* and allied species are found in the place of the small leafy shoots (spurs) in the axils of the scale-leaves of growing woody shoots, usually many in number and forming an inflorescence through which the mother-shoot has grown; the female flowers are in the place of one of the buds, one to four in number, which stand in a false whorl at the summit of the shoot, and develope into lateral branches. In *Gingko* the flowers are exclusively on the short lateral shoots which annually produce new rosettes of leaves, in the axils of the foliage-leaves or of the inner scales of the buds (Fig. 251 *A, B*).

The part of the floral axis beneath the sporangia or the sporophylls is densely covered with scale-leaves or foliage-leaves in the female plant of *Taxus, Juniperus, Pinus,* and others (Figs. 252, 253), but it is developed as a naked stalk in the Abietineae, *Gingko* (Fig. 251 *A, B*), the male plant of *Taxus, Podocarpus,* etc. The flowers of the Cycadeae and Coniferae are peculiar in the circumstance that the axis

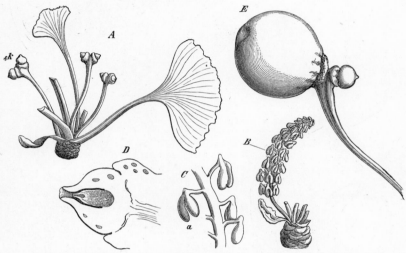

FIG. 251. *Gingko biloba,* natural size. *A* a short lateral leafy shoot with female flowers; *sk* macrosporangia. *B* a male flower. *C* a portion of a male flower magnified; *a* the pollen-sacs. *D* longitudinal section of an ovule of *A* enlarged. *E* a ripe seed by the side of an abortive seed on the flowering axis.

elongates, even when covered with sporophylls; if there are many of them, the whole flower is long and conical and resembles a catkin in outward appearance, and is in fact termed a catkin in the superficial language of many systematic botanists, though the amentum of Dicotyledons is an inflorescence while the apparent catkin of the Coniferae is a single flower. In the Angiosperms the flowering shoot usually undergoes a peculiar transformation throughout, the portion of the axis which bears the parts of the flower, the torus, remaining very short and becoming broader, and the floral envelope-leaves and the sporophylls appearing in positions very different from those of the vegetative shoots. But the difference between the flower and a vegetative shoot is much less in the Coniferae, as is seen chiefly in the relative positions of the leaves; if the leaves of the vegetative shoots are arranged spirally, those of the flower are usually arranged in the same way, as for instance in the Abietineae; if on the other hand they are in alternating whorls, as in the Cupressineae, the sporophylls are also in alternating whorls; occasionally however there are greater differences in the arrangement of the leaves in the flower as compared with that in the vegetative shoots; this is the case in *Taxus.*

The *male flowers* consist of an evidently elongated axis furnished with staminal
leaves or sporophylls and terminating above in a naked apex (Fig. 253 *A*), exactly
similar, for example, to a single sporangiferous spike of *Selaginella* or *Lycopodium*.
The staminal leaves are usually more delicate than the foliage-leaves and of a different
colour, and are generally differentiated into a slender stalk and a peltate lamina
which bears the microsporangia or pollen-sacs on its under side, as for instance in
Taxus, the Cupressineae, and Abietineae (Figs. 252 *A*, *B*, 253 *A*, *B*, 254 *A*); but

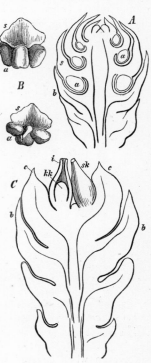

FIG. 252. *Taxus baccata. A* male flower
magnified; at *a* the pollen-sacs. *B* a stamen from
below with the pollen-sacs opened. *C* a piece of a
leafy shoot with a foliage leaf *b*, and the female
flower springing from its axil; *s* its envelope of
scales, *sk* the ovule. *D* longitudinal section of the
same magnified; *i* the integument, *kk* nucellus, at
x the aborted extremity of the shoot. *E* longitudinal section through an ovule in a more advanced state of development before fertilisation;
i integument, *kk* nucellus, *e* endosperm, *m* arillus,
s s leaves of the envelope.

FIG. 253. *Juniperus communis. A* longitudinal section of the male flower. *B* a stamen
seen from the front and the outside (the upper
figure), and one seen from behind and within
(the lower figure). *C* longitudinal section of the
female flower. *a* denotes the pollen-sacs, *s* the
peltate lamina of the staminal leaf, *b* lower leaves
of the flowering axis, *c* carpels, *sk* ovules, *kk* the
nucellus, *i* the integument. *A* and *C* magn.
about 12 times.

there may be no flat expansion at the end of the stalk, as in *Gingko* (Fig. 251 *C*),
where it is reduced to a small knob from which the pollen-sacs are suspended. That
the structures that bear the pollen-sacs in the Coniferae are undoubtedly metamorphosed leaves is shown by their form, and still more clearly by their position which
has been described above and by the history of their development. The pollen-sacs
are usually attached by a narrow base to the under side of the support and do not
unite together as they grow; their number is always much smaller than in the
Cycadeae and much more variable than in the Angiosperms; the peltate portion of

the staminal leaf in *Taxus baccata* bears from three to eight (Fig. 252), in *Juniperus communis* and most of the Cupressineae three roundish pollen-sacs (Fig. 253); those of *Abies, Pinus,* and their allies lie in pairs parallel to or obliquely beside one another beneath the peltate scale right and left along its stalk, which resembles the connective of the Angiosperms; in *Araucaria* and *Dammara* on the other hand the long cylindrical pollen-sacs hang down free in larger numbers.

The pollen-sacs or microsporangia have special contrivances of different kinds for their protection while they are still young. In *Pinus, Abies,* and other genera they are more or less sunk like the sporangia of *Ophioglossum* in the tissue of the sporophyll or staminal leaf; in *Gingko* they have a thick wall of several layers of cells; in *Cupressus, Thuja,* and many species of *Juniperus* they are covered by a special growth of the tissue on the under side of the staminal leaf, which then appears like a continuation of the expanded portion of the stamen[1]. This formation is no doubt analogous to the indusium of the sori of the Ferns, and may therefore be called an indusium. A similar formation, *mutatis mutandis,* is also found in the leaves, in the axils of which the macrosporangia are placed.

The development of the microsporangia (pollen-sacs) agrees entirely, as far as it is known, with that of the sporangia of *Lycopodium,* that is, the sporogenous tissue is the product of an archesporium and is surrounded by tapetal cells. The microspores (pollen-grains) are formed by division of the mother-cells into four daughter-cells.

The usually delicate wall of the pollen-sacs at length bursts longitudinally and releases the pollen-grains or microspores, which are produced in extraordinarily large quantities, since they are dependent for the most part on the wind for conveyance to the female organs of the same or of some other tree. The pollen-grains which happen to fall on the orifice of the micropyle of the ovules are retained there by a drop of liquid which issues from the micropyle; this liquid fills the canal of the micropyle at this time, but it afterwards dries up and so draws the captive pollen-grains down to the nucellus, where they at once send in their tubes into its loose tissue. This arrangement is sufficient in the Taxineae, Cupressineae and Podocarpeae, where the micropyles project free to the outer air; but in the Abietineae, where they are more concealed among the seminiferous and bract-scales, these structures themselves form suitable canals and grooves at the time of pollination, by means of which the pollen-grains are conducted to the micropyles[2]. The large number and lightness of the pollen-grains is favourable to their transportation by the wind over considerable distances; in the true Pines and the Podocarpeae their buoyancy is still further aided by the distension of the exine into hollow vesicles, represented in Fig. 255 *IV, V.*

The formation of a rudimentary prothallium inside the pollen-grain takes place in the Coniferae as in the Cycadeae (Fig. 248), and before pollination. The process is very simple in *Taxus, Podocarpus,* the Cupressineae, *Araucaria,* and the true Pines, where the contents of the grain divide by a transverse wall into a large and a small cell, the latter of which undergoes no further change (Fig. 255); in the rest of the Abietineae the dividing wall bulges out into the space enclosed by the intine (Fig. 255 *I, II, III*); in this apparently unimportant fact we have another instance

---

[1] See Beitr. z. Vergl. Entwicklungsgeschichte d. Sporangien, II (Bot. Ztg. 1881).
[2] See Strasburger, *loc. cit.* on page 319.

of resemblance to other microspores and especially to those of the Marsiliaceae, in which the swelling endosporium protrudes in the same way out of the exosporium.

The *structure of the female flowers* varies much in the different divisions of the Coniferae; the position of the ovules (macrosporangia) is especially variable, and resembles in this respect the position of the sporangia in Vascular Cryptogams. In *Taxus* the macrosporangia terminate a small leafy axis; in *Gingko* they are placed more than one together on a peculiar branch; in the Cupressineae on a projection in the axil of a scale-leaf; in most other species immediately upon a leaf, or on a

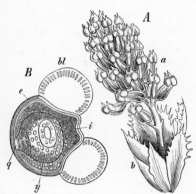

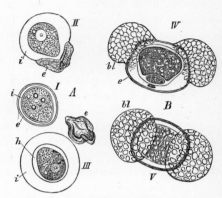

FIG. 254. *Abies pectinata*. *A* a male flower; *b* delicate bud-scales forming a sort of perianth, *a* the stamens. *B* a pollen-grain; *e* its exine which forms the two large bladdery swellings *bl*. *B* after Schacht.

FIG. 255. *A* pollen of *Thuja orientalis* before pollination; *I* fresh, *II, III* after lying in water, in which case the exine *e* is stripped off by the swelling of the intine *i*; *h* space left beneath the intine. *B* pollen of *Pinus Pinaster* before the bursting of the pollen-sac; *e* the exine with its bladder-like swellings *bl*, magn. 550 times.

placenta formed on a leaf and often of very peculiar construction. In *Taxus*, for example, each macrosporangium is a female flower; in other genera, as *Pinus*, the female flowers have the well-known cone-form, and consist of a number of scale-leaves which bear one or more macrosporangia on their upper or dorsal surface.

The simplest forms of female flowers are to be found in the Araucarieae, and these are closely allied to the male 'catkins' above described and to analogous structures in most of the Vascular Cryptogams. But while the microsporangia (pollen-sacs) are on the under side of the sporophyll (staminal leaf), the macrosporangia are inserted on the upper side of the leaf that bears them. The genus *Dammara* presents the simplest case (Fig. 256, 1, 2). The scales of the cone bear on their upper side a macrosporangium with an integument (Fig. 256, 2 *Jnt*), which shows one or two wing-like expansions (Fig. 256, 1, 2 *fl*). The micropyle is turned towards the axis of the cone (Fig. 256 *Mi*). The macrosporangium is formed originally, according to Dickson[1], close to the base of the scale and carried further upwards by the intercalary growth of the basal portion. The arrangement is quite similar in the genus *Araucaria*, only there the part of the integument which is turned towards the scale is not free, and therefore the macrosporangium is only covered by an integument on its outer side (Fig. 256, 3). In this case there is an outgrowth from the scale of the cone above the macrosporangium (Fig. 256 *i*), which in

---

[1] Transactions of the Botan. Soc. of Edinburgh, 1861.

Cunninghamia has the form of a narrow membrane with toothed margin rising above the three macrosporangia (Fig. 256, 4 *i*).   This 'ligular' outgrowth certainly has to do with the protection of the microsporangia, and may therefore be compared to the indusium-like formation covering the microsporangia in the staminal leaves of the Cupressineae.   In *Sciadopitys* there are seven or eight macrosporangia on each scale which has a thick broad cushion instead of the membranous border of *Cunninghamia*.

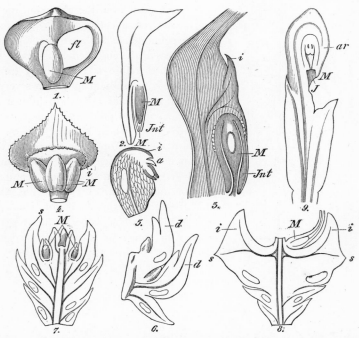

FIG. 256. Female flowers of Coniferae. 1. *Dammara australis*, a leaf-bearing macrosporangia from the inside; *M* the macrosporangium (ovule) with winged integument *fl*, slightly magnified. 2. Longitudinal section of 1; *Jnt* the integument, *M* macrosporangium, the micropyle *M* (should have been *Mi*) is directed downwards. 3. Longitudinal section through a cone-scale of *Araucaria excelsa*; *i* outgrowth of the scale above the macrosporangium; vascular bundles enter the outgrowth. 4. *Cunninghamia sinensis*, a cone-scale with three macrosporangia *M* from the inside; *i* membranous outgrowth of the scale above the ovules. 5. Longitudinal section through a cone-scale of *Microcrachys tetragona*; *a* the aril, the ovule is inserted near the tip of the scale, *i* outgrowth of the scale above the ovule. 6. *Cryptomeria japonica*, portion of a longitudinal section through a young cone ; the ovules are in the axil of the scales *d*, which form an outgrowth above them.   7 and 8. *Cupressus Lawsoniana*.   7. Longitudinal section through a young cone, two (axillary) ovules included.   8. Part of a longitudinal section through a half-ripe fruit ; the point *s* of the scale is forced outwards by the outgrowth *i* formed on the inner surface (upper side) of the scale. 9. *Podocarpus macrophylla*, female flower in longitudinal section, ovule anatropous ; *ar* the aril ; 1, 2, 4—8 after Eichler, 3 after Strasburger.

The Taxodineae closely resemble the Araucarieae in the mode of formation of their female flowers ; but the outgrowth on the upper side of the scale which bears the macrosporangia is much larger than in the Araucarieae, and develops into a special scale known as the *seminiferous scale* (*squama fructifera*) or fruit scale, which by the time the cones are ripe may rise considerably above the cone-scale from which it springs, and which is termed the *bract-scale*.   Fig. 256, 6, gives a longitudinal section through a young cone of *Cryptomeria japonica*, in which the dorsal outgrowth from the scales of the cone, that is, the rudimentary seminiferous scale, is still small, while in the ripe cone the toothed seminiferous scale is more than twice the height of the bract-scale.

In the Abietineae the well-known cones (Fir-cones, Pine-cones) are the female flowers or fruits.   The cone is a metamorphosed shoot with a large number of crowded woody scales arranged spirally on its axis, and the ovules are formed on the scales rarely singly, generally two and sometimes several together on each scale.   In the Abietineae in the narrower sense (*Abies, Picea, Larix, Cedrus, Pinus*) the semi-niferous scales (squamae fructiferae) (Fig. 257 *A, B, s*) are apparently axillary structures

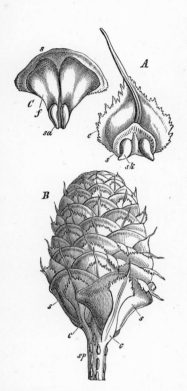

in the axils of small leaves (*c*), the scales of the cone which grow from the axis ; but the observation of very young cones of *Abies pectinata* shows that the seminiferous scale arises as a protuberance on the base of the so-called bract-scale (the cone-scale) and therefore is not axillary (see below). While the latter subsequently grows very little or not at all larger, this outgrowth from it increases greatly in size and produces on its upper surface the two ovules, which adhere to it by one side and turn their micropyles to the axis of the cone ; the seminiferous scale of these genera must therefore be regarded as a *placenta* of large dimensions growing out of a carpellary leaf (Fig. 257 *c*), the latter being naturally small or stunted in its growth.   The whole cone is therefore a single flower with numerous small open carpels, usually termed bract-scales, which are far outstripped in growth by their seed-bearing placentas, the semi-niferous scales.

The development of the seminiferous scales which are flat in *Abies* and *Larix* when the seeds are ripe, and thickened at the apex in *Pinus*, has been closely followed in *Pinus Pumilio* (the dwarf Pine) by Strasburger, who regards them as reduced shoots.   The cones which are intended to flower in the next spring begin to form in the autumn of the preceding year, and take the place of one of the buds which are disposed in false whorls on the summit of the shoots, and from which long shoots are subsequently developed.   A considerable number of large scale-leaves are formed at the

FIG. 257. *Abies pectinata*. *A* a leaf detached from the female flowering axis and seen from above, *s* the seminiferous scale with the ovules *sk* ; magnified. *B* upper part of the female flower (the cone) in the mature state ; *sp* axis of the cone (floral axis), *c* its leaves (bract-scales), *s* the seminiferous scales highly magnified. *C* a seminiferous scale *s* with the two seeds *sa* and their wings *f*, reduced.

base of the shoot, and may still be seen on ripe cones.   The seminiferous scales appear in the axils of the bract-scales, and therefore some of the tissue of the vegetative apex of the axis of the cone contributes to their formation, though they are always in connection with the bract-scales [1]; they take the form of a flattened transverse

---

[1] The seminiferous scales cannot in this case be regarded as outgrowths of the bract-scales, which is Eichler's view.   But it is not clear why such a placental growth should not arise even in the axil of the carpel (the bract-scale), without being necessarily therefore a metamorphosed shoot.

cushion in the middle of which a protuberance is soon apparent which subsequently developes into a stalk; this stalk may be seen in Fig. 257 *A*, on the anterior side of the seminiferous scale between the macrosporangia. The lobes of the young scale swell up on both sides of this elevation, and on them the macrosporangia are formed. These appear as flat protuberances, and are each surrounded at once by a distinct two-lipped wall, the rudiment of the integument. The seminiferous scale now grows chiefly on its upper and outer margin, so that the keel comes to be on the inner face of the scale (Fig. 257); but some growth also takes place in the region of insertion of the macrosporangia, so that these as they develope are completely girt round with the tissue of the scale and partly adhere to it (Fig. 257 *sk*). Thus the micropyles of the macrosporangia or ovules are turned towards the axis of the cone. The seminiferous scale in this species has a special system of vascular bundles distinct from that of the bract-scale, while the smaller outgrowths on the bract-scale of *Araucaria* for example only receive a branch from the bundle which enters the scale; we shall recur to this point further on.

In the Cupressineae the macrosporangia are on a slight swelling in the axils of scales, which are arranged in whorls containing two or more members and are united together in comparatively small numbers to form a diminutive cone. There is no seminiferous scale here as in the Abietineae; the scales of the cone at flowering time differ but little from vegetative leaves, but after fertilisation they grow vigorously and reach a considerable size. They cohere and envelope the seeds, and thus form a fleshy or dry fruit which is developed differently in the different genera. In *Biota orientalis* the cone is formed of three decussating pairs of scales, of which the two lower pairs only are fertile, the upper ones having no macrosporangia in their axils. The cones occupy the extremities of short lateral branches of the same year, and the scales bearing macrosporangia are fully developed when the first rudiments of the sporangia make their appearance. The macrosporangia are formed on a slight axillary protuberance, singly on the lower scales, on the upper in pairs. In the succeeding spring the scales and the axillary protuberance begin to enlarge immediately above the insertion of the macrosporangia, and a dark-coloured wall is formed at the base of the scale which swells up so considerably, that the apex of the scale when the cone is matured appears to be inserted beneath this enlargement, which is more or less distinctly separated from the scale (Fig. 256, 7, 8). The small cones of *Juniperus communis* (Fig. 253 *C*) consist of three scales, which form a whorl of three members beneath the naked extremity of a small shoot springing from the axil of a foliage-leaf. In the axil of each scale is a macrosporangium, not in front of the centre of the scale but on one side of it, so that the three macrosporangia (ovules) appear to alternate with the scales. The scales swell after fertilisation, cohere as they grow and become fleshy, and form the soft substance of the blue berry in which the ripe seeds are completely enclosed. In *Juniperus Sabina* also the fruit is like a berry; in other Cupressineae (*Thuja, Cupressus, Callitris*) the scales together with the enlargement subsequently formed become woody, and develope into stalked shields or into valves, as in *Frenela*, the lateral margins of which approach one another and remain closely joined during the development of the seed, but afterwards separate to allow the ripe seeds to fall out. In *Juniperus Sabina* and *Callitris quadrivalvis* (Fig. 258) there are only two decussating pairs of scales which separate in a stellate manner at the time of flowering; in the former species the ovules or macrosporangia are placed in pairs in the axils of the lower scales to the right and left of the median line, and are seldom abortive. *Callitris* has more than two, usually three ovules in the axils of the outer scales (Fig. 258), the upper pair being either sterile or having only a few ovules. In *Cupressus* the number of ovules at the base of the scales is still larger. The fruits of *Arceuthos drupacea* and *Frenela*

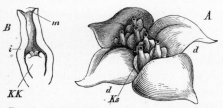

FIG. 258. *Callitris quadrivalvis. A* the female flower, magnified; *d d* two pairs of decussate leaves (the carpels) with six ovules *Ks* in their axils. *B* an ovule in vertical longitudinal section through its broader diameter; *KK* the nucellus still without an embryo-sac, *i* the integument prolonged into a tube with the micropyle *m*.

verrucosa in the collection at Würzburg consist of alternating whorls of scales each containing three members, which open in the latter species after the seeds are ripe, like a six-valved capsule; in this case the inner side of each scale is swollen up into a thick placenta ascending from the base to the apex, and bearing numerous winged seeds disposed three side by side in a transverse row; there are from four to six rows in each carpel, the entire inner surface bearing seeds nearly to the apex.

In the last group also, the Taxineae, the macrosporangia (ovules) are formed both on leaves and in the axils of leaves. The first kind occurs in a very remarkable form in the Tasmanian genus *Microcachrys*. The scales of the cone bear their solitary macrosporangium so near the upper end of the inner surface (Fig. 256, 5), that it projects between the summits of the scales; in *Dacrydium* it is placed on or even below the middle of the scale, and in this genus no cone is formed, the scales simply standing singly or two together at the extremity of a branch. In both genera the macrosporangium is surrounded when the seeds are ripe by the integument and by an outer envelope, which is still quite short in the flowering time but after fertilisation grows into a cup-shaped fleshy brightly coloured structure, the *aril*, a formation which is generally characteristic of the Taxineae, but is absent in *Cephalotaxus* and *Gingko*. In the peculiar genus *Podocarpus* the aril is present as early as the flowering time in the form of a second outer integument, which makes its appearance after the proper inner integument. In *Podocarpus dacryoides* the ovule is inverted (anatropous), and grows on the inner surface of a scale (Fig. 256, 9) immediately beneath the apex, adhering to it along its whole length. In other species of *Podocarpus* the position is somewhat different; the macrosporangium has the form of the anatropous ovule in the Angiosperms, and does not adhere to the scale. The small flowering shoots proceed in *P. chinensis* from the axils of foliage-leaves, in *P. chilina* from the axils of minute scale-leaves at the end of elongated leafy shoots, and consist of an axis which is slender and stalk-like below and enlarged and angular above, and bears three pairs of very small decussate scales. Usually only one scale of the second pair is fertile, and bears the anatropous macrosporangium on its inner surface with the micropyle directed downwards towards the apex of the contracted flowering shoot. The leaves of the shoot in many species unite together to form a fleshy body, the so-called 'receptacle.' In *Phyllocladus* the lower lateral members of the shoot-system with its bilateral and leaf-like branches are changed into female flowers, which are raised on a stalk and are swollen and club-shaped above. They bear small alternating boat-shaped scales, of which only the two, three or four lower ones are fertile, and bear one macrosporangium in their axil. In *Gingko* the female flowers spring from the axils of scale-leaves or foliage-leaves on short lateral shoots, which produce new rosettes of leaves each year (Fig. 251 *A*). The single flower consists of an elongated stalk-like axis which bears two lateral macrosporangia immediately beneath its apex, and sometimes a second pair above the first and alternating with it, though one of the two is as a rule abortive. *Cephalotaxus* has inflorescences with from four to eight decussate pairs of fertile bracts above an elongated basal internode ; in the axil of each bract is a naked shoot which bears a macrosporangium right and left; in this case therefore the flowers are disposed in spike-like inflorescences. The ovules (macrosporangia) of *Taxus* are placed singly on diminutive shoots (primary flowering shoots, Fig. 252 *D*) which spring from the axils of the foliage-leaves of elongated woody shoots, and are furnished with two bracteoles and a number of small imbricated scales. One of the upper scales has an axillary bud, which pushes the growing point of the primary flowering shoot to one side and looks like the continuation of its axis. This secondary shoot bears three decussate pairs of scales and is crowned by the terminal macrosporangium. Sometimes the scale next below on the primary flowering shoot is also fertile, that is, bears a macrosporangium in its axil; this indeed is generally the case in *Torreya nucifera*, which is closely allied to *Taxus*. If we adhere to the terminology hitherto employed, we shall call each macrosporangium in *Taxus* and *Torreya* a flower; but the Taxineae as a rule do not have their flowers in the cone-form which is so characteristic of most of the Coniferae, and the seeds are invested with an aril except in the cases already mentioned.

It has been stated that the *macrosporangia* (*ovules*) of the Coniferae have always one integument and are originally erect and orthotropous ; they retain this position in the Cupressineae, but undergo subsequent changes in this respect in *Podocarpus*, the Abietineae and other divisions. They consist when fully developed of the central portion of the sporangium (Fig. 259 *Nu*), a mass of tissue beneath or in which are the sporogenous cells and which here and in the Angiosperms we name after Strasburger the *nucellus*, and of the *integument*[1], which usually projects some distance above the nucellus and forms a comparatively broad and long micropylar canal ; through this canal the pollen-grains (microspores) find their way to the apex of the nucellus which is sometimes depressed[2]. Lateral outgrowths of the integument often cause the macrosporangium and subsequently the seed to appear winged, as in *Dammara* (Fig. 256 *I*), *Callitris quadrivalvis* (Fig. 258), *Frenela*, and other genera. But the wing-like appendages of the seed of *Pinus* and *Abies* are thin plates of tissue which have separated from the seminiferous scale and adhere to the ripe seed.

The structure of the female flowers of the Coniferae has been the subject of much discussion up to the most recent times. According to one view, which rests chiefly on the history of development, the integument is an ovary, for it appears in many cases in the form of two separate prominences, and this does not agree with the nature of an integument, but seems rather to point to an ovary composed of two carpellary leaves ; each macrosporangium would then be a single female flower. On the other

---

[1] For the aril of the Taxineae, see above under that division.
[2] Compare the 'pollen-chambers' of the Cycadeae.

side there is the close affinity with the Cycadeae in which the envelope is undoubtedly a true integument, and the absence of the stigma which is so characteristic a feature in the ovary of the Angiosperms. This view which would prove the Gymnosperms to have no title to their name, has been lately abandoned by Strasburger who was once its chief supporter. Opinions also are still divided with respect to the relation between the seminiferous scale and the bract-scale; but it may be claimed for the view given above and proposed before by Sachs, that it adapts itself to the facts without violence and without the aid of hypotheses. Strasburger, resting on the history of development and the anatomy of the parts, looks upon the seminiferous scale of the Abietineae as an axial structure, a compressed branch bearing two ovules. But anatomical characters cannot be used to decide morphological questions in this or in any case, for their value is only secondary, and the facts of development are equally compatible with the view represented above. Then in the Cupressineae and Araucarieae Strasburger assumes a more or less complete coherence of the seminiferous scale, which he thinks is present here, with the bract. Now in the Cupressineae we simply see a luxuriant growth make its appearance after fertilisation on the upper side of the scale, in the axils of which the macrosporangia are placed, a growth which we are able to compare directly with that which, as I have shown, covers the microsporangia on the under side of the staminal leaves. That this extensive growth should contain a system of vascular bundles was to be expected, because their presence is in accordance with the universal rule, and they afford therefore no ground for calling the growth itself a seminiferous scale. Lastly, in the Araucarieae this would be a very forced explanation of the phenomena, while the view that the leaf which bears the macrosporangia is a single one gives here as everywhere a clear reflection of the facts [1].

The mode in which the *macrospore* or *embryo-sac* is formed from the archesporium in the Coniferae has recently been made known to us by the researches of Strasburger. The *archesporium* in the Abietineae is a hypodermal cell, which is covered above by *primary tapetal cells*, as in *Isoetes* [2]. Later the archesporium is seen to be sunk in the tissue of the macrosporangium, because the layers of cells of the sporangium above the archesporium undergo rapid growth combined with copious cell-division. In *Larix* then (Fig. 260 *I*) the archesporium divides into a lower and an upper cell, and the latter again divides into two cells. The lower cell which does not divide again becomes the *macrospore* at once without the previous division into four which occurs in the rest of the Archegoniatae. It now displaces the two upper cells which become disorganised, and at the same time exercises the dissolving and destructive effect on the adjacent cells of the macrosporangium, which we saw, for example, in the case of the macrospore of *Isoetes*. The young macrospore at this stage of its existence, which is reached at different times in different genera, lies therefore free in the loosened cells of the tissue of the macrosporangium. In other cases, as in *Cupressus sempervirens* and *Callitris quadrivalvis* (Fig. 259), the arche-

---

[1] [Dickson, in Trans. Bot. Soc. Edin. xvi, 1885, gives a useful résumé of the views which have been advanced respecting the morphology of the parts of the cone, adhering to Baillon's hypothesis that the seminiferous scale is a cladode and the integument an ovary.

[2] See page 294; and with regard to the 'primary tapetal cell,' see the note under development of pollen-sacs in Angiosperms on page 363.]

sporium undergoes further divisions and a group of cells is developed from it, as in the Cycadeae, a *sporogenous tissue* therefore, the cells of which however, with the exception of one which produces the macrospore or embryo-sac, are sterile and are displaced by the growing macrospore. Here too the *prothallium* or *endosperm* is formed entirely within the macrospore. The nucleus of the latter divides, and by frequent repetition of the process a number of free nuclei are produced round which cells are formed, and these soon unite laterally and grow in a radial direction, and divide in such a manner that the macrospore becomes filled with the parenchymatous tissue of the prothallium.

The *archegonia*, formerly termed corpuscula[1], are formed at the apex of the macrospore from single superficial cells of the prothallium, in exactly the same manner as in other higher Archegoniatae. The mother-cells swell and are densely filled with protoplasm, and divide by a transverse wall parallel to the surface of the macrospore (Fig. 260 *II*). In this way a large inner cell is formed, the *central cell* of the

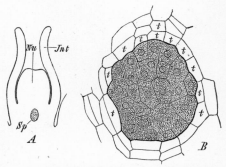

FIG. 259. *Callitris quadrivalvis.* Longitudinal section through the ovule, *A* slightly, *B* highly magnified. *Jnt* integument, *Nu* nucellus, *Sp* the sporogenous cell-group, the cells of which however are all sterile with the exception of one which becomes the macrospore (embryo-sac). *B* shows the portion of Fig. *A* marked *Sp* more highly magnified; *t* tapetal cells.

archegonium, and an upper smaller cell (Fig. 260 *II h*) lying against the wall of the macrospore, from which the *neck* of the archegonium proceeds. The neck remains simple and one-celled in *Abies canadensis* and elongates to an extent corresponding with the increase in size of the prothallium; but in most cases the original neck-cell divides into several cells which either lie in one plane or form several tiers one above another, as in *Picea excelsa* and *Pinus Pinaster*. The neck-cells seen from above appear as rosettes of four or, as in *Picea excelsa*, of eight cells. A *ventral canal-cell* is also formed by the separation of a small portion of the contents of the large central cell beneath the neck from the remaining part, the *oosphere*, after preliminary division of the nucleus. This happens in the Abietineae shortly before fertilisation, in *Juniperus virginiana* and others after the appearance of the pollen-tube; in these species the canal-cell is very soon disorganised and may be easily overlooked. The cells of the tissue of the prothallium which surround the central cell of the archegonium in the Coniferae develope by further divisions into a parietal layer round the central cell, as in the Cycadeae and other Archegoniatae. In the Abietineae each archegonium is separated from its next neighbour by at least one and often by many layers of cells; those of the Cupressineae on the contrary are in contact with one another laterally (Fig. 262). The archegonia of *Taxus* (Fig. 261) are very short; in those of the Abietineae the central cell is elongated, but in the Cupressineae it is rendered angular by the pressure of the adjoining cells. The number of archegonia formed at the apex of the prothallium varies greatly; in the Abietineae, according to Hofmeister and Strasburger, there are from three to five, in the Cupressineae from

---

[1] [See note on page 300.]

five to fifteen or even, according to Schacht, to thirty, in *Taxus baccata* from five to eight.   Continued growth of the adjacent parts of the prothallium gives rise to funnel-shaped indentations in its substance above the archegonia, which in many of the Abietineae are shallow, but in *Pinus Pinaster, P. Strobus*, and other species are deep and narrow ; in these species each funnel leads down to the neck of an archegonium ;

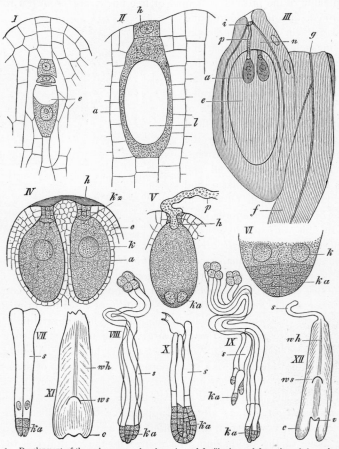

FIG. 260. Development of the embryo-sac and archegonia, and fertilisation and formation of the embryo in the Abietineae. *I* apex of the nucellus of *Larix Europaea* showing the rudiment of the embryo-sac ; above the sac are two of its sister-cells which are formed with it from a mother-cell, the archesporium ; magn. 430 times. *II* the young archegonium of *Abies canadensis* soon after the formation of the neck-cell, magn. 150 times. *III* longitudinal section of a young ovule of *Abies canadensis* and a part of the seminiferous scale to which it is attached, magn. 12 times. *IV—VI Picea vulgaris. IV* apex of the embryo-sac with two mature archegonia, magn. 40 times. *V* an archegonium shortly after fertilisation with four nuclei at the posterior extremity of the oospore, of which two only are visible, magn. 50 times. *VI* the posterior extremity of the oospore with three tiers of four cells each, and four free nuclei *k* above it, magn. 80 times. *VII—XII* formation of the embryo in *Pinus Pumilio, VII, VIII*, and *X* magn. 50 times, *IX* 30 times, *XI* 25 times, *XII* 12 times. *e* denotes the embryo-sac (macrospore), *a* the central cell of the archegonium, *h* the neck of the archegonium, *l* the cavity of the central cell, *i* the integument, *p* the pollen-tube, *n* the nucellus, *f* the seminiferous scale, *g* vascular bundle, *kz* the canal-cell, *ka* the rudiment of the embryo, *k* in *IV* and *VI* the nucleus of the oosphere, *ws* the apex of the root, *wh* the root-cap, *c* the cotyledons, *v* the growing-point of the stem, *s* the suspensor. From drawings by Prof. Strasburger.

in the Cupressineae (*Callitris, Thuja, Juniperus*), where the archegonia are crowded together, the prothallium grows up round the whole group, and thus one funnel is formed which is common to them all, and continues to be covered over by the wall of the macrospore.

Fertilisation. The pollination of the macrosporangium takes place before the archegonia begin to be formed in the prothallium. The pollen-grains (microspores) which have reached the apex of the nucellus thrust their tubes at first only a little way into the tissue of the nucellus and then remain inactive for a time; when the archegonia are fully formed in the prothallium, the pollen-tubes begin to grow again in order to reach them. In *Gingko biloba* fertilisation takes place in October in the

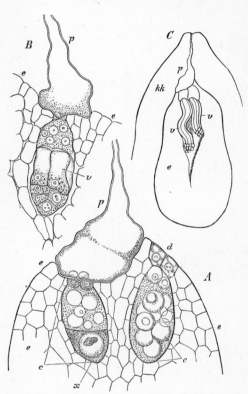

macrosporangia (seeds) which have fallen ripe from the tree, and the embryo forms in the seed during the winter. In the rest of the Coniferae in which the seeds ripen in the year this interruption in the growth of the pollen-tubes only lasts for a few weeks or months; where the seed takes two years to mature, as in *Juniperus sibirica*, *J. communis*, *Pinus sylvestris*, and *P. Strobus*, it continues till June of the ensuing year. In the Abietineae and Taxineae each pollen-tube fertilises only one archegonium, several pollen-tubes therefore enter at the same time; in the Cupressineae on the other hand one tube is sufficient for the whole group of archegonia at the end of the broad funnel of the prothallium; the pollen-tube fills the funnel completely and lays its broad extremity on the necks of them all. Short narrow protuberances on the extremity of the tube now grow into the separate archegonia, thrusting the neck-cells apart and destroying them, and they finally reach the oosphere. The process is similar in the Abietineae and Taxineae, where the tube which had become broader grows narrow again and enters the neck of one archegonium only, making its way ultimately to the oosphere. A

FIG. 261. *Taxus canadensis.* *A* longitudinal section through the upper extremity of the prothallium (endosperm) *ee* and the lower extremity of the pollen-tube *p*; *cc* the archegonia, *d* their neck-cells; the archegonium to the left is fertilised (June 5th). *B* portion of the endosperm with an archegonium, the elongating suspensor-cells of which *v* are already in an advanced state of development, with the embryo at the extremity; *p* the pollen-tube (June 10th). *C* longitudinal section of a nucellus on June 15th; *kk* nucellus, *e* endosperm, *p* pollen-tube, *vv* two suspensors with embryos at their extremities proceeding from two oospores. Numerous vacuoles are visible in the oospheres of the archegonia; the nucleus of the oosphere is not given. After Hofmeister. *A* magn. 300, *B* 200, *C* 50 times.

thin spot, a pit, may be recognised at the apex of the protuberance on the thick-walled pollen-tube, and evidently facilitates the transmission of the fertilising substance; probably the pressure of the superior tissue on the portion of the tube outside the archegonium assists the operation. The processes in the pollen-tube are thus described by Strasburger:—The small vegetative cells, that is, the cells of the prothallium, in the pollen-grain (microspore), one or more in number, take no part in the formation of the pollen-tube, but the nucleus of the large cell moves to the apex of the tube. There it divides, as can be seen with especial distinctness in *Juniperus virginiana*, and cell-formation takes place round each of the new nuclei by the gathering of protoplasm round them. While the upper one of the two primordial cells does not usually divide again, the lower divides once or twice, and the new cells spread themselves out in one plane at the lower extremity of the tube. The nucleus of the oosphere, which has increased in size and contents, advances towards the middle

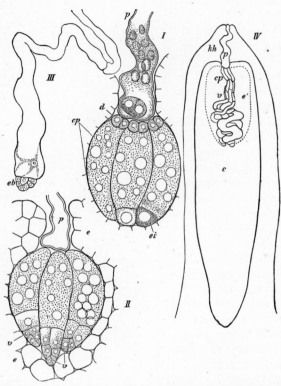

FIG. 262. *Juniperus communis. I* three archegonia closely side by side *cp*, two of them having the oosphere fertilised; *d* neck-cells, *p* pollen-tube (July 28). *II* a similar preparation; *e e* the prothallium (endosperm), *v v* the pro-embryos. *III* lower end of one of the longitudinal cell-rows of a pro-embryo with the rudiment of the embryo *e b. IV* longitudinal section of the nucellus *hh*; *e* the endosperm, *e'* the portion of the endosperm which has become loose and spongy, *p* the pollen-tube, *cp* the archegonia, *v* suspensors (beginning of August). After Hofmeister. *I* magn. 300, *IV* 80 times.

of the oosphere, while the canal-cell becomes disorganised. During fertilisation the small nuclei in the pollen-tube over the archegonia disappear, and their substance must in some way or other pass into the archegonia. A round cell-like body is found in the oospheres of the archegonia in front of the extremity of the pollen-tube, and Strasburger has named it the *sperm-nucleus* (male pro-nucleus). This object, which must be considered to have passed from the pollen-tube into the oosphere, moves towards the *nucleus of the oosphere* (female pro-nucleus) and coalesces with it. It follows that in this case also fertilisation consists in the union of the constituents of two cells, for it is plain that there is here not only a coalescence of two nuclei, but a union of the protoplasm of the pollen-tube with the protoplasm of the oosphere. After fertilisation the definitive nucleus, the *germ-nucleus*, which results from the coalescence of the sperm-nucleus with the nucleus of the oosphere, moves into the part of the oospore which is opposite to the neck (Fig. 260 *V*), and here the formation of the pro-embryo begins. The small lower part of the oospore (Fig. 262 *I ei*) which is to develope into the pro-embryo and contains the germ-nucleus is either at once divided off from the upper and larger part, or this does not take place till the nucleus has divided several times and cells have formed round the daughter-nuclei[1].

The *formation of the embryo* varies to a remarkable extent in the different divisions; but in all of them the considerable elongation of certain cells of the suspensor thrusts the rudimentary embryo at its apex out of the oospore of the archegonium into the prothallium, where the embryo proceeds to develope.

In the Cupressineae the lower third of the oospore (Fig. 262 *II*) divides into three cells lying one above another; in *Thuja occidentalis* the two upper only of these cells, which are towards the neck of the archegonium, divide each into four cells, while the lower one becomes the apical cell of the young embryo. By the elongation of the upper cells forming the suspensor the rudiment of the embryo is thrust forth from the archegonium into the prothallium. In this case therefore each archegonium forms only one embryo, which grows at first with a two-sided apical cell, but this soon disappears. In *Juniperus* on the other hand the lowest of the three cells which lie above one another divides by intersecting longitudinal walls into four cells, which are pushed out by the elongation of the upper ones, round themselves off and separate from one another, and each gives rise to a rudimentary embryo; in this case therefore four rudimentary embryos proceed from one archegonium, but one only developes into a perfect embryo. The commencement of the formation of the embryo is different in the Abietineae (Fig. 260 *VII–XII*). The germ-nucleus moves to the bottom of the oospore, and by its division forms two and then four nuclei, and four cells lying in a transverse plane beside one another are formed by the accumulation of protoplasm round these nuclei. The four cells divide by transverse walls into three tiers one above the other; the cells of the second tier develope into very long and sinuous tubes, while those of the upper tier form a rosette which remains fixed in the archegonium. The four cells of the lowest tier, which have been thrust out into the endosperm by the elongation of the cells above them, divide repeatedly and so contribute to the elongation of the suspensor; then the four rows of cells of the suspensor separate from one another, each bearing a terminal cell, which forms the rudiment of the embryo in such a manner as to preclude from the first the existence of an apical cell[2]. Thus in the Abietineae also each archegonium gives birth to four rudimentary embryos; but *Picea vulgaris* agrees with *Juniperus*, inasmuch as the lowest of the three primary cells of the suspensor does not divide but forms only one rudiment. In *Taxus baccata* the embryonic structure consists of two or three tiers, the upper one of which elongates and forms the tubular cells of the suspensor; the lower tier consists of from four to six cells, but only one of them ultimately produces the

---

[1] [See Goroschankin, Ueber d. Befr. Process b. *Pinus Pumilio*, 1883.—Strasburger, Neue Unters. ü. d. Befruchtungsvorg. b. d. Phanerog. 1884.]

[2] *Pinus strobus* forms an exception, in which the rudimentary embryo grows by an apical cell, as in the Cupressineae; but according to modern views on the relationship of growth to cell-formation this is not a matter of serious importance.

embryo; there is no separation of the tubes of the suspensor. In *Gingko,* where the formation of the embryo does not begin till after the fall of the ovules from the tree, the germ-nucleus in the oospore first divides, and the repeated division of the daughter-nuclei gives rise to a large number of separate cell-nuclei, which lie free in the protoplasm of the oospore. When the fixed number of these cells is completed, they become surrounded with threads of protoplasm and cell-walls are formed between them, and the entire oospore appears to be filled with a body of tissue which forms the embryo. In this case therefore only one embryo is formed in each archegonium, and a true suspensor is not formed; it is only indicated by the cells which are towards the neck of the archegonium developing into short cells. In *Cephalotaxus Fortunei* and *Araucaria brasiliensis,* as Strasburger has recently ascertained, the growing point of the embryo is not the apex of the rudiment but is formed inside the rudiment, while the original apex serves only as an organ of penetration and protection, and is afterwards thrown off.

It appears then that in the Coniferae one or more embryos are formed from one oospore, and their number inside a prothallium (endosperm) is increased by the circumstance that several archegonia are fertilised at the same time; *polyembrony* therefore, which is exceptional in Angiosperms, is the rule among the Coniferae and generally among Gymnosperms, but only in the rudimentary state, for usually one rudiment only developes into a vigorous embryo, such as has been described above. The endosperm also grows rapidly during the development of the embryo, and its cells become filled with reserves of food-material (fat and albuminous substances); the embryo-sac also which incloses it enlarges at the same time and ultimately displaces the tissue of the nucellus, while the tissue of the integument hardens into the seed-coat; in *Gingko* a thick outer layer of tissue produces the pulpy investment which makes the seed resemble a plum (drupe). The tubular cells of the suspensor usually disappear during these processes, but are said by Schacht to persist in *Larix.*

The Coniferae like the Cycadeae are essentially distinguished from the Vascular Cryptogams by the presence of a primary root. In the young pro-embryo the lower part which is rich in protoplasm, the embryo proper, is clearly distinguished from the upper part, the suspensor. The differentiation of the root begins in *Thuja,* when the lower part of the rudimentary embryo has reached a length of four-tenths of a millimetre; it commences at some depth in the tissue of the embryo, about a tenth and a half of a millimetre below its apex. Tangential divisions first appear in a layer of cells disposed in a half circle and enclosed on all sides by the tissue of the rudimentary embryo; consequently the first rudiment of the root is covered from the beginning on the side towards the suspensor by several layers of cells. The differentiation of the root proceeds in a similar manner in the rest of the Coniferae. The cotyledons are formed beneath the apex of the rudimentary embryo as was stated above.

While the seeds are ripening the parts in their vicinity are subjected to further growth and changes of consistence; in *Taxus* the aril, which afterwards becomes red and pulpy, grows up round the seed as it ripens (Fig. 252 *Fm*); in *Podocarpus* the aril, which had been formed before, becomes pulpy; in *Juniperus* and *Sabina* the united bract-scales, which had contracted, develope into the blue berry which encloses the seeds; in most of the other Cupressineae and in the Araucarieae the scales grow larger, unite by their sides and become woody, while in *Pinus*, *Abies*, *Cedrus*, and *Larix* it is the seminiferous scales which increase greatly in size after fertilisation, outgrow the bract-scales, become woody and form the ripe cones. In all these cases, with the exception of *Podocarpus*, *Gingko*, and *Taxus*, the seed is shut up close and tight within the scales; it ripens inside the fruit, the parts of which do not open or drop off, as in *Abies pectinata*, to allow of the dispersion of the seeds, till they are fully ripe.

Taxonomic Summary of the Coniferae.

I. **Araucariaceae.** The female flowers form perfect cones; scales of the cones (sporophylls) either simple or with a basilar or axillary placental growth (seminiferous scale), or furnished with outgrowths above the insertion of the ovules either before or after fertilisation.

1. ARAUCARIEAE. Scales of the cone (bract-scales) arranged spirally, simple (without seminiferous scales), bearing the ovules on their base, free (*Dammara*) or adhering; ovules on the scales in numbers which vary in the different genera, one in *Dammara* and *Araucaria*, three in *Cunninghamia*, anatropous; no outgrowth (*Dammara*), or only a small one on the scale above the ovule.

2. TAXODINEAE. Scales of the cone (bract-scales) arranged spirally; seminiferous scale present as an outgrowth from the bract-scale and more or less separate from it; in *Sequoia* and *Arthrotaxis* the ovules are moved upwards and on to the seminiferous scale, at first orthotropous then anatropous.—*Taxodium*, *Cryptomeria*, *Glyptostrobus*, *Sequoia*, *Arthrotaxis*, *Widdringtonia*.

3. SCIADOPITYEAE. Scales of the cone (bract-scales) arranged spirally; an outgrowth (the seminiferous scale) is formed from and becomes larger than the bract; ovules moved upwards and on to the seminiferous scale, from six to nine, anatropous, free.—*Sciadopitys*.

4. ABIETINEAE. Scales of the cone (bract-scales) in spirals; in the axils of the scales are formed placentae which increase greatly in size and assume the form of scales (seminiferous scales), on which the ovules are placed in pairs.—*Abies*, *Larix*, *Picea*, etc.

5. CUPRESSINEAE. Monoecious or dioecious; scales of the cone (bract-scales) in alternating whorls of two, three, or four members; the ovules are on a slight placental projection which arises in the axil of the bract-scale and does not develope into a seminiferous scale, singly or in pairs or more together, orthotropous, free; after fertilisation a considerable enlargement is formed on the upper side of the bract-scale above the ovules. Staminal leaves peltate in front through formation of indusium on the under side. Embryo with two, rarely with three or nine cotyledons.—*Frenela*, *Thuja*, *Biota*, *Libocedrus*, *Chamaecyparis*, *Callitris*, *Juniperus*, *Cupressus*, *Fitzroya*, *Diselma*, *Actinostrobus*.

II. **Taxaceae.** Always dioecious; cones none or imperfect, ovules sometimes terminal. Staminal leaves of different form, bearing two, three, or four to eight dependent pollen-sacs. The ripe seed usually with a fleshy aril or with the outer layer of the seed-coat fleshy. Embryo with two cotyledons.

1. TAXINEAE. Ovules sometimes with rudimentary bracteoles.—*Taxus*, *Cephalotaxus*, *Torreya*, *Gingko*.

2. PODOCARPEAE. Ovules without bracteoles. — *Phyllocladus*, *Dacrydium*, *Podocarpus*, *Microcachrys*.

C. GNETACEAE[1].

This division includes three genera of strikingly different habit.   The Ephedrae
are shrubs which have no large foliage-leaves, but long slender cylindrical branches
with a green rind which bear two opposite minute leaves at their joints; these leaves
cohere and form a bidentate sheath, and lateral branches grow from their axils.   In
Gnetum the leaves are also opposite to one another on the jointed axis, but they are
large and stalked, with a broadly lanceolate lamina and pinnate venation.   Finally,
Welwitschia mirabilis, a very remarkable plant in other respects also, has only two
foliage leaves of enormous size, which are placed crosswise with respect to the deciduous cotyledons, and when old are split up and lie stretched out on the ground.   The
stem is always short, rising only a little way above the ground, is broad above with a
furrow over the apex, and swells out below where it passes into the tap-root[2].

The flowers of the Gnetaceae are unisexual in dioecious (*Ephedra*) or monoecious
inflorescences; these inflorescences have a clearly defined form and spring in *Ephedra*
and *Gnetum* from the axils of the opposite leaves.   The male flower of these genera
consists of a small bipartite perianth with a central stalk-like filament, which in *Gnetum*
is bifid above and bears two bilocular anthers, and in *Ephedra* has a larger number
of anthers crowded together into a small head.   The female flower also, according to
Eichler[3], has a perianth[4] which is flask-shaped in *Gnetum* and in three divisions in
Ephedra, and encloses a centrally placed ovule which has one integument in *Ephedra*
and two in *Gnetum*, the inner one being prolonged like a style.   A small cell is
separated off in the pollen-grain of *Ephedra* as in that of the Cupressineae;   the
prothallium of the macrospore (the embryo-sac) produces from three to five archegonia with an elongated central cell, and a very long neck divided by transverse
walls and with a ventral canal-cell distinctly visible at its base (Strasburger).   In
Gnetum the inflorescence which springs from the axil of a foliage-leaf consists of a
jointed axis with verticillate leaves, in the axils of which the male and female
flowers are crowded together.   But the female flowers in the apparently hermaphrodite
inflorescences are not capable of development, and are distinguished from the fertile
flowers of the female inflorescences by having two only instead of three envelopes,
the middle one being abortive.   The inflorescences of *Welwitschia mirabilis* are
dichotomously branched cymes nearly a foot high; they spring from the circumference of the broad apex of the stem above the insertion of the huge leaves.   The
round and jointed branches of the inflorescence proceed from the axils of the bracts,
and bear rather long erect cylindrical cones; the cones are covered with from seventy
to ninety broadly ovate scale-leaves standing in four rows closely one above another,
in the axils of which are the single flowers, male and female being distributed on
different cones.   The male flowers are pseudo-hermaphrodite and have a perianth of

---

[1] Strasburger, as quoted under the Coniferae.

[2] For further information on this strange plant, see Flora, 1863, p. 459, and Bower, On Welwitschia (Q. J. M. S. 1881).

[3] *Flora*, 1863, pp. 463, 531.

[4] This is considered by Strasburger to be a simple outer integument, and so *Ephedra* would
have two and *Gnetum* three integuments.   How we name these envelopes appears to me to be
unimportant, but the analogy of the other forms is in favour of the designation given by Strasburger.

two pairs of small decussate leaves; the lower ones are entirely free, falcately curved and acuminate, the upper ones broadly spathulate and cohering at the base into a compressed tube. Inside this tube are six stamens, monadelphous below, with cylindrical filaments and terminal spherical trilocular anthers opening by a three-rayed fissure at the apex. The centre of the flower is occupied by a single erect orthotropous sessile ovule with a broad base, and with no investment except a simple integument which is prolonged into a style-like tube with its margin expanded into a disk; but the nucellus has no embryo-sac and is sterile. In the female flowers the perianth is tubular and much compressed, slightly winged and quite entire; there is no indication of male sporophylls; the ovule, which of course has an embryo-sac, is completely enveloped in the perianth and is of the same shape as the ovule in the male flower, with the difference only that the elongated apex of the integument is only simply slit and not expanded into a disk. The

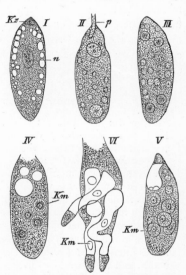

FIG. 263. Commencement of formation of the embryo in *Ephedra altissima. I* oosphere before fertilisation with only one nucleus *n. II* After fertilisation; the nucleus has divided. *III* four nuclei in the oosphere. *IV* formation of cells round the nuclei. *V* completion of formation of cells. *VI* development of the pro-embryos, which have each divided off a small cell at their apex. *Kz* canal-cell, *n* nucleus, *p* pollen-tube, *Km* pro-embryo. After Strasburger, magn. about 30 times.

cones when ripe are nearly two inches long and scarlet in colour; the scales are persistent; the perianth increases considerably in size and becomes broadly winged, and its cavity narrows above into a slender canal, through which the apex of the integument passes. The seed, which is of the same shape as the ovule, contains a copious endosperm, in the centre of which is the dicotyledonous embryo; the embryo is thick at its radicular end and attached by it to a very long spirally-coiled suspensor. The embryo-sac (macrospore) is formed in exactly the same way as in the Coniferae, in *Larix* for example; *Gnetum Gnemon* has several 'embryo-sac-mother-cells.' The mode of development of the embryo from the oospore is peculiar[1]. In *Ephedra* (Fig. 263) the nucleus of the oospore divides first into two free daughter-cells; by repeated bipartition four and then eight nuclei are formed. Then cells are formed round these free nuclei; they collect protoplasm, which is disposed round them in radiating lines and then invests itself with a cell-wall. Each of the free pro-embryonal cells thus formed develops into a tube which pierces the side-wall of the archegonium, and parts off at its apex a small cell containing much protoplasm from which the embryo is formed; but one only of these many rudimentary embryos comes to complete development. This mode of development of the embryo is not so very different from that which has been already described in the case of *Pinus*, for example, as may at first sight appear; the chief distinction is that

---

[1] [According to Bower, The Germination and Embryology of Gnetum Gnemon (Q. J. M. S. 1882), the embryo in *Gnetum Gnemon* is not found at the extremity of the suspensor until after the seed is separated from the parent plant, and its development corresponds closely with the type in Gymnosperms. A 'feeder' is formed on the hypocotyledonary axis as in *Welwitschia*.]

the nuclei produced by the division of the nucleus of the oospore in *Ephedra* continue free, while in *Pinus* they very soon become centres of union for cells lying in the lower part of the oospore, but they may also occasionally remain free (Strasburger). In *Welwitschia* the archegonium is reduced to a single cell surrounded by a cell-wall. These rudimentary archegonia, from twenty to thirty in number, grow out of the embryo-sac and penetrate into canal-like spaces in the nucellus, where fertilisation is effected by the pollen-tubes which grow towards them and lay themselves along them, while the wall of the archegonium swells up at the point of contact. The oospore with its cell-wall elongates into a tube, and a cell is separated off at its extremity and becomes a rudimentary embryo; when several cells have been formed in the rudiment the cells behind it also grow into long tubes, so that the embryo when thrust downwards into the pro-thallium terminates at its upper radicular extremity in unusually long embryonal tubes; but only one embryo is developed as the result of fertilisation in from two to eight archegonia. An outgrowth, an organ of suction, is formed on the hypo-cotyledonary portion of the embryo, which remains in contact with the endosperm and supplies the young plant with nutriment from it.

Appendix on the Histology of the Gymnosperms.

From the abundant material which has been collected and critically examined in De Bary's Comparative Anatomy, we can here only call attention to a few points which are characteristic of the division.

The *vascular bundles* are on the whole similar to those of the Dicotyledons; there is a system of common bundles, and their leaf-traces as they descend in the stem are disposed in a circle, in which by means of interfascicular cambium a closed cambium-ring is formed and gives rise to permanent growth in thickness; the ascending limb of each leaf-trace, which bends out into the leaf itself, assumes in the Cycadeae more or less the character of a closed bundle, but retains the appearance at least of an open bundle in the leaves of many Coniferae. No cauline bundles are formed in the stem of the Coniferae or of *Ephedra*; the leaf-trace-bundles descend through a number of inter-nodes, and then lay themselves along older and deeper leaf-trace-bundles either on one side only or on both sides by dividing into two limbs (Fig. 264). The leaves in the Coniferae, with the exception of *Gingko*, receive only one bundle from the stem, which usually divides in the leaf into two equal parts running alongside one another; if the leaves are broader, the bundle that comes from the stem divides at the point where it leaves the stem into several bundles which enter the leaf, as in *Dammara* and the broad-leaved Araucarieae; if the leaf forms a broad flat lamina, as in *Gingko* and *Dammara*, the bundles ramify in it but without forming reticulations; in *Gingko* they form repeated bifurcations. These bundles seldom form prominent veins in the lamina of the leaf in the Coniferae, but run through the middle of the tissue. In *Ephedra* each leaf receives two, in *Gnetum* four or five bundles (*G. Thoa*, De Bary, *loc. cit.*). Many bundles enter the two huge leaves of *Welwitschia*, and their parallel ramifica-tions run in the middle layer of tissue. Two bundles also enter the large pinnate leaves of the Cycadeae, and these bend till they are almost horizontal in the cortical tissue of the stem and divide in the leaf-stalk, when it is thick, into a number of strong bundles elegantly arranged as seen in a transverse section; in *Cycas revoluta* for example they have the form of an inverted Ω; they run parallel to one another in the rhachis of the leaf and give off branches into the pinnae, where they either run parallel in the middle layer of tissue, as in *Dioon*, or branch dichotomously, as in *Encephalartos*; in *Cycas* they form a mid-rib which projects on the under surface. The course of the bundles in the leaves of the Cycadeae is obviously very like that of many Ferns (see on page 313).

The woody body of the stem is formed of the descending leaf-trace-bundles, which are at first completely isolated, but are soon united into a closed ring by the cambium which bridges over the medullary rays. The protoxylem, the medullary sheath in older stems, which consists of the xylem of the several leaf-trace-bundles, contains in all Gymnosperms, as in Dicotyledons, long narrow elements with annular or spiral thickening-bands, and towards the outside reticulately thickened or scalariform elements. The secondary wood produced by the cambium-ring after growth in length has ceased

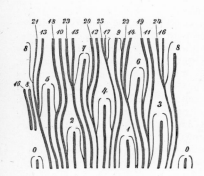

FIG. 264. *Pinus sylvestris.* Diagrammatic representation of the course of the bundles in the young shoot, the surface of the cylinder being expanded into a plane. Leaves in a right-handed spiral with a divergence of $\frac{8}{21}$. The numbers indicate the leaf-trace-bundles in their order of succession which appear as broad bands. The bundles which converge in pairs, shown by the thin lines by the side of the prominent leaf-trace-bundles o—9, run each pair to an axillary shoot. The foliar bundles unite each with the eighth below it. From De Bary, Vergl. Anatomie, after Geyler.

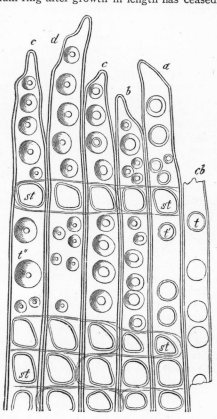

FIG. 265. *Pinus sylvestris.* Radial longitudinal section through the wood of a vigorous branch; *c* cambial wood-cells, *t t′ t″* bordered pits of older wood-cells (tracheides), *s* large pits where medullary rays are in contact with the wood-cells.

consists in the Coniferae of long prosenchymatic tracheides having a few large bordered pits, which in later-formed wood at least are usually circular; between these tracheides and the spiral vessels of the medullary sheath all possible intermediate forms may be found. The characteristic difference between the secondary wood of the Coniferae and that of the Dicotyledons is that the former has only this prosenchymatous[1] form of cell, and none therefore of the wide dotted shortly articulated vessels which traverse the compact narrow-celled woody mass of the Dicotyledons. On the other hand, this predominance of prosenchymatous tracheides recalls the

---

[1] Wood-parenchyma is either not formed at all or only in small quantities.

Vascular Cryptogams, in which the vascular bundles, except in a very few cases, contain only tracheides. The bordered pits in the Coniferae are usually developed only on the cell-walls which are turned towards the medullary rays, and in one or two rows ; in *Araucaria* they are in several rows and closely crowded together. The Gnetaceae approach the Dicotyledons in the structure of their secondary wood, as they do in that of the flower and in habit ; in *Ephedra* wide vessels are found along with the ordinary tracheides in the inner part of the ring of secondary wood, but their constituent parts are separated by oblique septa and are therefore still prosenchymatous, and are pierced with several roundish holes ; their lateral walls like those of the tracheides show bordered pits.

In *Gnetum*, as in the Cycadeae and many Dicotyledons, the growth in thickness from the first cambium-ring ceases after a time, and a new zone of meristem is formed in the secondary cortex outside the ring ; in this zone xylem-strands are formed on the inside and phloem-strands on the outside alternating with medullary rays. As this process is repeated more than once, a transverse section of an older stem or branch of *Gnetum scandens*, for example, shows several concentric rings of growth, each consisting of a xylem-ring and a phloem-ring.

The stem of the Cycadeae shows at first the typical structure of the Gymnosperms and Dicotyledons ; a ring of xylem, bast, and cambium proceeds from the primary leaf-trace-ring and separates the outer cortex from the pith. Both pith and cortex contain gum-passages and mucilage-passages. The xylem of the vascular bundles is formed of tracheides ; the innermost and first formed have spiral threads, as in the Coniferae, the others have scalariform thickenings. The tracheal elements of the secondary wood are tracheides, which either have bordered pits arranged transversely in several rows, as in *Cycas* and *Encephalartos*, or a combination of scalariform and reticulate thickenings, as in *Zamia*. *Zamia, Dioon*, and *Stangeria* retain this structure, the network of primary bundles and the increase from the normal cambium-ring, all their life. But in *Cycas* and *Encephalartos*, as in *Gnetum*, growth in thickness from this source is limited, and a new ring of growth is formed on the outer edge of the phloem-layer ; and as this process is repeated, old stems of *Cycas* are found with from six to eight successive rings of growth. *Cycas* also has a system of bundles in the cortical tissue, *Encephalartos* in the pith[1].

The gnetaceous genus *Welwitschia* which is peculiar in many respects has also anomalies in its anatomical structure, on which De Bary should be consulted.

The *medullary rays*[2] of the secondary wood are very narrow in the Coniferae, often not more than one cell broad, and their cells are strongly lignified and have closed pits on the walls which meet the adjoining tracheides. They are broader in the Cycadeae, and their tissue is more like the parenchyma of the pith and cortex; their number and breadth make the whole woody body appear loose in texture; and its prosenchymatous elements are much curved in different directions in a tangential section. The phloem-portion of the vascular bundles of Gymnosperms resembles that of the Dicotyledons ; it consists usually of true much thickened fibres, cambiform cells, sieve-tubes and parenchyma, which in the Coniferae are formed in alternate layers ; the soft-bast generally predominates.

The *fundamental tissue* of the stem of Gymnosperms is separated by the woody cylinder into pith and primary cortex. Both these are largely developed in the Cycadeae, the pith especially, and consist of true parenchyma ; the mass of wood is much smaller. In *Welwitschia* also the parenchymatous tissues predominate, but the larger part of them must be formed by an outer meristematic zone in the stem. A large number of the so-called spicular cells are found scattered about in all the organs of this remarkable plant ; they are fusiform or branched with greatly thickened walls,

---

[1] See De Bary, Vergl. Anat. p. 612, English translation.
[2] [Kleeberg, Die Markstrahlen d. Coniferen (Bot. Ztg. 1885).]

in which many finely-formed crystals are imbedded close to one another. Similar forms are also found in the Coniferae.

The parenchymatous fundamental tissue of the Coniferae is very much diminished in quantity as the age of the stem and root increases; besides the slender pith the stem is now exclusively composed of the products of the cambium-ring, as the primary cortex, and then the outer continually developing layers of the secondary cortex are used to form bark. In the Cycadeae, which have but small growth in thickness, there is very little formation of cork, and in *Welwitschia* there appears to be none[1]; but this is perhaps doubtful.

Sap-conducting *intercellular passages* are widely distributed in the Gymnosperms, and are lined with secreting epithelial cells. In the Cycadeae they traverse all the organs in large numbers and contain gum, which exudes from transverse sections in large viscid drops; in the Coniferae they contain oil of turpentine and resin, and occur in the pith of the stem, in the whole of the wood, in the primary and secondary cortex, and in the leaves; like the gum-passages of the Cycadeae they always follow the longitudinal direction of the organs. In many Coniferae with short leaves roundish resin-glands are also found in the leaves, as in *Callitris, Thuja,* and *Cupressus,* according to Thomas; *Taxus* has no resin-passages at all[2].

The *foliage leaves* of the Cycadeae and Coniferae are usually covered with a stout strongly cuticularised epidermis with numerous stomata, and each stoma has two guard-cells. In the Cycadeae the stomata are found only on the under surface of the leaf and more or less sunk in its tissue, and are either scattered irregularly or placed in rows between the veins (Kraus). In the Coniferae also, according to Hildebrandt[3], the guard-cells are always sunk in the epidermis of the leaves, and the stoma therefore always has a vestibule. The stomata in the Coniferae occur on both sides or only on one side of the leaf; if the leaf is broad, as in *Dammara* and *Gingko,* they are scattered about without any order, if the leaves are acicular they are usually arranged in longitudinal rows; they are arranged in rows even in the large leaves of *Welwitschia.* The firm texture of the leaves of the Cycadeae and Coniferae is due to a hypodermal layer, often of considerable thickness, consisting of cells which are usually long and fibre-like with much-thickened walls and lying parallel to the surface of the leaf; in the leaf of *Welwitschia* this hypodermal tissue is loose and succulent and is traversed by fibre-bundles[4], and it acquires firmness by means of a mass of spicular cells. Beneath the hypodermal layers is the tissue containing chlorophyll, which in the Cycadeae and in the Coniferae with broader leaves is developed on the upper side of the leaf in the form of palisade-tissue, that is, the cells are elongated in a direction perpendicular to the surface of the leaf and are closely crowded together; the cells containing chlorophyll in the leaf in the genera *Pinus, Larix, Cedrus* have infoldings of their cell-wall. The middle layer of the tissue of the leaf, in which the vascular bundles run, is developed in a peculiar manner in most Gymnosperms; in the Cycadeae and Podocarpeae it consists of cells which are elongated in a direction transverse to the axis of the leaf and to the bundles, but lie parallel to the surfaces of the leaf, and leave large intercellular spaces (the transverse parenchyma of Thomas, the transfusion-tissue of Mohl); in the acicular leaves of the Abietineae the divided vascular bundle has an investment of colourless tissue which is clearly distinguished from the surrounding chlorophyll-tissue; it is parenchymatous and marked by a large number of peculiar pit-like formations (Fig. 266)[5].

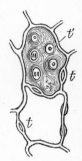

FIG. 266. *Pinus pinaster.* Two cells of the colourless parenchyma surrounding the vascular bundle of the leaf; at *t t* the pit-like formations seen in section, at *t'* the same seen from the surface.

---

[1] Flora, 1863, p. 473.　　[2] For further information see De Bary, Vgl. Anat., p. 137.
[3] Bot. Ztg. 1869, p. 149.　　[4] Flora, 1863, p. 490.
[5] Mohl in Bot. Ztg. 1871, Nos. 1–2.—Zimmerman in Flora, 1879.

Appendix. The CORDAITEAE. This group belongs to a type which existed in the Carboniferous period, and cannot, as far as we know at present[1], be united either with the Cycadeae or Coniferae or Gnetaceae. Grand' Eury describes them as trees from thirty to forty metres high, and branched only in the upper part; the leaves were from twenty centimetres to a metre in length, simple and unbranched, and from fifteen to twenty centimetres broad.

The male flowers were in cones inserted on the stem but not in the axils of the leaves. The cones were composed of sterile and fertile leaves arranged spirally, the fertile somewhat narrower than the sterile, and had at their apex three or four microsporangia (pollen-sacs), which did not however hang down as in *Gingko* but stood erect in the prolongation of the plane of the leaf. The macrosporangia had two integuments and a 'pollen-chamber' at the extremity of the nucellus, as in the Cycadeae; they were on long stalks which sprang several together as branches of an axillary shoot from the axil of a bract, and were surrounded at their base by a number of small leaves, like the female flowers of some of the Taxineae; these partial inflorescences appear to have been united into a spike-like general inflorescence. The anatomical structure, on the other hand, of the stem and leaf shows various points of agreement with that of the Coniferae.

It is to be hoped that the recent discovery of the organs of fructification of the Sigillarieae will enable us to determine whether those peculiar plants, which have been hitherto ranked by many botanists with the Vascular Cryptogams, do really belong to the Gymnosperms.

II. ANGIOSPERMS[2].

The Angiosperms agree with the Gymnosperms in producing a seed, but differ from them in the circumstance that the ovule is formed inside a chamber, the *ovary*, and further in the processes of development which go on inside the embryo-sac (macrospore). No prothallium bearing archegonia at its apex is formed in them before fertilisation as in the Gymnosperms, but three naked cells are found at the apex of the embryo-sac at the time of fertilisation, one of which is the oosphere; the nucleus of the embryo-sac lies in the middle of the sac, and its division after fertilisation is the commencement of the formation of a tissue, which more or less completely fills the embryo-sac and is known as the *endosperm*. The development on the other hand of the pollen-grains or microspores is the same in all essential points as that which takes place in the Gymnosperms. At the same time the Angiosperms are distinguished from other Vascular plants by many peculiarities of structure, especially in the formation of the flowers and fruit, in which the ordinary morphological conditions suffer such peculiar changes and combinations, that a more detailed account of them must be given before we proceed to describe the special characteristics of the two classes.

The Flower[3]. The flower of the Angiosperms is only occasionally terminal in the sense, that the primary stem which is the development of the axis of the embryo

---

[1] Renault, Cours de Bot. fossile, première année, Paris, 1881.—[Heer in Bot. Centralbl. 1882.]

[2] The word is derived from the Greek ἀγγεῖον, a receptacle, and σπέρμα, the seed.

[3] The most complete account of the flower of the Angiosperms is to be found in Eichler's Bluthendiagramme, I and II, Leipzig, 1875 and 1878, where the literature of the subject is also very fully given. The most important work on the history of the development of the flower is Payer's Traité d'organogénie de la fleur, Paris, 1857, with 154 splendid copper plates. [The admirable account of the flower given by Asa Gray in his Structural Botany (1880) should also be consulted.]

terminates in a flower, the plant being therefore uniaxial; when this is the case a sympodial (cymose) inflorescence is usually developed by the formation of new shoots with terminal flowers beneath the first flower. Usually the shoots of the second, third or some higher order are the first to end in a flower, so that the plant may in this respect be described as having two, three or more axes.

In Gymnosperms the flowers are as a rule unisexual (diclinous), but hermaphroditism decidedly predominates in Angiosperms, though monoecious and dioecious species, genera and families are not altogether uncommon. The male flowers sometimes differ essentially in structure from the female, as in the Cupuliferae and Cannabineae; but more often the diclinism is owing to partial or complete abortion of the androecium in some flowers and of the gynaeceum in others, the flowers being in other respects constructed after the same type (Fig. 267 *A*); in such cases hermaphrodite flowers may also be found on the same plant with the male and female flowers, as in *Fraxinus excelsior, Saponaria ocymoides, Acer*, and others, which are therefore said to be *polygamous*. But even in hermaphrodite flowers with male and female sporophylls,

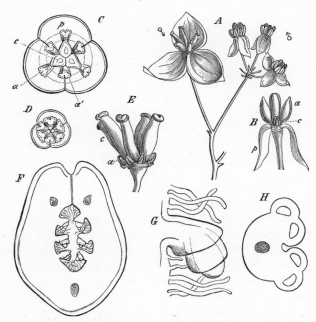

FIG. 267. *Akebia quinata. A* a part of the inflorescence; ♀ female, ♂ male flowers. *B* longitudinal section of male flower; *c* its sterile carpel. *C* transverse section of a female flower magnified. *D* transverse section of a male flower. *E* the gynaeceum of the female flower with the small stamens *a*. *F* an ovary in transverse section. *G* an ovule. *H* transverse section of an anther. *a* outer, *a'* inner stamens, *c* carpel, *p* perianth.

structurally and functionally perfect, fertilisation is effected by the conveyance of the pollen of one flower to the gynaeceum of another flower or even of the flower of another plant of the same species, either because pollination within the same flower is rendered impossible by its organisation, as in *dichogamous* flowers, or because the pollen is effective only when applied to the ovule of a different flower, as in the Orchideae, *Corydalis*, etc.

The floral axis in the Gymnosperms is usually so elongated, that the sporophylls, especially if they are numerous, can be readily seen to be arranged one above another in alternate whorls or ascending spirals; in the Angiosperms, on the contrary, that portion of the floral axis which bears the floral envelopes and sporophylls is so abbreviated, that space has to be obtained for the insertion of the different foliar structures by a corresponding expansion or increase in circumference of the *torus*; this swells out into the shape of a club both before and during the formation of the floral leaves, and is not unfrequently flattened like a disk or even hollowed out into a cup in such a manner that the apex of the floral axis occupies the lowest point in the depression, while the cup encloses the carpels, as in the *perigynous* flowers, or even

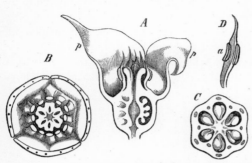

FIG. 268. *Asarum canadense.* A a flower in longitudinal section; *p* the perianth. B transverse section of the flower above the ovary. C transverse section of the sex-locular ovary. D a stamen with the lateral anthers.

takes part in the formation of the ovary which in this case is inferior (Fig. 268). The effect of this as regards the outward aspect of the flowers is that their parts do not usually appear to be arranged one above another, but in concentric circles or in scarcely ascending spiral lines, and hence the illustration of the relative position of the parts of the flowers by diagrams or ground-plans, such as those which will be explained more fully below, seems especially suitable in the case of the Angiosperms. This abbreviation of the torus is evidently the chief cause also of the unions and displacements which are nowhere found so abundantly as in the flowers of Angiosperms; and since the small development in length of the floral axis itself arises from the early cessation of apical growth, even the acropetal succession of the floral leaves may be disturbed by formation of intercalary zones of growth [1], though even in these cases the disturbance of the general regularity is inconsiderable. However the acropetal succession is in most cases strictly preserved, and sometimes the apical growth of the floral axis continues long enough for the foliar structures to be evidently arranged in circles one above the other or in ascending spirals, as is the case in the Magnolieae, Ranunculaceae, and Nymphaeaceae. Occasionally single sections of the axis are much elongated within the flower, as in *Lychnis* (Fig. 273) between the calyx and corolla, in *Passiflora* between the corolla and the stamens, in the Labiatae between the androecium and the ovary.

The flower of the Angiosperms like that of the Gymnosperms is a metamorphosed shoot, a leaf-bearing axis; but the Angiosperms are specially distinguished by the high degree of metamorphosis in the flowering shoot, and by the peculiar characters of the floral leaves and their relative positions, which are quite different

---

[1] These intercalary zones of growth have the properties of growing points, and new formations arise on them, as in the present case, and in such a manner that the latest is nearest to the growing point; the succession therefore is acropetal or progressive; but new formations may also be interposed between the older.

from those of the purely vegetative shoots. Hence to the eye alone the flower of the Angiosperms appears a peculiar structure and altogether distinct from the rest of the organism; and this impression is heightened by the peculiar character of the floral axis and especially by the presence of the floral envelopes, and above all by the circumstance that the floral leaves are with few exceptions arranged in rosettes, even when the leaves of the vegetative shoots are placed singly and at a distance from one another, or in two rows or in other ways. Usually the perianth, the androecium, and gynaeceum of the flower are each composed of several members arranged in concentric whorls or in closely coiled spirals, one or more whorls of perianth-leaves being succeeded by one or more whorls of stamens, which are followed by the gynaeceum in the centre of the flower; but sometimes one sometimes another of these whorls may be absent, or single whorls are represented by one member only, as in *Hippuris* (Fig. 272), where only one stamen and one carpel are developed inside a small perianth; in rare cases the whole flower is reduced to a single sporophyll, as the female flower of the Piperaceae and the male and female flowers of some Aroideae; it much more often happens that the whorls which follow one another from without inwards (from below upwards) are of the same number or are multiples of the same number [1], and spread in every direction like a rosette from a common centre, though

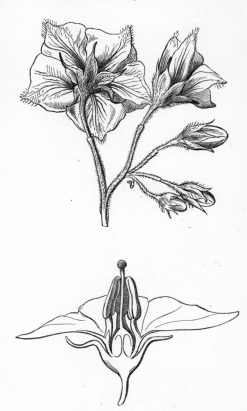

FIG. 269. Inflorescence and flower of *Solanum tuberosum,* the latter in longitudinal section.

this character is often partially concealed by subsequent bilateral development and by abortion.

The floral envelope (*perianth, perigone*) is seldom entirely wanting, as in the Piperaceae and many Aroideae; it is more often simple, that is, it consists of one whorl of two, three, four, five, or more rarely of more leaves (Figs. 267, 268); in this case the perianth is often inconspicuous and composed of small green leaves, as in the Chenopodiaceae and Urticaceae, but sometimes also large, of delicate structure and gaily coloured (*corolline*), as in *Aristolochia, Mirabilis* [2] and some others. But usually the perianth in both classes of Angiosperms is composed of two alternating

---

[1] [This is symmetry in the sense of French and English botanical writers (see pp. 411, 423).]

[2] *Mirabilis* has what looks like a calyx, but the formation is rather of the nature of an involucre. See p. 353.

whorls containing the same number of members, usually from two to five, rarely more. The structure and appearance of the two whorls is different in most Dicotyledons and in many Monocotyledons; the outer whorl, the *calyx*, is composed of

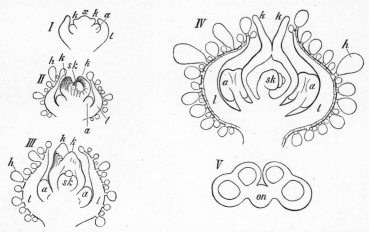

FIG. 270. *Chenopodium Quinoa. I—IV* development of the flower (longitudinal section); *II* the calyx with glandular hairs *h*, *a* anthers, *k k* carpels, *sk* ovule, *x* apex of the flowering axis. *V* transverse section of an anther with four pollen-sacs on the connective *on*, highly magnified.

usually smaller and coarser green leaves, the inner, the *corolla*, of usually larger leaves of delicate structure and colourless or coloured; it is convenient however, as Payer has suggested, to call the inner whorl the corolla, and the outer the calyx, even where

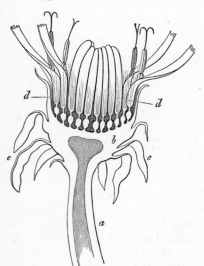

FIG. 271. Longitudinal section of an inflorescence of *Taraxacum officinale* partly diagrammatically represented. The flowering axis *a* is expanded at the summit *b* and bears the ligulate flowers *d*; the axis has a number of involucral leaves *c* beneath the inflorescence.

both whorls have the same structure, for the sake of greater brevity of expression, and also because these structural differences are not infrequently absent, the leaves of both whorls being *sepaloid*, as in the Juncaceae, or both *petaloid*, as in the Liliaceae; in *Helleborus, Aconitum,* and others, the leaves of the outer whorl only, the calyx, are petaloid, those of the inner, the corolla, have been changed into nectaries. In many Dicotyledons the perianth is not formed of alternate whorls, but of a few or more or even many turns of a spiral arrangement of leaves, the number of which is then usually large or indefinite; the outer (lower) leaves may then be sepaloid, the inner only petaloid, as in *Opuntia*, or they are all petaloid as in *Epiphyllum* and *Trollius*, or there is a gradual passage from the sepaloid through the petaloid to the staminal structure, as in *Nymphaea.*

Sometimes in place of sepaline or petaline leaves for the envelopes of the flower we find structures of a quite different kind. The female flowers of *Typha*, for example, and of some Cyperaceae are surrounded by hair-like bristles, and in the Compositae there is a circle of hairs, the *pappus*, outside the corolla in place of a calyx. The Gramineae have neither calyx nor corolla developed, the flowers being enclosed in *glumes* which are forced apart from one another when the flowers unfold by peculiar expanding bodies, the *lodicules*; these are small colourless scales of delicate texture, and have been generally supposed to be a rudimentary and imperfect perianth. It has already been mentioned that in *Aconitum, Helleborus* and other plants, the leaves of the corolla are changed into peculiarly shaped nectaries.

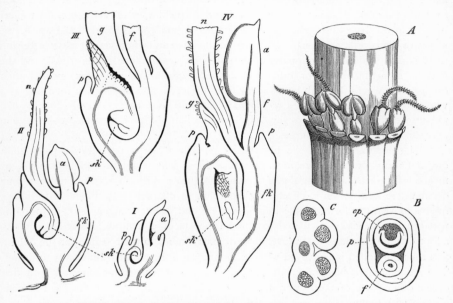

FIG. 272. *Hippuris vulgaris. A* a piece of an erect stem with the leaves of the whorl cut off, and flowers in their axils. *B* transverse section of a flower above the ovary. *C* transverse section of the anther. *I* to *IV* longitudinal sections through flowers in different stages of development. *a* anthers, *f* filament, *n* stigma, *g* style, *p* perianth, *fk* inferior ovary, *sk* the pendulous anatropous ovule; *cp* in *B* the carpel.

If the perianth is composed of one or two whorls, the leaves of one whorl or of both often appear to cohere or coalesce laterally, forming a shallower or deeper cup or tube or similar figure, and the number of the coherent leaves of calyx or corolla is usually shown by that of the marginal teeth. These coherent perianth-whorls are due to the elevation, by intercalary growth in the form of an annular lamella, of the common zone of insertion of the rudiments of the isolated leaf-structures formed on the circumference of the torus; the lamella assumes as it developes the structure of the foliar whorl which it replaces. The coherent cup-shaped or tubular portion therefore is not formed of parts originally free and subsequently united by their sides, but it grows up from the first as a whole which may be said to be intercalated at the base of the perianth-leaves; the leaves which were at first free are the marginal teeth of the common basal portion. Since a leaf of a calyx is called a *sepal*, and a leaf of a corolla a *petal*, a calyx composed of coherent leaves is said to be *gamosepalous*, and a corolla composed of coherent leaves *gamopetalous*; if the leaves of the perianth are not coherent but free, the fact is expressed by the terms *chorisepalous* and *choripetalous*[1], which, though here used in a figurative sense only, are at all events better than the terms *polypetalous* and *dialypetalous* which have also been used. If there is only one whorl of perianth-leaves present, and it is desired to express that it is composed of coherent or of free leaves, the best terms to use are *gamophyllous* and *choriphyllous*; in some cases there are two perianth-whorls, but they cohere into a single whorl, as in *Hyacinthus* and *Muscari*, where two alternating trimerous whorls unite to form a single tube with six teeth.

If the leaves of the outer and inner perianth are free and form a distinct calyx and corolla, certain differences of form may usually be observed in them in addition to the differences of structure before mentioned; the leaves of the calyx are usually broader at the base and sessile, of very simple outline and pointed at the apex; the leaves of the corolla are usually narrower at the base and often very broad above, and there is often a distinction apparent between stalk (*claw*) and lamina (*limb*), and the limb is sometimes cleft or otherwise divided; *ligules* often appear on the inner (upper) side where the limb bends away from the claw, and these when regarded as a whole in a flower are termed a *corona*, as in *Lychnis*, *Saponaria*, *Nerium*, the Hydrophylleae, etc.; if the corolla is gamopetalous, the parts of the corona also cohere, as in *Narcissus* where it is very large.

The general form of the perianth, especially when it is distinctly petaloid in character and of some size, always stands in a definite relation to pollination by means of insects, and large gaily-coloured delicate strongly-scented flowers only occur where fertilisation is effected by them; these characters are intended to induce insects to visit the flowers; the infinite variety and often strangeness of form in the perianth are specially calculated to compel insects of a definite size and species to adopt definite positions and movements of their bodies in their search for the nectar, and thus the pollen is conveyed without intention on their part from flower to flower. The multilateral or bilateral symmetry of the perianth is usually connected with that of the other parts of the flower, and will be discussed therefore further on in connection with them.

Besides the perianth in the narrower sense which we have hitherto been describing, other forms of envelope also occur not unfrequently in the single flower. In the Malvaceae and in some other cases the calyx proper appears to be surrounded by a second calyx, the *epicalyx* or *calyculus*, which, however, is not a calyx morphologically; in *Malope trifida*, for example, the three parts of the epicalyx represent a sub-floral bract with its two stipules, in *Kitaibelia vitifolia* an epicalyx of six parts is formed out of two similar sub-floral leaves with their four stipules (Payer)[2]. But the epicalyx may also be only apparent, as in the Roseae and Potentilleae, where the true calyx-leaves produce stipular structures which unite in each case in pairs, and form a small and apparently simple leaf. In *Dianthus*, *Caryophyllus*, and other genera, a kind of epicalyx is formed by two decussate pairs of small bracts immediately beneath the calyx; in the terminal flowers of the Anemoneae there is a whorl

---

[1] From χωρίς, *separate*.

[2] Eichler doubts the correctness of Payer's view of the epicalyx of the Malvaceae, and the point will have to be again investigated.

of foliage-leaves a little way beneath the flower, and this in the allied plant *Eranthis hyemalis* becomes a kind of epicalyx. The epicalyx of the small flowers of the Dipsaceae is particularly interesting : each flower within the crowded inflorescence is surrounded by a membranous sac, which forms an epicalyx. If, when the perianth and sporophylls of the flower are already formed, a growth takes place from the peduncle beneath the flower, at first as an annular swelling which afterwards developes into the form of a cup and produces scaly or spinous emergences, the structure thus formed is called a *cupule*; of such a kind is the cup in the acorn of some species of *Quercus*[1] ; in this case the cupule only surrounds a single flower, but in *Castanea* and *Fagus* it envelopes a small inflorescence, and this spiny cupule afterwards opens by valves from above downwards to release the ripened fruits. If an inflorescence is surrounded with a peculiarly developed whorl or with a rosette of leaves, as in the Umbelliferae and Compositae, this envelope is termed an *involucre*; if a single sheath-like leaf envelopes an inflorescence belonging to its own axis, it is called a *spathe*. Both involucre and spathe may assume a petaloid structure; the former, for instance, in *Cornus florida*, the latter in many Aroids.

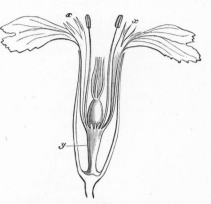

FIG. 273. Longitudinal section of the flower of *Lychnis flos-Jovis* ; *y* the elongated portion of the axis between calyx and corolla, *x* ligule of the petals (corona).

The *androecium* is the collective name for all the male sporophylls of a single flower ; each one of them is called a *stamen*, and consists of the *anther* and of the *filament* on which it is placed; the filament is usually filiform, but sometimes broad and leaf-like. The anther is formed of two equal longitudinal lobes placed on the upper part of the filament right and left of its median line ; the part of the filament which bears the anther-lobes is distinguished as the *connective*.

The position of the stamens on the floral axis or torus in all hermaphrodite and in most purely male flowers is unquestionably lateral. From this lateral position of the stamens, from their exogenous origin from the primary meristem next the growing point of the floral axis, from their acropetal development and their frequent monstrosities in which they assume more or less the character of floral or even of foliage-leaves, they must be regarded in the morphological sense as foliar structures, and may be suitably termed staminal leaves. The lateral position is liable to exception in a variety of cases. In *Naias* the vegetative cone of the male floral axis becomes a quadrilocular anther[2] by the formation of pollen-mother-cells in four longitudinal peripheral strips of its tissue, and a similar arrangement occurs in *Casuarina*[3] and in the unbranched stamens of *Typha*. In *Cyclanthera* also the

---

[1] On its development, see Hofmeister, Allg. Morphologie, p. 495.

[2] Magnus, Beitr. z. Morphol. d. Gattung *Naias*, Berlin, 1870. See also Bot. Ztg. 1869, p. 771.

[3] Kaufmann, Ueber d. männl. Blüthe von *Casuarina* (Bulletin de la soc. imp. d. sc. nat. de Moscou, 1868).

peculiar anther proceeds from the floral axis itself[1]; it has two annular loculaments, an upper and a lower. Since the rest of the Cucurbitaceae have distinct
staminal leaves of the normal form, comparative morphology considers the one anther
of *Cyclanthera* as formed of five anthers completely fused together, though there are
none but phylogenetic reasons for this view, there being no visible signs of any such
amalgamation. The four loculaments of an anther are simply sporangia sunk in the
swollen tissue of the anther[2], and their development agrees perfectly in all points with
that of the microsporangia of the Gymnosperms and of the sporangia of the Equisetaceae and Lycopodieae[3]. Two loculaments are formed in the anterior and two in
the posterior angles of the young stamen; but the position of the loculaments is often
different from this in the mature state of the stamen; either two are lateral on the
stamen, and two are on its dorsal side, that is, the side towards the floral axis, or the
loculaments all appear to belong either to the dorsal or to the opposite and ventral
side. Displacements of this kind are caused by subsequent processes of growth in
the young anther, especially in the region of the connective[4]. Anthers in which the
loculaments are turned outwards are said to be *extrorse*, as in *Aristolochia, Tamarix,*
and *Iris,* those with loculaments turned inwards are *introrse,* as in *Cypripedium* and
Nuphar. Before proceeding to the consideration of the pollen-sacs and their
contents, we will return for a moment to the subject of the entire stamen and the
androecium. The stalk or support of the anther (the filament with the connective) is
either simple or articulated; the simple stalk may be filiform (Fig. 269), or dilated
and leaf-like (Fig. 268 *D*), or sometimes even very broad, as in the Asclepiadeae and
Apocynaceae, or it is enlarged below (Fig. 275 *f*) or above; it usually terminates
between the two anther-lobes, but is sometimes prolonged above them (Fig. 268 *D*)
as a projecting point or in the shape of a long process, as in *Oleander.* If the upper
part, the connective, is broad, the two anther-lobes are distinctly separated (Fig. 268,
274); if it is narrow, they lie close together. The articulation of the filament is very
frequently due to the sharp demarcation of the filament from the connective by a
deep constriction; the connection is kept up by so slender a piece of tissue that the
anther and connective together oscillate and turn freely on the filament (*versatile
anther*); the point of attachment may be at the lower or upper end or in the middle
of the connective (Fig. 275); sometimes the connective attains a considerable size
and forms appendages beyond the anther (Fig. 276 *A, x*), or it developes as a cross-
bar between the two anther-lobes, so that filament and connective form a T, as in
Tilia and still more notably in *Salvia,* in which the transverse connective has only a

---

[1] Warming, Ueber pollenbildende Phyllome u. Caulome in Hanstein's Abh. II. Bd. I.—Engler,
Beitr. z. Kenntn. d. Antherenbildung d. Metaspermen (Angiospermen) in Pringsheim's Jahrb. f. wiss.
Bot. x. p. 275.

[2] It is necessary therefore in dealing with the anther to distinguish carefully between the tissue
of the stamen (the sporophyll) and the microsporangia; the old explanations, which were founded
on malformations and are now obsolete, often enough neglected this distinction, though the right
conception is to be found in Cassini and Roeper. In malformations (phyllomorphy, frondescence)
we get the stamen in different states according to the stage of its development at the time that it
experienced the metamorphosis into a vegetative leaf, and these states, though very interesting in
themselves, have given occasion to some absurd notions.

[3] See Goebel, *loc. cit.,* on page 325.

[4] Warming, *loc. cit.*; Engler, *loc. cit.*

half anther at the extremity of one arm, the other arm remaining sterile and serving to other ends. It depends on the nature of the connection of the connective with the two anther-lobes whether these are parallel to one another, in which case they usually adhere to the connective along their whole length, or whether they are connected together below and are separated above, or are free below and united

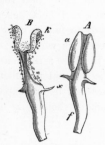

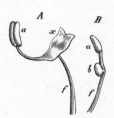

FIG. 274. *A* stamen of *Mahonia Aquifolium*. *B* the same with anther open. *a* anther-lobe, *k* ruptured valve of anther, *x* hook-like process, *f* filament.

FIG. 275. Stamen of *Arbutus hybrida* with the anther *a* open; *f* filament, *x* appendage.

FIG. 276. Stamens of *Centradenia rosea*. *A* a larger fertile, *B* a smaller sterile stamen. *f* filament, *a*, *b* anthers, *x* appendage of connective.

above, in which latter case they may diverge from one another to such an extent as to lie in one line above the top of the filament, as in the Labiatae. The filament frequently has appendages, such for instance as the membranous expansions or appendages, like stipules, right and left of the lower part of the filament in *Allium*, or a hood-shaped out-growth behind, as in the Asclepiadeae, or ligular structures in

FIG. 277. Longitudinal section of the flower of *Calothamnus*, one of the Myrtaceae; *f* the ovary, *s* the calyx, *p* the petals, *g* the style, *st* branched stamens.

FIG. 278. Part of a male flower of *Ricinus communis* in longitudinal section; *ff* the basal portions of the repeatedly branched stamens, *a* the anthers.

front, as in *Alyssum montanum*, or hook-like processes on one side beneath the anther, as in *Crambe*, or on both sides, as in Fig. 274 *x*.

A phenomenon of the greatest importance for the understanding of the morphology of the flower is the branching of the stamens which occurs in many Dicotyledons, and which was often confounded by the older botanists with their cohesion, though the two things are fundamentally distinct.   Sometimes the branching is bilateral in one plane right and left of the median line, as in foliage-leaves, so that the branched stamen appears to be pinnate, as in *Calothamnus* (Fig. 277 *st*), where each pinna bears an anther; but in other cases it is in the nature of a polytomy, as in *Ricinus* (Fig. 278), where the separate filaments emerge from the torus as simple protuberances, and each protuberance repeatedly produces new protuberances, which ultimately develope by intercalary growth into a filament with many and repeated ramifications bearing anthers on all their free extremities.   In the Hypericineae, after the formation of the corolla, from three to five large broad protuberances appear on the circumference of the floral axis (Fig. 279, *II–IV, a*), each of which gradually developes smaller roundish prominences from the apex to the base; these are the rudiments of stamens and are connected at the base in the original protuberance, being branches of it.   A transverse section through the flower-bud before expansion shows, especially in *Hypericum calycinum*, the numerous filaments belonging to one

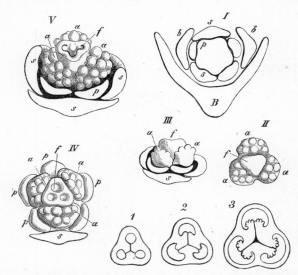

FIG. 279.   Development of the flower of *Hypericum perforatum. I* young flower-bud in the axil of its bract *B* with two bracteoles *b b*; *s* the sepals, *p* first indication of petals.   *II* middle portion of a somewhat older bud; *f* rudiment of the ovary, *a a a* the three stamens with their branches appearing as protuberances.   *III* a flower-bud of nearly the same age as *II*, but seen from the side; *s* a sepal, *a a* the stamens, *f* the ovary.   *IV* and *V* buds in a more advanced state, the letters denoting the same parts as in *I, II, III.*   1, 2, 3 are ovaries in various stages of development and cut through transversely.

origin closely crowded together into one bundle.   In this and similar cases the common primordial base of the stamen remains very short, while the branches elongate considerably and appear later as a tuft of filaments springing from the torus, so that their true nature could only be known from the history of development[1]; if, on the other hand, the primordial basal portion elongates as in *Calothamnus* and *Ricinus*, the stamen in the matured condition is readily seen to be branched.

The coherence of the stamens which stand side by side in the same whorl is not less important for recognising the general plan of the structure of a flower and the

---

[1] Beitr. z. Morphol. u. Physiol. d. Blattes, III (Bot. Ztg. 1882).

real relations of number and position in its parts. In *Cucurbita*, for example, there are the rudiments of five stamens, while at a later period only three are found, but two of these are broader than the third ; each of the two is formed by the lateral cohesion of two stamens; the filaments unite to form a central column, on which the pollen-sacs growing more rapidly in length than the filaments form vermiform convolutions (Fig. 280, *III*).

FIG. 280. *Cucurbita Pepo.* Development of the androecium ; in the three figures the simple stamen is to the right, one double stamen formed by coherence of two simple ones is behind, and one to the left. The anthers grow vigorously in length and form convolutions. After Payer.

The conditions are more complicated and more difficult to understand when cohesion and branching of the stamens occur simultaneously, as in the Malvaceae. In *Althaea rosea*, for example, the androecium forms a closed membranous tube completely surrounding the gynaeceum ; outside this tube are five vertical double rows of long filaments (Fig. 281 *B*, *f*) parallel to each other, each of which divides into two arms (*t*) each carrying a half anther. The history of development and comparison with allied forms shows that the tube is formed by the lateral cohesion of five stamens, but the cohering margins produce double rows of lateral branches, which

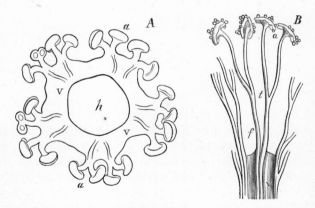

FIG. 281. *Althaea rosea.* *A* transverse section through the young androecium. *B* a piece of the tube of a fully formed androecium with a few stamens. *h* cavity of the tube, V substance of the tube, *a* the anthers, *t* the point where the filament divides, *f* the point where two filaments spring from the tube. *A* is much more highly magnified than *B*.

are the filaments, and each of these divides into two arms. The transverse section of the young tube in Fig. 281 *A* shows these double rows of divided filaments quite clearly ; the part (V) which lies between two of them must be considered to be the body of a stamen, the margins of which right and left bear each a single row of filaments as laciniae or branches[1]. In *Tilia*, where the five primordial stamens

---

[1] This view of the matter will cease to seem strange if we consider the nature of an unilocular ovary, in which the margins of the cohering carpels form parietal projections, and the ovules arise in

branch at their margins in the same manner and form anthers on the branches, the stamens remain free below ; but in other points the conditions are the same [1].

The stamens not unfrequently suffer remarkable displacements caused by the intercalary growth of the tissue of the torus at the place of their insertion, and these displacements are also commonly treated as cases of coalescence of parts. Thus the stamens frequently unite with the calyx or with the corolla; in this case in the mature state the filaments seem to grow from the inner surface of the perianth-leaves ; but the early stages of development show that the perianth-leaves and the stamens emerge one after the other and separately from the torus ; it is not till afterwards that intercalary growth begins at the spot in the torus at which they both appeared, and thus a lamella grows up which is in structure the basal portion of the perianth-leaf, and at the same time bears the stamen, which thus appears to grow from the middle of the

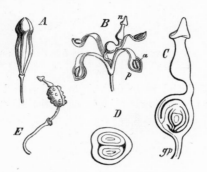

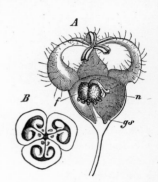

FIG. 282. Flower of *Manglesia glabrata*, one of the Proteaceae. *A* before the opening of the flower. *B* the flower unfolded. *C* the gynaeceum; *gp* the gynophore. *D* transverse section of the ovary. *E* fruit ripening on its stalk.

FIG. 283. *A* flower of *Sterculia Balanghas*; *gs* the gynophore, *f* ovary, *n* stigma. *B* transverse section of the ovary.

inner face of the perianth-leaf. In Fig. 282 *B*, *p* is a perianth-leaf, *a* an anther which is sessile upon it; these stood at first separately one above the other on the young torus, and the portion of the leaf underneath *a* and *p* was formed some time after by intercalary growth, and carried up with it the true perianth-leaf *p* and the stamen *a* together. This mode of coalescence is especially frequent in flowers in which the parts of the corolla are united laterally into a tube, as in the Compositae, Labiatae, Valerianeae and other families. But the stamens may also unite in various ways with the gynaeceum. In *Sterculia Balanghas* (Fig. 283 *A*) the connection is only apparent and simply arises from the fact, that the small sessile stamens immediately beneath the ovary are carried up with it by the elongation of a part of the torus, and appear from their small size to be mere appendages of the large ovary ; the part that bears the two organs, the *gonophore*, is here therefore an internode of

---

double rows on the cohering margins (placentas); that which takes place here inside in regard to the ovules takes place in the other case outside in the formation of the filaments; at the same time a fresh comparative investigation of the history of development in the flower of the Malvaceae is desirable.

[1] See Payer, *l. c.*, on page 346.

the flowering axis [1]. Much more complicated is the mode of formation of the true *gynostemium* above an inferior ovary, as in the Aristolochiaceae and still more in the Orchideae, in which these unions and displacements of the parts of the flower are combined with the abortion of certain members. As the subject will be further explained in the appendix, it will be sufficient in this place to examine Fig. 284, which represents the flower of *Cypripedium* after removal of the perianth *pp* in *A* from the side, in *B* from behind, in *C* from the front; *f* is the inferior ovary, *gs* the gynostemium produced by the adhesion of three stamens—two of which *a a* are fertile and the third *s* a sterile staminode—with the carpel, the anterior part of which bears the stigma *n*. In this case the gynostemium is entirely composed of floral structures which have coalesced together, namely of the basal portions of the stamens and carpels, both of which spring from the upper margin of the hollow torus which forms the inferior ovary *f*. (See below on the development and interpretation of the flowers of the Orchideae.)

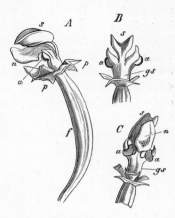

FIG. 284. Flower of *Cypripedium Calceolus* after removal of the perianth *p p* (see the text).

The size and shape of the stamens is often different in the same flower; in the Cruciferae, for instance, there are two shorter and four longer stamens, in the Labiatae, two shorter and two longer; in these two cases the androecia are termed *tetradynamous* and *didynamous* respectively; in *Centradenia* they are not only of different sizes but also differently articulated, as is shown in Fig. 276 *A* and *B*. Supported by the history of development and a comparison of relationships of number and position in allied flowers we are even justified in speaking of stamens without anthers, that is, without that which is physiologically their characteristic mark. Thus in *Geranium* there are two whorls of fertile stamens, but in its near ally *Erodium* the stamens of one of the whorls have no anthers; these sterile staminal leaves or *staminodes* usually undergo further changes, becoming unlike the fertile stamens and often petaloid,

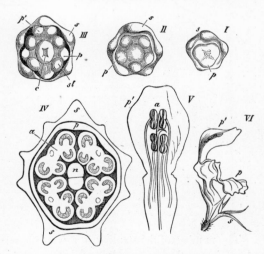

FIG. 285. Stages in the development of the flower of *Lamium album*. *I, II, III* very young buds seen from above; *I* after the formation of the rudiments of the sepals *s*, *II* after the appearance of the petals *p*, *III* after that of the stamens *st* and carpels *c*. *IV* transverse section of an older bud. *s* the tube of the gamosepalous calyx, *p* that of the gamopetalous corolla, *a* anthers, *n* stigmas. *V* upper lip of the corolla with the epipetalous stamens. *VI* the entire mature flower seen from the side.

---

[1] [An elongation of this character below the gynaeceum alone is a *gynophore*, one below the androecium is an *androphore*.]

like the innermost stamens of *Aquilegia*, or they assume special forms, as in *Cypripedium* (Fig. 284 *s*); in some Gesneraceae a gland-like structure, a nectary, takes the place of a posterior stamen (see Fig. 352). Metamorphoses of this kind may be considered as the first steps in abortion, which may go so far that an empty place is ultimately left in the flower where a stamen ought to have been, as in the Labiatae, the near allies of the Gesneraceae, where the staminode has disappeared and there is nothing in its place; there are only four stamens instead of the five required by the plan of the flower, and the first rudiment even of the fifth, the posterior stamen, is wanting, as Fig. 285 shows. Instances of this kind completely justify us in assuming abortion in cases also in which the absent organ does not disappear during development but is wanting from the beginning, provided that a comparison of the number and position of the parts in nearly allied plants gives ground for supposing that there is something missing; but it is the modern theory of descent which supplies certain grounds for the assumption of abortion of this kind.

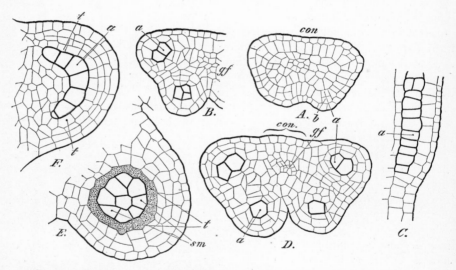

FIG. 286. Development of the microsporangia (pollen-sacs) of Angiosperms. *A—D Doronicum macrophyllum.* *A* transverse section of a very young anther; at *a* a cell of the periblem has divided into an inner cell *a*, the archesporium, and an outer *b*, the primary tapetal cell; *con* the connective. *B* transverse section through a lobe of a somewhat older anther; the archesporium *a*, or the cells formed from it are denoted by stronger outlines. *C* part of a longitudinal section in which the archesporium *a* appears as a cell-row. *D* transverse section of an older anther, the cells of the primary tapetal layer have divided and the inner layers which adjoin the archesporia *a* are becoming tapetal cells; *gf* rudimentary vascular bundle of the connective *con*. *E* a microsporangium (pollen-sac) of an older anther of *Menyanthes trifoliata* in transverse section; *sm* pollen-mother-cells (sporogenous cell-group) surrounded by the tapetal cells *t* (darker); the wall of the anther is of several layers through the division of the cells of the primary tapetal layer. *F* transverse section of a loculament of an anther of *Mentha aquatica*; *a* archesporium, *t* tapetal cells. After Warming.

The number of the stamens in a flower is seldom limited to one or two; like the perianth-leaves they are generally present in larger numbers, and are then arranged in the form of rosettes, either spirally or in whorls. If the perianth-leaves are arranged spirally, the stamens also are generally so arranged, and in that case their number is usually large (*indefinite*), as in *Nymphaea, Magnolia, Ranunculus* and *Helleborus*, though it may be small (*definite*). But it is more common to find the stamens in one or more whorls, and where there are several whorls the number of the stamens in each is the same, and the same as that of the parts of the perianth;

the whorls also alternate with one another and with those of the perianth; yet there are many cases of deviation from this rule, often due to the abortion of single members or of entire whorls, or to the multiplication of both, or to the superposition of consecutive whorls; two or even more stamens not unfrequently make their appearance close to one another instead of a single one; such cases are often difficult to explain, but they are of great value for determining natural affinities and must be examined again further on.

Development of the pollen and anther-wall [1]. The following account refers only to the ordinary cases, in which the pollen is produced in four loculaments or compartments of the anther, in other words where there are four microsporangia present, and in which it forms isolated grains which fall out on the dehiscence of the anthers; some of the more important exceptions will be noticed below.

Immediately after the leaves of the perianth or those of the innermost whorl first become visible as roundish protuberances on the circumference of the torus, the rudiments of the stamens make their appearance in similar form, but they usually grow

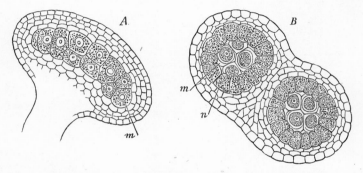

FIG. 287. *Althaea rosea.* *A* pollen-sac seen from the side. *B* transverse section of an anther-lobe showing the two pollen-sacs. *m* the pollen-mother-cells, in *A* still connected together into a tissue, in *B* already divided each into four pollen-grains, *n* the tapetal cells. Each anther-lobe consisting of two pollen-sacs is here borne on a long branch of the filament.

more rapidly than the corolla, which often remains for a considerable time in a very rudimentary condition. The young stamen which is composed of homogeneous protomeristem soon shows the outlines of the two anther-lobes united by the connective; the filament is at this time still very short and for a while grows slowly, but ultimately before the opening of the flower it increases rapidly in length by the elongation of its cells. When the protuberances which answer to the four future pollen-sacs begin to be visible externally on the young anthers, the differentiation of the mother-cells of the pollen from the hitherto homogeneous tissue begins in each of the protuberances. The development of the sporangia in the Angiosperms agrees entirely with that of the sporangia in the Vascular Cryptogams, as for example in the Lycopodiaceae. In both cases the young anther consists of a small-celled protomeristem

---

[1] Nägeli, Zur Entwicklungsgesch. d. Pollens, Zürich, 1842.—Hofmeister, Neue Beitr. z. Kenntn. d. Embryobild. d. Phanerog. I. Monocot.—Warming, Unters. ü. pollenbildende Phyllome u. Caulome in Hanstein, Bot. Abh. Bd. II. 1873.—Engler, Beitr. z. Kenntn. d. Antherenbildung in Pringsh. Jahrb. Bd. X.

(Fig. 286 *A*), from which a vascular bundle is usually formed, passing through the middle of the connective, while the outermost peripheral layer forms the dermatogen or young epidermis. According to Warming's minute investigations it is only the layer of tissue immediately under the epidermis, the outermost layer of periblem, which gives rise both to the archesporium and to the parietal layers which surround the archesporium in each pollen-sac. In other words this layer next beneath the epidermis in each of the four longitudinal protuberances separates into

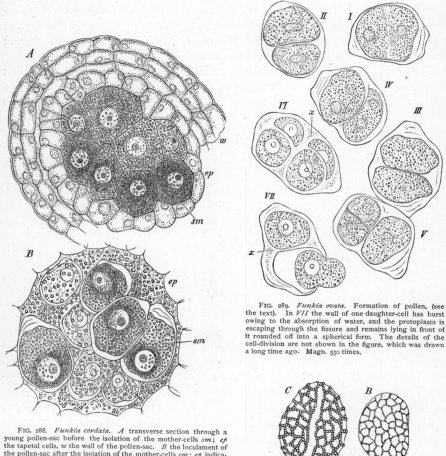

FIG. 289. *Funkia ovata.* Formation of pollen, (see the text). In *VII* the wall of one daughter-cell has burst owing to the absorption of water, and the protoplasm is escaping through the fissure and remains lying in front of it rounded off into a spherical form. The details of the cell-division are not shown in the figure, which was drawn a long time ago. Magn. 550 times.

FIG. 288. *Funkia cordata. A* transverse section through a young pollen-sac before the isolation of the mother-cells *sm*; *ep* the tapetal cells, *w* the wall of the pollen-sac. *B* the loculament of the pollen-sac after the isolation of the mother-cells *sm*; *ep* indication of the tapetal cells. For the further development of the pollen-mother-cells and of the pollen see Figs. 289 and 290. Magn. 500 times.

FIG. 290. *B* a young pollen-cell of *Funkia ovata*; the bead-like thickenings which project outwardly are still small, but larger in the older cell *C*; they are disposed in lines connected into a network.

two layers, the innermost of which is the *archesporium.* The cells of the archesporium very soon become distinguished by their size as compared with those of the surrounding tissue, and when seen in a transverse section of the anther they usually

form a band of several cells, concave towards the inside, in each of the four protuberances (Fig. 286 *F*), but in some cases the transverse section shows only one
archesporial cell in each protuberance, and there is therefore only a longitudinal row
of these cells in each; this is the case in the Compositae and Malvaceae (Fig. 286 *C*);
still more rarely only single archesporial cells are formed, as in the Mimoseae. There
is usually but little division of the cells of the archesporium before the formation of
the tetrads; consequently the number of the pollen-mother-cells is usually not much
greater than that of the cells of the archesporium; but it does sometimes happen
that the original simple layer or row of archesporial cells divides in all directions and
produces several layers or a cylindrical mass of mother-cells (Fig. 286 *E*). The
layer of cells (*primary tapetal layer*[1]) formed, as was stated above, by the longitudinal
division of the layer from which also the layer of primary mother-cells is derived, and
lying between the latter and the epidermis, divides according to Warming usually
into three layers, in which radial, horizontal and tangential walls are formed alternately. The innermost of these three layers (Fig. 288 *A ep*, Fig. 287 *B n*), supplemented by a corresponding layer on the side of the group of mother-cells next the
axis of the anther, developes into the *tapetum*, which becomes disorganised as the
sporangium matures, as in many of the Vascular Cryptogams. The same fate befalls
the cells of the next outer layer, which do not however assume the glandular appearance of the tapetal cells. The outermost of the three layers, which lies therefore
immediately beneath the epidermis of the loculament, forms the layer of fibrous cells
which causes the dehiscence of the anther (Fig. 299 *G*, *β*), and to which we shall
return again a little later. The large pollen-mother-cells (Fig. 288 *A*, *sm*) are at
first thin-walled; but their walls become considerably and in most cases unequally
thickened (Fig. 288 *B*), and the thickening material is usually distinctly stratified. In
many Monocotyledons the mother-cells now become completely isolated, the loculament
enlarges, and the cells float singly or in groups in a granular fluid which fills the cavity
(Fig. 288 *B*), a circumstance which at once recalls the formation of spores in the Vascular Cryptogams. But in many Dicotyledons, as *Tropaeolum, Althaea*, and other genera,
the very thick-walled mother-cells do not become isolated but completely fill the loculament, and usually separate after the disruption of the wall of the anther in water.

As the cell-wall of the pollen-mother-cell becomes thickened, the protoplasmic
body rounds itself off, and the large central nucleus divides when the preparation for
the formation of *pollen-grains* (*microspores*) commences. The latter process[2] presents
two modifications. In one, which is the most frequent in the Monocotyledons, the
division of the nucleus of the pollen-mother-cell is followed by the formation of a wall
between the two daughter-cells, so that the mother-cell is now divided into two cells

---

[1] ['Primary tapetal cell,' 'primary tapetal layer,' are adopted as renderings of 'Schichtzelle'
and 'Schicht zwischen Archespor und Epidermis,' that is, the cell or layer cut off from the periblem-
cell or layer, the other portion of which forms the archesporium. A distinctive term for this cell or
layer is wanted, and the one here adopted appears suitable, implying as it does that the cell or layer
is that from which the tapetum is derived; the other cells or layers formed from it may be
distinguished as 'parietal cells,' 'parietal layers.' In the ovule the primary tapetal cell is Strasburger's 'tapetal cell' (see page 386). The occurrence of this cell or layer has been already referred
to in Lycopodineae and Gymnosperms (see pp. 294, 332).]

[2] Strasburger, Zellbildung u. Zelltheilung, III. Ed., Jena, 1880, p. 130.

lying beside one another (Fig. 289), and as each cell divides again, the four 'special mother-cells' are formed, and the contents of each of these becomes a pollen-grain or microspore. In most Dicotyledons the process is somewhat different; the division of

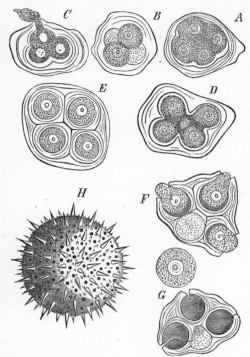

the pollen-mother-cell is not followed by the formation of a firm wall of cellulose, but the daughter-nuclei divide again at once in intersecting planes. The four nuclei then take up a position to one another answering to the four angles of a tetrahedron, and it is only then that firm walls are formed, which divide the mother-cell into four daughter-cells disposed tetrahedrally. Ridge-like projections appear first on the inner wall of the pollen-mother-cell (Fig. 291 *A, D*) corresponding in position to the cell-plates between the four nuclei. Then partition-walls form very rapidly between the separate cells and attach themselves to these projections. The pollen-mother-cell thus divided into four is called a tetrad.

The mass of cellulose round each separate cell of the tetrad is differentiated into concentric systems of layers (the 'special mother-cells'), and these are surrounded by

Fig. 291. *Althaea rosea. A—E* division of the mother-cells of the pollen into four. *F* and *G* a tetrad, in which the walls of the special mother-cells are bursting under the influence of water and allowing the protoplasm of the young pollen-grains to escape. *H* a mature pollen-grain seen from without and magnified the same number of times as the other figures.

the common layers which encompass the whole tetrad (Figs. 291 *E*, 294); if the tetrads lie some time in water, the layers often burst, and the protoplasmic bodies of the young pollen-grains escape through the rent and become rounded off into a spherical

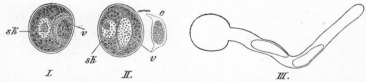

Fig. 292. *Leucojum aestivum.* Pollen-grains (microspores) with vegetative cells. *I* shows the pollen-grain after division into the vegetative cell *v* and the larger cell with the nucleus *sk.* In *II* the vegetative cell has become detached; *o* is the vegetative cell after treatment with osmic acid. *III* a pollen-grain which has put out a tube (the contents not shown) with two similar nuclei. After Elfving. Magn. 400 times.

form (Fig. 289 *VII* and Fig. 291 *F, G*). Soon after the conversion of the pollen-mother-cell into a tetrad, each of the daughter-masses of protoplasm invests itself with a new and at first very delicate cell-wall, which is not connected with the innermost layer of the concentric system of wall-layers, as is shown clearly by its separation from it after contraction in alcohol; this is the true wall of the pollen-grain, and it now becomes rapidly thicker and differentiated into an outer cuticularised layer, the *exine*, and an inner one of pure cellulose, the *intine*; the former becomes covered on the outer surface with spikes (Fig. 294 *ph*), warts, ridges, combs, &c., while the latter often forms considerable thickenings, which project inwards at certain spots (Fig. 294 *v*), and take part at a later period in the formation of the pollen-tube. During these processes the layers of cellulose surrounding the tetrads slowly dissolve, their substance is converted into mucilage and their form finally disappears; their disorganisation may commence on the inner side of the wall of the mother-cell (Fig. 289 *VII, x*) or on the outer side (Fig. 294 *sg*). By the dissolution of the chambers in which the young pollen-grains were till now enclosed, they are set at liberty and separate from one another and float in the granular fluid which fills the cavity of the loculament, and there attain to their ultimate development and size; in this process the fluid is used up, and the ripe pollen-grains are at length a powdery mass filling the anther-chamber.

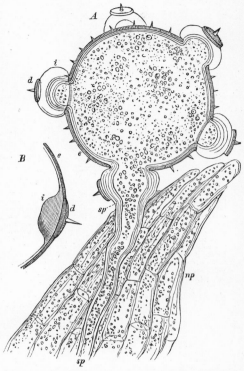

FIG. 293. *Cucurbita Pepo.* *A* a pollen-grain putting out its tube *sp* which is penetrating into a papilla of the stigma *np*. The intine is much thickened at certain spots *B i*; the exine forms a round lid *d* upon each thickening-mass; when the grain prepares to germinate, the thick layers of the intine swell, and lift off the piece of exine which forms the lid; pollen tubes are formed from one or two of these thickening-masses. Magn. 550 times.

Similar processes take place in the ripe pollen-grains or microspores of the Angiosperms to those with which we are acquainted in the microspores of the Gymnosperms, as Strasburger has recently discovered[1]. The pollen-grain either immediately after its formation, or at some later time but always before pollination, becomes divided into two cells, a larger cell and a smaller 'vegetative' or prothallium-cell

---

[1] Strasburger, Ueber Befruchtung und Zelltheilung, Jena, 1878.—Elfving, Studien ü. d. Pollenkörner d. Angiospermen (Jen. Zeitschr. f. Naturw. Bd. XIII, N.F. Bd. VI).—On the external sculpturing etc. see Schacht in Jahrb. f. wiss. Bot. II. 149, and Lürssen in the same publication, VII. p. 34. [Strasburger's more recent views regarding the homologies of the pollen-grain and the nature of the processes which go on within it are referred to in a note on page 310. In the case of Angiosperms the small cell, the so-called prothallium-cell, is, he maintains, the progamous cell, its nucleus combining with the nucleus of the oosphere, and it will therefore be the homologue of the large cell in Gymnosperms.]

(Fig. 292 *v*), the latter of which may divide and form a tissue of two or three cells, but most commonly remains undivided. The vegetative cell is only separated from the large cell by a layer of protoplasm which is soon absorbed; in isolated cases only a more substantial membrane, perhaps of cellulose, has been observed. The pollen-tube is formed as in the Gymnosperms from the large cell, and sometimes the vegetative cell or cells take no part in this process, and only the contents of the large cell pass into the tube. But usually, as was said, the wall or layer between the small vegetative cell, the prothallium, and the large cell is absorbed, and the former becomes detached from the inner wall of the pollen-grain and assumes a peculiar fusiform or crescent-shaped appearance (Fig. 292 *II*); this proceeding we may consider to be a retrogressive metamorphosis. The free-floating vegetative cell may itself divide, and the cells thus produced also pass into the pollen-tube and there disappear. The mode of formation of vegetative cells in the pollen-grain is the same therefore in Angiosperms as in Gymnosperms, but in Angiosperms these cells are either not separated by firm walls of cellulose from the cells which form the tube, or they are rarely so separated, and this produces the small complications above described.

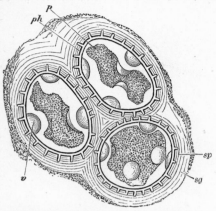

FIG. 294. Mother-cells of the pollen of *Cucurbita Pepo*; *sg* the external common layers of the mother-cell in process of dissolution, *sp* the so-called special mother-cells consisting of masses of layers of the mother-cell which surround the young pollen-grains, and are also subsequently dissolved, *ph* the wall of the pollen-grain, the spikes of which grow outwards and pierce through the special mother-cell, *v* hemispherical deposits of cellulose on the wall of the pollen-grain, from which the pollen-tubes are subsequently formed, *p* the protoplasm of the pollen-grain contracted; the preparation was obtained by making a section through an anther which had lain some months in absolute alcohol. Magn. 550 times.

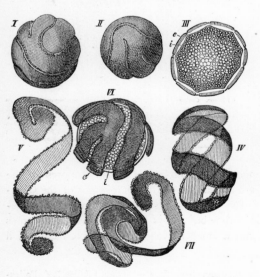

FIG. 295. Pollen of *Thunbergia alata*. *I* and *II* in concentrated sulphuric acid. *IV*, *V* and *VII* in the same acid after solution of the intine. *III* in Schulze's solution, in optical transverse section. *VI* in strong solution of potash. *e* the exine, *i* the intine. The fissures in the exine are evidently due to subsequent internal differentiation.

The pollen-tube is a protuberance of the intine which breaks through the exine usually at definite spots prepared beforehand; there are often several or even very many such points of exit in a grain (Figs. 296 *a*, 297 *o*), and it is possible therefore for as many pollen-tubes to be formed from it; but usually one only developes vigorously and effects fertilisation. Apart from the sculpture which has already been described on the exine, the external form and the structure of the outer coat of the pollen-grain depends chiefly on the number and arrangement of the points of exit, and on the condition and behaviour of the exine at these points; whether it is simply thinner there while the intine protrudes as a wart (Fig. 296), or whether roundish pieces like lids are detached from it, as in the Cucurbitaceae (Fig. 293), or *Passiflora*, or whether it splits up into ribands by spiral fissures, as in *Thunbergia* (Fig. 295), and so on. The intine is usually thicker at the points of exit, and often forms semi-circular protuberances which supply the first material for the formation of the tube (Fig. 296 *i*), or the exine only forms thinner longitudinal striae which are furrows in the dry pollen-grain, as in *Gladiolus*, *Yucca*, *Helleborus*, and others. But in many plants the intine is uniformly and continuously thickened, as in *Canna*, *Strelitzia*

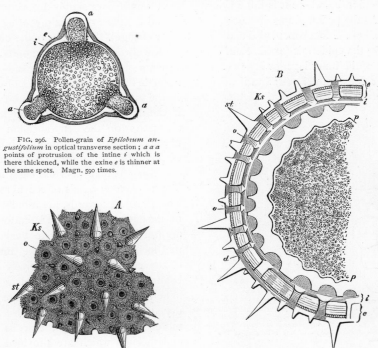

FIG. 296. Pollen-grain of *Epilobium angustifolium* in optical transverse section; *a a a* points of protrusion of the intine *i* which is there thickened, while the exine *e* is thinner at the same spots. Magn. 590 times.

FIG. 297. Pollen-grain of *Althaea rosea*. *A* portion of the exine seen from without. *B* the half of a very thin aequatorial section of the grain. *st* large spikes, *Ks* small spikes of the exine, *o* holes in the exine, *e* the exine, *i* the intine, *p* the protoplasm of the grain retracted from the intine. Magn. 800 times.

Musa, *Persea*, and then according to Schacht no points are prepared beforehand for the exit of the tube. The number of these peculiarly organised points of exit is a fixed one in each species, and often in whole genera and families; one in the majority of Monocotyledons and in a few Dicotyledons; two in *Ficus*, *Justicia*, and some others; three in the Onagrarieae, Proteaceae, Cupuliferae, Geraniaceae, Compositae, and Boragineae; from four to six in *Impatiens*, *Astrapaea*, *Alnus*, and *Carpinus*; many in the Convolvulaceae, Malvaceae, Alsineae, etc. (see Schacht *loc. cit.*). The exine is not often smooth, and has usually the sculpturing mentioned above on its outer surface. If it is more than usually thick, it often shows layers of different structure and consistence, and differentiations sometimes appear in it passing through its thickness in a radial direction (Fig. 297), and making it appear to be composed of rod-like prismatic pieces or honey-comb-like lamellae or the like,—structural con- ditions which recall the episporium of the Marsiliaceae. The contents of the ripe pollen-grain, the *fovilla* of the older botanists, usually consists of dense coarsely- granular protoplasm, in which grains of starch and small drops of oil may be detected; if the grain is ruptured in water, the fovilla appears in masses of a coherent mucilage which often form long vermiform convolutions. Oil of a yellow or of some other colour is often found on the outer surface of the exine, often in perceptible drops, which makes the pollen sticky and adapted for conveyance by insects from flower to flower; in a few plants only it is dry and powdery, as in the Urticaceae and many of the Gramineae, where it is flung violently from the anthers or simply drops from them.

As the pollen-grains approach maturity and the flower-bud is preparing to open, the wall of the loculament also undergoes further change[1]. The walls of the outer layer of cells, the epidermis (exothecium of authors), are always smooth (Fig. 299 *G, H*), and those of the inner layer or layers (the endothecium of authors[2]) are also smooth, if the anther does not dehisce; but if valves are formed (Fig. 274 *K*), the cells of the inner layers are furnished with thickening-bands on the valves only, that is are fibrous, while if the loculaments dehisce longitudinally, all parts of the endothecium contain fibrous cells; there is usually only one layer of this kind, sometimes several, in *Agave americana* as many as from eight to twelve. The thickening-bands of the fibrous cells, which project inwards, are usually wanting on the outer wall; on the lateral walls they are usually perpendicular to the surface of the loculament, and on the inner wall of the cells they run transversely and are connected in a reticulate or stellate manner. When the walls of the mature anthers dry up, the epidermal cells contract more strongly than the cells of the endothecium which are provided with the

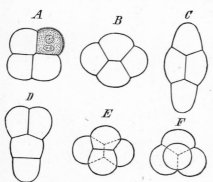

FIG. 298. Pollen-tetrads of *Neottia Nidus avis*, one of the Orchideae. The disposition of the four daughter-cells varies much according to the shape of the pollen-mother-cell before division. The contents are shown in *A* in one of the right hand cells, which contains two nuclei, one belonging to the 'vege- tative' cell.

thickening-bands, and consequently exert a force which tends to make the wall of the anther concave outwards and to rupture it at the weakest spot. The modes in which the pollen-sacs dehisce are very various, and have a close and constant relation to the rest of the arrangements for pollination in the flower, whether by insects or by some other means. Sometimes a short fissure only is formed at the apex of each anther- lobe, as in *Solanum* and the Ericaceae (Fig. 275), by which the pollen escapes from both the adjoining loculaments, or, and this is the commonest case, the wall parts

---

[1] H. v. Mohl, Verm. Schriften, p. 62.—Purkinje, De cellulis antherarum fibrosis, Vratislaviae, 1830.

[2] [If Purkinje's terms exothecium and endothecium are to be retained (and they might be dropped with advantage), they should only be used in describing the state of the anther-wall at the period of maturity and dehiscence and without reference to development, exothecium being the epidermal layer (a single one), endothecium all the layers visible beneath it.]

down the length of the furrow (*suture*) between the two loculaments, while at the same time the tissue that divides them is more or less torn and so both loculaments are opened simultaneously by the longitudinal fissure (Fig. 299); this it was that caused such anthers to be strangely called bilocular; but they must be called quadrilocular, if our nomenclature is to be scientific, in contradistinction to the really bilocular anthers of the Asclepiadeae and to those of many of the Mimoseae which have eight loculaments. In some cases the anther-lobes open at the apex by a pore formed simply by the destruction of a small portion of tissue at the spot (Hofmeister). But we still want a more detailed and comparative investigation of these processes, which are of great physiological importance and at the same time very various; here we can only add the remark, that it is an important point for purposes of classification whether the anther-lobes open inwards, towards the gynaeceum, or outwards, and this depends on whether the pollen-sacs are on the inner or outer side of the filament.

More or less important deviations [1] from the course of development and from the ultimate structure of the pollen as described above occur in several families of Monocotyledons and Dicotyledons. In *Naias* and *Zostera* the difference is that the walls of the mother-cells are not thickened, and the pollen-grains themselves have very thin walls; the latter have a very unusual appearance in *Zostera*, being long narrow tubes which lie parallel to each other in the anther, instead of having the ordinary rounded form. There are more considerable deviations however in the formation of compound pollen-grains; either the four daughter-cells (the pollen-grains) of a mother-cell remain more or less closely connected, as in the case of the tetrads (four-fold grains) of some of the Orchideae (Fig. 298), of *Fourcroya, Typha, Anona, Rhododendron*; or the whole products of a primary mother-cell do not separate, but form one mass of eight, twelve, sixteen, thirty-two or sixty-four pollen-grains all connected together, as in many species of Mimoseae, Acacieae, and others [2]; in these cases the cuticle (exine) on the free outer surface of the grains which lie at the circumference of the mass is more strongly developed and covers the whole as a continuous membrane, from which thin ridges only project inwards between the individual cells. All gradations occur in the different divisions of the Orchideae from the ordinary isolated pollen-grains of the Cypripedieae through the four-fold grains of the Neottieae (Fig. 298) up to the Ophrydeae, in which all the pollen-grains formed from a primary mother-cell remain in connection, and thus a number of pollen-masses (*massulae*) lie together in each loculament, and finally to the *pollinia* of the Ceriorchideae, in which all the pollen-grains of a loculament are united into a cellular mass. In this case, as in the Asclepiadeae with bilocular anthers in which the pollen-grains of each loculament are held fast together by a wax-like substance,

---

[1] Hofmeister, Neue Beitr. II (Abhandl. d. K. Sächs. Ges. VII).—Reichenbach, De pollinis Orchidearum genesi, Leipzig, 1852.—Rosanoff, Ueber den Pollen d. Mimoseen (Jahrb. f. wiss. Bot. VI. 441).—[Corry, Struct. and Developm. of the Gynostegium &c. in Asclepias Cornuti (Trans. Linn. Soc. London, 1884).]

[2] The anthers in many of the Mimoseae have eight loculaments, and a still larger number have been observed (Engler, *loc. cit.* on p. 354). In the Onagrarieae also, as in *Gaura* and others, more than four loculaments occur, but the history of development requires closer investigation in these cases. In the plurilocular Mimoseae the pollen-sacs are filled with groups of eight, sixteen or thirty-two cells, which have originated in one primary mother-cell.

it is obvious that there can be no scattering of pollen-dust, nor can the pollen-masses fall of themselves out of the anthers; the parts of the flower are disposed in special ways to cause honey-seeking insects to draw the pollinia or the coherent pollen-masses from the pollen-sacs, and to deposit them on the stigma of other flowers of the same species.

The *gynaeceum*[1] of the Angiosperms consists of one or more closed chambers in which the ovules are formed; the lower hollow enlarged portion of the chambers, which encloses the ovules, is called the *ovary*; the spot or the mass of tissue from which the ovules immediately arise in the ovary is a *placenta*. Above the ovary the

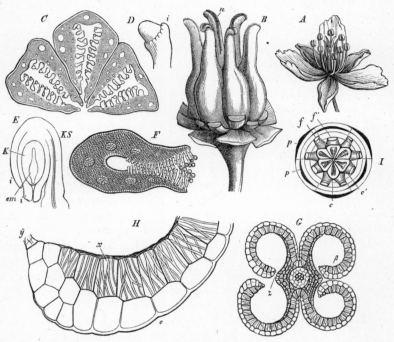

FIG. 299. *Butomus umbellatus.* *A* flower, the natural size. *B* the gynaeceum after removal of the perianth and the stamens, magnified; *n* the stigmas. *C* transverse section through three of the monomerous ovaries, each carpel bearing on its inner surface a number of ovules. *D* a young ovule; *i* commencing integument. *E* a similar one immediately before fertilisation; *ii* the integuments, *K* the nucellus, *KS* the raphe, *em* the embryo-sac. *F* transverse section through the stigmatic portion of a carpel highly magnified; pollen-grains are attached to the hairs of the stigma. *G* transverse section of an anther which is quadrilocular, but afterwards appears bilocular by the separation of the valves *β* at *z*. *H* part of a valve of the anther answering to *β* in *G*; *y* the point where it has separated from the connective, *e* the epidermis, *x* the fibrous cell-layer (endothecium). *I* diagram of the whole flower; the perianth *pp* consists of two alternating whorls of three members each, the androecium of the same number of whorls, but the stamens of the outer whorl are doubled *f*, those of the inner *f'* are simple and thicker. The gynaeceum also consists of two whorls of three members each, an outer *c* and an inner *c'*. There are present therefore six alternating whorls of three members, the members of the first whorl of stamens being doubled.

chamber narrows into one or more slender stalk-like formations, the *styles*, which bear the *stigmas*; these are glandular swellings or expansions of varying shape, which retain the pollen conveyed to them and stimulate it by the moisture which they secrete to put forth the pollen-tubes.

---

[1] The views of Payer, which differ in some important points, should be compared with the text; see his Organogénie de la fleur, p. 725.

The gynaeceum is always the terminal structure of the flower. When the floral axis is sufficiently elongated it occupies the highest place in it; if that is flat and expanded, the gynaeceum is in the centre of the flower; if the axis is hollowed out and cup-shaped, the gynaeceum is at the bottom of the cavity, in the centre of which is the apical point of the floral axis. In the diagram of the flower (Fig. 299 *I*), in which each outer circle represents a genetically lower transverse section, and each inner circle a morphologically higher one, the gynaeceum always appears as the innermost central structure of the flower, the longitudinal displacements on the floral axis being disregarded in the construction of the diagram.

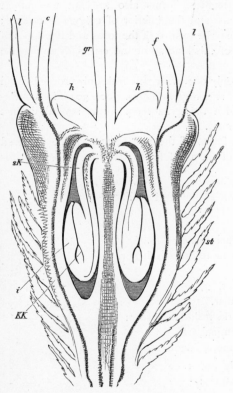

FIG. 300. Longitudinal section of the inferior ovary of *Eryngium campestre*; *ll* sepals, *c* petal, *f* filament, *gr* style, *h* disc, *KK* nucellus of the ovule, *i* integument, *s* funiculus, *st* spikes.

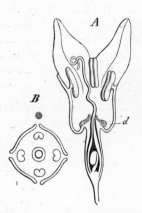

FIG. 301. Flower of *Elaeagnus fusca*, *A* longitudinal section, *d* disc. *B* diagram of flower.

If the axial portion of the flower, the torus, is so far elevated in the centre that the base of the gynaeceum lies plainly above the stamens or at least in the middle of the androecium, the perianth and androecium, or even the whole flower, are said to be *hypogynous*, and the ovary is *superior* (Fig. 299); if on the other hand the torus is hollowed out into a cup and bears the perianth and stamens on its annular margin, while the gynaeceum springs from the bottom (Fig. 301 *A*), the flower is said to be *perigynous*; it is obvious that intermediate forms are possible between typical hypo-gynous and perigynous flowers, and such forms are in fact frequent, especially in the

Rosiflorae. In both these forms of flowers the gynaeceum is free; the torus takes no part in the formation of the wall of the ovary, though it appears to do so sometimes in many perigynous flowers, as in *Pyrus* and *Rosa*. Lastly the flower is *epigynous*, when it has a really *inferior* ovary; this is distinguished from the ovary which is sunk in the torus of the perigynous flower by having its wall formed from the torus itself, which is hollowed out into the shape of a cup or even of a long tube, while the carpels, which form the entire wall of the free superior ovary, spring like the perianth and androecium from the margin of the hollow torus and only close its cavity above, being there prolonged into the style and bearing the stigmas (Fig. 300). Intermediate forms also are not uncommon between the superior ovary of hypogynous and the inferior of epigynous flowers; for instance, the lower half of the ovary may be formed of the torus and the upper of the coherent carpels; transitional forms of this kind are found especially among the Saxifragaceae.

If the gynaeceum of a flower forms only one ovary, one fruit only proceeds from it, and the flower may then be termed *monocarpous* (Figs. 300, 301) in contradistinction to *polycarpous* flowers, in which the gynaeceum forms several distinct ovaries and as many or fewer fruits (Fig. 299).

The understanding of the different forms of the gynaeceum will be rendered more easy by a separate consideration of the chief forms; we may distinguish for this purpose [1] :—

I. Gynaeceum superior; stamens hypogynous or perigynous.
    A. Ovules springing from the carpels :
        a. Ovary monomerous:
            a. Ovary one in each flower,
            β. Ovaries two or more in each flower.
        b. Ovary polymerous :
            γ. Ovary unilocular,
            δ. Ovary plurilocular.
    B. Ovules springing from the torus inside the ovary:
            ε. Ovules one, terminal,
            ζ. Ovules one or more, lateral.

II. Gynaeceum inferior; stamens epigynous :
    C. Ovules springing from the carpels :
            η. Ovary unilocular,
            θ. Ovary plurilocular.
    D. Ovules springing from the torus inside the ovary:
            ι. Ovule single, terminal,
            κ. Ovules one or more, lateral.

---

[1] [The terms *monocarpellary* and *polycarpellary* applied to gynaecea formed respectively of one and of more than one carpel and the terms *syncarpous* and *apocarpous* indicating the union or non-union of the carpels in a gynaeceum are familiar to English-speaking botanists. But as monomerous and polymerous, monocarpous and polycarpous as used and defined in the text are not quite coextensive with them, it has been found necessary to retain the terminology of the German edition.]

The important point in the *superior gynaeceum* is that it is essentially a foliar formation, constituted by the carpellary leaves or carpels, which usually also produce the ovules; the ovules as a rule spring from the margins of the carpels, as in Fig. 302, but sometimes also from the whole inner surface, as in Fig. 299 *C*. The ovary is *monomerous* when it is formed of one carpel only, the upper or inner surface of which is curved concavely inwards and the margins are applied to each other and

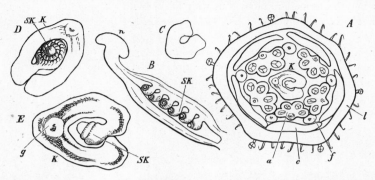

FIG. 302. *Phaseolus vulgaris. A* transverse section of the flower-bud; *i* calyx-tube, *c* corolla, *f* filaments of the outer, *a* anthers of the inner circle of stamens, *K* the carpel. *B* longitudinal section of the carpel with the ovules *SK* and the stigma *n*. *C, D, E* transverse section of carpels of different ages; *SK* their marginal ovules, *g* mid-rib of the carpel.

cohere, so that the mid-rib runs along its back, while the ovules, when they are marginal, are placed opposite to it in two rows; but the inflexed margins of the carpel may swell up and form thicker placentas, as in Fig. 303, and produce several rows of ovules, while on the other hand the number of ovules is not unfrequently reduced to two, as in *Amygdalus*. In monocarpous flowers there is only one such

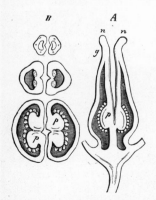

FIG. 303. Gynaeceum of *Saxifraga cordifolia. A* in longitudinal section; *g* the style, *n n* the stigmas. *B* transverse sections at different heights; *p* the placentas.

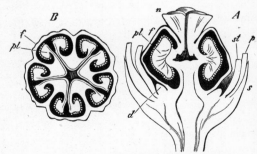

FIG. 304. Gynaeceum of *Pyrola umbellata. A* in longitudinal section; *s* sepals, *p* petals, *st* filaments of the stamens, *f* ovary, *n* stigma, *d* nectar-glands. *B* transverse section through the ovary; *f* its wall, *pl* the placentas.

carpellary leaf, as in Figs. 301, 302; in polycarpous flowers there may be two, three, or more, or even many; if there are two, three or five they are usually arranged in a whorl; if there are four, six or ten, they are usually in two alternating whorls (Fig. 299 *B, I*); if there are a considerable number of monomerous ovaries in a flower, as in the Ranunculaceae, Magnoliaceae and some other families, the portion of the axis which bears them is usually elongated, in *Myosurus*, for instance, very considerably elongated, and their arrangement is spiral. The monomerous ovary when first formed is always unilocular, but it may subsequently become plurilocular by luxuriant growth of the inner surface of the carpel forming ridges which divide the cavity longitudinally, as in *Astragalus*, or transversely, as in *Cassia fistula*. Such ovaries may be termed monomerous with false loculi or spurious dissepiments, but ought not to be called polymerous.

A *polymerous* ovary is in all cases produced by the union of all the carpellary leaves of a flower, which are usually formed two, three, four or five together in a whorl, in the centre of which is the apex of the floral axis. If the several carpels remain open and cohere in such a manner that the right margin of one carpel unites with the left margin of the adjoining carpel, the result is a *unilocular* polymerous ovary;

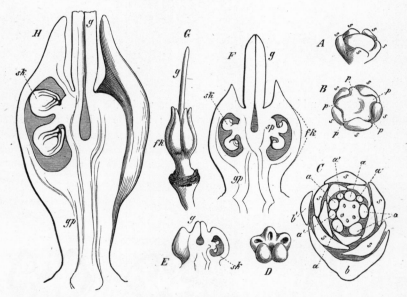

FIG. 305. *Dictamnus Fraxinella. A* young flower-bud after appearance of the sepals *s. B* older bud after appearance of the petals *p. C* still older with the rudiments of the five stamens *a* between which five other stamens *a'* have begun to be formed, three being already visible ; *b* the bract, *b'* the bracteole. *D* to *H* development of the ovary *fk* ; *sk* the ovules, *gp* the gynophore, *g* the style.

such an ovary has parietal placentas, if the coherent margins project only a little inwards, as in *Reseda, Viola,* &c.; but if the margins project farther inwards, the cavity of the ovary becomes plurilocular, but the compartments are open in the centre towards one another, as in *Papaver,* where the incomplete partition-walls are covered on both sides with numerous ovules. A *bilocular* or *plurilocular* polymerous ovary is formed when the carpels push their lateral margins so far into the cavity of the ovary that they meet or cohere in or about its axis, and to this the elongated floral axis in the centre often contributes. There are variations in the mode in which the carpels cohere to form a plurilocular ovary, according as their inflexed margins cohere along their whole length, or only below, in which case the upper portions have rather the appearance of a whorl of monomerous ovaries (Figs. 303, 304, 305, 306). If the inflexed margins of the carpels form placentas in the centre of the ovary, the ovules make their appearance in the central angles of the loculi, as in Fig. 305; but they not unfrequently divide at the centre into two lamellae, which are recurved and swell out into placentas in the middle of the loculi, as is shown in Fig. 304; it is obvious, that the two placentas inside a loculus correspond to the margins of the carpel which forms the outer wall of the loculus.

Spurious dissepiments may be formed in polymerous as well as in monomerous ovaries; if the polymerous ovary is bilocular, it may in this way become quadrilocular, if it has properly five loculi, these may become ten. The former case is common in the Labiatae and Boragineae; Fig. 307 shows that the ovary is formed by the union of two carpels, the margins of which projecting inwards (*I* to *IV*) form a right and left placenta (*pl*), and on each placenta, which corresponds to a margin of a carpel, is a posterior and an anterior ovule; but a growth inwards from the median line of the carpel thrusts itself in between the two ovules of a loculus (*IV* and *VI x*) and divides it into two one-seeded lobes. As the outer part of the wall of each of the four lobes subsequently becomes strongly convex outwards and upwards (Fig. 307 *B*), the separation of the ovary, composed originally of two carpels, into four separate parts becomes still more marked, and finally these parts

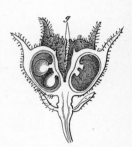

FIG. 306. Ripe fruit of *Dictamnus Fraxinella*, the anterior carpel being removed, and the two lateral opened; *g* the style. Natural size.

separate as one-seeded lobes (nutlets), as is seen most completely in the Boragineae. In *Linum* on the other hand the division of the five compartments of the ovary into ten by false dissepiments is incomplete, since the ridges which project from the median line of the carpels do not reach as far as the centre of the ovary.

Before going on to consider ovaries with axial placentas, it must be mentioned, that there are cases, in which the present state of our knowledge does not allow us to determine with certainty, whether the ovules proceed from the axis or from the margins of the carpels which are united to it, and these doubtful cases are perhaps more numerous than is supposed. In the Caryophylleae, according to Payer's observations on *Cerastium* and *Malachium*, the broad extremity of the floral axis becomes considerably elevated even before the formation of the carpels, which then make their appearance in a whorl with their margins united, and attached by them to the axis which rises above them; each, so to speak, forms a pocket which hangs by the side of the axis; as the axis lengthens, the margins of the carpels form radial dissepiments along it and between the pockets which enlarge into loculi of the ovary; ultimately the carpels outgrow the apex of the axis, the dissepiments becoming raised above it in *Cerastium* and other genera as free lamellae which do not meet in the middle, so that the ovary has five loculi below but continues unilocular above. The ovules appear in two parallel rows on the axile side of each compartment, and appear to be formed from the axis. There are genera in the Caryophylleae in which it is more probable that the placenta is axial, others where it seems to belong rather to the carpels.

Among *superior ovaries with axial* [1] *placentation* those of *Naias* [2] and the Piperaceae specially deserve attention, in which the very simple female flower consists merely of a small lateral shoot transformed into an ovary with a central ovule. The apex of this shoot is itself said to become the terminal nucellus of the ovule, round which

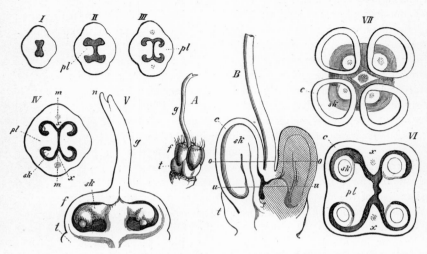

FIG. 307. Development of the ovary of *Phlomis pungens*, one of the Labiatae; age according to the order of the numerals *I* to *VII*; *V* is a longitudinal section, the rest are transverse sections. *A* a mature gynaeceum seen from without. *B* a similar one in longitudinal section. The lines *o* and *u* in *B* answer respectively to the transverse sections *VII* and *VI*; *pl* denotes the placenta, *x* the spurious dissepiments, *f* compartments of the ovary, *sk* the ovule, *c* the wall of the carpel, *t* the disc, *n* the stigma, *g* the style, *m* to *m* the median plane of the carpels.

an annular wall grows up from beneath and overtopping it at length closes over it, and forms the wall of the ovary; in *Typha* [3] a single style only with a stigma rises above the ovary, and the latter is therefore considered to be formed of a single carpel, which rises up from the floral axis as an annular wall; but in the Piperaceae the stigma which is sessile on the apex of the ovary often has several lobes or is placed obliquely; this, like the two to four styles on the ovary of *Naias*, indicates that the ovary is formed not of one but of several carpels, which like the leaf-sheaths of the Equisetaceae are at first an undivided annular growth and afterwards separate into teeth at the upper margin. This view appears the more admissible because in other Angiosperms, in which comparison with allied forms justifies the assumption of a number of coherent carpels, these grow up as an undivided annular wall, which developes into the ovary and above it into the style and stigma, as in the Primulaceae (Fig. 309). In the Polygonaceae on the contrary, the ovary, which is there also eventually a unilocular chamber enclosing the central ovule, is seen to be formed

---

[1] [Axial placentation (that is, placentas upon the floral axis) as distinct from carpellary placentation must not be confounded with 'axile' placentation of many English text-books, which according to the views expressed in this work is a carpellary form.]

[2] Magnus, Zur Morph. d. Gattung Naias (Bot. Ztg. 1869, p. 772).—Hanstein u. Schmitz, Ueber Entw. d. Piperaceenblüthen (Bot. Ztg. 1870, p. 38).—Schmitz, Die Blüthenentwickl. d. Piperaceen in Hanstein, Bot. Abhandl. II. Bd., 1 Heft.

[3] The ovule in this case is not terminal on the floral axis, as has been stated, but grows from the bottom of the carpel.

by the cohesion of two or three carpels, both from the corresponding number of the styles and stigmas and from the fact that the carpels are at first separate on the floral axis, and unite only as they develope, their zone of insertion rising at an annular wall. Since in all these cases the wall of the ovary does not form placentas, the number and position of which would indicate the number and position of the carpels, we are driven to direct observation of the early stages of development and the numerical relations of the styles and stigmas. We have to deal moreover in this case with morphological relations, which are not yet made out with sufficient certainty, notwithstanding the many researches that have been made into the development of the flower.

Beside the number of carpels which have united to form the ovary, it is important also to know in this division whether in any given case the ovule appears

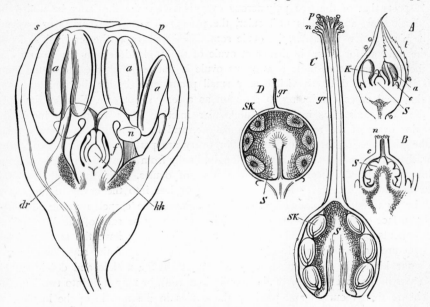

FIG. 308. *Rheum undulatum*. Longitudinal section of the flower; *s* leaf of the outer, *p* leaf of the inner perianth-whorl, *a* the anthers, three only of the nine being visible, *f* the ovary, *n* the stigma, *kk* nucellus of the ovule, *dr* glandular tissue at the base of the filaments forming the nectaries.

FIG. 309. *Anagallis arvensis*. *A* young flower-bud in longitudinal section; *l* sepal, *c* petal, *a* anther, *K* carpel, *s* the apex of the floral axis. *B* older gynaeceum after formation of the stigma *n* and the ovules on the axial placenta *S*. *C* gynaeceum ripe for fertilisation; *p* pollen-grains on the stigma *n*, *gr* the style, *S* the axial placenta bearing the ovules *SK*. *D* unripe fruit; *gr* the style; the placenta *S* has become pulpy and so swollen that it fills the spaces between the seeds *SK*.

as the terminal structure on the floral axis, or laterally on the axis. It is obvious that the ovule may be a terminal structure of the floral axis, where there is only one ovule springing from the base of the ovary, as in the Piperaceae, *Naias*, and the Polygonaceae &c., and it has been shown in fact by the researches of Hanstein and Schmitz, Magnus and Payer that not only the ovule as a whole, but the nucellus itself is to be considered as a terminal structure. But it cannot be concluded from this that every ovule which springs from the bottom of the cavity of the ovary necessarily represents the apex of the floral axis, for it is conceivable that the axis may produce an ovule at the side of its apex, though it is not itself advancing, a case

which we shall meet with presently in the inferior ovary of the Compositae.   It does
not often happen that the axis rises free inside the wide cavity of the ovary and
produces ovules laterally, as in Primulaceae (Fig. 309) and Amarantaceae (*Celosia*
according to Payer).

The *inferior ovary* of epigynous flowers is due to the retardation or entire
cessation of the growth of the young floral axis at its apex, while the tissue of the
circumference rises up as an annular wall and produces the perianth-leaves, the
stamens and carpels on its free margin (Fig. 310, 311); the hollow structure thus
formed is at first open above, but is afterwards roofed over by the carpels which
close together above it; the apical point of the axis lies at the bottom of the cavity
which is cup-shaped or elongated into a tube.   Notwithstanding this remarkable
displacement of the axial parts, the structure of the inferior ovary resembles in almost
all respects that of the free polymerous ovary; it can like the latter be unilocular
or plurilocular, and if it is unilocular, the placentation may be basilar or parietal.
If the placentation is basilar, the ovule sometimes appears as the terminal structure
of the axis, as for example the erect ovule of the Juglandeae; in the Compositae
on the other hand the single anatropous ovule is not terminal but lateral, the floral
axis being often distinctly visible as a small prominence beside the funiculus, and
in abnormal cases continuing to grow on as a leafy shoot.   In *Samolus* the apex
of the floral axis rises inside the unilocular inferior ovary as it does inside the
superior ovary of the rest of the Primulaceae, and forms numerous lateral ovules.
If the placentas of the unilocular inferior ovary are parietal, they form two, three,
four, five or more elevations running longitudinally from above downwards or from
below upwards, and bear two or more rows of ovules, as in the Orchideae and
Opuntia; these placentas, which project more or less into the cavity of the ovary,
may be regarded as prolongations of the margins of the carpels running down the
inner surface of the wall of the ovary.   The same may be said of the longitudinal
dissepiments of the plurilocular inferior ovary, which may have the same varieties
of structure as have been already described in the case of the superior ovary of
the same kind; the dissepiments may either meet in the middle and develope their
placentas in the inner angles of the loculi (Fig. 268), or may split into two lamellae
which are then recurved and produce the ovules in the middle of the loculus, as
in the Cucurbitaceae.   Usually two, three or more carpels take part in the formation
of the upper portion of the inferior ovary, and the prolongations of their margins,
as was said above, run downwards and form the parietal placentas of the unilocular
or the dissepiments of the plurilocular ovary; in such cases the inferior ovary like
the similarly constructed superior ovary must be termed polymerous, since the
name refers to the number of the carpels.   Examples of a monomerous inferior
ovary appear to be very rare; *Hippuris vulgaris* (Fig. 272) is one, with a single
carpel containing one pendulous anatropous ovule.

The *style* is formed by the prolongation of the carpel above the ovary; in the
monomerous ovary there is therefore only one style (Figs. 299, 301), but this may
be branched; if the ovary is polymerous, the style consists of as many parts as
there are carpels; these parts may be free from immediately above the ovary
(Fig. 303), or they cohere for a certain distance above it and then separate higher
up, or lastly they cohere along their whole length (Fig. 305 *G*, Fig. 307).   Though

the style is formed from the upper part of the young carpel, it may come to be placed on the axile side of the monomerous ovary, if the carpel bulges out considerably owing to the stronger growth of the ovary on its dorsal side, as in *Fragaria* and *Alchemilla*; if this happens to the individual carpels of a polymerous ovary, the ovary itself appears to be depressed in its centre, and the style rises from out of the depression (Fig. 304, 305). The same thing occurs in the Labiatae and Boragineae in an exaggerated form, where the four lobes of the bicarpellary ovary bulge out very strongly above (Fig. 307 *A, B*), so that the style at length appears to rise from between four parts of the ovary which seem almost entirely unconnected, and is known as a *gynobasic* style.

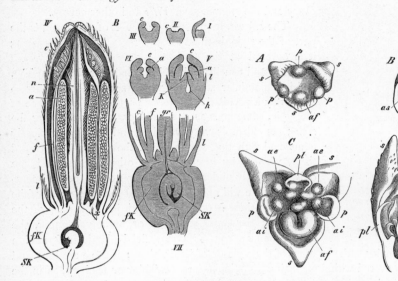

FIG. 310. Development of the flower of *Helianthus annuus*, the numerals from *I* to *VII* show successive stages (*IV* and *VI* have been transposed by mistake); *c* corolla, *l* calyx, *f* filaments of the stamens, *a* their anthers, *x* the basal portion which becomes later the lower part of the corolla-tube bearing the epipetalous stamens, *fK* the inferior ovary, *SK* the ovule, *k* the carpel, *gr* the style.

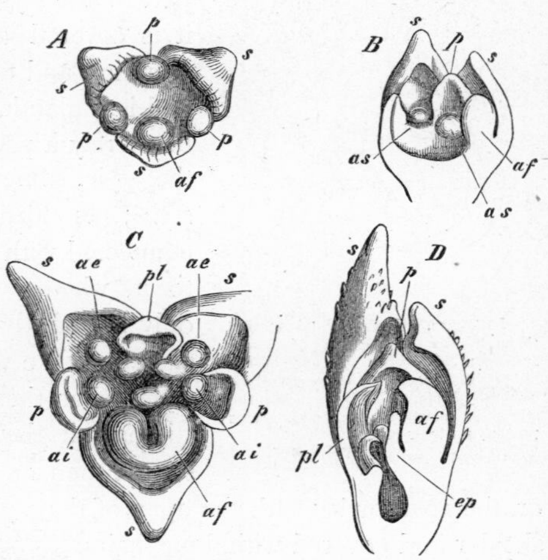

FIG. 311. Development of the flower of *Calanthe veratrifolia* in successive stages from *A* to *B*. *A* and *C* seen from above, *B* and *D* in longitudinal section; *s* the sepals, *p* the petals, *pl* the petal which developes into the lower lip, *af* the single fertile anther, *ae* and *ai* abortive anthers of the outer and inner circle; *as* in *B* denotes the sterile stamens, *ep* in *D* one of the three carpels. After Payer.

The style may be hollow, that is, may be traversed by a longitudinal canal which is a narrow continuation of the cavity of the ovary, as in *Butomus* (Fig. 299 *B, F*) where the canal is open up to the hairy surface of the stigma, and in *Viola* (Fig. 312) in the same way, where it is broad and ends in the round open cavity of the stigma; in *Agave* also and in *Fourcroya* the style is hollow along its whole length and open at the stigma, but the canal divides below into three branches which run into the loculi of the ovary, an arrangement which occurs also in other Liliaceae; sometimes the style is hollow at first, as in *Anagallis* (Fig. 309 *B*), and is afterwards filled up by the growth of the tissue. But in most cases there is no open passage to be found in the style of the mature gynaeceum, or at any rate not in its upper portion, but it is filled with a loose tissue, the *conducting tissue*[1], in which the pollen-tubes grow

----

[1] See on p. 403. A description of this tissue will be found on a subsequent page.

downwards till they reach the cavity of the ovary. The outer form of the style is usually elongated-cylindrical, or filiform, or columnar, or sometimes prismatic or flat and riband-like; it is of considerable size in most of the Irideae; very long and tripartite and with each division hollowed out into a deep cup in *Crocus*; the genus *Iris* has three free broad petaloid coloured styles. Sometimes the

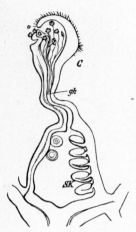

portion of the style belonging to each carpel is branched, as for instance in the Euphorbiaceae, where the tripartite style corresponding to the three carpels is divided above into six branches. The style often remains quite short, and it then appears like a mere constriction between the ovary and the stigma, as in *Vitis* and other genera.

The *stigma*, in the narrower use of the term, is the part of the style destined for the reception of the pollen; it is covered at the time of pollination with a viscid secretion and usually with delicate hairs or short papillae, and is a glandular structure which sometimes appears to be merely a peculiarly developed portion of the surface of the style, sometimes as a special organ surmounting the style; its form is very variable and is always closely connected with the way in which the pollen is conveyed to it, whether by insects or by other means, and can only be rightly understood by reference to these circum-

FIG. 312. Longitudinal section through the gynaeceum of *Viola tricolor*; *SK* ovules, *gk* canal of the style, *o* its orifice; in the cavity of the capitate stigma, which is filled with the stigmatic moisture, are pollen-grains putting out their tubes.

stances. We will only say here that the open canal of the style, when there is one, has its exit in the surface of the stigma; if the canal is closed or entirely wanting, the stigma then appears as a superficial glandular formation on the apex or beneath the apex of the style or of its divisions; if these are long and slender and covered with long hairs, the stigmas are *penicillate* or feathery, as in the Gramineae; in the Solanaceae and Cruciferae the moist stigmatic surface covers a knob-like notched thickening at the extremity of the style, in *Papaver* it forms a many-rayed star on the lobed style. Sometimes the stigmatic portion of the style is greatly enlarged, as in the Asclepiadeae, where the two monomerous ovaries which are elsewhere separate cohere by these stigmatic heads; the true stigmatic surface, into which the pollen-tubes penetrate, lies concealed in this case on the under side of the stigma [1].

Nectaries. Wherever pollination is effected by insects, glandular organs are found in the flowers, and these organs either secrete or contain in their delicate tissue juices with a strong smell and taste (usually sweet), which can easily be obtained from them by suction. These juices are all included under the term *nectar*, and the organs which produce them are called *nectaries*. The distribution, form and morphological significance of nectaries are very various, and are always in direct relation to the specific contrivances in the flower for its pollination by insects. The nectaries are in some cases merely gland-like groups of cells on the leaves or on the axial parts of the

---

[1] On the position of the lobes of the stigma in relation to the placentas in different plants see Brown in Bot. Ztg. 1843, p. 193.

flower, or they are cushions of more delicate tissue, or sessile or stalked protuberances, or the entire foliar structures of the perianth, the androecium and even the gynaeceum, are transformed into peculiar organs for secreting and storing nectar. As no general morphological account can be given of these organs[1], a few examples will serve to show where the nectaries are to be sought for in different flowers. In *Fritillaria imperialis* the nectaries are shallow pits on the inner face of the perianth-leaves above their base, which distil large clear drops of nectar; in *Elaeagnus fusca* (Fig. 301 *d*) they form a glandular projecting ring in the gamophyllous perianth; in *Rheum* they are slight glandular protuberances at the base of the stamens (Fig. 308 *dr*); in *Nicotiana* they are annular weals outside and at the base of the superior ovary; in the Umbelliferae a fleshy cushion forming a disk above the inferior ovary at the base of the styles (Fig. 300 *h, h*), and the same in the Compositae also at the base of the style (Fig. 310); in *Citrus, Cobaea scandens*, the Labiatae, Ericaceae and other plants, the nectary is a luxuriant growth of the torus forming an annulus beneath the ovary; in the Cruciferae (Fig. 314 *k*) and in *Fagopyrum* (Fig. 315 *k*) it takes the form

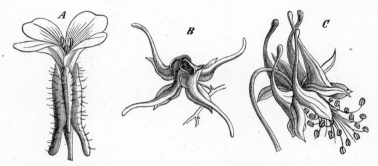

FIG. 313. Flowers with spur-like formations on the sepals (*A*) and petals (*B, C*). *A Biscutella hispida. B Epimedium grandiflorum. C Aquilegia canadensis.*

of four or six roundish or club-shaped outgrowths or warts between the filaments; in the Gesneraceae an abortive stamen becomes a nectary; in *Cucumis Melo* and other species, a nectary takes the place of the androecium in the female flower and of the gynaeceum in the male. Generally the nectaries are found deep down among the other parts of the flower, and if they secrete nectar, it collects at the bottom of the flower, as in *Nicotiana* and the Labiatae; but sometimes special hollow receptacles are formed for this purpose; such especially are the sac-like *spurs* formed by the leaves of the perianth (Fig. 313). In *Viola* only one perianth-leaf forms a hollow spur, which contains two appendages from two of the stamens and receives the nectar which they secrete. The cup-shaped stalked petals of *Helleborus* and the slipper-shaped petals of *Nigella* secrete nectar at the bottom of their cavity and collect it there[1].

The *ovule*. The ovule in Angiosperms usually consists of a distinct and sometimes even very long stalk, the *funicle* (*Opuntia* and the Plumbagineae), though this is sometimes wanting, as in the Gramineae, and one or two integuments surrounding the

---

[1] See Behrens, Die Nektarien d. Blüthen (Flora, 1879), for the anatomy of nectaries, and also for the literature of the subject.

nucellus; most gamopetalous Dicotyledons and some other plants have only one integument; nearly all Monocotyledons have two, and sometimes a third integument is subsequently formed, the *aril*, as in *Myristica, Euonymus, Asphodelus luteus* and *Aloe subtuberculata.* The ovule is often straight or *orthotropous* when it is the terminal

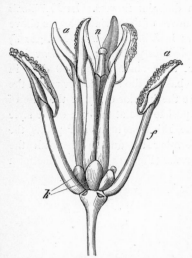

structure of the floral axis, and the funicle remains short, as in the Piperaceae and Polygonaceae ; it is comparatively rarely *campylotropous*, in which case the nucellus with its integuments is itself curved, as in the Gramineae, Caryophyllaceae and others ; its usual form in Angiosperms is the *anatropous*, in which the nucellus with its integuments is inverted, being turned round on the summit of the funicle towards its base, to which the micropyle is therefore directed (Figs. 299 *E*, 300); in this case the funicle where it runs along one side of the ovule and adheres to it is termed the *raphe*. The *micropyle*, especially in the Monocotyledons, is often formed by the inner integument (*secundine*) only projecting above the nucellus ; sometimes, especially in the Dicotyledons, the outer integument (*primine*) grows up above the mouth of the inner one, and the micropylar canal is then formed at its outer extremity, the *exostome*, by the outer integument, at its inner portion, the *endostome*, by the inner. If there are two or three integuments, the innermost is always formed first, and then the outer, and lastly and usually much later the third, the aril; the integuments therefore in respect to the axis of the ovule are formed in basipetal succession. The transverse zone from which the one or two true integuments spring is termed the *chalaza*, or base of the ovule. The integuments are usually only a few layers of cells in thickness, and appear like membranes, especially when they enclose a

FIG. 314. *Brassica Napus.* Flower after removal of the sepals and petals ; *a* anthers, *f* filaments, *n* stigma, *k* nectaries in the form of club-shaped outgrowths.

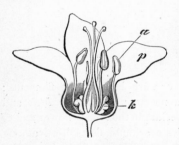

FIG. 315. Longitudinal section of a flower of *Polygonum Fagopyrum* ; *a* anthers, *p* perianth, *k* nectaries.

large nucellus (Fig. 299 *E, i*); but if only one integument is formed, the nucellus usually remains very small, while the integument is thick and solid and far overtops the nucellus, forming the chief mass of the ovule before fertilisation, as in *Hippuris* (Fig. 272), the Umbelliferae (Fig. 300) and Compositae (Fig. 310) ; see also Fig. 317.

The history of the development of the ovule is as follows[1]. The ovule makes its first appearance as a small protuberance, which either occupies the apex of the floral axis or originates in a group of cells of the placenta; the epidermis together

---

[1] Warming, De l'ovule (Ann. d. sc. nat. 1878).—Strasburger, Die Angiospermen u. d. Gymnospermen, 1879.—Jönsson, Om embryosäckens utveckling hos Angiospermernae (Lunds Univ. Årsskrift, T. XVI).

with the cells of the layer next beneath it, or sometimes even those of deeper-lying layers, arches outwards to form the protuberance; the ovule is never formed from superficial cells, as is the case with the sporangia of many Vascular Cryptogams. The apical portion of the protuberance becomes the nucellus, the basal the funicle (sporangium-stalk). Then the integuments begin to grow from beneath the nucellus, and an annular wall is formed which grows up completely over the nucellus; if a second and outer integument is added to the first, it is formed in a similar manner

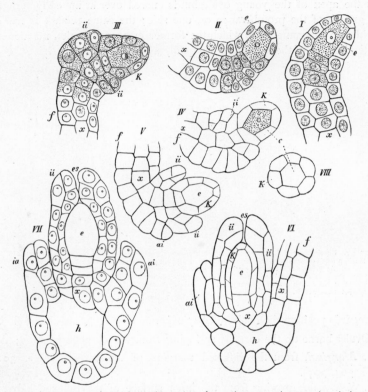

FIG. 316. *Orchis militaris.* Development of the ovules, magn. 550 times; successive stages shown in the order of the numerals *I* to *VII.* *VIII* is a transverse section of *I.* *I—VI* are side views and in optical longitudinal section. *VII* is a front view and the funiculus is behind. The letters *xx* denote the axile cell-row, the upper cell of the row being the mother-cell of the embryo-sac *e* (the archesporium), *f* the funiculus, *ii* the inner, *ia* and *ai* the outer integument, *K* the nucellus, *es* the micropyle, *h* an intercellular space; in *VII* the embryo-sac *e* has entirely displaced the tissue-layer of the nucellus.

from beneath the first and grows over it. Terminal ovules usually continue straight (orthotropous); those which are afterwards anatropous appear at first as a straight or only slightly curved projection, but soon become distinctly curved at the spot where the first or the only integument originates (Fig. 316 *II, III, IV*); the apical part which is enclosed by the integuments forms the nucellus, while the basal portion beneath them is the funicle. As the integuments develop the curvature increases, and the nucellus is at length inverted even before the outer integument is quite formed, and consequently the latter does not develope on the side of the ovule which is towards the raphe but spreads over the free parts of the ovule, growing up to the

raphe on the right and left of it. (Fig. 316 *V, VI, VII*.) When there is only
one integument present, which is usually strongly developed on the outer side, and
the nucellus is slender, consisting in many cases of only a central row of cells
and a layer of cells round it, the nucellus often has the appearance in the
middle stages of development of being a lateral secondary projection from beneath
the apex of the young conical funicle (Fig. 317 *II*). But the history of development shows that here also the integument arises from beneath the nucellus, which
occupies the apex of the young ovule but is curved over at an early period by the
stronger growth of the protuberance on one side; the same remark is true also of
ovules with two integuments, to which the former erroneous notion mentioned above
of the lateral origin of the nucellus was equally applied[1].

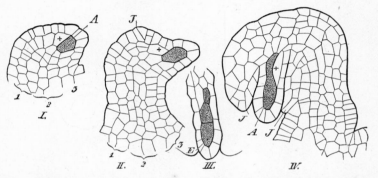

FIG. 317. Development of the anatropous ovule of *Verbascum phoeniceum* in axile longitudinal section. In *I* the
ovule is still a small conical body, the longitudinal axis of which is already curved by the stronger growth of the left
(convex) side. At *J* in No *II* is the rudiment of the (single) integument; the rudiment of the nucellus arises at this spot
and apparently laterally on the young ovule. *III* division of the mother-cell of the embryo-sac into three cells. *IV* an
older stage than No. *II*, the mother-cell of the embryo-sac not yet divided. *A* mother-cell of the embryo-sac (archesporium), + the cell next it. After Warming.

As regards position the ovules of Angiosperms may be grouped as follows :—

I. Ovules borne on the carpels, springing from the carpellary leaves; these are

    1. *Marginal*, from the inflexed margins of the carpels (Figs. 302, 303,
        304, 307).

    2. *Superficial*, growing from the inner surface of the inflexed halves of the
        carpellary leaves (Figs. 267, 299); in the genus *Cabomba* of the Nym-
        phaeaceae any portion of the carpel, even the mid-rib, may produce ovules;
        in *Brasenia*, another genus of the same family, the ovules are all on the
        mid-rib, and the same is the case in *Astrocarpus*, a genus of the Resedaceae,
        which has only one ovule[2].

---

[1] The views which have been entertained with regard to the morphological value or dignity of
the ovule need not be noticed here, for their interest is now purely historical. The history of
development has shown that the ovule of the Angiosperms like that of the Gymnosperms is a
macrosporangium, which is distinguished from that of the Vascular Cryptogams only by the integuments which spring from the rudimentary sporangium itself. The consideration of the malformations of ovules has generally caused confusion and prevented a true understanding of the matter.

    [2] Eichler, Blüthendiagr. II. p. xvii.

3. *Basal* or *axillary*, springing from the base of the upper side of the carpel or from the axil of the carpel, as in *Ranunculus, Sedum, Zannichellia* according to Warming[1].

II. Ovules borne on the axis and springing from the prolongation of the floral axis within the ovary, the carpels themselves being sterile; these are

4. *Lateral*, when they arise beside or below the apex of the axis which either rises as a column and bears numerous ovules, as in Fig. 309, or ceases to grow after forming one ovule, so that this may appear to be terminal, as in Fig. 310.

5. *Terminal*, when the apex of the axis itself becomes the nucellus, as in Fig. 308, the Piperaceae, *Naias*, etc.

The question, to which of these types the ovules of any given plant belong, must be decided in each individual case, but the ovules that are marginal on the carpels are much the most common in Angiosperms, while the superficial and the axillary positions are confined to single families or genera. If we compare the position of the ovules in Angiosperms and Gymnosperms, we find that the ovules of the Cycadeae belong to the marginal class, those of *Dammara* and *Araucaria* to the superficial, those of the Cupressineae to the axillary; those of *Gingko* are lateral upon the axis, those of *Taxus* are terminal. Similar varieties of position are found in the sporangia of the Vascular Cryptogams, though none are terminal upon the axis; the sporangia of *Ophioglossum*, for example, are produced laterally on a leaf, those of many Ferns are superficial on a leaf, those of *Lycopodium* and *Selaginella* are axillary or basal; the latter may also be considered as being upon the axis and lateral, of which kind the sporangia of the Psilotaceae most be regarded as the most striking examples.

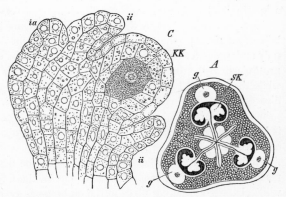

FIG. 318. *Funkia cordata. A* transverse section of young superior trilocular ovary; two ovules *SK* are visible in each compartment growing from the revolute margins of the carpels, *g* vascular bundles surrounded by transparent parenchyma. *C* young ovule in optical longitudinal section; *KK* tissue of the nucellus, *ii* integument, *ia* outer integument. *A* is slightly, *C* is very highly magnified; the dark-coloured cell is the mother-cell of the embryo-sac.

The ovules are sometimes rudimentary; those of the Balanophoreae and Santalaceae have no integuments, the nucellus being naked and in many species consisting of only a few cells. The same is the case with the Loranthaceae[2], where the ovules are produced, as in the Santalaceae, from an axial placenta; but the latter becomes so closely united at a very early period with the tissue of the carpel, that when the flower opens it is no longer possible to distinguish the ovules by any

---

[1] Warming, Recherches sur la ramification des Phanérogames, Kopenhagen, 1872, page xxii, Taf. xi, Fig. 1–10. Axillary ovules are as little to be regarded as shoots (stems) as are the axillary sporangia of the Lycopodieae and Selaginelleae; and there is as little ground for regarding marginal ovules as leaf-tips or pinnae.

[2] Treub, Observations sur les Loranthacées (Ann. du jard. bot. de Buitenzorg, 1881).

definite outline in the apparently homogeneous tissue, their position being indicated only by their embryo-sacs.

Before the formation of the integuments certain differentiations take place in the nucellus introductory to the formation of the *embryo-sac* (*macrospore*), differentiations similar to those observed in the macrosporangia of the Coniferae and in other sporangia, and especially in the microsporangia or pollen-sacs of Angiosperms. The researches of Strasburger and Warming have made us acquainted with these important processes, and have supplemented and corrected Hofmeister's earlier observations. A good example is afforded by *Polygonum divaricatum* which was carefully examined by Strasburger. The ovule occupies the summit of the floral axis, and is therefore terminal upon the axis. The hypodermal terminal cell of the axile row of cells of the nucellus (Fig. 319 *I b*) is the *archesporium* or mother-cell of the embryo-sac or macrospore. This cell divides into an upper and a lower and larger cell. The former (Strasburger's tapetal cell) may be termed the primary tapetal cell[1] (Fig. 319 *t*); it increases considerably in size in many ovules and divides repeatedly, so that the archesporium (Fig. 319 *em*) is sunk deep in the tissue of the. nucellus. There it divides, as is shown in Fig. 319 *II* and *III*, by transverse (anticlinal) walls first of all into two and then into four cells, while the *primary tapetal cell* is also divided by a longitudinal and a transverse wall. The transverse walls in the mother-cell of the embryo-sac are marked by their power of refracting light, and have the appearance of being swollen. Of the four cells into which the mother-cell is now divided, the lower only undergoes further development and becomes the embryo-sac or macrospore. The protoplasm of the three upper cells (*cap-cells*) becomes grumous and strongly refractive, while the lower cell as it grows squeezes them together, and at the same time has the disorganising effect, commonly observed in sporangia, on the cells formed from the primary tapetal cell, the lowest of which must be considered as the *tapetum*; there is left at last only a cap of a strongly refractive substance, covering the apex of the embryo-sac (macrospore), and the embryo-sac as it enlarges exerts a similar destructive influence on the adjacent lateral cells of the tissue of the nucellus (Fig. 319 *V*), resembling in this the macrospores of *Isoetes*, the Cycadeae and Coniferae[2]. Meanwhile changes are taking place in the embryo-sac or macrospore itself. The nucleus divides and one of the two daughter-cells moves into the upper or micropylar end of the embryo-sac, the other into the lower extremity. The upper nucleus gives rise to the *egg-apparatus*, the lower to the *antipodal cells*; each of them divides again (Fig. 319 *VI*) and the division is repeated in each of the daughter-cells. There are now therefore four nuclei at the upper and four at the lower end of the embryo-sac. Three out of each group of four now become invested with protoplasm and are naked cells. The three upper cells[3], which have no cell-wall, together form the egg-apparatus, and one of the three lying deeper in the embryo-sac than the other two (Fig. 319 *VII*, *o*) is the *oosphere*, the others which assist only in the process of fertilisation are termed the *synergidae*. The three lower cells, which in this and in many other cases are invested with a wall of cellulose, are the antipodal cells; they take no part in the processes which follow, and they eventually disappear. In both

---

[1] See on page 363.

[2] See pages 294 and 332.

[3] Formerly known as germinal vesicles.

the upper and lower group of cells there is still an unemployed nucleus (*polar nucleus*). These two nuclei move towards the middle of the embryo-sac and there coalesce and form a larger nucleus (Fig. 319 *VIII, sek*), which is now the nucleus of

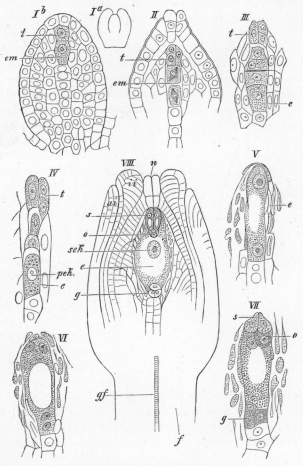

FIG. 319. *Polygonum divaricatum.* Ovules and development of the embryo-sac. *Ia* longitudinal section through a young ovary; the ovule terminates the floral axis. *Ib* longitudinal section through a rudimentary ovule before the formation of the integument; *em* mother-cell of the embryo-sac (archesporium), *t* primary tapetal cell. *II* older stage, the mother-cell of the embryo-sac has divided into two cells, in both of which the nucleus is in the act of dividing. *III* mother-cell of the embryo-sac divided into four (sporogenous mass of cells); the lowest of these cells *e* displaces the rest and becomes the embryo-sac in *IV*; *peh* is the primary nucleus of the embryo-sac and has divided in *V* into two daughter-nuclei, which in *VI* and *VII* form the egg-apparatus and the antipodal cells; *o* the oosphere, *s* synergidae, *g* antipodal cells. *VIII* is a longitudinal section through a mature ovule with the inner integument *ii* and the outer *ai*, the nucellus *n* and the vascular bundle *gf* entering the funiculus *f*, *sek* secondary nucleus in the embryo-sac. After Strasburger.

the embryo-sac (*secondary nucleus*). The perfected embryo-sac therefore contains the egg-apparatus consisting of the two synergidae and the oosphere, the nucleus of the embryo-sac and the antipodal cells, and these elements are found with slight variations in all embryo-sacs.

A comparison of Angiosperms with Gymnosperms shows that there is an almost perfect agreement between them in the matter of the formation of the embryo-sac (macrospore). The mother-cell of the embryo-sac in both Angiosperms and

Gymnosperms is the archesporium, but it undergoes only a few divisions. Of the sporogenous tissue which is thus formed, and which in *Polygonum* is composed of four cells, one cell displaces the others and becomes the macrospore or embryo-sac. The antipodal cells are a rudimentary prothallium, but it at present remains uncertain whether the egg-apparatus can be looked upon as a rudimentary formation of archegonia.

The structural characters of an anatropous ovule have already been briefly described and illustrated; Fig. 321 shows its development. The ovule in this case consists of only a single axile row of cells surrounded by an outer layer of cells. The inner integument is seen in process of formation in Fig. 321 *I, ii.* The mother-cell of the embryo-sac here, as in many other cases, gives off no primary tapetal cell above. It divides into three daughter-cells, the lower of which displaces the upper ones and developes into the embryo-sac, in which the egg-apparatus and the antipodal cells are formed exactly as in the instance of *Polygonum* which we have just examined; but the antipodal cells disappear at an early period (Fig. 321 *VI, g*). In other cases the growth and repeated division of the primary tapetal cell, which lies above the mother-cell of the embryo-sac and of its daughter-cells, makes the embryo-sac descend deep into the tissue of the

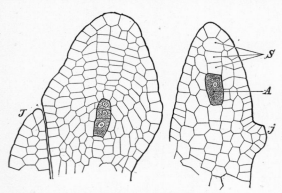

FIG. 320. *Mercurialis annua.* Longitudinal sections through the nucellus of the ovule, to the right a young, to the left an older stage of development. *A* the mother-cell of the embryo-sac (archesporium); the primary tapetal cell *S* above it has divided into three cells, which still show considerable growth and divide by transverse and longitudinal walls. By this means the mother-cell of the embryo-sac is sunk deep in the tissue of the nucellus. In the left-hand figure it has divided by transverse walls into three cells, the lowest of which supplants the other two and becomes the embryo-sac, *J* integument. After Jönsson.

nucellus. This proceeding which puts us in mind of the Coniferae, but does not seem to be very common in Angiosperms, may be illustrated by *Mercurialis annua* (Fig. 320). The occurrence moreover of two or more mother-cells of embryo-sacs, produced perhaps by the division of a single one, is not very rare; they are found for instance in *Chrysanthemum Leucanthemum, Helleborus cupreus, Thesium intermedium* and some species of *Rosa*, etc. In *Rosa* several embryo-sacs have been found even in the mature ovule. Strasburger saw four hypodermal embryo-sac-mother-cells in the young ovule of *Rosa livida*, and each of them gave off a primary tapetal cell above. These primary tapetal cells, like the cells of the nucellus above them, divide further by transverse walls, so that a cap of tissue lies over the embryo-sac-mother-cells (archesporial cells), each of which then divides by repeated bipartitions into from one to six daughter-cells, and the uppermost usually of these, not as is the rule in other cases the lowest, becomes the embryo-sac; sometimes both the upper cells become embryo-sacs, which then destroy the circumjacent tissue.

This case shows that each of the cells, into which the archesporium or embryo-sac-mother-cell is divided, may under certain circumstances develope into an embryo-sac, and this gives support to the view, that we are dealing here with sporogenous tissue which has become rudimentary in the course of development, and that one usually of its cells and sometimes two may develope into macrospores directly, and without previous division into four cells[1].

In ordinary cases then the embryo-sac so far displaces the tissue above it, that it is at last covered by only a thin layer of it, or even comes into contact with the inner surface of the inner integument, as in the Orchideae (Fig. 316 *VII*); in such cases the tissue of the apex of the nucellus may remain intact, as in the Aroideae and some others, or the apex of the embryo-sac may destroy it and project beyond it, either extending into the micropyle, as in *Crocus* and the Labiatae, or even growing out beyond it in the form of a long tube, as in *Santalum*. Sometimes also the embryo-sac extends itself in its middle and lower parts and encroaches on the surrounding tissue; in many gamopetalous Dicotyledons it puts out vermiform prolongations, which penetrate into and destroy the tissue of the integument, as in some Labiatae, *Rhinanthus* and *Lathraea*.

The egg-apparatus does not often show any variation from its normal number of three cells. *Santalum*[2] as a rule has two oospheres, the origin of which is still not certainly known. The synergidae in *Santalum* and other plants (*Watsonia, Gladiolus, Crocus, Zea, Sorghum, Polygonum*) have a long tubular prolongation with distinct longitudinal striation[3]. The apex of the embryo-sac in *Crocus, Gladiolus* and *Santalum* is pierced by the synergidae, as Schacht correctly stated and Strasburger has confirmed, and their prolongations extend therefore beyond the embryo-sac. But in the great majority of Monocotyledons and Dicotyledons the synergidae are not developed in so peculiar a manner and remain covered by the wall of the embryo-sac. The cells of the egg-apparatus often conceal each other, and their number therefore was often in former times incorrectly given. In all plants hitherto examined there are as a rule two synergidae and one oosphere, but in *Santalum*, as has been said, there are too oospheres, an occurence which has been exceptionally observed also in *Siningia*, a genus of the Gesneraceae. Since the oosphere is more deeply placed in the embryo-sac than the synergidae, the contents of the pollen-tube, when this has applied itself to the apex of the embryo-sac, reach the synergidae first, or rather one of them; these however never experience any further development, but on the contrary disappear, while the oosphere developes into the embryo, though it does not come into contact with the pollen-tube[4]. The function therefore of the synergidae in the process of fertilisation is only ancillary; they serve to convey the fertilising substance from the pollen-tube to the oosphere.

---

[1] Goebel, Beitr. z. vergl. Entwicklungsgeschichte d. Sporangien, II (Bot. Ztg. 1881).

[2] [Strasburger in Ber. Deutsch. Bot. Ges. III, 1885, shows that in *Santalum* there is but one oosphere; the synergidae are large and constricted in the middle by processes of the wall of the embryo-sac, and the portions below the constrictions have been taken for two oospheres, the oosphere itself having been overlooked.]

[3] Once known as the filiform apparatus.

[4] That only one of the cells of the egg-apparatus (the germinal vesicle) can be regarded as the oosphere, while the others, one or both, have only really the duty of conveying the fertilising substance to the oosphere, has already been insisted on by Sachs in pages 560 and 561 of his 4th edition. [See also Strasburger on *Santalum* in Ber. Deutsch. Bot. Ges. 1885, and his Neue Unters. ü. d. Befruchtungsv. b. d. Phanerog.]

Fertilisation[1]. The pollen-grains which germinate on the stigma send their tubes through the canal of the style, when there is one, or more commonly through the spongy conducting tissue in the interior of the solid style, down into the cavity of the ovary[2]; the micropyle often lies so close to the bottom of the style, both in erect basal ovules (Fig. 308) and in pendulous anatropous ovules, that the descending pollen-tube can enter it at once; but in the majority of cases the pollen-tubes must continue to grow on after their entrance into the cavity of the ovary in search of the orifices of the ovules, and they are led in the right way by various contrivances; such are the papillae frequently found on the placentas or on other parts of the wall of the ovary, along which the tubes advance; in our European Euphorbias a tuft of hairs conducts them from the base of the style to the neighbouring micropyle; in the Plumbagineae the tissue of the style forms a descending conical projection which serves as conductor of the pollen-tube to the micropyle; and other similar aids may be observed.

As each ovule requires a pollen-tube for its fertilisation, the number of tubes entering the ovary is proportionate on the whole to the number of ovules which it contains; still the number of the tubes which enter the ovary is generally larger than that of the ovules; where these are very numerous, the number of the tubes is also large, as in the Orchideae for instance, where they may be seen with the naked eye in the ovary as a bundle of white silky threads.

The time which elapses between pollination and the entrance of the pollen-tubes into the micropyle depends not only on the length of the route which is often considerable, as in *Zea* and *Crocus*, but also on specific characters in the plants; thus according to Hofmeister the pollen-tubes of *Crocus vernus* require only from twenty-four to seventy-two hours to pass through the style which is six to ten centimetres in length, while those of *Arum maculatum*, which have a distance of scarcely two or three millimetres to traverse, take at least five days, those of the Orchideae ten days or even weeks and months, during which time the ovules are being developed in the ovary or in many cases only begin to be formed.

The pollen-tube is usually very narrow and thin-walled while it is rapidly lengthening; when it has made its way into the micropyle its wall soon becomes very considerably thickened, chiefly, it would appear, through swelling, so that the lumen is only a narrow canal, as is the case in the Liliaceae, Cactaceae and *Malva*; Hofmeister compares it in this state to the tube of a thermometer; sometimes the lumen also enlarges, as in *Œnothera* and Cucurbitaceae. The pollen-tube contains a granular protoplasm, usually with numerous grains of starch. The nuclei of the pollen-grain are according to Strasburger's account dissolved in the tube, in *Orchis* only after the apex of the tube has reached the embryo-sac[3].

---

[1] Besides the works cited above, see Hofmeister's Historical account in Flora, 1875, p. 125, which gives the literature of the subject, and Strasburger, Ueber Befruchtung u. Zelltheilung, Jena, 1878, [and Neue Unters. ü. d. Befr. b. d. Phanerog. Also D'Arcy Thompson, Catalogue of Books and Papers relating to the Fertilisation of Flowers, 1883].

[2] Regarding the passage of the pollen-tube see references in note on page 306.

[3] The analogy of the Gymnosperms would lead us to suspect that the nucleus of the pollen-tube is not dissolved in the Angiosperms, but takes part directly in the fertilisation.

The pollen-tube having passed through the micropyle either encounters the exposed apex of the embryo-sac, or, as in *Watsonia* and *Santalum*, the projecting synergidae; but very frequently a portion of the tissue of the apex of the nucellus is still in the way, and the tube must penetrate it to reach the embryo-sac. The wall of the latter is often weak and is sometimes indented by the advancing end of the tube, or even, as in *Canna*, pierced by it.

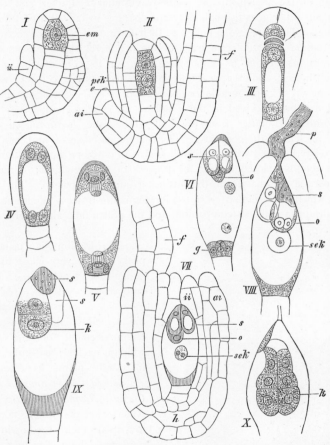

FIG. 321. Development of the embryo-sac, fertilisation and embryogeny in an orchidaceous plant, a combination of figures of *Gymnadenia Conopsea* and *Orchis pallens*. *I* rudiment of the mother-cell of the embryo-sac, and of the inner integument. *II* division of this mother-cell of the embryo-sac into three sister-cells, the lowest of the three being the rudimentary embryo-sac. *III* displacement of the two upper sister-cells by the growing embryo-sac; two nuclei in the sac. *IV* doubling of the two nuclei. *V* further division of these nuclei. *VI* the egg-apparatus in the anterior extremity of the embryo-sac consisting of the two synergidae and the oosphere beneath them; the three antipodal cells are in the posterior end of the embryo-sac, and there are two free nuclei in its cavity. *VII* the mature ovule before fertilisation; the two free nuclei of the embryo-sac have coalesced and formed a secondary nucleus which still contains two nucleoli. *VIII* fertilisation by means of one of the synergidae (the one to the right) which appears to be changed into a homogeneous highly refractive protoplasmic body; there are two nuclei, the sperm-nucleus and the nucleus of the oosphere. *IX* pro-embryo consisting of two cells. *X* further development of the pro-embryo. The letters *em* denote the mother-cell of the embryo-sac (archesporium), *e* the embryo-sac, *pek* the primary nucleus of the embryo-sac, *sek* the secondary nucleus of the same, *s* the synergidae, *o* the oosphere, *g* the antipodal cells, *p* the pollen-tube, *k* the pro-embryo in process of differentiation, *ii* the inner, *ai* the outer integument, *f* the funiculus, *h* an intercellular space. From drawings by Prof. Strasburger. *VII* is magn. about 200 times, the rest about 300 times.

The contact of the tube with the apex of the embryo-sac or with the filiform apparatus of the oosphere is sufficient for the transference of the fertilising substance;

the transference is accomplished according to Strasburger in the following manner. In a suitable subject, as in *Torenia asiatica*, the pollen-tube may be seen to attach itself firmly to the synergidae as soon as it has reached them, and breaks before it will allow itself to be separated from them.   Then the contents of one of the synergidae become turbid, its nucleus (?) and its vacuole disappear, its protoplasm becomes finely granular and afterwards very strongly refractive, and now agrees entirely with the contents of the pollen-tube in density, granular character and colour.   The companion cell either goes through the same changes or takes no part in the process of fertilisation.   The synergidae next lose their form, and pieces of them break away and attach themselves to different parts of the oosphere, which must take into itself shapeless portions of one or both synergidae, for its contents become richer in granular substances, and it appears to be invested with a cell-wall as a result of impregnation.   In cases favourable for observation, as in the Orchideae and *Monotropa*, two nuclei can be perceived in the oosphere after impregnation, one of which is certainly formed of matter from the pollen-tube (the sperm-nucleus), while the other is the nucleus of the oosphere.   The two nuclei coalesce, and then the oospore which is already invested with a cell-wall begins to develope into the embryo.   The pollen-tube remains closed during the process of impregnation; it must therefore remain uncertain in what form the fertilising substance passes.   The one of the synergidae which is not employed in the impregnating process persists for a time and ultimately disappears like its companion, and the pollen-tube also after a time can no longer be recognised.

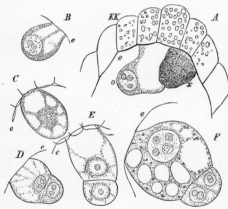

FIG. 322. *Funkia cordata. A* apex of the embryo-sac *e* covered by a layer of cells of the nucellus *KK*; *x* one of the synergidae, beside it the peculiarly shaped oospore with its onucleus. *B, C* ospores before division   *E* after division   *F* the pro-embryo differentiating into the spherical suspensor-cell and the two-celled rudiment of the embryo.   Magn. 550 times.

Fertilisation is usually accomplished in a very short time after the pollen-tube reaches the apex of the embryo-sac; yet the cases are not few in which a long time elapses between the arrival of the pollen-tube and the commencement of the development which it excites; several days or weeks in woody plants as *Ulmus, Quercus, Fagus, Juglans, Citrus, Æsculus, Acer, Cornus, Robinia*, almost a year in the American oaks which take two years to ripen their seed; in *Colchicum autumnale* the pollen-tube reaches the embryo-sac at the latest by the beginning of November, and it is not till the May of the next year that the embryo begins to form (Hofmeister) [1].

Even the penetration of the pollen-tube into the conducting tissue of the style and to the cavity of the ovary often causes extensive changes in the flower; if the perianth is delicate it usually loses its turgidity at this time, withers, and soon falls to the ground; it is common in the Liliaceae for the ovary to begin to increase rapidly in size before

[1] Hofmeister, Neue Beitr. (Abh. d. K. sächs. Ges. d. Wiss. Bd. VI. and VII).

fertilisation is effected in the ovules (Hofmeister). In the Orchideae pollination not only stimulates the ovary to a vigorous and often long-continued growth, but makes the ovules capable of fertilisation, and even in some cases is the cause of their first appearance on the placentas which till then were sterile (Hildebrand).

Results of fertilisation in the embryo-sac ; formation of the endosperm. The first results of fertilisation are those which have just been described as appearing in the egg-apparatus and in the oospore. The formation of the endosperm begins very often before the division of the oospore, at the latest during its transformation into the pro-embryo ; it begins in all cases with the division of the (secondary) nucleus of the embryo-sac, and continues with the repeated division of the daughter-nuclei or daughter-cells. Of this process of division there are two modifications[1]. In a large number of Dicotyledons the division of the nucleus in the embryo-sac is combined with cell-division ; the embryo-sac after the division of its nucleus is divided by a transverse wall into two cells, as for example in *Monotropa*, Loranthaceae, *Orobanche*, Labiatae and Campanulaceae, and the further division of these cells gives rise to the tissue of the endosperm, which in this case often fills only certain parts of the embryo-sac. In some cases the embryo-sac also divides by a transverse division into two daughter-cells, the upper one of which contains the rudiment of the embryo and produces a small quantity of endosperm in a way which will be described presently ; examples of this proceeding are found according to Hofmeister in *Nymphaea, Nuphar, Ceratophyllum* and *Anthurium*. The second mode of formation of endosperm is by free cell-formation and occurs in Monocotyledons and most Dicotyledons. In this case the embryo-sac is not at first divided into compartments by cell-walls, but the nucleus

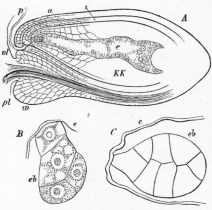

FIG. 323. *Viola tricolor.* *A* longitudinal section of the anatropous ovule after fertilisation ; *pl* the placenta, *w* cushion on the raphe, *a* outer *i* inner integument, *KK* nucellus, *p* the pollen-tube which has penetrated into the micropyle, *e* the embryo-sac containing the embryo to the left and numerous free nuclei. *B* and *C* the convex apices of two embryo-sacs *e*, with the differentiating pro-embryo *eb* attached to them, the suspensor in *B* being formed of two cells.

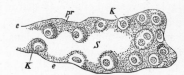

FIG. 324. *Viola tricolor.* Posterior portion of the embryo-sac ; *e* its wall, *S* sap-cavity, *K* free nuclei imbedded in the protoplasm *pr*.

divides and the two daughter-nuclei repeat the division, and the further continuance of the process gives rise to a large number of free nuclei lying in the protoplasm which lines the embryo-sac. These nuclei are almost always distributed as a simple layer on the lateral walls of the embryo-sac, but a thicker layer of protoplasm is in many cases collected at its two extremities about the oospore and about the antipodal cells, and the nuclei then form several layers at the same points. Meanwhile the embryo-sac has increased considerably in size, and cell-formation does not begin till

---

[1] Strasburger, Zellbilding u. Zelltheilung, III ed. Jena, 1880.

after its growth has ceased. Portions of protoplasm, in the centre of each of which there is usually a single nucleus[1], become separated off from one another by walls perpendicular to the wall of the embryo-sac, and are then invested on their inner side also with walls of cellulose. In this way the embryo-sac is first lined with a single layer of cells, and by several layers only at the parts indicated above. The cells of this layer at once begin to multiply and thus ultimately fill the entire sac with endosperm, provided the latter is not early displaced by the growing embryo. The cell-formation round the free nuclei is not usually simultaneous throughout the whole embryo-sac, but advances in it in a given direction; it may have begun at the two extremities, while free formation of nuclei is still going on in the central parts. If the embryo-sac increases greatly in size, it may be a long time before it is filled with endosperm, as in *Ricinus*. The centre of the sac in unripe seeds is filled with a clear vacuole-fluid; in the embryo-sac of the coco-nut which grows to an enormous size this fluid, the milk of the coco-nut, is still found when the seed is fully ripe, and the tissue of the endosperm forms a layer of only a few millimetres in thickness lining the inner side of the seed coat. The formation of endosperm by free cell-formation, that is by division of nuclei, at first without the formation of cells, these being only formed subsequently, occurs, as has been already intimated, in plants whose embryo-sac attains very large dimensions or grows very rapidly, while in narrow and slowly growing sacs it is produced by the division of the sac itself into cells. In a few families only, the formation of endosperm is rudimentary, being limited to the temporary appearance of a few free nuclei or cells, as in *Tropaeolum, Trapa,* the Naiadaceae, and Alismaceae; even this rudimentary formation is wanting in the Orchideae.

During the formation of endosperm the embryo-sac usually increases in size, and displaces whatever tissue of the nucellus there may still be surrounding it; in a few cases only is the nucellus wholly or partially preserved, and then it becomes filled with food-material, like the endosperm, and takes its place as a receptacle of reserve-material for the embryo; in the Scitamineae (*Canna*) this tissue, the *perisperm*, is largely developed, the endosperm being entirely absent; in the Piperaceae and Nymphaeaceae there is a small endosperm present in the ripe seed, but it lies in an excavation in the much more copious perisperm.

The *seed-coat* is meanwhile being developed from the integuments, and increases with the increase in size of the embryo-sac and the endosperm which it contains. In *Crinum capense* and in some other Amaryllideae, according to Hofmeister, the growing endosperm bursts the seed-coat and even the wall of the ovary, its cells produce chlorophyll, and its tissue continues succulent and forms intercellular spaces, which does not happen elsewhere; in *Ricinus* a similar growth takes place in the germination of the ripe seed in moist ground: by this means the seed-coat is ruptured and the endosperm previously about eight to ten millimetres in length is hanged to a flat broad sac some twenty or twenty-five millimetres in length, which encloses the growing cotyledons till they have exhausted its food-material.

---

[1] In some cases (*Corydalis cava, Staphylea pinnata, Armeria vulgaris* and others) there are several, two, three or four nuclei; these then coalesce in a remarkable manner, as Strasburger has shown, *loc. cit.*, p. 26, and form a single nucleus.

In Monocotyledons and many Dicotyledons the embryo within the endosperm remains small, and is either enveloped by it or is placed on one side of it, as in the Gramineae; the cells of the endosperm leave no intercellular spaces and are filled till the seed is ripe with protoplasmic substance and fatty oil or starch or both, and in this case remain thin-walled; the endosperm then appears as the mealy (rich in starch) or oily kernel of the ripe-seed, with the embryo in the middle of it or by its side; it sometimes becomes horny from a considerable thickening of its cell-walls which have the power of swelling, as in the Date and other Palms, in the Umbelliferae, *Coffea*, etc.; if this thickening is excessive, the endosperm may fill the seed-coat as a stony substance, as in *Phytelephas*, 'vegetable ivory'; in these cases the thickening-masses of the cells are dissolved during germination and serve with the protoplasmic and fatty cell-contents to feed the young plant. The endosperm, when fully formed and copiously developed, has usually the shape of the entire ripe seed and is uniformly covered by its coat; its external form therefore is usually simple and often rounded; but considerable deviations from this condition occur not unfrequently and especially among the Dicotyledons; this is the case, for example, in the well-known coffee-bean (*Coffea*), which with the exception of the minute embryo concealed in it is entirely composed of the horny endosperm; but this, as a transverse section shows, is a plate with its edges folded inwards. The marbled appearance of the *ruminate* endosperm which forms the kernel of the nutmeg, the seed of *Myristica fragrans*, and of the Areca-nut, the seed of the areca palm, is due to an inner dark layer of the seed-coat which grows inwards in the form of radiating lamellae into narrow folds in the clear endosperm. The ripe endosperm is either a solid body of tissue, or it has a cavity, which in *Strychnos nux-vomica*, for instance, is a broad flat narrow fissure; in these internal cases the endosperm as it grows from

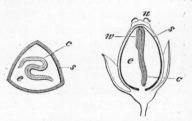

FIG. 325. *Polygonum Fagopyrum.* To the left a transverse, to the right a longitudinal section through a mature ovary; *n* dried stigmas, *s* testa, *e* endosperm. *c* cotyledons folded in a sinuous manner, as is shown in the transverse section, *w* root.

the outside of the embryo-sac inwards leaves a central space unfilled; this space in the coco-nut, as has been already mentioned, is large and contains a fluid, while the endosperm itself is a hollow thick-walled sac enclosing a roundish or fissure-like cavity.

In very many families of the Dicotyledons the first leaves of the embryo, the cotyledons, grow before the seed is ripe into bodies of such a size that they displace the endosperm which is already formed, and at length fill the whole space enclosed by the embryo-sac and the seed-coat, while the axial part of the embryo and the bud which lies between the bases of the cotyledons remain comparatively small; such cotyledons are thick and fleshy or leaf-like and then usually folded, and contain the reserve of protoplasmic substance and starch or fatty matter which in other cases is stored up in the endosperm to be used during the unfolding of the young plant. The cotyledons appear to obtain this copious supply of food-material from the endosperm, and therefore the difference between the seed which in its mature state has no endosperm and one which contains endosperm is simply, that in the former the reserve of food in the endosperm has passed into the embryo before germination, but passes in the latter during germination. The occurrence of ripe seeds with or without endosperm is more or less constant within large groups of plants and is therefore of systematic value; among the better-known families, for example, the Compositae, Cucurbitaceae, Papilionaceae and Cupuliferae (Oak, Beech) have seeds without endosperm. Sometimes the embryo grows within the seed to such a size, that the endosperm is only like a rather thin membrane surrounding it.

To return once more to the recently formed oospore; in Angiosperms as in Gymnosperms it is not as a rule at once transformed into the embryo; the end which is towards the micropyle becomes attached to the wall of the apical convexity of the embryo-sac, and the free extremity is directed towards the base of the ovule; it then elongates and undergoes in doing so one or more transverse divisions. The embryo is usually formed from the two terminal cells of this row of cells and the suspensor from the others [1].

The embryos of *Alisma Plantago* and *Capsella Bursa-pastoris* which have become well known since Hanstein's researches may serve to illustrate the development of the embryo. We desire to know how and where the first organs of the embryo (the *radicle*, the *plumule* and the *cotyledons*) are formed, and how the dermatogen, the periblem and plerome are differentiated. The first point to notice is, that the root (extremity of the radicle) is always formed at the posterior extremity of the embryo which is towards the point of attachment, and that the plumule is lateral (Monocotyledons) or terminal at the free extremity which is remote from the point of attachment. *Capsella* affords the best illustration of the development of the embryo in Dicotyledons. The oospore first elongates considerably and assumes the form of a tube, the upper or micropylar end of which is divided by a number of transverse walls. The embryo is chiefly formed from the terminal cell of this row of cells. Three stages may be distinguished in the development of this cell; in the first it becomes spherical in form without external differentiation, while the different layers of meristem are already separated from one another in its interior; in the second stage the embryo becomes differentiated into radicle, stem and cotyledons, and in the third it grows in all its parts into the state in which it is ready for germination. The development of the embryo begins with the increase in size of the terminal cell, which then divides into halves by a radial wall (Fig. 326 *I*, 1). As commonly happens in the case of cells developing into organs which are nearly spherical in shape, for example in the embryos of the Vascular Cryptogams, a second longitudinal wall follows the first and at right angles to it (lying in Fig. 361, *I* in the plane of the paper), and then a transverse wall at right angles to the two former walls (Fig. 326 *I*, 2), so that the small embryonic sphere is now composed of the octants of the sphere.

The cotyledons and the plumule or *epicotyledonary* portion of the young plant subsequently proceed from the upper half of the embryo which is cut off by the

---

[1] The embryonic body in the condition before the differentiation into suspensor and embryo is termed the pro-embryo. On the development of the embryo see Hanstein, Entwicklungsgesch. d. Keims der Monocot. u. Dicot. in his Bot. Abh., I. Bd.—Westermaier, *Capsella bursa-pastoris* (Flora, 1876), and Hegelmaier in Bot. Ztg. 1874, p. 631.—Koch, *Orobanche* in Pringsheim's Jahrb., XI Bd. p. 218.—Famintzin, Embryol. Studien (Mém. de l'Acad. imp. de St. Pétersbourg, Sér. XXVI). See also below.

transverse wall (Fig. 326, *II*), and the radicle or *hypocotyledonary* portion from the lower; but first of all an outer and an inner cell are usually separated from one another in each octant by its periclinal wall.   The outer cells which are dark in Fig. 326 *II* are the *dermatogen* or young epidermis, and its cells continue to divide only by walls at right angles to the outer surface, i.e. by anticlinal walls, no periclinal walls being formed; the inner cells produce the *periblem* and *plerome*.   The figures *III* and *IV* will give a clear idea of the divisions in these cells.   According to Famintzin the initial layers of cells, from which the periblem and plerome proceed, are very early separated from one another and continue to be so; (Fig. 326 does not give this quite correctly and Fig. 327 should be consulted).   Subsequently the spherical

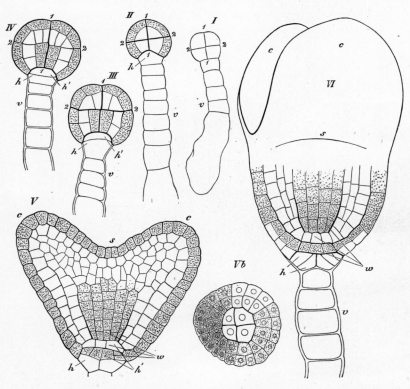

FIG. 326.   Embryogeny of *Capsella Bursa-pastoris*.   Stages of the development in the order of the figures *I* to *VI*; *Vb* extremity of the root seen from below, 1 1, 2 2 first divisions of the terminal cell of the pro-embryo, *hh'* the hypophysis, *v* the suspensor, *c* the cotyledons, *s* apex of the axis, *w* the root.   The dermatogen and plerome are shaded.   After drawings by Hanstein.

embryo is flattened and becomes first triangular and then cordate in shape (Fig. 326 *V*) by the appearance of two large protuberances, the cotyledons, on the sides of its apex.   Meanwhile further differentiations have taken place also at the radicular end of the embryo.   The cell of the suspensor adjoining the embryo is made use of to build up the embryo; its lower transverse wall becomes concave downwards, so that the cell of the suspensor appears as part of the spherical embryo, as the termination of its posterior extremity (Fig. 326 *h*); it then divides by a

transverse wall into two cells, of which the one next the suspensor takes no further
part in the development of the embryo.   The upper of the two cells (the *hypophysis*
of Hanstein) divides into two cells lying one above the other by a transverse wall
which is curved like a watch-glass (Fig. 327).   These two cells are first divided by
longitudinal walls, as is shown in Fig. 326 *V*, and then the lower one of them by a
transverse wall.   The cells which proceeded from the upper of the two cells of the
hypophysis form the termination of the periblem of the root, while the lower one
gives rise to a layer of cells, shaded in Fig. 326 *V*, which connects with the dermatogen and forms the first layer of the root-cap; as Fig. 329 shows, the root-cap is
produced by the continued growth of the root accompanied by corresponding
divisions by cell-walls, and may therefore be described simply as a luxuriant growth
of the dermatogen.   The peripheral layer of tissue, which elsewhere remains single
and passing into permanent tissue forms the epidermis, becomes thicker where it
covers the growing point of the root, and suffers tangential divisions (parallel to the
surface) which are repeated periodically; of the two layers thus formed at each

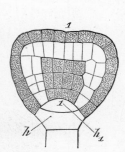

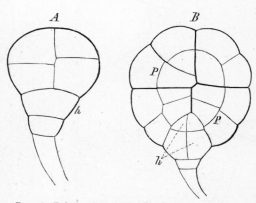

FIG. 327.   *Capsella Bursa-
pastoris*. Embryo about half developed (shortly before the appearance of the cotyledons) in optical longitudinal section, somewhat diagrammatically rendered.
The hypophysis has divided into
the cells *h* and *h₁*. After Hanstein.

FIG. 328. Embryos of *Orobanche*. The cell-divisions agree on the
whole with those in *Capsella*, but among other variations the anticlinal line
first makes its appearance in the left upper octant, and then the periclinal *P*.
Similar irregularities occur also sometimes in *Capsella*. *h* hypophysis, *P* the
periclinal wall which divides off the dermatogen. After Koch. .

division the outer becomes a layer of the root-cap (Fig. 329, 2 and Fig. 333 *wh*),
while the inner remains dermatogen and repeats the same process.   The dermatogen
which covers the vegetative cone of the root behaves therefore in the same way as a
layer of phellogen, but with this difference, that the cells produced by the cork-
cambium become at once permanent cells, whereas those of the root-cap continue
capable of division, and thus each layer of cells separated off from the dermatogen
gives rise to several layers of cells of the root-cap, the growth of which is most active
in the centre and lessens towards the circumference.   The formation of the root-cap
is different from this in other Angiosperms, and will be touched upon presently.

Alisma Plantago may serve as an example of the development of the embryo
in a monocotyledonous plant.   Fig. 330 *I* shows the stage in which the embryo
consists of three cells, the proximal cell (*q*) of the pro-embryo being in this case swollen
out into a vesicle.   The middle cell (*r*) now divides by a number of transverse walls

which appear in basipetal succession, while longitudinal walls are formed at the same time in the terminal cell, and with the result, as in *Capsella*, that two walls are formed at right angles to one another. But in this case the chief portion of the embryo does not proceed solely from the terminal cell of the pro-embryo, but the other cells *m* and *n* also take part in its formation, as appears from Fig. 330 *III*. The separation of the dermatogen by periclinal walls takes place later in *Alisma* than in *Capsella*, but the

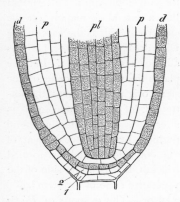

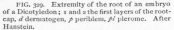

FIG. 329. Extremity of the root of an embryo of a Dicotyledon; 1 and 2 the first layers of the root-cap, *d* dermatogen, *p* periblem, *pl* plerome. After Hanstein.

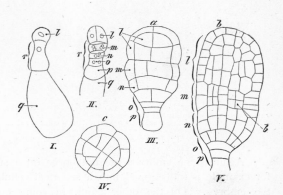

FIG. 330. Embryogeny in *Alisma Plantago*. *I* pro-embryo, consisting of three cells. The cell *q* subsequently swells into a spherical shape, the cotyledon springs from *l* and portions of the embryo and suspensor from *r*; four cells are formed by three transverse walls in basipetal succession from the middle cell *r* in No. *II*, *m*, *n*, *o*, *p*; from *m* the plumule is developed, *n* gives rise to the greater part of the radicle, *o* and *p* to the hypophysis. *III* upper part of an older embryo, in which the dermatogen has been formed by periclinal walls; *l* denotes those cells which proceeded from the terminal cell *l* of the preceding figure. *IV* optical transverse section of the same embryo. *V* an older embryo, in which the rudiment of the plumule may be seen on the side to the right, where are the larger cells of the dermatogen. The letters indicating the groups of cells also indicate the cells from which they are formed (see also Fig. 332). After Famintzin.

layers which produce the periblem and plerome are as distinctly marked off from the first, according to Famintzin, in the one case as in the other. But the origin of the organs is different in the two embryos. In *Alisma* the whole of the terminal mass of tissue occupying the apex of the embryo becomes the cotyledon, which is therefore terminal on the embryo, while the growing point of the stem is placed laterally upon it, where a slight depression appears on the right side of *V* in Fig. 330. This separation may be traced back to the first cell-divisions. The cotyledon is produced from the terminal cell *l* and from the cells formed by its division, the cell next below *m* forms the middle portion, which is distinctly marked off from the cotyledon and from the radicle and gives rise to the plumule, and the third cell *n* becomes the radicle; *o* and *p* form the hypophysis, and *p* therefore a part also of the embryo. Fig. 332 shows that the termination of the radicle proceeds from the hypophysis in the same way as in *Capsella*.

The two examples which have been now briefly described do not however at all supply schemes of development of the embryo that are generally applicable to Monocotyledons and Dicotyledons. Other forms that have been examined show variations in almost all the processes of differentiation observed in *Capsella* and *Alisma*. As regards the position and origin of the organs, the important point of difference between Monocotyledons and Dicotyledons has been already noted, that in the former the cotyledon is terminal, while in the latter the two cotyledons are of lateral origin at the upper extremity of the embryo, though they often, as for instance in *Capsella*, take up so much of the upper part of the embryo that the plumule cannot be recognised as a distinct projection between them.   Moreover there are monocotyledonous embryos, as Solms-Laubach has shown[1], in which the cotyledons are not a terminal but a lateral formation on the embryo.   This is the case in the Dioscoreaceae and some, perhaps all, the Commelinaceae.   In these plants the vegetative cone of the stem originally occupies the extremity of the embryo, and is afterwards moved into a lateral position by the development of the cotyledon which is formed beneath, that is, at the side of the vegetative cone of the stem[2].

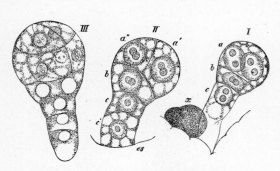

FIG. 331.   Embryos of *Allium Cepa* in different stages of development.   In *I* the spherical cell at the end of the suspensor contains two nuclei.   In *II* it has divided into *a'* and *a''*, and *c* in *I* into *c* and *c'* in *II*; *x* is the remains of one of the synergidae, *es* embryo-sac wall.

Again, some embryos are not borne on a suspensor.   The oospore of *Pistia* for example is transformed into a spherical cellular body, which directly represents the embryo.   On the other hand, in some Orchideae the suspensor assumes the peculiar form of a row of cells with transverse walls which grows out of the micropyle and attaches itself to parts like the placentas, where food-material is present, in order to convey it to the embryo[3].   In species of *Lupinus* the cells of the long suspensor separate at an early period of their existence, and the embryo then lies free in the embryo-sac at a distance from the micropyle[4].

There are many variations also in the external form of the embryo and consequently in the arrangement of its cells, and also in the mode of formation of the root-cap.   These variations are found, as we learn from Hegelmaier[5], in allied plants, and are connected with the number of the cells of the pro-embryo which are employed in the formation of the embryo; in the Cruciferae and other plants the number of cells is two (compare *Capsella*), in other cases three or more.   The differentiation of the apex of the root takes place in some cases, as in the Gramineae, deep within the tissue of the embryo, and the apex is therefore covered by a layer of tissue which it

---

[1] H. Graf zu Solms-Laubach, Ueber monocotyle Embryonen mit scheitelbürtigem Vegetationspunkt (Bot. Ztg. 1878, p. 65).

[2] As far as the morphological nature of the cotyledons is concerned it is a matter of indifference where and how they are formed in the embryo, for that they must be considered foliar structures is established by the fact that they are often but slightly different in the fully developed state from the first foliage-leaves.

[3] Treub, Notes sur l'embryogenie de quelques Orchidées (Naturkund. verhandl. d. k. Akad. Deel XXI, 1879).

[4] Strasburger, Ueber vielkernige Zellen u. Embryogenie von *Lupinus* (Bot. Ztg. 1880).—Hegelmaier, in same place.

[5] Hegelmaier, Vergl. Unters. ü. Entw. dicotyl. Keime, Stuttgart, 1878.

must break through in germination, and which is termed the *coleorhiza* or root-sheath; a similar state of things is found also in Dicotyledons, in *Geranium* for instance, where there is no appearance of a hypophysis as in *Capsella*, but the apex of the root is bounded on the posterior side by the tissue of a many-celled suspensor. It is not uncommon for lateral roots as well as the primary root, which we have hitherto been considering, to be formed in the embryo before the seed is ripe, as for example in many of the Gramineae and in some Dicotyledons, such as *Impatiens* according to Hanstein and Reinke and in *Cucurbita* according to Sachs; in *Trapa natans* the primary root soon ceases to develope and lateral roots are formed from

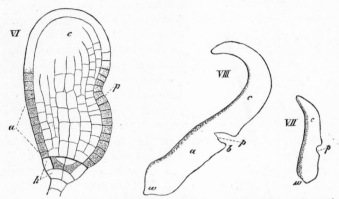

FIG. 332. Older embryos of *Alisma Plantago*; *c* cotyledon, *p* growing point of the stem, *a* hypocotyl, *w* root, *h* hypophysis. In *VI* the dermatogen is shaded. From drawings by Hanstein.

the hypocotyledonary portion of the axis (*hypocotyl*). The degree also of development which the embryo reaches in the seed is very different in different seeds. In some plants the plumule has several leaves besides the cotyledons while it is within the seed, whereas the embryo of many Angiosperms which live as parasites or saprophytes is an undifferentiated mass of cells with no sign of root or cotyledons.

Adventitious embryos and polyembryony. Great as are the variations in the development of the embryo in the cases which have now been described, they have this feature in common, that the embryo proceeds from the oospore. But, according to Strasburger's interesting discovery[1], there are a number of Monocotyledons and Dicotyledons in which the embryos never or seldom come from the oospore, but are shoots from cells of the nucellus adjoining the embryo-sac. To the list of such plants belong *Funkia ovata, Nothoscordum, Citrus Aurantium, Mangifera indica, Coelebogyne ilicifolia. Funkia ovata* (Fig. 334) has an egg-apparatus composed as usual of two synergidae and an oosphere; the oosphere also is fertilised, but the oospore seldom or never developes into an embryo. Instead of this, adventitious embryos of the kind above-mentioned make their appearance after fertilisation. Cells of the nucellus covering the apex of the embryo-sac (Fig. 334 *I*) become filled with protoplasm, swell up and divide (Fig. 334 *II*), and as a considerable number of the cells of the nucellus put out these shoots, we have here an evident case of polyembryony.

---

[1] Strasburger, Ueber Befruchtung u. Zelltheilung, Jena, 1878;—Id., Ueber Polyembryonie (Jen. Zeitschr. für Naturwiss. Bd. XII).

The adventitious embryos thus formed continue to grow into the cavity of the nucellus, pushing the embryo-sac before them, and assume altogether the habit of true embryos. A similar proceeding has been observed in *Nothoscordum fragrans*. In *Citrus Aurantium* the adventitious embryos originate in single cells of the nucellus lying either at the apex of the embryo-sac or lower down, and may even be separated from the embryo-sac by several other cells. *Coelebogyne ilicifolia* is interesting from the fact that it has hitherto been adduced as an instance of *parthenogenesis* in Phanerogams. Though the female plant of this dioecious species is the only one cultivated in Europe, it nevertheless often produces seeds capable of germination, and these often have more than one embryo. Here too there is a normal egg-apparatus, but the oosphere cannot be fertilised as there is no pollen, and soon perishes. This therefore is no case of parthenogenesis, which would only occur if an embryo proceeded from the unfertilised oosphere, as in *Chara crinita*, (p. 64), but embryos are formed, as in *Funkia* and *Nothoscordum*, as shoots from cells of the nucellus. This is evidently a parallel case to that of the apogamous prothallia of the Ferns which have been described above, in which the formation of an embryo is replaced by asexual formation of a shoot. Whether the oosphere of *Coelebogyne* is not still capable of fertilisation and development is not certainly known.

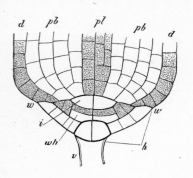

FIG. 333. Diagrammatic representation of the formation of the primary root in Monocotyledons and its connection with the stem ; *v* suspensor, *h* hypophysis, *w w* boundary-line f root and stem, *wh* layer of the root-cap, *d* dermatogen, *pb* periblem, *pl* plerome, *i* initial cells. From a drawing by Hanstein.

Polyembryony may occur in Angiosperms in other ways than by the formation of adventitious embryos. Two seeds are often found in the embryo-sac of some Orchideae, as in *Gymnadenia conopsea*, the result probably of duplication of the oosphere before fertilisation. Abnormal cases also are found of two nucelli in an integument, each of which may produce an embryo. It was stated above that more than one embryo-sac is formed in some ovules; but as only one developes, no occasion is given for polyembryony, at least in the cases as yet observed.

Development of the seed and fruit. While the endosperm and embryo are being formed in the embryo-sac, development takes place both in the ovule and in the wall of the ovary which surrounds it. The seed-coat is formed from certain layers of cells of the integuments or from the whole of their tissue, and its structure varies greatly ; the ovule becomes the seed when the changes above detailed take place within it as the result of the act of fertilisation. The wall of the ovary, the placentas, and the dissepiments increase in volume and undergo manifold changes in external form and still more in internal structure ; they and the seeds together form the *fruit*. The altered wall of the ovary now bears the name of *pericarp*; if an outer layer is specially differentiated in it, it is called the *epicarp* and the inner layer the *endocarp*; not unfrequently there is a third layer lying between the two, the *mesocarp*. A series of typical forms of fruit are distinguished according to the original form of the ovary and the structure of its tissue in the ripe state, the nomenclature of which will be given in the appendix. In many cases the long series of far-reaching changes set up by fertilisation extends to parts, which do not belong to the ovary or even to other parts of the flower; and since these parts belong physiologically to the fruit and are usually combined with it to form a single whole which is distinctly separate from the other parts of the plant, a structure of the kind, the fig (Fig. 335), the strawberry and the mulberry, for example, may be termed a *pseudocarp*.

At a certain time either the fruit with its seed becomes detached from the plant, or the seed separates by itself from the opened fruit; this is the time of maturity. In many species the whole plant dies down when it has ripened its fruit; such a species is termed *monocarpic*, as bearing fruit only once; monocarpic plants may be distinguished into those which bear fruit in the first period of vegetation (*annual plants*), or not till the second (*biennial plants*), or lastly not till several or many vegetative periods have passed (*monocarpic perennial* plants, as *Agave americana*). Most Angiosperms however are *polycarpic*, that is the vitality of the plant is not exhausted by ripening

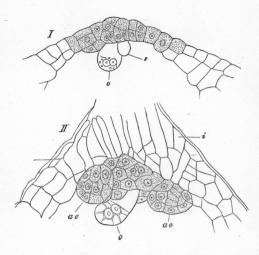

FIG. 334. Formation of adventitious embryos in *Funkia ovata. I* the cells at the apex of the nucellus filled with cell-contents; beneath it the oospore with two nuclei and the remains of one of the synergidae. *II* several adventitious embryos have formed in the cells of the nucellus; the nucellus is displaced, and strongly thickened cells of the integument are in contact with the embryo-sac. The oospore is present and has divided into three cells. *o* denotes the oospore, *s* a synergid, *ae* the adventitious embryos, *i* the cells of the integument. After Strasburger. Magn. about 150 times.

its fruit, but the plant continues to grow and fructify periodically, and is *polycarpic perennial*.

Anatomy of the flower. Of the structural details of the flower which have been already described two will be again noticed here, the conducting tissue and the nectaries, our knowledge of which has been increased by the labours of various investigators in quite recent times.

Conducting tissue[1]. The tubes which the pollen-grains develope on the viscid surface of the stigma have often a considerable distance to travel in order to reach the ovules. The conducting tissue has a double duty to perform; first to supply the pollen-tubes with plastic material for their growth, for they soon exhaust the food-material stored up in the pollen-grain, and secondly to assist the tubes to find their way to the micropyle and to enter it. For this purpose a conducting tissue is necessary in the style first and afterwards in the ovary or on the ovule itself. This tissue is formed in plants whose style has no canal by conversion into mucilage of the outer layers of the walls of the cells in the tissue which occupies the place of the canal, and which is thus converted into conducting tissue; in plants which have a canal, the cells that line it show a similar secretion to that on the papillae of the stigma. It is only occasionally, for

---

[1] Behrens, Ueber d. anat. Bau d. Griffels u. d. Narbe (Dissert. Göttingen, 1875).—Capus, Anat. du tissu conducteur (Ann. d. sc. nat. Bot. 6. sér. T. VII, 1878).—Dalmer, Ueber d. Leitung d. Pollenschläuche bei d. Angiospermen (Jen. f. Zeitschr. Naturw. Bd. XIV).—[Strasburger, Neue Unters. ü. d. Befruchtungsvorg. b. d. Phanerog. 1885. See also note on page 306.]

instance in the erect orthotropous ovules of *Polygonum* noticed above, that the micropyle lies almost immediately opposite to the lower extremity of the style, so that the downward-growing pollen-tube must necessarily encounter it.   In the Compositae (Fig. 310), where there is also a single but anatropous ovule, the micropyle is directed towards the bottom of the ovary.   Here, as in *Senecio Doria*, two strips of conducting tissue are found in the ovary right and left from the median line of the ovule; these strips are continuous with the conducting tissue of the style, descend to the bottom of the ovary and there unite beneath the micropyle which is bounded by the funicle. The cells of the funicle which lie next the micropyle also assume the character of a conducting tissue; and thus a thread of mucilage stretches from the bottom of the ovary to the micropyle, and the pollen-tube has its way marked out for it from the stigma to the micropyle by the conducting tissue, in which the cell-walls are changed into mucilage.   In other cases the cells of the placenta (or of the outer integument) secrete a mucilage in which the pollen-tube developes.   Thus the stigma is always in connection with the cavity of the ovary or with the ovules, either by means of a spongy tissue or of a canal, the walls of which supply the secretion mentioned above, or this secretion is the product of the transformation of their membrane.   Each loculus

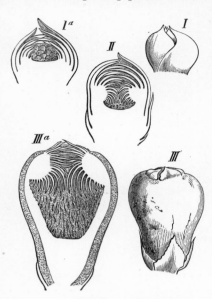

FIG. 335. Development of the inflorescence of *Ficus Carica*. *I*ᵃ and *II* young inflorescence from without surrounded by involucral leaves which in *III* are at the base of the inflorescence; *I*ᵃ, *II*, and *III*ᵃ are longitudinal sections. The axis of the inflorescence is depressed and becomes cup-shaped, while a number of involucral leaves grow out of the mouth of the cup, and the flowers from its inner surface.

of a plurilocular ovary is of course in communication with the style.   The presence of a cellular tissue explains the fact, that in the very great majority of cases pollinated flowers are found to have been fertilised.

As regards the arrangements connected with pollination in flowers[1], it has been already pointed out that in hermaphrodite flowers the stigmas are not usually dusted with pollen from the same, but from some other flower.   But *cleistogamous* flowers are systematically fertilised by their own pollen.   These are small flowers which never open, and are found on a number of plants, such as *Viola* and *Lamium amplexi-caule*, along with other and larger flowers which expand to the air and light; in cleistogamous flowers the conveyance of the pollen of one flower to the stigma of another (cross-pollination) is necessarily excluded.   The arrangements by which *cross-pollination* and *cross-fertilisation* are secured in ordinary expanding flowers are very various.   A few only can be briefly noticed here.   In many flowers the relative positions of anthers and stigmas render it impossible for the pollen of the one to reach the other.   Other flowers again are incapable of self-fertilisation, are *self-sterile*; if the pollen from the anthers of a flower reaches the stigma of the same flower, it either developes no tube,

---

[1] C. Sprengel, Das neuentdeckte Geheimniss d. Natur im Bau u. in d. Befruchtung d. Blumen, Berlin, 1793.—Hildebrand, Geschlechtvertheilung bei d. Pflanzen, Leipzig, 1867.—H. Müller, Die Befruchtung d. Blumen durch Insekten, Leipzig, 1873;—Id. Die Alpenblumen, ihre Befruchtung durch Insekten u. ihre Anpassungen an dieselben, Leipzig, 1880.—Darwin, On the various contrivances by which Orchids are fertilised, London, 1862;—Id., The effects of cross- and self-fertilisation in the Vegetable Kingdom, 1876.   [See also reference in note on p. 390.]

or the tube does not effect fertilisation ; normal fertilisation is produced only by pollen from another flower of the same species. Such a self-sterile plant is *Corydalis cava*, according to Hildebrand, in which the pollen of a flower falling on the stigma of the same flower is ineffectual, and only effects fertilisation when conveyed to a flower of another plant of the same species. Another plant of this kind is *Oncidium aricrochilum* ; according to Fritz Müller [1] the pollen-masses and the stigmas of the same plant in various species of *Oncidium* have actually a poisonous and deadly effect on one another.

One of the commonest and simplest means by which self-pollination is prevented is *dichogamy*, that is the development of the two kinds of sporophyll in a hermaphrodite flower at different times. Either the anthers discharge their pollen before the stigma is fully formed and in a condition to receive it, in which case the flower is *protandrous*, or the style is developed before the anthers, and the stigma is dusted before the pollen of the same flower has reached maturity and is discharged, and then the flower is *protogynous*. The stigmas of protogynous flowers can therefore only be dusted with pollen from older flowers, those of protandrous flowers only with that of younger ones. The Campanulaceae, Compositae, and Umbelliferae are protandrous, *Plantago* and *Aristolochia*, etc. are protogynous.

A further method for securing the mutual fertilisation of different plants of the same species is *heterogony* (*heterostyly*). In this case individuals of the same species differ in respect to their sporophylls ; one has only flowers with a long style and short filaments and with the stigma therefore placed high and the anthers low in the flower, while another has flowers with the stigma low down in the flower and the anthers placed high, with a short style therefore and long filaments. In this case then we have long-styled and short-styled flowers on different individuals of the same species, as in *Linum perenne*, *Primula sinensis*, and others of the Primulaceae. But there are also plants, as for instance *Lythrum Salicaria* and many species of *Oxalis*, in which the flowers of different individuals have sporophylls with three degrees of relative length ; beside the long-styled and the short-styled form of flower, there is another form with styles of medium length. In these cases of heterogony Darwin and Hildebrand have proved that fertilisation is only possible (*Linum perenne*), or at any rate has the best result, when the pollen of the long-styled flower is conveyed to the short-styled stigma, and that of the short-styled flower to the long-styled stigma of another plant. Where there are three different lengths of styles, fertilisation, by extension of the same rule, does best when the pollen is conveyed to the stigma of another flower which stands at the same height as the anther from which the pollen comes.

The conveyance of the pollen from one flower to another is effected either by the wind, as in the Cupuliferae, Urticaceae, *Potamogeton*, etc., or by insects ; less frequently by birds, as in *Colibris* of the Marcgraviaceae, or by snails, as in some Aroideae. Very various are the means by which insects are induced to visit flowers ; striking colours in the perianth, small secretion of nectar, are among the number ; a detailed description will be found in the writings of H. Müller cited on the preceding page.

Inflorescences. It is rare in Angiosperms for the flowers to appear singly on the summit of the primary shoot or in the axils of the foliage-leaves ; it much more frequently happens that peculiarly developed branch-systems are formed in these two positions bearing flowers usually in great profusion ; these systems, which are known as *inflorescences*, are distinguished by their collective form from the rest of the plant, and in polycarpic plants are even thrown off after the ripening of the fruit. Their habit depends not merely on the number, form and size of the flowers which they bear, but also on the length and thickness of the component branches, and on the degree of development of the leaves from the axils of which the branches spring ; these are usually much more simple in form and smaller than the foliage-leaves, and not unfrequently coloured (i. e. not green), or sometimes without colour. They are known by

---

[1] Bot. Ztg. 1868, p. 114.

the distinctive name of *hypsophyllary leaves* or *bracts*, and in this term are included also the small leaflets (*bracteoles*) which grow on the flower-stalks and often have no shoots springing from their axils; sometimes leaves of this kind are entirely wanting within the inflorescence or wanting at certain parts of it, and in that case the axes of the flowers or their parent-axes are not axillary (Aroideae, Cruciferae, and many others). The combination of these and other peculiar characters in various ways gives rise to a very great variety in the forms of inflorescences, each of which is constant in a particular species, and is often characteristic of a whole genus or family; the form of the inflorescence is often decisive of the habit of the plant and has also a systematic value.

It will be found that the most satisfactory classification of inflorescences is one that is founded chiefly on their mode of branching, because this is less variable than any other character and can be referred to a few types; it supplies also distinguishing marks for the primary groups, which will then fall readily into subdivisions according to the length and thickness of the different axes and other marks.

The branching of inflorescences is here as everywhere either *radial* or *dorsiventral* [1]. Dorsiventral inflorescences are those in which the axis of the inflorescence is not, like a radial inflorescence, developed uniformly in every direction but is seen to have two distinct sides, one of which (the side towards the primary axis in lateral shoots) is termed the dorsal side, while the side opposite to it is the ventral side. The two sides of the axis, which separate the dorsal and ventral sides, are the lateral faces or flanks. A chief mark of distinction between the dorsal and ventral sides is that one only bears flowers. The distinction is seen in a very striking manner in many papilionaceous inflorescences, as in *Vicia Cracca*, in *Urtica dioica*, and in the Boragineae, etc. Botanists generally have hitherto misunderstood this peculiarity or have attempted to refer it to irregular growth and displacement; but the history of development and a comparison with other dorsiventrally branched parts of plants show that these explanations are inadmissible. Intermediate forms are not wanting between the two modes of branching, being found, for example, in the inflorescence of the Gramineae. We will first consider radial inflorescences and proceed further on to the dorsiventral, observing only here that the branching of dorsiventral inflorescences is often extra-axillary, as will be shown more at length below.

The first point to observe is, that every inflorescence originates in the normal terminal branching of growing axes; this branching in Angiosperms, with the exception of the cases mentioned in section 14, is monopodial, that is, the branches arise laterally beneath the apex of the growing mother-shoot; if leaves (bracts) are distinctly developed on the latter, the lateral branches grow from their axils; if they are indistinct or abortive, the axes of the inflorescence are not indeed axillary, but their branching and other conditions of growth remain the same as if there were bracts present, and we need not lay any particular stress on this circumstance in determining the subdivisions. The presence of bracts is of practical importance, because it makes it more easy to perceive the true character of the branching even in fully developed inflorescences, the axillary shoot being always lateral; without this mark it is often difficult to say, in the mature state of the inflorescence, which is a parent-axis and which a lateral, for the latter often grows as vigorously or much more vigorously than the former. Of the many individual forms of inflorescence we shall here give only the more common ones, and without special regard to the question of symmetrical relationships within themselves [2].

---

[1] Goebel, Ueber d. Verzweigung dorsiventraler Sprosse (Arbeiten a. d. bot. Inst. in Würzburg, II. Bd. 3 Heft.

[2] Compare the dissimilar descriptions in Ascherson's Flora der Provinz Brandenburg (Berlin, 1864) and Hofmeister's Allgemeine Morphologie, sec. 7. [See also the remarks of Asa Gray in his Structural Botany, 1880, and the grouping of inflorescences given by Dickson in Balfour's Class-Book of Botany, 1871.]

A. Racemose (monopodial) inflorescences, in the widest sense of the term, are produced, when the primary axis or rhachis of the branch-system gives rise to
a larger or smaller number of lateral shoots in acropetal succession, in which
the power of development is less or at least not greater than that of the
portion of the primary axis which lies above their point of insertion.

a. *Spicate inflorescences* arise, when the lateral axes of the first order do not branch
and are all flowering axes ; the rhachis terminates with or without a flower.

(a) Spicate inflorescences with elongated rhachis :

1. *Spike.* Flowers sessile ; rhachis slender ; e.g. the so-called spikelet in the
Gramineae.
2. *Spadix.* Flowers sessile ; rhachis thick and fleshy; usually enveloped in a
long spathe ; bracts usually not developed; e.g. Aroideae.
3. *Raceme.* Flowers stalked ; e.g. the Cruciferae (without bracts), *Berberis,*
Menyanthes, Campanula with a flower terminating the rhachis.

(β) Spicate inflorescences with shortened rhachis :

4. *Capitulum.* Flowers sessile, densely covering the rhachis which is conical
or flattened or hollowed out into the shape of a cup ; bracts often wanting ;
e.g. the Compositae, Dipsaceae.
5. *Simple umbel.* Flowers stalked in a rosette and springing from a much
shortened rhachis ; e.g. *Hedera Helix,* etc.

b. *Panicled inflorescences* arise, when the lateral branches of the first order branch
and produce axes of the second and higher orders ; each axis may
terminate in a flower, or only those of the last order ; the power of development usually diminishes from below upwards on the primary axis and on the
lateral branches.

(a) Panicled inflorescences with elongated rhachis :

6. *True Panicle.* Lateral axes elongated, bearing stalked flowers ;e.g. *C rambe,*
Grape-vine.
7. *Panicle composed of spikes.* Lateral axes elongated, bearing sessile flowers ;
e.g. *Veratrum, Spiraea Aruncus,* Ears of Wheat, Rye, etc.

(β) Panicled inflorescences with shortened rhachis :

8. *Compact spike-like panicle.* Shortened lateral axes with their flowers on
a prolonged primary rhachis ; e.g. Ears of Barley, *Alopecurus.*
9. *Compound umbel.* Much shortened rhachis bearing a densely compact
rosette of partial umbels (*umbellules*) usually on long stalks (cf. No. 5) ; if
the umbel is surrounded by a group of leaves, this is the *involucre* ; if the
umbellule has one, it is the *involucel* ; one or both may be absent.

B. Cymose inflorescences[1] are produced by the branching of the primary axis or
rhachis immediately beneath the first flower in such a manner that each
lateral axis itself terminates in a flower after producing one or more lateral
axes, which also terminate in flowers and continue the system in a similar
manner ; the development of each lateral shoot is therefore stronger than
that of the parent-axis above its insertion (Figs. 336 and 337).

a. *Cymose inflorescences without a false axis.* Two or more lateral axes with a
terminal flower are developed beneath each flower of the inflorescence, and
the system is continued by lateral axes of a higher order.

10. *Anthela.* Lateral axes are formed in indefinite number on each axis that
terminates in a flower ; the lateral shoots growing vigorously overtop the
primary axis and develope in such a manner, that the entire inflorescence
does not acquire any definite outline (e.g. *Juncus lamprocarpus, J. tenuis,*

---

[1] Also termed centrifugal inflorescences, the racemose being known as centripetal.

J. alpinus, J. Gerardi, Luzula nemorosa, etc.)[1]. The anthela of these genera, and those of *Scirpus* and *Cyperus,* show many different forms that are transitions to the panicle and even to the spike, and on the other hand also to the formation of cymose inflorescences with false axes (e. g. *Juncus bufonius*) ; the inflorescence of *Spiraea Ulmaria* is included in this division by myself and others.

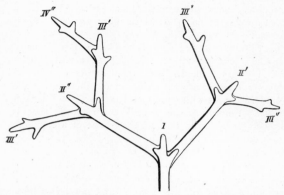

FIG. 336. Diagram of a dichasium (false dichotomy). The Roman numerals denote the order of development of the shoots of the system. The shoot *I* terminates with a flower and produces the shoots *II'* and *II''*, etc.

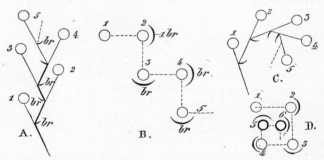

FIG. 337. Cicinnus or scorpioid cyme and bostryx or helicoid cyme in ground-plan and elevation. *A* elevation of cicinnus ; each shoot ends with a flower and produces an axillary shoot alternately right (as 2) and left (as 3). *B* ground-plan of the cicinnus. *C* elevation, *D* ground-plan of the bostryx.

11. *Cymose umbel.* A whorl of three or more equally strong axes spring from beneath the first flower, and these in their turn produce each a whorl of lateral axes beneath the terminal flower, and the process is repeated in the same manner ; the whole system has the habit of a true umbel ; very good examples are to be seen in the Euphorbiaceae, especially in *Euphorbia helioscopia* and *E. Lathyris* ; this form of cyme is not essentially different from the following one, the dichasium, and the cymose umbel often passes into it in the higher orders of shoots, e. g. in *Periploca graeca* even in the first branches.

12. *Dichasium.* Each axis of the inflorescence that terminates in a flower produces a pair of opposite or nearly opposite lateral axes, which terminate in a flower after they have in turn produced a pair of lateral axes, and so on ;

---

[1] Buchenau in Pringsh. Jahrb. f. wiss. Bot. IV. p. 393 and Taf. 28–30.

the whole system appears to be composed of bifurcations, especially when the older flowers have fallen off, as in many Sileneae, some Euphorbias, the Labiatae, etc. The dichasium easily passes into the sympodial development in the first or succeeding generations of lateral axes (Fig. 336).

b. Cymose inflorescences with a false axis (sympodial inflorescences). Only one similar axis is developed on each axis terminating in a flower, and this is repeated during several generations of axes. The basal portions of the successive generations of axes may lie more or less in a straight line and may become thicker than the flower-stalk (above the branching) ; in this way a *pseudaxis* or *sympodium* is formed, which curves first to one side then to the other or is straight, and the flowers appear to arise on it as lateral axes ; if the sympodium is clearly developed, it simulates a spike or raceme, but may be readily distinguished from it where there are bracts, because these are apparently opposite to the flowers ; but they are often liable to displacement, as in *Sedum.*

13. *Uniparous helicoid cyme or bostryx.* This is a sympodial inflorescence, in which the median line of each successive axis which builds up the system inclines away from that of the preceding one towards the same side, i. e. each new floral axis stands always right or always left of the median plane of the preceding axis (Fig. 337 *C, D*) ; as, for example, in the primary rays of the inflorescence of *Hemerocallis fulva* and *H. flava,* and in the partial inflorescences of *Hypericum perforatum* which are themselves arranged in a panicle (Hofmeister).

14. *Uniparous scorpioid cyme or cicinnus.* This is produced when the consecutive branches of the system arise alternately right and left of the median line of the preceding one, as in *Drosera, Scilla bifolia, Tradescantia* (Hofmeister). Of this kind also is the inflorescence of *Echeveria,* where the fully developed cicinnus has a false axis on which the flowers are opposite to the leaves. While the summit of the relatively primary axis is converted into a flower, a lateral axis is formed in the axil of its subfloral leaf ; this developes and forms a new leaf at right angles to the former one and ends in a flower, while a lateral axis appears in the axil of its leaf and continues the development ; the leaf formed on this last axis is in the same position as the first (Kraus).

It follows from what has been already said, that not only different forms of one of these divisions, but also forms from the two divisions (*A* and *B*) may make their appearance in an inflorescence composed of several generations of shoots, and produce mixed inflorescences ; a panicle in its last ramifications may form a dichasium, as in many Sileneae, a dichasial inflorescence may bear capitula (*Silphium*), the dichasium may in its first lateral branches or in those of a higher order pass into a bostryx or cicinnus, as in the Caryophylleae, Malvaceae, Solanaceae, Lineae, *Cynanchum, Gagea, Hemerocallis,* etc. In general the form of the branching in the inflorescence is different from that of the vegetative stem ; not unfrequently it passes suddenly from one to the other, but the two may be connected by intermediate forms of branching.

The older terminology has several other names of inflorescences, as cluster, corymb, etc., but they only indicate the habit or external shape of the system, and must be referred in a scientific description to one of the forms enumerated above or to some combination of them.

Even the inflorescences of the Boragineae which were formerly described as cicinnal are, at least in all the forms in which the history of development has been investigated, dorsiventral racemes. Two rows of flowers spring from the dorsal surface of the flowering axis which is rolled up in a circinate manner at its extremity, and a row of leaves is developed on each of the lateral faces and so placed that there is a leaf beneath each flower, an arrangement that is found in other dorsiventral inflorescences also, such as *Klugia notoniana, Aponogeton distachyon, Urtica canadensis.* The Urticaceae besides cymose inflorescences, such as occur in *Urtica urens* and *U. pilulifera,* have dorsiventral inflorescences of a very remarkable form. In *Urtica dioica* two rows of branches are formed on the dorsal side of the inflorescence, which produce cymose clusters of flowers on their dorsal face only. The flat flower-heads of *Dorstenia* owe their origin to peculiar conditions of growth in the ventral side of the flowering axis, which expands into a flat disk and branches dichotomously. In this case also the flowers grow only from one side of the head. The Papilionaceae also often have dorsiventral inflorescences, the flowers being placed always on the ventral side of the axis which is turned away from the primary axis, and this side is different in appearance from the dorsal side before the formation of the flowers, as in *Vicia, Orobus, Ononis* and other genera. In inflorescences of this kind with a large number of flowers, *Vicia Cracca* for

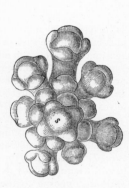

FIG. 338. Young inflorescence of *Isatis taurica* seen from above; *s* the apex of the inflorescence, beneath which the flower-buds arise in whorls of four members each; no bract is formed. The youngest buds are still quite leafless, the oldest show the beginnings of the four sepals.

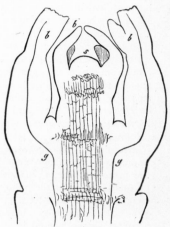

FIG. 339. Longitudinal section of the apical region of a shoot of *Clematis apiifolia*; *s* apex of the stem, *b b* leaves, *g* vascular bundle; small axillary shoots are seen in the axils of the youngest leaves, and are visible in the lower pair of leaves as hemispherical protuberances in their axils.

example, the flowers are seen to be arranged in oblique lines. For information with respect to other forms of inflorescence of this kind the student is referred to the treatise cited in note on page 406 [1].

On the *change in the mode of branching* in passing from the vegetative to the floral region of the shoot Warming [2] has made some important statements, from which it appears that many cases of apparently extraaxillary branching in inflorescences can be derived from axillary branching as the typical mode. He says that the axillary shoot and its subtending leaf must be taken together as a whole, in which the leaf which is one part, and the shoot which is the other, may be developed simultaneously or one before the other, and one more or less fully than the other. He then shows, that the subtending leaf is always formed first in the vegetative region, and at first at least grows more vigorously and rapidly than the shoot which belongs to it, and which does not make its appearance till a certain number of younger leaves have been already formed above the leaf in question (Fig. 339). In some inflorescences the formation of leaves anticipates that of the axillary shoots by a much less interval, as in the spikes and racemes

---

[1] [See also Čelakovský, Ueber ideale oder congenitale Vorgänge d. Phytomorphologie (Flora, 1884).]

[2] Recherches sur la ramification des Phanérogames, Kopenhagen, 1872.

of *Amorpha, Salix, Rudbeckia, Lupinus, Veronica, Digitalis, Orchis, Delphinium.* But there are other inflorescences in which the shoot is formed immediately after its subtending leaf, so that no rudiment of a leaf appears beneath the apex of the mother-shoot above the youngest shoot, as in *Plantago, Orchis, Epipactis*; sometimes the shoot and the leaf are formed simultaneously, as in the Gramineae, *Cytisus, Trifolium, Orchis, Plantago, Ribes*; or lastly the axillary shoot is formed before its subtending leaf, in which case the leaf attains only a slight development, there being an indication only of its presence, as in *Sisymbrium, Brassica* and other Cruciferae, Umbelliferae, *Anthemis, Valeriana,* the Asclepiadeae, *Bryonia, Cucumis*; or the subtending leaf is not developed, as in many Cruciferae (Fig. 338), Compositae, Gramineae, Umbelliferae, Papilionaceae, Boragineae, Solanaceae, Hydrophyllaceae, Saxifragaceae, *Potamogeton.* In all these inflorescences we find therefore the youngest flower-buds nearer the apex of the parent-shoot than any leaf, in so far as these have been formed at all; but the branching must not therefore be explained as a dichotomy of the parent-shoot; this only takes place when the formation of a shoot occurs so near the apex and with so much vigour that a continuation of the previous direction of growth of the parent-shoot is rendered impossible, and the apex divides into two or more apices, as happens according to Warming in *Hydrocharis, Vallisneria,* the Asclepiadeae, and some Cucurbitaceae[1]. That there is a connection between this tendency to dichotomy in plants in which the vegetative portion of the plant shows axillary branching and the suppression of the leaves in the inflorescences is to be inferred also from the fact, that the tendrils of *Vitis* and *Cucurbita,* in which also there is only a rudimentary formation of leaves, show the same inclination to dichotomy.

The axillary shoots of the vegetative region are usually so placed, that they spring at the same time from the base of the leaf and from the tissue of the stem; but it sometimes happens that the shoot moves quite on to the stem and therefore is detached from the leaf. In the floral region on the other hand it is not rare for the axillary shoot (the flower) to spring altogether from the leaf, as in *Hippuris, Amorpha, Salix nigricans*; but if the bract is formed later than the shoot (flower), it can spring from it, and in that case is no longer in direct connection with the parent-shoot, but appears to be the first (lowest) leaf of the lateral shoot; this is the case according to Warming in *Anthemis, Sisymbrium,* and the Umbelliferae, and to a lesser extent in Papilionaceae, Orchideae, Valerianeae, etc. These circumstances are usually most apparent in the earliest stages of development; the bract is often found moved more or less high up the stem in the fully developed state of the plant, as in *Thesium ebracteatum, Samolus Valerandi,* the Boragineae, Solanaceae, Crassulaceae, *Spiraea,* the Loranthaceae, *Ipomaea bona nox, Agave Americana, Ruta, Paliurus, Tilia* in which this is true of the large bract of the inflorescence, and others.

Bracteoles. The formation of the flower on the floral axis is usually preceded by the appearance of certain foliar structures, which cannot be regarded as forming part of the flower; they are known as bracteoles, and may be compared with the first scale-like leaves formed on rudimentary vegetative shoots. In Monocotyledons the bracteole is placed on the side of the shoot which is towards the parent-shoot, the dorsal side. Dicotyledons have usually two bracteoles placed right and left on the lateral faces of the branch; Monocotyledons in exceptional cases have two bracteoles and Dicotyledons one. The bracteoles are omitted in the diagrams in this work, because these are intended to show only the relative position of the parts of the flower.

Relative position and number of the parts of the flower[2]. As the forms of the

---

[1] The statements of Warming respecting dichotomy in the inflorescence of the Boragineae and others, at least in the majority of cases, are incorrect.

[2] [If in each of the three outer series of organs of the flower (calyx, corolla and androecium) there are five leaves or their number is a multiple of five, the flower is said to be *pentamerous*; similarly the terms *bimerous, trimerous,* etc. designate flowers in which the whorls of these organs have two

branching in the inflorescence are generally different from those in the vegetative stem, so the positions of the leaves in the floral shoot of the Angiosperms are not generally the same as those on the vegetative parts of the same plant. The cessation of the apical growth of the torus and its considerable expansion or even hollowing out before and during the formation of the leaves of the perianth and the sporophylls have an inevitable effect on the order of their succession and on their divergences. But while all other relations of form vary to an extraordinary degree, the true position of the foliar structures of the flower, though difficult to determine, is liable to a comparatively small amount of variation ; and a knowledge of this position is often of great use in ascertaining affinities and therefore in classification, especially if we take into account at the same time the frequent abortion of the separate parts, their multiplication under certain circumstances, and their branching and cohesion.

To render the representation of relations of this kind more easy, we must have recourse to certain diagrams and symbols.

It is important first of all to show the position of all the parts of the flower with respect to the mother-axis of the floral shoot. For this purpose the side of the flower which is turned towards the mother-axis is called the *posterior*, that which is turned away from it the *anterior* side ; if we now imagine a plane (longitudinal section) passing through the flower from front to back and including the axis of the flower and the axis of its mother-shoot, this is the median plane or section of the flower, and it divides it into a right and a left half. The foliar structures of the flower and the ovules and placentas, which are halved longitudinally by the median plane, are said to be in a median position, either median posterior or median anterior. Again, if we imagine a plane at right angles to the median plane and also including the axis of the flower, it may be termed the *lateral* plane ; it divides the flower into an anterior and a posterior half, and the parts of the flower which are bisected longitudinally by it are exactly right and left. Two planes which bisect the right angle between the median and the lateral planes may be called *diagonal* planes, and parts of the flower bisected by them are said to be diagonally placed. Foliar structures in flowers exactly posterior or exactly anterior are not uncommon ; they are much less frequently placed exactly laterally or diagonally, and we must generally have recourse to other expressions as obliquely posterior or obliquely anterior.

As regards the relative positions of the parts of the flower, it has been already stated that their arrangement is either *spiral* or in whorls (*cyclic*).

Flowers with their parts arranged spirally appear to be comparatively rare and to be confined to certain orders of Dicotyledons (Ranunculaceae, Nymphaeaceae, Magnoliaceae, Calycanthaceae). We may follow Braun in calling them *acyclic* when the passage from one foliar structure to another, as from calyx to corolla and from corolla to androecium, does not coincide with definite turns of the spiral, as in Nymphaeaceae and *Helleborus odorus* ; if it does so coincide, Braun names them *hemicyclic*, a term which may also be used when some of the foliar structures of a flower are cyclical, and others spiral, as in *Ranunculus*, in which the calyx and corolla form two alternating whorls and are succeeded by the spirally arranged sporophylls. Parts of the flower with a spiral arrangement are sometimes present in small and definite numbers, usually in larger and indefinite numbers.

If on the other hand the parts of the flower are arranged in whorls, the number of the whorls and the number of members in each whorl is usually a definite one in the same

---

or three leaves each or a multiple thereof. To this numerical relationship the term *symmetry* has been applied by English and French botanists, a *symmetrical flower* being one exhibiting this numerical relationship, while in an *unsymmetrical flower* the relationship fails in one or other of the whorls. In estimating this symmetry the gynaeceum is not taken into account. This specific use of the expression symmetry must be borne in mind in view of the wider and more general use of the term in biology and of its application to the flower by Sachs on page 423 of this book.]

species, and is constant within larger or smaller cycles of affinity. If the whorls of a flower have each the same number of members, and are so placed that the members of the different whorls stand over one another, forming orthostichies, they are said by Sachs and Payer to be *superposed* (the usual term is '*opposite*'); if the stamens are superposed on the calyx or corolla they are said to be *antisepalous* or *antipetalous*; if the members of a whorl lie between the median planes of the members of the whorl next above or below, the whorls *alternate*, and Braun terms flowers in which all the whorls have the same number of members and alternate *eucyclic*. But it sometimes happens that new and similar members are subsequently developed between the members of a whorl already formed, as for instance five later stamens between the five first formed in *Dictamnus Fraxinella* (Fig. 305 *C*), and probably in many eucyclic flowers with ten stamens; members thus subsequently introduced into a whorl may be termed *interposed*. (For further remarks on this subject see below.)

The consideration of the number of the parts of the flower is necessarily connected with that of their relative positions; but before we enter more at length into this point it will be well to explain the diagram of a flower.

The *floral diagram* is constructed in various ways according to the purpose which it is intended to serve. It is sometimes treated as a free drawing of an actual transverse section, and not only the number and position but approximatively also the form, cohesion, size, etc. of the parts of the flower are given in it; the purpose here intended is however best attained by preparing accurate drawings of actual transverse sections

FIG. 340. Floral diagram of Liliaceae.

FIG. 341. Floral diagram of *Celastrus* (Celastrineae). After Payer.

FIG. 342. Floral diagram of *Hypericum calycinum.*

of flower-buds, which will then indeed contain much that for certain purposes is superfluous. But if the object is merely to show the number and position of the parts of the flower in such a manner as to make the comparison of a number of flowers in these respects as easy as possible, the best plan is to disregard all other considerations and to frame all diagrams upon one and that the simplest plan, so as to show only the relative numbers and positions of the parts in all their variations. The diagrams given below have exclusively this object in view, and Figs. 340—342 are examples of them. They are horizontal projections, the floral axis being supposed to be vertical. The transverse sections of the axis which bear the foliar structures, the sepaline, petaline, staminal and carpellary leaves, are drawn as concentric circles, on which the separate structures are inserted. The development being acropetal the outermost circle is the oldest and in many cases also the lowest. The dot above the diagram always indicates the position of the mother-axis of the flower, and therefore the lower part of the diagram is anterior. Though simple dots are quite sufficient to indicate the number and position of the parts of the flower, different signs have been chosen for the different foliar structures, to enable the eye quickly to catch the meaning of the diagram; the leaves of the perianth are represented by segments of a circle, those of the outer circle or calyx having an appearance of a mid-rib, that they may be distinguished at first sight from the leaves of the inner circle; the sign chosen for the stamens is like the transverse section of an anther, but there is no attempt to indicate the position of the pollen-sacs or of their dehiscence, whether inward or outward; the branching of the stamens is expressed by placing the signs in groups, as in Fig. 342, where the five groups answer to five branched stamens. The gynaeceum is treated as a simplified transverse section of the ovary, because it is thus more readily distinguished from the other parts of the flower; the smaller or larger dots inside the loculi of the ovary indicate the ovules but these are given only where their position can be correctly indicated in so simple a form of diagram. No indication is in any case given of the cohesion, size, or form of the separate parts[1]. The construction of these diagrams is founded partly on the careful investigations of Sachs, but chiefly on Payer's studies in the history of development and on the descriptions of other authors (Döll, Eichler, Braun).

Sachs distinguishes between *empirical* and *theoretical* diagrams; the empirical gives only the relative number and position of the parts, as they are found at once by careful examination of the flower; if the diagram also indicates the place where members are wanting, as can be proved by the history of development and by comparison with allied plants, and if it contains indications of circumstances which are suggested by purely theoretical considerations, he calls it a theoretical diagram. If the comparison of a number of diagrams shows that though empirically different, they yet yield the same theoretical diagram, he calls this common theoretical diagram the type or *typical* diagram, according to which the others were formed. The determination of the type facilitates the recognition of the mutual relations of the individual floral structures in a group of allied plants. But it must not be forgotten that such a type is purely artificial, a plan obtained by logical combination and abstraction. It has to be asked in each separate case, whether, taking our stand on the theory of descent, we are justified in regarding the type as a still existing or now extinct form, from which the flowers with 'derivative' diagrams have been formed by abortion or cohesion of particular members[2]. Experience shows that the neglect of this consideration often leads to more or less forced interpretations of the forms of flowers.

A few instances must first be given, in which the typical diagram is actually to be regarded as the original form of the flower in a group of allied plants.

It is to be so regarded for example in the Scrophularineae. In this order the flowers are typically pentamerous, as we see in *Verbascum* (Fig. 343 *A*). But the calyx does not show the number five in all species; the posterior sepal has entirely disappeared in *Veronica* and *Lathraea* (Fig. 343 *D*, *E*). In some species of *Pedicularis* and *Veronica* (e.g. *Veronica latifolia*) it is still perceptible as a minute tooth; in genera in which it has disappeared, the position of the other sepals and the structure of the corolla which has often five parts (Fig. 343 *E*) point to the fact, that the existence of a fifth sepal must be assumed in the theoretical diagram even where the early stages of development no longer show any indication of it. The corolla is generally pentamerous, but the two upper petals are often united into one, and it then appears to be formed of four parts as in *Veronica*. The posterior petal shows by its greater breadth that it occupies the place of two petals, but there is here no question of a cohesion. The external configuration of the mature corolla is of less importance for the diagram, but there are interesting points in the stamens. In some species the five stamens are all equally developed and all fertile, i.e. provided with anthers having pollen-sacs (microsporangia). In others the posterior stamen is sterile, rudimentary or suppressed (Fig. 343 *B*, *E*). In *Gratiola* (Fig. 343 *C*), the posterior stamen is suppressed, but the two obliquely anterior ones are at the same time sterile, being developed merely as staminodes. Lastly, in *Veronica* (Fig. 343 *D*) these are entirely suppressed. Other variations, such as the sterility and sometimes the entire suppression of the two obliquely posterior stamens need not be enlarged upon here. The diagrams show that the structure of the ovary is less liable to variation.

The diagram of the Liliaceae is the typical diagram of many Monocotyledons. The Orchideae depart from it to an antonishing degree, but even they may be referred to it

---

[1] A diagram showing these features is given in Fig. 343.

[2] The theory of types is also much older than that of descent.

by assuming the incomplete development of certain parts. Both whorls of the perianth are developed in a petaloid manner, and like the whole flower are zygomorphic or monosymmetrical (see below for this term). Of the typical androecium consisting

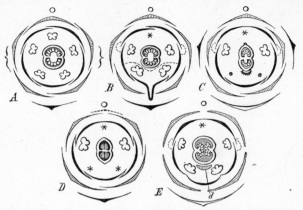

FIG. 343. Floral diagram of Scrophularineae. The shaded leaves are the calyx-leaves right and left of them in *A* and *C* bracteoles, beneath the flowers are their bracts, the aborted stamens are indicated by asterisks. *A Verbascum nigrum. B Linaria vulgaris*; the under lip is spurred, the dotted line shows the 'palate.' *C Gratiola officinalis*; the two anterior stamens are developed as staminodes. *D Veronica Chamaedrys* with tetramerous calyx and corolla. *E Lathraea squamaria*; *d* scale of the disk. After Eichler, Blüthendiagramme, I.

of two alternating whorls of three members each, only a single stamen, the anterior stamen of the outer circle (Fig. 344 *A*), is fully developed in most of the Orchideae, the others being abortive; but indications of them sometimes appear in the young bud, as in *Calanthe veratrifolia* according to Payer (Fig. 311), where at least the two obliquely anterior stamens of the inner whorl (not the posterior one of the same whorl) are represented by two small protuberances which however soon disappear. In *Cypripedium* on the other hand the place of the stamen which is elsewhere fertile is occupied by a large staminode in the front part of the flower (Fig. 284), while the two obliquely anterior anthers of the inner whorl are fully developed and fertile (Fig. 344 *B*). In place of these fertile stamens of *Cypripedium* two small staminodes are found in the Ophrydeae beside the gynostemium (Fig. 354 *D, st*); in *Uropedium* all three inner stamens are developed (Döll), in *Arundina pentandra* as many as five (Reichenbach fil.). The carpels which adhere to the androecium to form the gynostemium are not

FIG. 344. Floral diagram of Orchideae. *A* the common form. *B Cypripedium* (see Fig. 283); the dots denote stamens that are entirely wanting, the shaded figures rudimentary stamens which are abortive or developed as staminodes (see the text).

developed alike, but the difference is usually not perceptible in inferior ovaries, and is therefore not indicated in the diagram. The beginner who desires to investigate these points must observe that the long inferior ovary of most of the Orchideae suffers torsion at the time of flowering which brings the posterior side of the flower round to the front; but transverse sections of older buds show plainly the true position of the flower with reference to the parent-axis.

Like the Orchideae, many though not all monocotyledonous flowers may be derived from a type which is actually seen in the Liliaceae, and which represents a flower consisting of five alternating whorls of three members each, the two outer of which form the perianth, the two succeeding ones the androecium, and the innermost the gynaeceum; but the last may be represented by two whorls, and multiplication instead of abortion sometimes takes place within the separate whorls and two members appear in place of one, as in *Butomus* (Fig. 299).

Increase in the number of the members of a floral whorl may occur in different ways, as the following examples show. According to Eichler's[1] exhaustive investigations the flowers of the Fumariaceae may be referred to a type, in which there are six decussate pairs of members:

two median sepals,
two outer lateral petals,
two inner median petals,
two lateral stamens,
two median (always abortive) stamens,
two lateral carpels.

The two lateral stamens are however represented in some Fumariaceae (*Dicentra, Corydalis*) by two groups each of three stamens ; each group consists of a middle stamen and two on each side of it ; the former has a quadrilocular (entire) anther, the latter have each a bilocular (half) anther, and Eichler explains this by assuming that the two lateral stamens are stipular formations, branches therefore from the base of the middle stamen. In *Hypecoum* Eichler assumes a cohesion of each pair of opposite stipular stamens, so as to produce a staminal whorl apparently of four members.

FIG. 345. Floral diagram of Fumariaceae. After Eichler.

According to the same author the flowers of the Cruciferae and Cleomeae (a tribe of Capparideae) may be derived from a type which is represented in Fig. 346 *A*, and appears as the empirical diagram in *Cleome droserifolia*, in species of *Lepidium*, in *Senebiera* and *Capsella*. This typical flower consists of—

two outer median sepals,
two inner lateral sepals,
four diagonal petals in one whorl,
two outer lateral stamens,
two inner median stamens,
two lateral carpels.

Deviations from this type are caused by two or more stamens appearing in place of one of the inner stamens, in the Cruciferae usually two (Fig. 347), in the Cleomeae sometimes two, sometimes more (Fig. 346 *B*). Such a substitution of two or more stamens for one is called by Payer *dédoublement* (doubling, duplication), by Eichler and others *collateral chorisis*, and may apparently be regarded as branching which takes place at a very early period ; this is supported in the present case by the fact that in *Atelanthera*, one of the Cruciferae, the median stamens are only split and each branch in the split stamens has only a half anther, while in *Crambe* each of the four inner stamens puts out a sterile lateral branch, which may be explained as the beginning of a still further increase of the stamens, such as actually occurs in the Cruciferous genus *Megacarpaea* and in many Cleomeae. Though we may be unable to give a mechanical explanation of the increase in the typical number of the stamens of the inner whorl and the history of their development may be obscure, yet it seems certain that the instability of the number of the members of the androecium points to the view, that a deviation from the original typical number of two members has arisen in this part of the flower of the Cruciferae and Cleomeae, while the other floral whorls maintain a striking constancy ; in *Tetrapoma* and *Holargidium* only amongst the Cruciferae the gynaeceum so far varies as to have two median carpels in addition to the two lateral, and there is thus a four-valved ovary.

The theory of the duplication of an originally simple stamen has been applied in cases where it is inadmissible. In many cases this supposed simple formation is not to

---

[1] Ueber d. Blüthenbau d. Fumariaceen, Cruciferen u. einiger Capparideen (Flora, 1865, Nr. 28–35, u. 1869, p. 1), and Blüthendiagramme, p. 195, where other works are cited. The flowers of the Fumariaceae however admit of a different explanation (see on page 418).

be seen even in the most rudimentary stage of development, and then a 'congenital' duplication is spoken of, commencing at the first inception of the organ, but this expression only means that two rudiments make their appearance, where in other flowers only one is found. But this fact may in many cases be partly referred to the conditions of growth of the young organ[1]. It is a general rule, prevailing also in the vegetative region of the plant, that the number of rudiments of organs increases on a shoot for instance, if either the surface of the shoot continues of the same size but the size of the rudimentary formations suddenly diminishes, or if the producing surface of the shoot increases rapidly in size while the rudiments remain of the same size. An instructive instance of the first case occurs in the perianth-leaves of the flower-heads of *Typha*, which are arranged in two rows; in the lower part of the head each young

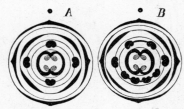

FIG. 346. Floral diagram of Capparideae. *A Cleome droserifolia. B Polanisia graveolens.* After Eichler.

FIG. 347. Floral dia-
gram of the Cruciferae.

perianth-leaf occupies half the circumference of the head at the point where it is inserted. Towards the top of the head the perianth-leaves are smaller, and here instead of one there are two or three rudimentary perianth-leaves quite separate from one another. To speak in this case of a congenital splitting would be only a needless circumlocution. The family of the Rosaceae supplies interesting conditions for the occurrence of similar processes in its flowers. These are usually pentamerous and sometimes also tetramerous. In some species the pentamerous corolla is succeeded by five stamens alternating with the petals (Fig. 348 *I*). But in some species the rudiments of the stamens diminish in size, and the first five stamens are followed not only by five but by ten other stamens, which range themselves in the intervals (Fig. 348 *II*), and each pair of these ten young stamens are closely connected with one of the five original stamens. I have shown at some length in another place that it is impossible in this case to suppose a duplication of five antisepalous stamens. In other Rosaceae (Fig. 348 *III*) the same process takes place on the first appearance of the stamens, that is, not five but ten rudiments of stamens are formed alternating with the petals, and each pair of these are closely connected with a rudiment of a petal. If the growth of the torus is everywhere uniform, ten more stamens may make their appearance in front of the intervals between the first ten stamens, and then we have an androecium consisting of two whorls of ten members each succeeding to a corolla of five members. But in many cases the growth of the separate parts of the torus after the formation of the rudiments of the first ten stamens is not uniform. In *Rubus Idaeus* for instance the parts in front of the sepals grow more vigorously than those in front of the petals, and consequently not one but several rudiments of stamens are formed in front of each sepal quite unconnected with one another; it seldom happens that one only is formed, the torus having grown very little in this part; the number is usually two, and then one or two more are intercalated (interposed) between them (Fig. 348 *d*), but two remarkably small rudiments appear in front of each petal, and these may be replaced by one larger one. In this case also

---

[1] Hofmeister, Allg. Morphol. d. Gewächse, p. 475.—Schwendener, Mechanische Theorie d. Blattstellungen, Leipzig, 1878.—Goebel, Beitr. z. Morphol. u. Physiol. d. Blattes, No. III, Ueber die Stellung d. Staubblätter in einigen Blüthen (Bot. Ztg. 1882).

[2]   E e

I have shown that there is no duplication, but that the number of the rudimentary organs in any given place depends merely on the space afforded, and on the size of the rudiments. In other species of *Rubus* on the contrary it is the region of the torus in front of the petals which grows most vigorously, and consequently more young organs are found here than in front of the sepals. For the rather large amount of details which have been collected on this subject the reader is referred to the author's treatise cited in the note on the previous page, where also it is shown that the number and position of the parts of the flower vary so much in the family of the Rosaceae that it is impossible to

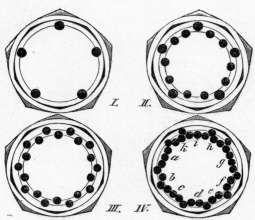

FIG. 348. Floral diagrams of various Rosaceae (carpels not included). *I. Sibbaldia cuneata* and some species also of *Agrimonia*. *II. Agrimonia odorata*; the first whorl of five stamens is followed by one of ten. *III. Potentilla*; the pentamerous corolla is succeeded by a whorl of ten stamens alternating with the ten stamens of a second whorl. *IV. Rubus Idaeus* (special case), the outermost staminal whorl only shown; the pentamerous corolla is followed by a whorl of ten stamens, and from one to four stamens according to the growth of the zone of the floral axis are interpolated in the intervals between each pair of the first stamens (not one only as in *III*), three at *a*, one at *b*, three at *c*, two at *d*, two at *e*, two at *f*, four at *g*, two at *h*, three at *i*, two at *k*.

frame a typical diagram. Similar facts are observed in other flowers also, as in *Citrus* and *Tetragonia*, and in *Alisma* and *Butomus* among Monocotyledons, where in the same way a whorl of three petals is succeeded by a whorl of six stamens. In the Fumariaceae mentioned above it seems to me more natural to assume, not that there has been a branching of the two stamens, but that after they were formed there was a sudden diminution in the size of the rudiments of the stamens, and that therefore four were formed instead of two and became connected in pairs with the two first formed, as occurs in *Agrimonia* (Fig. 348 *II*). This view appears to me to be most in accord with the facts observed in allied plants, such as the Papaveraceae, and to be supported also by the history of development.

In considering the relative positions of the parts of flowers the obdiplostemonous flower requires special notice. In many Dicotyledons the androecium is formed of two whorls, one of which alternates with the sepals and is opposite to the petals (corolline stamens), the other is opposite to the sepals (calycine stamens). Either the calycine or the corolline stamens may form the outer whorl; the former is the normal, that is, the usual case of alternation, and the arrangement is said to be *diplostemonous*; in the latter the corolline stamens are outside, the calycine further in, so that the normal alternation between the two whorls of stamens seems to be interrupted, and this is the *obdiplostemonous* arrangement. The case of obdiplostemony has received various explanations, all endeavouring to bring it into harmony with the normal arrangement of alternation of parts. Sachs is of opinion that new members of the same kind are formed on the same zone of the torus in the bud when still quite young between the members already formed, in other words, that new members are interposed. This he found was the case in *Dictamnus Fraxinella* (Fig. 305); it is shown in the diagram in Fig. 349, where the later formed stamens are not black like the first ones but only shaded. He considers himself entitled to conclude from Payer's figures and descriptions that the same proceeding takes place in the nearly allied *Ruta* and in the families of the Oxalideae, Zygophylleae, and Geraniaceae which belong to the same cycle of affinity, and that in them also five stamens are subsequently interposed between the five calycine stamens which were first formed. If we suppose the five interposed stamens removed, there remains a regular pentamerous flower with four whorls of five alternating members, such as is seen in the nearly related Lineae and Balsamineae. Whether the new stamens arise at the same height as those first formed (diplostemony) or lower than they, evidently depends on where more space is left free by the changes in the form of the growing torus. We have just seen instances of such interposition according to the conditions of space in the torus in the Rosaceae. But other facts of development are opposed to this explanation in the case of obdiplostemonous flowers [1]. According to Frank there can be no interposition here, but the corolline stamens are the older, and the calycine are formed afterwards in alternation with them. However this may be, it must be borne in mind that the normal alternation of the parts of the flower is only a fact of experience, which loses its validity as a general rule as soon as a number of opposing facts are known.

FIG. 349. Floral diagram of *Dictamnus Fraxinella* (see Fig. 305).

Floral formulae. The diagram may if necessary be partially replaced by a formula composed of letters and figures; in such a floral formula the relative positions cannot always be exactly given, but it has the advantage of being able to be expressed in ordinary type, and, which is perhaps of greater importance, it is capable of a wider generalisation since the figures may be replaced by letters as numerical coefficients.

The construction and application of such formulae will be easily made intelligible by a few examples [2].

The formula $S3\ P3\ St\ 3 + 3\ C3$ corresponds to the diagram of the Liliaceae (Fig. 340), and means therefore that each of the two perianth-whorls, the outer of sepals S and the inner of petals P, consists of three members; that the androecium St consists of two whorls of three members ($3 + 3$) and the gynaeceum C of one of the same kind; the diagram shows that these whorls of three members alternate without interruption, but as this is the normal case in flowers, it is not specially indicated. The formula $S3\ P3\ St3^2 + 3\ C3 + 3$ gives the numerical relations of the flower of *Butomus umbellatus* (Fig. 299); it differs from the previous one in the circumstance that the gynaeceum C consists of two whorls of three carpels each ($3 + 3$), and that in the androecium St the typical three stamens of the outer circle are replaced by two stamens, as is expressed by the sign 3^2. The formula $So\ P3\ St3 + 3\ C3$ answers to the diagram of the flower of *Bambusa* and differs from the first only in having So instead of $S3$, which means that the outer perianth whorl is absent. The numerical relations of the flower of the Orchideae (Fig. 344 A) would be expressed by the formula $S3\ P3\ St\ddot{\imath} + o\ C3$, in which the symbol $St\ddot{\imath} + o$ signifies that all the members of the inner whorl of the androecium are suppressed, but that only the two obliquely posterior stamens are wanting in the outer whorl, the anterior one being fully developed; the position of the two dots above the number $\ddot{\imath}$ means that the abortive members are the posterior ones; if they were anterior the dots would be placed beneath the number as in the formula $So\ Po\ St3 + o\ C2$, which

---

[1] Frank, Ueber d. Entw. einiger Blüthen mit besonderer Berücksichtigung d. Theorie d. Interponirung, in Pringsheim's Jahrb. f. wiss. Bot. Bd. X. p. 20.

[2] Grisebach (Grundriss d. syst. Bot. Göttingen, 1854) depicted the numerical relations of the parts of the flower in this way, by simply writing the numbers of the alternating members one after another, and indicating cohesions by strokes.

corresponds to the ordinary flower in the Gramineae. The formula $S2\ P2\ St2+2\ C2$ gives the numerical relations of the whorls in the flower of *Maianthemum bifolium* formed of decussate pairs, the formula $S4\ P4\ St4+4\ C4$ or $S5\ P5\ St5+5\ C5$ shows the flower of *Paris quadrifolia* consisting of whorls of four or five members. These and most other formulae for monocotyledonous flowers may be united in a general expression

$$Sn\ Pn\ Stn+n\ Cn\ (+n),$$

which means that the flowers belonging to this type are usually composed of five alternating whorls each with the same number of members, two of which are developed as perianth-whorls, two as staminal whorls and one usually as a carpellary whorl; the bracket $(+n)$ at the end of the formula indicates that occasionally there is a second whorl of carpels present; n may have the value of 3 or 2 or 4 or 5, as the examples show; usually $n = 3$. If there is a considerable increase in the number of members in a whorl and the number, as is usual in such cases, is a fluctuating one, the fact may be expressed by the sign ∞; the formula for *Alisma Plantago* is $S3\ P3\ St3+3\ C\infty$.

It has been already mentioned, that there is no sign to indicate the normal alternation of the whorls; an exception to the general rule may be expressed with more or less preciseness by concerted symbols; for instance in the formula for the flowers of the Cruciferae (Fig. 347) $S2+2\ P\times4\ St2+2^2\ C2\ (+2)$ the symbol $P\times4$ would mean that the decussate pairs of the calyx are succeeded by a corolline whorl of four members, which are placed diagonally to the members of the calyx; to show the superposition of two successive whorls, a vertical stroke might be placed after the number of the first whorl, e. g. $S5\ P5\ |\ St5^v\ C5$; in this which is the formula for *Hypericum calycinum* $St5^v$ might indicate that the androecium consists of five branched (5^v) stamens superposed on the members of the corolline whorl ($P5\ |\ St$); lastly, if it is desired to show that the members of a second whorl are interposed between the members of an original whorl at the same height, the number of the new members may be simply placed beside that of the first whorl, as in the formula $S5\ P5\ St5\ .\ 5C5$ which corresponds to the diagram in Fig. 349.

In the formulas hitherto given no occasional cohesions have been indicated; they too may be easily shown, if necessary, by concerted symbols. Thus in the formula for *Convolvulus* $S5\ \overparen{P5}\ St5\ \overparen{C2}$, the sign $\overparen{P5}$ would indicate a gamopetalous corolla of five members, $\overparen{C2}$ an ovary formed by the cohesion of two carpels; in the floral formula of the Papilionaceae $\overparen{S5}\ P5\ \overparen{St5+4}+1C1$ the symbol $\overparen{St5+4}+1$ would mean that the five stamens of the outer whorl and the four of the inner cohere and form a tube, while the posterior stamen of the inner whorl remains free[1].

The construction of the formulas must vary according to the special purpose which they are intended to serve; the greater number of relations it is desired to express the more complicated they must become, and we must take care not to render them obscure through the accumulation of many symbols.

All the formulae hitherto given express cyclical flowers; the spiral arrangement of the parts of flowers may be indicated by the mark placed before them, and the angle of divergence may be put after the number. For example, the formula $S\sim\frac{2}{5}5\,P\sim\frac{3}{8}8\,St\sim\frac{8}{21}\infty\,C\sim3$ will give the relative numbers and positions in *Aconitum* according to Braun's views, and mean that all the organs of the flower are spirally arranged, that the calyx consists of five leaves with the divergence $\frac{2}{5}$, the corolla of eight leaves with the divergence , and the androecium of an indefinite number of stamens with the divergence $\frac{8}{21}$; it would however be sufficient to put the symbol for the spiral arrangement once before the whole formula, since it recurs in all the parts of the flower, thus, $\sim S\frac{2}{5}5\ P\frac{3}{8}8\ St\frac{8}{21}\infty\ C3$.

In flowers arranged cyclically it is generally unnecessary to indicate the divergence, because the members of each whorl are usually formed simultaneously and so placed as

---

[1] See also Rohrbach in Bot. Ztg. 1870, p. 816.

to divide the circle into equal parts; if they are formed one after another succeeding one another in the circle with a definite divergence, as is the case in most calyces of three and five members, the fact may be indicated by placing the divergence after the number of the members, as for instance in the formula for the Lineae $S5\frac{2}{5}P5\,St5\,C5$. If on the other hand the members of a whorl arise one after another proceeding from front to back, this may be shown by an upright arrow ↑, as in the formula for the Papilionaceae $S5\uparrow P5\uparrow St\uparrow 5+5\uparrow C1$; if they succeed one another from back to front, the arrow may be reversed, as in the formula of *Reseda* $Sn\downarrow Pn\quad Stp\downarrow +q\downarrow Cr$, where letters are employed because of the variability of the numbers in the different whorls[1]. The position also of the ovary may be indicated in the floral formula. A stroke over the figure after the letter C, as $C\,(\overline{3})$, means that the ovary is inferior, a stroke under the figure, as $C\,(\underline{3})$, that it is superior. When the calyx and corolla are not distinguished from one another, they are called the perianth and designated by the letters *Per*, as in the formula for the Liliaceae *Per* $3+3\,St3+3\,C\,(\underline{3})$, or that of the Amaryllideae with an inferior ovary *Per* $3+3\,St3+3\,C\,(\overline{3})$.

Order of development of the parts of the flower. The foliar structures are formed on the axis of the floral shoot beneath the growing apex in the same acropetal order which obtains on the axes of other shoots; but in the formation of flowers it frequently happens that the apical growth of the axis ceases or becomes very slow, while the tissue of the axis (the torus) increases in circumference, and transverse zones of intercalary growth are at the same time developed. In such circumstances the acropetal succession is disturbed, and new floral whorls may be introduced between those already formed; and within the same whorl the separate members may appear in a very different order, according as the leaf-forming zone of the torus developes uniformly all round, as in polysymmetrical flowers, or the anterior or posterior side developes more vigorously, as is the case especially in monosymmetrical (zygomorphous) flowers.

These disturbances of the acropetal order of development are less marked in flowers whose parts are spirally arranged[2], the more numerous those parts are and the longer the apical growth of the floral axis continues; the spirally arranged parts are formed one after another in ascending order and the divergence may be constant or may change. Thus according to Payer in Ranunculaceae and Magnoliaceae the perianth-leaves and the stamens arise in a continuous spiral, but each cycle is formed of a larger number of stamens than of perianth-leaves; in *Helleborus odorus* for example, in which all the organs of the flower are spirally arranged, the corolline cycle contains thirteen, but each staminal cycle twenty-one members. According to Braun the calyx in *Delphinium consolida* is a cycle in which the parts have a $\frac{2}{5}$ arrangement[3]; then the divergence changes but the deviation is small; the first cycle after the change is formed by the corolla, the three next by the stamens, and one carpel forms the termination. In the section *Garidella* of *Nigella* the first cycle of the spiral with a $\frac{2}{5}$ divergence is formed by the calyx, the second by the corolla, then comes a change to a $\frac{3}{8}$ divergence, of which the stamens occupy two cycles and above them are three or four carpels; in the section *Delphinellum* of *Delphinium* the calyx forms a cycle with a $\frac{2}{5}$, the corolla one with a $\frac{3}{8}$ divergence, then follow two or three cycles of stamens with a divergence approaching to $\frac{3}{8}$, and the spiral ends with three carpels. In the section *Staphisagria* of *Delphinium* and in *Aconitum* the calyx forms one cycle of the spiral with the divergence of $\frac{2}{5}$, the corolla another of $\frac{3}{8}$, the stamens are in one or two cycles with an $\frac{8}{21}$ or a $\frac{13}{34}$ divergence, and from three to five seldom more carpels end the spiral. In these cases of relative position of parts it should be noticed that the members of the successive cycles form orthostichies, if the divergence is constant, but the orthostichies pass into oblique rows if the divergence undergoes a slight alteration.

---

[1] See next page.

[2] Payer, Organogénie, p. 707, and Braun, Ueber d. Blüthenbau d. Gattung *Delphinium* (Jahrb. f. wiss. Bot.).

[3] See however the remarks below on sepals and petals with $\frac{1}{3}$ and $\frac{1}{3}$ divergences (page 423).

In cyclic flowers we must first of all distinguish between the succession of the whorls among themselves and the formation of the members in each whorl, though the two are in fact closely connected. A disturbance of the acropetal order in the development of the whorls is observed, for example, when the carpels begin to form before all the stamens beneath them have made their appearance, as happens in *Rosa*, *Potentilla* and *Rubus*[1], or when the calyx is formed after the androecium as in *Hypericum calycinum* (Hofmeister), or when the calyx does not appear till after the development of the corolla is considerably advanced or even till after the formation of the stamens and carpels, as in the Compositae, Dipsaceae, Valerianeae, Rubiaceae.

One of the most remarkable deviations from the general rule for the order of development of the floral whorls occurs in the Primulaceae, where five primordia appear on the torus above the calyx, each of which developes into a stamen ; subsequently a lobe of the corolla arises from the dorsal (under) side of the base of each rudimentary stamen. Pfeffer, who observed this order of development[2], considers these corolla lobes as dorsal outgrowths of the stamens, dorsal ligular structures, such as are found in the form of hood-like nectaries on the stamens of the Asclepiadeae where there is a true corolla also. According to this view the flowers of the Primulaceae would be morphologically apetalous, since the corolla is not a true floral whorl but only an outgrowth from the staminal whorl. In other families of Dicotyledons superposed corollas and androecia arise separate from one another and in acropetal succession, as in the Ampelideae, and probably also in the Rhamneae, Santalaceae, Chenopodiaceae, and other families.

The separate members of a floral whorl, especially if the flowers afterwards become zygomorphous, may follow one another as they form from front to back or in the reverse

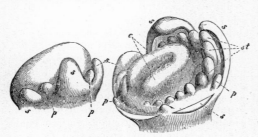

FIG 350. Development of the flower of *Reseda odorata*; to the left a younger bud, to the right an older bud with the anterior sepals removed and the posterior retained; *ss* sepals, *p p* petals, *st* stamens already of some size behind, but not begun to be formed in front, *c* carpel.

way ; thus for instance in Papilionaceae the anterior median sepal is first formed, then one right and one left of it simultaneously, and then the two obliquely posterior ones ; before these last appear, the two obliquely anterior petals are formed and after them the other three in the same order as the corresponding sepals ; the androecium, consisting of five alternating whorls of five members each, is formed in the same way, the parts succeeding one another from front to back[3]. In *Reseda* and *Astrocarpus*, on the other hand, the petals, stamens and carpels begin to be formed from behind according to Payer[4], and advance right and left towards the front (Fig. 350).

If the calyx consists of pairs of sepals, the sepals of each pair are formed, according to Payer, simultaneously ; but if the calyx is a whorl of from three to five sepals, they are formed as a rule successively with a $\frac{1}{3}$ or $\frac{2}{5}$ divergence ; the whorls that follow them, the corolla, androecium and gynaceum, usually appear as simultaneous whorls, apart from the exceptions that have been named above and will be named below. It should be remarked here, that an order of formation advancing from a certain point with a definite divergence of $\frac{1}{3}$ or $\frac{2}{5}$, for example, does not by itself prove that the arrangement is a spiral one[5], it may quite as well be a whorl ; the question depends on whether the foliar structures

---

[1] Hofmeister, Allgem. Morphol. p. 462, where Payer's observations on this point are also given.
[2] Jahrb. f. wiss. Bot. VII, p. 194.
[3] On the nearly related Cesalpinieae see Rohrbach in Bot. Ztg. 1870, p. 826.
[4] See also Goebel in Bot. Ztg. 1882.
[5] Compare the successive true whorls of the Characeae.

arise at an equal height, that is at an equal distance from the centre of the flower, or not ; if they do, the arrangement is that of a whorl ; but if the members arise in acropetal order at different heights, approaching the centre of the flower with each step in the divergence, the arrangement is spiral ; this appears actually to be the arrangement in many calyces, but it is a question whether it always is so, when the sepals are formed with a $\frac{1}{3}$ or $\frac{2}{5}$ divergence.

We must once more notice the cases which have been already mentioned, in which new members are formed between the original members of a whorl at the same height with them[1]. In the Oxalideae, Geraniaceae, Rutaceae and Zygophylleae an entire whorl of five members is interposed between the previously formed stamens[2]; in *Peganum Harmala*, according to Payer, a circle of ten stamens is thus formed in pairs, and not between the first five but below them at the base of the petals ; whether the later formed stamens arise at the same height as the first or below them obviously depends on whether more space is supplied by the changes in form of the growing torus. A still greater deviation from the usual rule occurs in the Acerineae, Hippocastaneae and Sapindaceae, where, according to Payer, a staminal whorl of five members is first formed alternating with the corolla, in which an imperfect whorl of from two to four stamens is subsequently interposed at the same height, as appears from that author's drawings. In *Tropaeolum* on the other hand we learn from Payer and Rohrbach[3] that three stamens first make their appearance after the commencement of the petals, and five others are afterwards formed between them, but at a greater distance from the centre of the flower than the three first formed.

Symmetry of the flower[4]. Actual symmetry and decided bilaterality occurs much more frequently in floral than in other shoots. Sachs avoiding the lax terminology of many botanists here also considers those forms to be *symmetrical* which can be divided into halves, each of which appears to be the exact reflection of the other ; if a flower can be divided in this manner by one plane only, he terms it a simple symmetrical structure or *monosymmetrical*; if it can be symmetrically divided by two or more planes, it is said to be doubly or repeatedly symmetrical (*polysymmetrical*) ; the term *zygomorphous* applied by Braun may be used equally for monosymmetrical flowers and for those doubly symmetrical ones, in which the median section gives differently shaped halves from those produced by the lateral section, *Dielytra* for instance. Sachs calls a polysymmetrical flower *regular*[5], only when the symmetrical halves produced by one section are the same as or very like the symmetrical halves produced by any other section, or which comes to the same thing, when a flower can be divided by two, three or more longitudinal sections into four, six or more equal or similar portions.

To determine exactly the relations of symmetry in a flower we must first distinguish between the relative positions of the parts as shown in the diagram and the form of the whole flower produced by the complete development of its organs.

---

[1] See on the other hand the statement of Frank concerning obdiplostemonous flowers mentioned above (page 419).

[2] See also Pfeffer in Jahrb. f. wiss. Bot. VIII, p. 205.

[3] Rohrbach however (Bot. Ztg. 1869, No. 50, 51) explains these observations in a different way ; but the equal or even greater distance of the later stamens from the centre of the flower proves decisively that we cannot in this case suppose a spiral formation advancing from without inwards.

[4] [See notes on pages 349 and 411. The older terms zygomorphous and actinomorphous are adopted by Eichler in his Blüthendiagramme for the monosymmetrical and polysymmetrical conditions of the text and are now in general use.

[5] English and French writers use the word 'regular' with a different and older signification as regards the flower. According to their terminology a calyx of which the sepals are all alike in form and size is a *regular calyx,* and similarly a corolla of which all the petals are alike in form and size is a *regular corolla,* and a flower which has a regular calyx and regular corolla is a *regular flower*. If one or more sepals or petals differ markedly in form and size from the other members of a calyx or corolla, the calyx or corolla is said to be *irregular* and the flower also becomes *irregular*.]

If the relative positions of the parts are first considered, it is obvious that they can never be symmetrically distributed in flowers with a purely spiral structure, but that in hemicyclic flowers the members at least that have a cyclical arrangement may possibly be symmetrically distributed. If on the other hand the parts of the flower are all arranged in whorls, they are also usually monosymmetrically or polysymmetrically distributed on the torus; thus the diagram in Fig. 340 may be divided symmetrically and regularly by three planes, that in Fig. 341 by four, that in Fig. 342 by five, while Fig. 344 can only be symmetrically halved by one plane, which is at the same time the median plane. The diagram in Fig. 345 may be divided by the median section into two symmetrical parts, which are different from those produced by the lateral section; the diagram is zygomorphous like those in Fig. 343 B, C and Fig. 344, but the latter are singly, the former is doubly symmetrical.

FIG. 351.   Flower of *Heracleum pubescens* with zygomorphous corolla.

The symmetry of the mature expanded flower is usually genetically connected with the relations of symmetry of the diagram which represents only the number and position of the parts, as is seen by comparing Figs. 352 and 354 with Fig. 344 A; but inasmuch as the general form of the mature flower is essentially determined by the outlines, dimensions, torsions and curvatures of the separate parts, these are the things which chiefly affect the relations of symmetry in the expanded flower, and they may affect them to such a degree that even flowers with their foliar structures arranged spirally may be monosymmetrically zygomorphous in reference to their general form, as is the case to a great extent in *Aconitum* and *Delphinium*. It must however be observed that in these instances the zygomorphous form is produced chiefly or exclusively by the calyx and corolla, in which the spiral arrangement may perhaps still be disputed, but which in any case are inserted on so narrow a zone of the torus that their position may be considered as equivalent to a cyclical (verticillate) one. If on the other hand the floral axis is sufficiently elongated for the ascending spiral arrangement to be distinctly shown, as in the perianth and androecium of the Nymphaeaceae and in the androecium and gynaeceum of the Magnoliaceae, the full development of the organs does not seem to produce a zygomorphous or any other really symmetrical general form.

On the other hand the zygomorphous and monosymmetrical form is frequently found in flowers, whose parts are arranged in whorls. Very distinct zygomorphism is often combined with partial or entire abortion of certain members, as in *Columnea* (Fig. 352) and other Gesneraceae, in which the posterior stamen is changed into a small nectary, while in Labiatae it is entirely wanting; in Orchideae, where of the six typical stamens only the median anterior outer stamen or two obliquely anterior inner stamens are developed, the abortion is still greater. Sometimes the subsequent monosymmetrical general form is to some extent provided for by the order of succession of the parts of the flower in the first rudiments, so far as these are not formed simultaneously in a whorl and do not follow one another in the circle with a definite angle of divergence, but their development begins with an anterior or posterior member and then proceeds simultaneously right and left of the median line to the opposite side of the whorl, in the manner already described in the Papilionaceae in the one case and in the Resedaceae in the other.

The diagram of the zygomorphous flowers of the Fumariaceae (Fig. 345), as has been already said, can be symmetrically divided by two planes in different ways; the anterior and posterior halves which are symmetrically alike are different from the right and left halves which are also symmetrically alike; and the general form of the mature flower corresponds to this arrangement of the parts in *Dicentra*; in *Fumaria* and *Corydalis* on the other hand the right side is developed differently from the left; the one produces a spur, the other does not, while the anterior and posterior sides are symmetrical; in this case therefore the plane of symmetry coincides with the transverse or lateral plane section. In the zygomorphous flowers of some Solanaceae the plane of

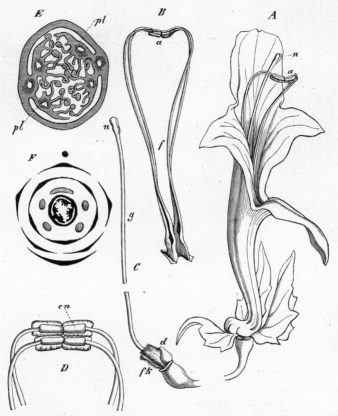

FIG 352. Zygomorphous flower of *Columnea Schiedeana*, one of the Gesneraceae. *A* an entire flower with two sepals removed. *B* the androecium. *C* the gynaeceum. *D* the coherent anthers enlarged and seen from behind. *E* transverse section of the ovary. *F* the diagram. The letters *a* denote the anthers, *cn* the connectives, *f* the filaments, *n* the stigma, *g* the style, *fk* the ovary, *d* the staminode developed as a nectary, *pl* the laterally oblique placentas.

symmetry and the median plane intersect one another at an acute angle[1]; but the large majority of zygomorphous, monosymmetrical flowers are so constructed, that the median plane is at the same time a longitudinal section which divides them symmetrically, as for instance in the Labiatae, Papilionaceae, Orchideae, Scitamineae, *Delphinium*, *Aconitum*, the Lobeliaceae and Compositae, etc.[2] The zygomorphous development is found especially in the lateral flowers of spikes, racemes and panicles,

---

[1] Such flowers are said to be obliquely zygomorphous; the expressions median zygomorphous and transverse zygomorphous require no explanation.

[2] In observations of this kind it is necessary to attend to torsions, such as occur in the ovary of the Orchideae, on the flower-stalk of the Fumariaceae, etc.

but occurs also in cymose inflorescences, in which all the flowers are terminal, as in the Labiatae; its appearance indeed would seem to be determined by the vigorous development of the primary axis of the whole inflorescence, whether the latest ramifications form cymose partial inflorescences or not, as is shown by the Labiatae, *Æsculus* and the Scitamineae.

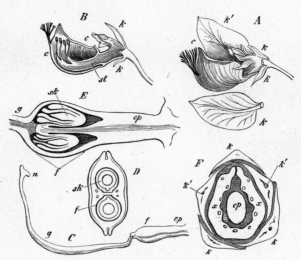

FIG. 353. Zygomorphous flower of *Polygala grandiflora*. *A* entire flower seen from the side after removal of a sepal. *B* a flower symmetrically divided without the gynaeceum. *C* the gynaeceum magnified. *D* transverse section of the ovary. *E* median longitudinal section of the same. *F* transverse section of the flower. The letters *k k'* denote the calyx, *c* the corolla, *st* the staminal tube, *cp* gynophore, *f* the ovary, *g* the style, *n* the stigma, *sk* ovule, *x x* the tube formed by the cohering and adhering petals and stamens.

The *fruit* in the Angiosperms is the ovary which has developed and become changed physiologically by the effects of fertilisation, and which contains the ripe seeds. In many cases the style and stigma fall off, as in *Cucurbita* and the Gramineae, and some of the ovules do not develope, so that the number of the seeds is less than that of the ovules. If all the ovules of one or more loculi of a plurilocular ovary disappear as the fruit ripens, the fertile loculus only developes, and the others are partially or wholly displaced and become more or less indistinguishable, and the plurilocular ovary produces therefore an unilocular and often one-seeded fruit; thus the trilocular ovary of *Quercus* with two ovules in each loculus becomes an unilocular one-seeded fruit, the acorn; there is a less complete obliteration of from two to four loculi with the ovules in the ovary of *Tilia* which has from two to five loculi, the fruit being usually one-seeded.

Parts on the other hand, which do not belong to the gynaeceum or even to the flower, are changed by fertilisation; the entire structure thus produced may be called a *pseudocarp*, which is therefore composed of a fruit or a number of true fruits, and the peculiarly developed parts surrounding it; the strawberry for instance is a pseudocarp, in which the axial portion of the flower is swollen into a fleshy pulp, and bears the true small fruits; in the hip or fruit of the rose the flower-stalk, which is hollowed out into the shape of an urn, surrounds the separate ripe fruits as a red or yellow succulent envelope; in the same way the apple also is a pseudocarp, and the mulberry is composed of an entire spike of flowers, the perianth-leaves of each flower having swollen and become fleshy, and surrounding the small dry fruits; in the fig the stalk of the entire inflorescence, hollowed out and covered on the inside with fruits, forms the pseudocarp.

If we accept the definition, that every ripe ovary is a fruit, then several fruits may be produced from one flower, if for instance there are several or many monomerous (monocarpellary) ovaries in a flower, or, which is the same thing, if the flower is poly-carpous; in this case the mature gynaeceum forms an *aggregate fruit*, for which the term *syncarp* would be preferable. Thus the small fruits of a flower of *Ranunculus* or *Clematis* and the larger ones of *Paeonia* and *Helleborus* form together an aggregate fruit; the blackberry is a similar structure, being formed of a number of plum-like fruits from one flower; in like manner the pulpy torus of the hip encloses an aggregate fruit, but the enclosed fruits are dry, not pulpy. The aggregate fruit must not be confounded with the pseudocarp formed from an inflores-cence, like the mulberry and fig already described, or the pine-apple or that of *Benthamia fragifera*.

The single plurilocular ovary of a flower may develope in such a manner as to produce two or more parts each containing a seed, and appearing to be a separate fruit; each of these may be called a *mericarp* or partial fruit, and the whole fruit is a *schizocarp*. This separation may commence at an early stage, as in *Tropaeolum*, in which each loculus with one seed rounds itself off and finally separates from the rest as a closed mericarp, and in the Boragineae and Labiatae, in which each of the two carpels forms two one-seeded projections, which finally separate into four distinct mericarps surrounding the style and known as *cocci*. Sometimes the separation is caused by the splitting and rending of certain layers of tissue in the ripe fruit, as in the Umbelliferae and in *Acer*, where the fruit by longitudinal division of the dissepiment separates into one-seeded halves (mericarps); the quinquelocular fruit of *Geranium* splits in the same manner into five one-seeded mericarps.

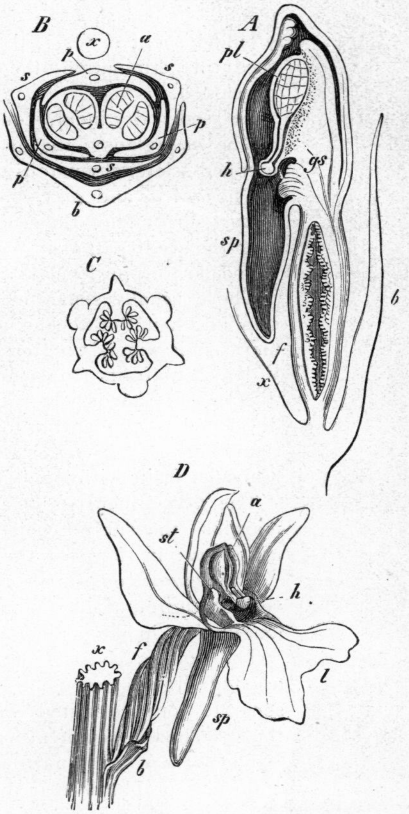

True single fruits are generally unilocular or plurilocular according to the structure of the ovary; but the unilocular ovary may become a plurilocular fruit owing to the presence of spurious dissepiments, that is, such as cannot be considered as the inflexed margins of the carpels; the loculi thus formed may lie above or beside one another; in the

FIG. 354. Zygomorphous flower of *Orchis maculata*. *A* bud divided symmetrically through the middle. *B* transverse section of the bud. *C* transverse section of the ovary. *D* entire flower fully developed after removal of a lateral leaf of the perianth. The letter *x* denotes the mother-axis of the flower, *b* the bract, *s* the outer, *p* the inner perianth-leaves, the posterior one of which becomes the labellum *l*, *a* the single anther, *st* staminodes, *gs* gynostenium, *pl* pollinium, *h* its viscid disk, *sp* the spur of the labellum, *f* the inferior ovary which is twisted in *D*.

lomentum of some Leguminosae, *Cassia fistula* for instance, they lie one above the other, in the legume of *Astragalus* beside each other. The plurilocular ovary may on the contrary produce an unilocular fruit by the suppression of one or more loculi, as in the oak and lime. Fruits therefore cannot, like ovaries, be divided into monomerous and polymerous, these terms having now a different meaning.

The wall of the ovary developes into the wall of the fruit or *pericarp*. If the pericarp is sufficiently thick it can generally be distinguished into two or three layers of tissue of different structure; the outer layer (often only an epidermis) is then called the *epicarp*, and the inner the *endocarp*; if there is still a third layer between these, it is termed the *mesocarp*, and if it is fleshy (pulpy) the *sarcocarp*.

Two principal forms of true fruits each with two subordinate forms may be distinguished for purposes of classification and in conformity with the traditional terminology, according as the pericarp in the ripe state has fleshy, succulent layers or not, and according as the ripe fruit opens to discharge the seeds which become detached from the placentas or remains closed, namely :

A. Dry fruits : pericarp woody or tough and leathery, the cell-sap having disappeared from all its cells.

I. Dry indehiscent fruits : the pericarp does not open, but envelopes the seed till germination; the seed-coat is thin and membranous, and little developed.

(*a*) One-seeded dry indehiscent fruits (achenial-fruits) :—

The *nut* (glans) : the dry pericarp is thick and hard, and is composed of lignified sclerenchymatous tissue, as in *Corylus*.

The *achene* and *caryopsis* : the dry pericarp is thin, tough and leathery, closely surrounding the seed and separable (true achene) or not (caryopsis) from the seed-coat, as in *Ranunculus*, the Gramineae, and Compositae.

(*β*) Bilocular, or plurilocular dry indehiscent fruits :—

These usually separate into mericarps, that is, are *schizocarps*, each resembling a nut or achene, as in Umbelliferae and Geraniaceae ; in *Acer* the mericarp is winged and termed a *samara*.

2. Dry dehiscent fruits (capsular fruits) : the pericarp dehisces when fully ripe to release the seeds, which are in this case themselves clothed with a strongly developed usually hard or tough seed-coat ; the fruits have usually more seeds than one.

(*a*) Capsular fruits with longitudinal dehiscence :—

The *follicle* consists of a single carpel which opens along the coherent margins (the suture) which bear the seeds, as in *Paeonia* and *Illicium anisatum* ; in *Asclepias* the thick placenta is also detached.

The *legume* consists also of a single carpel, which opens not only along the ventral suture but also along the dorsal median line, and thus separates into longitudinal halves, as in *Phaseolus* and *Pisum*.

The *siliqua* consists of two carpels which form a bilocular fruit with a longitudinal (spurious) dissepiment ; the pericarp opens by two valves which separate from the united margins of the carpels (*replum*) ; between these is the stretched dissepiment which remains behind, as in the Cruciferae.

The *capsule* in the narrower use of the word is formed from a polymerous unilocular or plurilocular ovary, and parts longitudinally into two or more valves which separate part of the way from the apex downwards, as in *Cerastium*, or down to the base. If the longitudinal fissures pass through the dissepiments in a plurilocular fruit, the dehiscence is *septicidal*, as in *Colchicum* ; but if the fissure is in the middle between each pair of dissepiments, the dehiscence is *loculicidal*, as in *Tulipa* and *Hibiscus* ; in these cases a half dissepiment may remain attached to each edge or an entire dissepiment may remain attached to the middle of each valve ; but if a part of each dissepiment or the entire dissepiments remain attached to a central column, which is thus winged and from which the valves are detached, the dehiscence is *septifragal, septicidally* or *marginicidally* septifragal, as in *Calluna* and *Rhododendron,* or *locucidally* septifragal, as in *Datura.* If the capsule comes from an unilocular polymerous ovary, the separation of the valves may take place in the sutures and correspond to the septicidal dehiscence, as in *Gentiana*, or midway between them and answer to the loculicidal dehiscence, as in *Viola*.

(*β*) Capsular fruits with transverse dehiscence :—

The *pyxidium* or circumscissile capsule opens by the separation of an upper portion of the pericarp, which falls off like a lid, while the lower portion remains in the form of an urn on the flower-stalk, as in *Plantago, Hyoscyamus, Anagallis.*

(γ) Capsular fruits opening by pores :—

By the term *pore-capsule* may be designated a capsular fruit in which by the removal of small portions of the pericarp at certain spots, small openings are formed through which the diminutive seeds are shaken out by the wind, as in *Papaver* and *Antirrhinum.*

B. Succulent fruits : the tissue of the pericarp or certain layers of it remain succulent till the ripening of the fruit or assume a fleshy or pulpy consistence.

3. Succulent indehiscent fruits : the succulent pericarp does not burst, and the seeds are not discharged.

The *drupe* or *stone-fruit* : inside a thin epicarp is a usually thick mesocarp of fleshy consistence ; the endocarp forms a hard thick layer, the stone (*putamen*) which usually encloses a single seed with a thin seed-coat, as in *Prunus.*

The *berry* : inside a more or less tough or hard epicarp the rest of the tissue of the pericarp is developed as a succulent pulp in which the seeds, which have a firm or even hard seed-coat, lie imbedded ; the berry is distinguished in general from the drupe by the absence of a hard endocarp and usually contains more than one seed, as in *Ribes, Cucurbita,* and *Solanum* ; it sometimes is one-seeded as in the date. Allied to the berry is the fruit of the species of *Citrus,* known as *hesperidium,* the pericarp of which consists of a firm tough outer layer, and a pith-like inner layer; from the innermost layer of tissue of the wall of the plurilocular ovary pluricellular protuberances are developed at an early stage, which gradually fill the cavity of the loculi of the ovary as isolated closely packed succulent lobes of tissue and form the pulp.

4. Succulent dehiscent fruits : the succulent but not pulpy pericarp bursts and discharges the seeds, the seed-coat of which is usually strongly developed.

The term *succulent capsule* might be applied to fruits in which the succulent pericarp opens by valves and releases the seeds, as in *Aesculus* and *Impatiens.* Corresponding with the drupe is the fruit of *Juglans,* in which the outer succulent layer bursts, and a stony endocarp surrounds the seed and its thin coat ; it is the *tryma* of authors and might be called a dehiscent drupe.

The fruit of *Nuphar* is more like the berry but is distinguished from it by the bursting of the outer stout layer of the pericarp; this in *Nuphar advena* detaches an inner lining of each loculus of the fruit, which at first floats on the water like a sac containing the seeds ; the fruit may be called a *dehiscent berry.*

The enumeration here given contains only the more common forms of fruits ; there are a number besides, which do not fit into any of the above categories and do not bear any special name [1].

The *ripe seed* depends for its external character on the development of the pericarp ; in general the seed-coat is thick, hard and firm, if the pericarp is soft, especially if it bursts and discharges the seeds ; but if the pericarp is tough and woody and encloses the seeds till they germinate, as in the achene, nut, drupe and mericarp of schizocarps, the seed-coat remains thin and soft, as it does when the strongly developed endosperm becomes very hard and encloses the small embryo, as in the date and in *Phytelephas,* etc. The seed-coat of the seeds of dehiscent fruits is

---

[1] For other recent attempts to classify fruits see reference by Vines in 2nd ed. of Engl. Transl. of Sachs' Lehrb. p. 617, note.

usually clothed with a distinctly differentiated epidermis, on the configuration of which it depends whether the seed has a smooth appearance as in beans and peas, or shows a variety of sculpturings, such as pits, warts, ridges and the like, as in *Datura, Hyoscyamus, Papaver, Nigella*; the epidermal cells not unfrequently develope into hairs; cotton, for example, consists of the long woolly hairs which clothe the seeds of *Gossypium*; only a penicillate tuft of long hairs is developed in some cases, as in *Asclepias syriaca*. The epidermal cells of many seeds, as in *Plantago psyllium, P. arenaria, P. Cynops, Linum usitatissimum* and *Cydonia vulgaris*, contain layers of cell-wall which have become converted into mucilage, and swelling up strongly in water envelope the moistened seeds in a layer of mucilage. Pericarps which do not open and which contain small seeds often assume the character of the seed-coat of the seeds of dehiscing fruits; this is especially the case in the achene and caryopsis, which are therefore popularly called seeds. The circle of hairs, which serves as an apparatus of flight for the dissemination of many seeds of dehiscent fruits, is developed in many achenes as an appendage of the pericarp, as, for example, the pappus of the Compositae, which really occupies the place of the superior calyx. The wings answering the same purpose, which are a development of the seed-coat of some seeds of dehiscent fruits and are well shown in *Bignonia*, occur again on the pericarp of indehiscent fruits, as in *Acer*. The mucilaginous epidermis of the seeds of dehiscent fruits mentioned above is seen in the epidermis of the mericarps of *Salvia* and other Labiatae. These and a number of other facts show that in the formation of the pericarp and seed-coat the chie object is to provide the greatest variety of methods for the dissemination of seeds, and in carrying this object into effect structures which are quite distinct morphologically attain the same physiological development, and those which are morphologically similar are very variously developed from the physiological point of view.

To complete the account of the terminology it should be remarked in conclusion that the spot at which the seed is detached from the funicle, and which is generally easy to be seen in the seeds of dehiscent fruits, is termed the *hilum* or umbilicus. The micropyle also is often to be distinguished, lying in anatropous and campylotropous seeds close to the hilum (*Corydalis, Faba, Phaseolus*), usually in the form of a wart with a depression in the middle. Outgrowths on seeds along the raphe, as in *Chelidonium majus, Asarum, Viola*, or as a cushion covering the micropyle, as in *Euphorbia*, are termed *crests, strophioles* or *caruncles*. The *aril*, which wraps the base of the ripe seed or the entire seed in a fleshy succulent envelope, and is easily detached from the true firm seed-coat, has been already mentioned [1].

A. MONOCOTYLEDONS.

The *seed* usually contains a strongly developed endosperm and a comparatively small embryo, the disproportion being very remarkable in the large seeds of *Cocos, Phoenix, Phytelephas, Crinum* and some others; in the Naiadaceae, Juncagineae, and Alismaceae the endosperm is absorbed before the formation of tissue in the embryo-sac; in the Orchideae it is wanting from the first, and in the Scitamineae where it is also wanting, it is replaced by copious perisperm.

The *embryo* is usually straight and cylindric or conical, sometimes considerably elongated and then spirally coiled, as in *Potamogeton* and *Zannichellia*, sometimes conical or obconical owing to the thickening of the cotyledon at the upper end. The axis of the embryo is usually very short, and small in proportion to the cotyledonary

---

[1] [By the term aril should be designated, as Baillon has pointed out, all growths on the outside of the seed-coat, whatever be their form and position; the hairs mentioned above, the crests, strophioles, caruncles, etc., are all different kinds of aril.]

leaf; but in the Helobiae the axial portion forms the larger part of the embryo (*macropodous embryo*). The rudiment of the primary root is at the posterior end of the axis, and near it in the Gramineae are the rudiments of two or more lateral roots, which like the primary root are enclosed in a root-sheath (Fig. 355). The embryo of the Gramineae is further marked by having an outgrowth from the axis beneath the cotyledon, which envelopes the whole of the embryo like a mantle and forms a thick peltate plate on the dorsal side, where it is in contact with endosperm; this outgrowth is known as the *scutellum*. In the Orchideae, *Apostasia* and Burmanniaceae the embryo in ripe seeds is still a roundish undifferentiated body, in which the plumule is not formed before the commencement of germination [1].

In *germination* [2] either the roots begin at once to elongate, and their emergence in the Gramineae ruptures the sheath which envelopes them and which remains attached to the axis as the *coleorhiza*, or, which is more commonly the case, the lower part of the cotyledon elongates and pushes the radicular end with the plumule enveloped by the sheath of the cotyledon out of the seed (Fig. 356), while its upper part remains as an organ of suction in the endosperm till the food contained in the latter is exhausted: in the Gramineae the whole of the plumule issues from the seed, the scutellum only remaining in it to convey the food-material of the endosperm to the embryo.

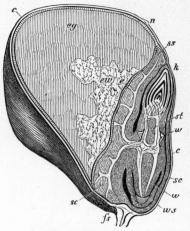

FIG. 355. Longitudinal section of fruit of *Zea Mais* *c* rind of the fruit, *n* appendage of the stigma, *fs* base of the fruit, *eg* yellowish firm part of the endosperm, *ew* its white and looser part, *sc* the scutellum of the embryo, *ss* its tip, *e* its epithelium, *k* the plumula, *w* (below) the primary root, *ws* root-sheath, *w* (above) secondary roots springing from the first internode of the primary stem *st*. Magn. about six times.

The *primary root* of the Monocotyledons soon ceases to grow, even though it may develope strongly during germination, as in Palms, Liliaceae, *Zea*, etc.; its place is taken by lateral roots, which spring from the axis and are stronger the higher up they are formed in it. The Monocotyledons have therefore no persistent root-system developed from the primary root, like that of Gymnosperms and many Dicotyledons; sometimes indeed no roots are ever formed, as is the case in some saprophytes without chlorophyll among the Orchideae, as *Epipogum* and *Corallorhiza*.

The *plumule* of the embryo is in most cases completely enclosed in the first sheath-like leaf, the cotyledon, which either developes into a sheathing scale-leaf, or becomes at once the first green foliage-leaf of the young plant, as in *Allium*. There is usually a second leaf present within the cotyledon, in the Gramineae even a third or fourth, which lengthen by intercalary growth at their base and emerge during germination from the sheath of the cotyledon; these and the succeeding leaves are stronger, the later they are formed on the growing axis, which usually continues very short during germination and forms no distinct internodes, as in *Allium*, the Palms

---

[1] No primary root is developed in the Orchideae even in germination.
[2] See Sachs in Bot. Ztg. 1862 and 1863.

and other plants, but sometimes elongates and becomes marked out into distinct internodes, as in Zea and other Gramineae.

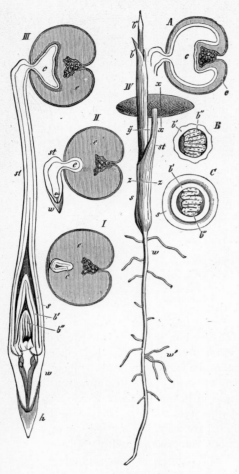

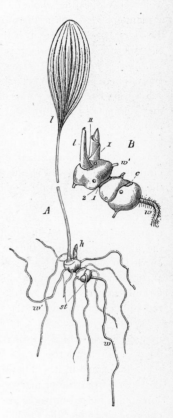

FIG. 356. Germination of *Phoenix dactylifera*. *I* transverse section of the resting seed. *II, III, IV* stages of germination (*IV* the natural size). *A* transverse section of *IV* at *xx*, *B* at *xy'*, *C* at *zz*. *e* the horny endosperm, *s* sheath of the cotyledon, *st* its stalk, *c* its summit developed as an organ of absorption which gradually exhausts the endosperm and finally takes its place, *w* the primary root, *w'* secondary roots, *h* root-cap, *b' b''* the leaves which come after the cotyledon, *b''* becoming the first foliage-leaf. In *B* and *C* is a transverse section of its folded lamina.

FIG. 357. Plant of *Polygonatum multiflorum* in its second year. *B* its stem magnified. The unbranched primary root is seen at *w*, *w'* lateral roots springing from the stem *st*, *l* the foliage-leaf of the second year, *k* its bud, *c* the scar of insertion of the cotyledon, 1 and 2 the insertions of the two first sheath-leaves which precede the foliage-leaf *l*. *I, II* the succeeding sheath-leaves (scale-leaves) of the bud in *B*.

The plant may increase in size and strength from such vigorous growth of the axis of the embryo, that the latter ultimately becomes the primary stem of the full-grown and fertile plant, as for instance in most Palms, *Aloe, Zea,* etc.; if the axis of the embryo remains short while it strengthens, it may increase greatly in thickness and form a tuber (Fig. 359), or a bulb if the bases of the leaves become thicker, as in *Allium Cepa*. If the axis of the embryo becomes the primary stem, whether it grows erect or creeps in the form of a rhizome, it first assumes the form of an inverted cone, which is short or elongated according to the length of the internodes; this peculiarity, which is common to Ferns and Monocotyledons, is due to the absence of secondary growth in thickness; the portions of the stem first formed preserve their original thickness, while each succeeding portion is larger; the transverse sections of the stem are thicker the nearer they are to the apex. So long as this process is going on, the stem is increasing in strength; but a time comes sooner or later when each portion of the stem is only as thick as the preceding one, and then the stem forms a cylinder, or is broad and compressed, as in many rhizomes, but in either case grows on with uniform strength; the lateral shoots also grow in a similar manner, when they spring low down on the primary stem, as in *Aloe* and other plants. But it not unfrequently happens that the primary shoot formed by the embryo soon dies away after producing lateral shoots; these grow more vigorously than the parent, and then hand on the further development to new shoots, which produce from generation to generation thicker axes, larger leaves and stronger roots, till at length a more constant state of things supervenes and each successive generation produces shoots of

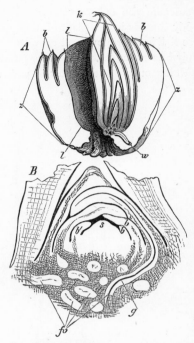

FIG. 358. Bulbs of *Fritillaria imperialis* in November. *A* longitudinal section of the whole bulb reduced in size; *zz* the coherent lower portions of the bulb-scales, *bb* their free upper portions; they enclose a cavity *l* which contains the decayed flower-stem; the next year's bud *k* is formed in the axil of the innermost scale; its first leaves will form the new bulb, while its axis developes into the new flower-stem; the root *w* springs from the axis of this bud. *B* longitudinal section of the apical region of the new bud; *s* the apex of the stem, *b, b' b''* the youngest leaves, *fv* and *g* vascular bundles.

uniform strength. If the portions of the axes of the shoots beneath the points of origin of their daughter-shoots are maintained, sympodia are formed, as for example in *Polygonatum multiflorum*; but in many cases each shoot disappears entirely after it has produced a shoot to replace it, as happens in our native tuberous Orchids, in *Fritillaria imperialis* (Fig. 358) and *Colchicum autumnale* (Fig. 360)[1].

The normal *branching* of Monocotyledons is monopodial and usually axillary; in most cases a bud is formed in the axil of every leaf, but all do not develope, so that the number of branches that can be seen is often much less than that of the leaves, as in *Agave, Aloe, Dracaena*, Palms, and many Gramineae. But sometimes several buds are formed in the axil of a leaf, and beside one another where the insertion of the leaf is broad, as in many bulbs; in *Musa* a number of flowers stand side by side in the

---

[1] A detailed account of these very varied phenomena will be found in Irmisch, Zur Morphol. d. monocotyl. Knollen u. Zwiebelgewächse, Berlin, 1850, and Biol. und Morphol. d. Orchideen, Leipzig, 1853.

axil of a bract, and in *Musa Ensete* two rows even one above the other. In the Spadiciflorae the bracts are often wanting, and the flowers grow without them from the axis of the inflorescence, but are nevertheless of distinctly lateral origin. The branching also of *Lemna*, where there are no foliage-leaves, is lateral; the vegetative body consists in this plant of disc-shaped or much swollen portions of the axis which are rich in chlorophyll and grow laterally from one another, and are connected together only by slender stalks or soon separate; the plane of branching coincides apparently with the surface of the water on which the plants float; each shoot produces only one

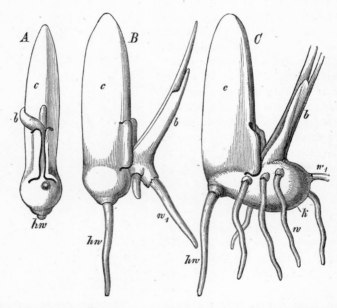

FIG. 359. Germination of *Aponogeton distachyum*; *hw* primary root, *c* cotyledon, *b* first leaf, *w1* first secondary root springing from the stem, which soon thickens into a tuber *k*, and developes fresh secondary roots *w*, *w*; to the left the youngest, to the right the oldest stage. After Dutailly.

or two lateral shoots which are originally dorsal but become afterwards lateral[1], and the branching is therefore distinctly cymose-sympodial or as in *Lemna trisulca* dichasial.

Besides the formation of shoots by the branching of the axis, *adventitious shoots* also are occasionally formed on the leaves and fulfil the part of gemmae, as in *Hyacinthus Pouzolsii* and on the margins of the leaves of some Orchideae according to Döll. The large gemmae which appear very regularly on the leaves of *Atherurus ternatus*, one of the Aroideae, should be specially mentioned; they grow at the point of union of the leaf-sheath and the stalk, and at the base of the lamina; but the small bulbs on the aerial stems of *Lilium bulbiferum* are normal axillary shoots, as are

---

[1] The shoots grow from the upper (dorsal) side of the axis that bears them, but are at an early period enclosed in a pocket by the luxuriant growth of the axis, and moved into an apparently lateral position.

probably those found on the inflorescence of many species of *Allium*. Hofmeister states that adventitious buds are produced on the roots of *Epipactis microphylla*; and the transformation of the tips of the roots into shoots has been observed in *Neottia Nidus avis* and *Anthurium longifolium*.

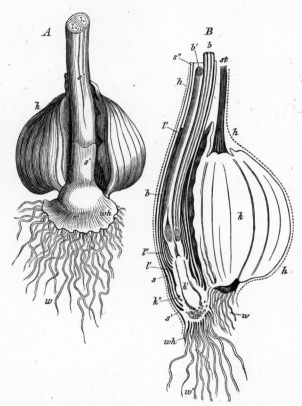

FIG. 360. *Colchicum autumnale*, the underground portions of a flowering plant. *A* seen in front and from without; *k* the tuber, *s'* and *s''* scale-leaves which envelope the flower-stalk, *wh* its base from which the roots *w* proceed. *B* longitudinal section of the preceding, the plane of section being perpendicular to the paper; *hh* a brown skin which covers all the underground parts of the plant, *st* the stalk of the flower and leaf of the previous year, which is dead and has left only its basal portion swollen into a tuber *k* as a reservoir of food-material for the new plant just coming into flower; this plant is a lateral shoot from the base of the tuber *k* and consists of an axis, from the base of which the roots *w'* proceed, while its middle part *k'* enlarges into a tuber in the following year, the old tuber *k* disappearing; the axis bears the sheath-leaves *s*, *s'*, *s''* and the foliage-leaves *l'*, *l''*; in the axils of the uppermost foliage-leaves are the flowers *b*, *b'*, and the axis itself terminates free between them. The foliage leaves are still small at the time of flowering, and appear with the fruits above the ground in the ensuing year; the portion *k'* of the axis then swells into the new tuber, on which the axillary bud *k''* is developed into a new flowering axis, while the sheath of the lowest foliage-leaf is transformed into the brown membranous envelope.

The *leaves* of Monocotyledons are seldom verticillate, the foliage leaves of *Elodea* and the bracts of *Alisma* being exceptional in this respect; their arrangement in two alternating rows, as in the Gramineae, Irideae, *Phormium*, *Clivia*, *Typha*, etc., is very common, and either prevails over the whole shoot and its secondary shoots, or appears at first and subsequently passes into spiral arrangements which often lead to the formation of rosettes of leaves spreading in every direction, as in *Aloe*, *Agave*, Palms, etc. The arrangement with the $\frac{1}{3}$ divergence is much less common, and is found in some species of *Aloe, Carex* and *Pandanus*; spiral arrangements with smaller divergences than $\frac{1}{3}$ are sometimes found, as in *Musa*; in *Musa rubra* according to Braun the foliage-leaves have a divergence of $\frac{3}{7}$, the bracts of $\frac{4}{11}$; in *Costus* the angle of divergence of the foliage-leaves is $\frac{1}{4}$ or $\frac{1}{5}$, &c. The axillary shoot of the

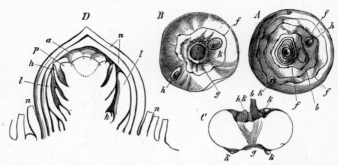

FIG. 361. *Crocus vernus. A* the tuberous stem seen from above, *B* from beneath, *C* from the side in longitudinal section. The lines of insertion of the scale-leaves *f f f* are seen forming closed circles, and the axillary buds *k k* belonging to these leaves; *b* the base of the dead leafy and flowering stem, and by its side *h k* in *C* the new bud, from which a new tuber and a new flowering stem are formed. *D* longitudinal section through the new bud; *n n* its scale-leaves, *l* foliage-leaves, *h* bract, *p* perianth, *a* anthers; *k* a bud in the axil of a foliage-leaf.

Monocotyledons usually begins with a leaflet which is generally two-keeled and has its dorsal surface closely applied to the primary axis; such a leaf for instance is the upper palea in the flower of the Gramineae, which is itself a shoot axillary to the lower palea; where the leaves of the successive generations of shoots alternate in two rows it follows that an entire system of shoots may be bilateral, and divisible by a plane which divides the leaves into halves, as in *Potamogeton* and *Typha*. The insertion of the scale-leaves and foliage-leaves, and often also of the bracts (for instance of the spathe which is so common), is usually either wholly or to a great extent amplexicaul, and the lower part of the leaf is consequently sheathing; there is an obvious connection between this and the absence of the stipules which are so common in Dicotyledons. The scale-leaves, rudimentary arrested states of foliage-leaves, and many bracts are reduced to this sheathing portion, which in the foliage-leaves usually passes immediately into the green lamina, though a comparatively long and slender stalk occurs between the lamina and the sheath in the Scitamineae,

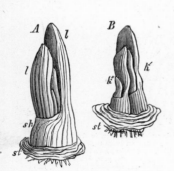

FIG. 362. *Allium Cepa.* Bud inside the bulb after removal of the bulb-scales; *st* the broad short portion of stem in which the bulb-scales are inserted. *A* shows the lamina at *l* and the sheaths of the foliage-leaves at *sh* which are still short. In *B* the outer leaves of *A* are removed, and an axillary bud *k''* is discovered by the side of the terminal bud *k'*.

Aroideae, Palmae and some other forms. If there is no stalk and the lamina and sheath are sharply distinguished, there is often a ligule present at the point where they meet, as in the Gramineae and *Allium* (Fig. 363).

The lamina is usually entire and of very simple outline, often long and narrow (ribbon-shaped), seldom roundish and discoid (*Hydrocharis*), or cordate or sagittate (*Sagittaria* and some Aroideae); branching of the lamina is of rather rare occurrence, and appears either in the form of lobes united by a broad base, or less frequently of deep division, as in some Aroideae (*Amorphophallus, Atherurus, Sauromatum*); the fan-shaped and pinnate leaves of the Palms owe their division not to branching at an early period of their growth, but to the tearing of their substance at the time of unfolding, caused by the drying up of certain strips of tissue in the lamina which is up to that time entire and is folded in sharp plaits.

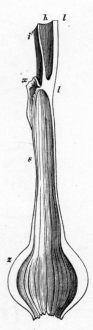

FIG. 363. A leaf of *Allium Cepa* divided longitudinally into halves; *z* the thickened base of the sheath, which remains behind as a bulb-scale after the decay of the upper part of the leaf, *s* the membranous part of the sheath, *l* the lamina, *h* the cavity and *i* the inner side of the lamina, *x* the ligule.

FIG. 364. Leaf of *Convallaria latifolia.* The nerves of the leaf are left white.

The *venation* of the foliage-leaves differs from that of most Dicotyledons in the circumstance that the weaker veins do not usually project on the under side of the leaf, but run through the mesophyll; in smaller foliage-leaves the projecting midrib is also wanting, but it is strongly developed in the large stalked leaves of the Spadiciflorae and Scitamineae and is traversed by numerous vascular bundles. If the leaf is ribbon-shaped and with a broad insertion, the vascular bundles run nearly parallel to one another; in broader leaves without a distinct mid-rib they run in curves from the central line of the leaf to the margins, as in *Convallaria* (Fig. 364); but if there is a strong mid-rib in a broad lamina, as in *Musa*, etc., the vascular bundles of the mid-rib give off slender lateral bundles which run in large numbers parallel to one another to the margin of the leaf; these parallel veins crossing the leaf are sometimes connected by short straight anastomoses into a lattice-like network, as in *Alisma Costus* and *Ouvirandra*, in the last of which the mesophyll which is present in the meshes of the young leaves is wanting in the older[1]. In a few cases only projecting lateral veins proceed from the mid-rib and give rise to a delicate reticulated venation, as in some Aroideae.

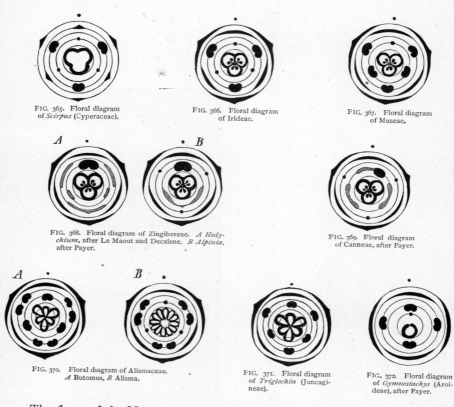

FIG. 365. Floral diagram of *Scirpus* (Cyperaceae).

FIG. 366. Floral diagram of Irideae.

FIG. 367. Floral diagram of Museae.

FIG. 368. Floral diagram of Zingibereae. *A Hedychium*, after Le Maout and Decaisne. *B Alpinia*, after Payer.

FIG. 369. Floral diagram of Canneae, after Payer.

FIG. 370. Floral diagram of Alismaceae. *A* Butomus, *B* Alisma.

FIG. 371. Floral diagram of *Triglochin* (Juncagineae).

FIG. 372. Floral diagram of *Gymnestachys* (Aroideae), after Payer.

The *flower* of the Monocotyledons usually consists of five alternating isomerous whorls, an outer and an inner perianth-whorl, an outer and an inner staminal whorl, and a carpellary whorl followed by a second only in the polycarpous flowers of the Alismaceae and Juncagineae. The most common typical floral formula is therefore $Sn\,Pn\,Stn+n\,Cn\,(+n)$. The number of the staminal whorls is increased in the Hydrocharideae only and in a few other cases; where, as in *Butomus*, there is an increase in the typical number of the stamens, this takes place without multiplication of the whorls. The number of the members in a whorl is two only in some isolated cases scattered through very different families, as $S\,2\,P\,2\,St\,2+2\,C\,2$ in *Maianthemum* and some Enantioblastae; it is sometimes four or even five in *Paris quadrifolia* and some Orontiaceae. The usual number of parts in a whorl is three and consequently the typical formula is $S\,3\,P\,3\,St\,3+3\,C\,3\,(+3)$.

---

[1] Observed in specimens in the Botanic Gardens at Strassburg.

In the large division of Liliiflorae, in some Spadiciflorae, in many Enantio-blastae, Juncagineae and Alismaceae[1] this formula is at once obtained empirically; in most other cases single members or whorls are wanting, but their suppression is usually at once suggested by the position of the parts that are present. In the Scitamineae with only one or even with only half an anther the rest of the members of the androecium are present in an imperfect condition, having been changed into petaloid staminodes. The flower of our European Gramineae has no perianth but is enclosed in two paleae, the lower of which is the bract, the upper the bracteole of the flower. The two small scales, known as the lodicules, which force the paleae apart by their strong turgescence and thus cause the flower to open, have been regarded as a rudimentary perianth. It is true that they are by their origin lateral portions of one leaf-rudiment, as the history of development in some cases shows[2]. But they are not a perianth, but the flower is enclosed in a number of bracts arranged in two rows, the two lowest of which are the paleae, while one of the upper ones is rudimentary and its lateral portions (or in place of these two smaller independent rudiments) are the lodicules, and the fourth is usually quite abortive, but in the Stipeae is developed as a posterior lodicule. The arrangement of the perianth-leaves is different in some of the tropical Gramineae. In *Oryza* for instance the second staminal whorl is developed, in *Bambusa* also and in some others. It has been already pointed out that the flower of the Orchideae may be referred to the pentacyclic trimerous type; the following theoretical diagrams will show the same thing in the case of the more important of the other families.

If we take the pentacyclic flower with the formula $Sn\ Pn\ Stn + n\ Cn\ (+n)$ as typical for Monocotyledons, it appears that in the great majority of families in which the numerical relations deviate from the type[3], the difference is simply that single members or whole whorls are wanting, but the typical position of those that are present is not disturbed; it is to the effects produced by abortion therefore that the variety in the forms of flowers in this class is chiefly due; the cases consequently are not rare in Monocotyledons, in which abortion is carried to such a point that nothing is at last left of an entire flower but a single naked ovary or a single stamen, as is the case in many Aroideae[4], in which this mode of explaining the present state of the flowers is rendered easy and obvious by the occurrence of typically constructed flowers and of a variety of intermediate forms in which partial abortion only has taken place. It is chiefly in small and closely crowded flowers that a great reduction of the typical number of parts is observed, as for example in the Spadiciflorae, while in large flowers placed further apart the whorls are usually present in full number or in more than their full number (*Butomus, Hydrocharis*), and any deviations consist chiefly in the appearance of petaloid staminodes in the place of fertile stamens, as in

---

[1] The dimerous flowers of Potamogeten $S2\ P2\ St2 + 2\ C\ 4$ (see Hegelmaier in Bot. Ztg. 1870, p. 287) differ only in the simultaneous appearance of the four carpels, which are placed diagonally to the previous pairs. The leaves of the perianth are formed in this case as outgrowths (scales from the connective) of the stamens, as in the case undoubtedly in *Ruppia*.

[2] Hackel, Untersuch. ü. d. Gräser in Engler's Jahrb. I. p. 336.

[3] Compare what is said on the subject of abortion on p. 414 and in the introduction to the Angiosperms.

[4] Engler, Araceae in De Candolle's Monographiae Phanerogamarum, Vol. II. 1879.

Scitamineae. Considering the extensive abortion in small flowers it may sometimes be a question whether in a group of stamens and carpels we have a single flower before us, or an inflorescence of several flowers reduced by abortion, as for instance in *Lemna*.

When both the *perianth-whorls* are developed, they are generally of the same structure; and in large flowers they are usually delicate and petaloid and either coloured or not, as in the Liliaceae and Orchideae; in small flowers on the contrary they are firm, dry and membranous (*glumaceous*), as in the Juncaceae and Eriocauloneae. But sometimes the outer whorl is green and sepaloid, as in *Canna*, *Alisma*, *Tradescantia*.

The *stamens* are generally composed of a filiform filament and a quadrilocular anther; but variations are not infrequent, especially in the form of the filament and of the connective. Among the most remarkable are the petaloid staminodes of the Canneae and Zingiberaceae. *Naias* and *Typha*[1] appear to supply exceptions to the rule that the stamens are of foliar origin, as has been already pointed out (p. 353). The branching of stamens, which is of so frequent occurrence in the Dicotyledons, scarcely ever occurs in the Monocotyledons, and this corresponds to the usual absence of branching in the other foliar formations; if the diagram of the flower of *Canna* (Fig. 369) founded on Payer's statements is correct[2], the petaloid staminodes are branched.

The *gynaeceum* usually consists of a trilocular ovary; it is less often unilocular and trimerous; in both cases it may be superior or inferior, the latter only in plants with large flowers, as *Hydrocharis*, the Irideae, Amaryllideae, Scitamineae, and series of the Gynandrae. Three or more monomerous ovaries, polycarpous flowers therefore, are found only in the Juncagineae and Alismaceae, in which also the usual number of the members and whorls of the gynaeceum is exceeded, reminding us of the Polycarpicae among the Dicotyledons.

Cohesions and displacements are usually neither so frequent nor so complicated in the flower of Monocotyledons as in Dicotyledons. Among the most remarkable cases of the kind are the formation of the gynostemium in the Orchideae, the cohesion of six similar perianth-leaves into a tube in *Hyacinthus*, *Convallaria*, *Colchicum*, etc., the epipetalous and episepalous position of the stamens in some plants; this last peculiarity is much less constant within fixed limits in Monocotyledons than in Dicotyledons.

Terminal flowers on a leafy primary shoot are very rare in Monocotyledons (*Tulipa*), terminal inflorescences are more common.

As the flower increases in size it exhibits a tendency on the whole to the zygomorphism which is in many cases only feebly indicated, but appears most fully developed in the Scitamineae and Orchideae.

The *ovules* usually spring from the margins of the carpels, rarely from their inner surface, as in *Butomus*; the single orthotropous ovule of *Naias* is formed, according to Magnus, by the transformation of the extremity of the floral axis; one

---

[1] Bot. Ztg. 1882, p. 405.

[2] This is not quite the case according to Eichler's careful researches. But the construction of the flower in this genus is so difficult, that we must not attempt to describe it here. See Eichler, Blüthendiagramme, I.

or more ovules are placed at the bottom of the cavity of the unilocular ovary of some Aroideae and of *Lemna*. The prevailing form of the ovule is anatropous ; campylotropous ovules occur in the Scitamineae, Gramineae and some other cases ; orthotropous, both erect and pendulous, are found in the Enantioblastae and certain of the Aroideae. The nucellus is almost invariably surrounded with two envelopes ; *Crinum* is an exception.

The *embryo-sac*[1] usually continues to be covered by a layer of the tissue of the nucellus up to the time of fertilisation ; in some cases the apex of the nucellus is destroyed and the embryo-sac protrudes, as in *Hemerocallis, Crocus, Gladiolus*, etc., but it often remains intact as a cap of tissue covering the apex of the embryo-sac, as in some Aroideae and Liliaceae ; in Orchids the growing embryo-sac completely destroys the layer of tissue that surrounds it together with the apex of the nucellus ; the same thing happens after fertilisation in all other Monocotyledons that form an endosperm, and sometimes the embryo-sac even attacks and destroys the inner integument, as in *Allium odorans* and the Ophrydeae.

In the majority of Monocotyledons fertilisation is soon followed by a copious development of *endosperm-cells* by free cell-formation ; the nuclei formed by division first of the nucleus of the embryo-sac and then of its daughter-cells are imbedded in the layer of protoplasm which lines the wall of the sac, and become centres of cell-formation. Narrow embryo-sacs are filled by the growth of the free endosperm cells first formed ; in some cases the free cells formed in the parietal protoplasm float loose in it at first, and afterwards unite into a tissue as in *Leucojum* and *Gagea* ; the narrow embryo-sac of *Pistia* is filled with a row of broad discoid cells, which lie in it like transverse compartments and may perhaps be produced by the division of the sac itself. In some Aroideae one part only of the embryo-sac is filled with endosperm, while the rest has none. The endosperm continues to grow after it has filled the sac, while the seed which it fills also increases in size ; it was mentioned above (p. 394) how considerable this growth is in *Crinum*.

In all Monocotyledons which form an endosperm, the endosperm ultimately forms a continuous tissue enveloping the embryo before the latter has ceased to grow ; the growth therefore of the embryo displaces a part of the endosperm that surrounds it, and it is this displacement which causes the lateral position of the embryo of the Gramineae by the side of the endosperm, and the absence of endosperm in some Aroideae. In Monocotyledons in which the mature seed has no endosperm (exalbuminous seed), the Naiadaceae, Hydrocharideae, Juncagineae, Alismaceae, Canneae, and Orchideae, no endosperm is formed at all, or only transitory preparations for its formation are observed.

The first formation of the embryo has been described in the Introduction to the Angiosperms.

In respect of their **histology**[2] Monocotyledons differ from Dicotyledons and Gymnosperms chiefly in the course of the vascular bundles in the stem and in the absence of a true cambium-layer. The transverse section of the stem of most Monocotyledons does

---

[1] Hofmeister, Neue Beitr. (Abh. d. K. Sächs. Ges. d. Wiss. VII) ; see also the works cited above, pages 382 and 390.

[2] See De Bary, Vgl. Anat. p. 262 of the English Edition, and the literature cited in that work.

not show the bundles arranged in a simple ring, as in the Coniferae and Dicotyledons ; but inside the peripheral zone of cortex which has no bundles there is a circular surface, in which either a number of rows of bundles irregularly disposed are concentrically ranged round the central portion which is without bundles, as for instance in the stems of many Grasses which subsequently become hollow ; or the bundles lie scattered over the whole surface. This arrangement of the bundles, to which however there are many exceptions, is due to the obliquely radial course of the leaf-trace-bundles.

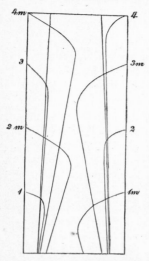

FIG. 373. Diagrammatic representation of the course of the vascular bundles in the Palms, the leaves being supposed to alternate in two rows and to embrace the stem. The successive leaf-traces are numbered in order; *m* the median bundle. After de Bary, Vergl. Anatomie.

These enter the stem in numbers side by side from the broad insertions of the leaves, run obliquely downwards penetrating to some depth into the stem, then bend again outwards and as they descend again approach the surface of the stem ; the bundles do not all penetrate equally far into the stem, as Fig. 373 shows, some even keeping near the surface throughout their course. The common bundle is usually thickest and most highly developed at the bend where it has reached farthest into the stem, while the extremity which bends upwards into the leaf and the descending portion become gradually slenderer and more simple in construction. A transverse section of the stem passes through the different leaf-trace-bundles at different heights in their course and shows therefore bundles of different structure and size ; a radial longitudinal section through the bud or through fully developed stems with short internodes (Palms, thick rhizomes, bulbs, etc.) shows how the bundles which descend from the different leaves, the curvatures of which lie at different heights, cross each other in the radial direction, some running inwards at the spot where others are already turning their course outwards. All bundles descend through many internodes, and finally unite in the outer part of the vascular cylinder with bundles which emerge lower down by applying themselves to them in a radial or oblique direction. In elongated internodes, as in the stalks of grasses, the stems of such Palms as *Calamus* and the long scapes of *Allium*, the bundles run nearly parallel to one another and to the surface ; the places where the bundles bend and cross one another, easily observed at the apex of such stems, are to be found also in the transverse plates (nodes) which have not lengthened between each pair of internodes, where they often form a net-work of horizontal bundles, as may be seen very distinctly in *Zea Mais*.

The course of the bundles as here described necessarily excludes such a distinction of the fundamental tissue of the stem into pith and cortex, as we find in Conifers and Dicotyledons ; the parenchymatous fundamental tissue between the usually numerous bundles is uniform in its character ; but sometimes it is divided into an outer peripheral layer and an inner mass by the formation of a layer of tissue between them, with its cells thickened and lignified in a peculiar manner, the strengthening zone, as in most of the thicker rhizomes and in the hollow scape of *Allium*.

Since the leaf-trace-bundles in the stem of the Monocotyledons are not parallel to one another and are irregularly distributed on the transverse section, they are not adapted to unite into a closed cylinder by the formation of interfascicular cambium, as is the case in other Phanerogams, and it is in accordance with this that they have also no active cambium-layer between the phloem and xylem ; in other words they are closed bundles. When the growth in length of any given portion of the stem comes to an end the whole of the tissue of the bundles becomes permanent tissue, and there is therefore as a rule no subsequent growth in thickness ; each portion of the stem when once formed retains the thickness which it had already reached in the bud near the apex of the stem. But in *Dracaena, Aloe* and *Yucca* of the Liliaceae a further growth in thickness begins subsequently at a considerable distance from the apex of the stem, and may continue even for hundreds of years and be the cause of considerable though slow increase in the diameter of the stem. But the process is very different from that in Conifers and Dicotyledons. A layer of the fundamental tissue parallel to the surface of the stem is changed into a meristem which continually produces new closed vascular bundles and between them parenchymatous permanent tissue; in this way a more or less evidently stratified net-work of slender anastomosing bundles is produced, the arrangement and connection of which are easy to recognise in stems in which the parenchyma between the bundles has perished from exposure to the weather. This compact net-work of closed bundles forms a kind of secondary wood which surrounds in the form of a hollow cylinder the space in which the original common bundles of the stem run isolated and loosely compacted as long threads. This mass of new thickening tissue in the arborescent Monocotyledons resembles the secondary wood of the Conifers and Dicotyledons in belonging entirely to the stem, and in having no genetic connection with the leaves, in which latter respect it differs from the original common bundles. Exceptions to the course of the vascular bundles as briefly described above occur in different Monocotyledons. Slight modifications arise by the bundles forming in their course oblique or transverse connecting branches (anastomoses), as in the tuberous stems of the Aroideae, the elongated internodes of the stems of many of the Cyperaceae, and in some other instances; or they may unite with bundles from lower leaves before they reach the periphery of the vascular bundle-cylinder, as in *Pandanus* and the Bromeliaceae, or cortical bundles may appear outside the cylinder, as in many Palms, the rhizomes of *Carex hirta,* etc. More important deviations also occur, for which De Bary's Comparative Anatomy must be consulted. We will only add here that the vascular bundles are arranged in the leafy stems of *Tamus* and *Dioscorea Batatas* as in Dicotyledons, that is, with the bundles in a circle round the pith; it has been already stated (p. 400) that the embryo in the Dioscoreaceae resembles that of Dicotyledons in the growing point of the stem being apical, not lateral as in most other Monocotyledons.

The following **systematic arrangement** of the subdivisions of the Monocotyledons is that of Eichler in his Syllabus[1]. The brief diagnoses of the orders are only intended to point out a few of the characters which are important for purposes of classification. It would be possible in the space here at command to describe each separate family of the Monocotyledons; but to do the same for the Dicotyledons would far exceed the limits of this work, and for uniformity's sake therefore we must be content simply to name them.

Series I. Liliiflorae.

Inflorescences very various, racemose or cymose; large flowers sometimes solitary; flowers pentacyclic and trimerous, with a few exceptions of dimerous and tetramerous or even pentamerous whorls; inner staminal whorl wanting in Irideae; perianth-whorls usually similar, inconspicuous and glumaceous (Juncaceae), but usually both petaloid (Liliaceae, Irideae, Taccaceae, Haemodoraceae, Pontederiaceae) and often large, or outer perianth developed as a calyx, inner as a corolla (Bromeliaceae); sometimes all six leaves cohering into a tube (Haemodoraceae, etc.); stamens often epipetalous and episepalous; ovary superior (Juncaceae and Liliaceae), superior or

---

[1] Eichler, Syllabus d. Vorlesungen über specielle medicinisch-pharmaceutische Botanik, 2nd Ed. 1880. [The details of the arrangement of the Monocotyledons given here and of the Dicotyledons differ in some respects from those given by Eichler. For a more satisfactory arrangement of the genera of Flowering Plants in orders and larger groups the reader is referred to Bentham and Hooker's Genera Plantarum.] See also Warming, Handb. den systematiske botanik, 1879.

inferior (Bromeliaceae), elsewhere inferior, usually forming a trilocular capsule or berry; embryo enclosed in endosperm, by the side of it in Bromeliaceae. Plants of very different habit; strong aerial woody stems with secondary growth in thickness in *Dracaena, Aloe, Yucca* (belonging to Liliaceae); more often underground rhizomes, tubers, bulbs, from which spring herbaceous annual shoots; leaves usually narrow and long, in Dioscoreaceae with a broad lamina and slender stalk.

Families.
1. Juncaceae.
2. Liliaceae.
3. Irideae.
4. Dioscoreaceae.
5. Taccaceae.
6. Haemodoraceae.
7. Pontederiaceae.
8. Bromeliaceae.

Series II.   Enantioblastae.

Flowers in crowded cymose inflorescences (Commelinaceae), inconspicuous (Restiaceae and Eriocauleae) or conspicuous (Xyrideae and Commelinaceae), pentacyclic usually trimerous (Restiaceae and Eriocauleae), often dimerous; perianth-whorls glumaceous (Restiaceae and Eriocauleae), developed as a calyx and corolla (Xyrideae and Commelinaceae); capsule superior, bilocular or trilocular with loculicidal dehiscence; ovule orthotropous, the embryo (βλάστη) therefore opposite to (ἐναντίος) the base of the seed. Plants with habit of grasses (Restiaceae, Eriocauleae and Xyrideae), or succulent herbs (Commelinaceae).

Families.
1. Restiaceae.
2. Eriocauleae.
3. Xyrideae.
4. Commelinaceae.

Series III.   Spadiciflorae.

Inflorescence a spadix or panicle with thick branches (Cyclanthaceae), usually enveloped in a large sometimes petaloid spathe (Aroideae); bracts small or wanting; perianth never petaloid, usually inconspicuous or abortive (Aroideae, Pandaneae, Typhaceae, Cyclanthaceae); flowers frequently unisexual; fruit always superior and often very large (Pandaneae and Palmae); seed usually large or very large with copious endosperm, except in Lemnaceae and Naiadaceae; embryo small straight. Plants mostly large and robust, with a strong usually aerial stem and many large leaves with the lamina broad branched or apparently pinnate or flabelliform (Aroideae, Palmae, Cyclanthaceae) and with a stalk and sheath; without a stalk and very long and narrow (Pandaneae). The Lemnaceae have small branched leafless floating stems (vegetative rhachis) usually with true dependent roots. The Naiadaceae are branched submerged plants with slender stalks and long leaves; the Lemnaceae and Naiadaceae were formerly grouped together as Centrospermae from the central position of the seed.

Families.
1. Aroideae, including Lemnaceae.
2. Pandaneae.
3. Typhaceae.
4. Cyclanthaceae.
5. Palmae.
6. Naiadaceae.

Series IV.   Glumiflorae.

Inflorescence a spike or panicle without a spathe; flowers very small and inconspicuous concealed among closely crowded dry bracts (glumes or paleae); perianth wanting or replaced by hair-like structures or scales; fruit superior small dry 1-seeded indehiscent; embryo within the base of the endosperm and very small (Cyperaceae) or by the side of the endosperm, largely developed and with a scutellum (Gramineae). Plants with subterranean elongated persistent rhizomes; aerial shoots erect with long slender internodes and long narrow foliage-leaves in two or three rows (Gramineae).

Families.
1. Cyperaceae.
2. Gramineae.

Series V.   Scitamineae.

Flowers trimerous and zygomorphous or asymmetrical; both perianth-whorls or the inner only petaloid (Zingibereae and Canneae); posterior stamen of the inner whorl suppressed (Museae), but the only fertile one in the other two families has only a half anther, the others being developed as petaloid staminodes (Figs. 367—369); fruit inferior, a trilocular berry or capsule; endosperm wanting, perisperm copious. Usually handsome herbaceous shrub-like plants, often large in Museae, growing from a persistent rhizome with large leaves usually differentiated into a broad lamina, stalk and sheath.

Families. 1. Museae.
2. Zingibereae.
3. Canneae. (Maranteae.)

Series VI. Gynandrae.

The entire flower is zygomorphous in its early and in its matured state ; by torsion of the long inferior ovary in Orchideae the anterior side of the developed flower is usually posterior ; the two trimerous perianth-whorls are petaloid, the posterior leaf of the inner whorl (labellum) usually spurred ; of the six typical stamens of the two whorls the anterior only are developed, and in the Orchideae (with the exception of Cypripedium) only the anterior stamen of the outer whorl is fertile and has large anthers, the two obliquely anterior stamens of the inner whorl forming small staminodes ; but it is these which are fertile in *Cypripedium*, while the anterior stamen of the outer whorl forms a large staminode ; the case is the same in Apostasieae, or the three anterior stamens are fertile ; the filaments of the fertile and sterile stamens coalesce with the three styles to form a gynostemium ; pollen in single grains, tetrads, masses or pollinia ; ovary inferior unilocular with parietal placentas (Orchideae), or trilocular with central placentas (Apostasieae) ; ovule anatropous ; seeds very numerous and small without endosperm ; embryo undifferentiated. Small herbs or shrubby plants ; tropical Orchideae often epiphytic with peculiar aerial roots ; our native species are perennial with underground rhizomes or tubers ; some Orchideae are saprophytes and destitute of chlorophyll, and some have no roots (*Epipogum, Corallorhiza*).

Families. 1. Orchideae.
2. Apostasieae.

The Burmanniaceae with cymose inflorescence, three or six fertile epipetalous stamens, a free tripartite style and unilocular or trilocular inferior ovary, are connected with the Gynandrae by their small seeds without endosperm and their undifferentiated embryo ; some of these plants, which are usually of small size, are also saprophytes and destitute of chlorophyll.

Series VII. Helobiae.

Flowers actinomorphous with more or fewer whorls than the typical number in Monocotyledons; gynaeceum of three or more monomerous ovaries with one or more seeds ; ovary in Hydrocharideae inferior; seeds with little or no endosperm. Marsh or water plants, dioecious or polygamous in Hydrocharideae.

Families. 1. Juncagineae.
2. Alismaceae.
3. Hydrocharideae, with Vallisnerieae and *Stratiotes*.

B. DICOTYLEDONS.

The ripe *seed* of the Dicotyledons contains either a large endosperm and a small embryo, as in the Euphorbiaceae, *Coffea*, *Myristica*, the Umbelliferae, Ampelideae, Polygonaceae, some Caesalpinieae, etc., or the embryo is comparatively large and the endosperm occupies but a small space, as in the Plumbagineae, Labiatae, Asclepiadeae and many others, or lastly the endosperm is wanting, and the embryo alone fills the space enclosed by the seed-coat, in which case the mature embryo often reaches a very considerable size, as in *Aesculus, Quercus, Castanea, Juglans, Cucurbita, Tropaeolum, Phaseolus, Faba*; in small seeds however it is of proportional size, as in the Cruciferae, Compositae, Rosiflorae, etc.   The absence of endosperm is generally

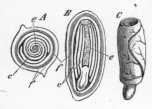

due to its displacement by the rapid growth of the embryo before the seed reaches maturity; it is only in a few cases, as in *Tropaeolum* and *Trapa*, that the endosperm is rudimentary from the first; in Nymphae-aceae and Piperaceae the embryo and the endosperm surrounding it continue small, the rest of the space inside the seed-coat being filled with perisperm.

FIG. 374. *Chimonanthus fragans. A* transverse section of the fruit before it is quite ripe. *B* longitudinal section of the same. *f* the thin pericarp, *e* remains of the endosperm, *c* cotyledons. *C* embryo taken from the seed, showing the cotyledons wrapped round each other with the extremity of the root below.

The *embryo* in parasites and saprophytes destitute of chlorophyll and with small seeds is usually very small and continues undifferentiated till the seed is ripe; in *Monotropa* it contains only from five to nine cells, and even in *Pyrola secunda* which contains chlorophyll it has only from eight to sixteen cells (Hofmeister); the ripe seeds of the Orobanchaceae [1], Balanophoreae and Cytineae [2], etc., contain a very small undifferentiated embryo in the form of a roundish mass of cellular tissue; the embryo of *Cuscuta* is indeed comparatively large and long and has a root [3], but its root is remarkable for showing no sign of a root-cap.   The embryo of some species of *Cuscuta* also has no rudiments of leaves.   *Viscum* on the other hand, one of the Loranthaceae, a parasite but with abundance of chlorophyll, has a large and well-developed embryo.   In plants also that are not parasitic the differentiation of the organs in the embryo is sometimes imperfect.   The embryo of *Utricularia* [4] for instance shows no rudiment of a root; as the plant subsequently developes no roots, it behaves in this respect in exactly the same way as *Salvinia*, which is also a water-plant (p. 234) and forms no rudimentary root in the embryonic stage.   On the other hand the embryo of *Utricularia* is provided with a large number (11–13) of rudimentary leaves of a peculiar character.

If the embryo in a ripe seed is differentiated, as it usually is, it consists of an axis and two opposite first leaves, between which the axis terminates as a naked vegetative cone, as in *Cucurbita* or sometimes as a bud with several leaves, as in *Phaseolus, Faba* (Fig. 376), *Quercus*, etc.; instead of two opposite cotyledons a whorl of three leaves is not unfrequently found in plants which normally have only two (*Phaseolus, Quercus, Amygdalus* and many others) [5].   The opposite cotyledons are usually of similar form and of the same size; but in *Trapa* one is much smaller than the other, and there are even isolated cases in which there is only one cotyledon; this is the case in

---

[1] Koch, Ueber d. Entw. d. Samens von *Orobanche* (Jahrb. f. wiss. Bot. XI).   On *Cuscuta* see Hanstein in Bot. Abhandl. Bd. II. Heft 3.

[2] Solms-Laubach, Ueber d. Bau d. Samen in d. Familien d. Rafflesiaceae u. Hydnoraceae (Bot. Ztg. 1874).

[3] The root performs its functions for a short time only, that is only until the seedling plant has succeeded in finding a host; then the root and the whole of the lower part of the plant dies off, and the rest of the plant lives on its host without any connection with the ground.

[4] Kamienski, Vergl. Unters. ü. d. Utricularieen (Bot. Ztg. 1877, p. 701).

[5] For numerous other cases see Bot. Ztg. 1869, p. 875.

Ranunculus Ficaria[1], where it is sheathing below, and in *Carum Bulbocastanum*, in which, as Hegelmaier[2] has shown, the *pseudo-monocotyledonous* form of the embryo, that is the presence of an apparently single terminal cotyledon, is due to the almost complete abortion of one cotyledon, the other being usually lateral in its origin. A similar explanation probably applies to *Ranunculus Ficaria* also, and to *Bulbocapnos*, a section of *Corydalis*. The two cotyledons usually form much the largest part of the mature embryo, so that the axis appears as a small conical

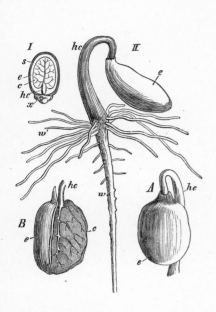

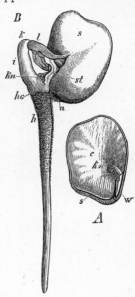

FIG. 375. *Ricinus communis. I* the ripe seed cut through longitudinally. *II* the young plant with the cotyledons still fixed in the endosperm, as shown more distinctly in *A* and *B. s* the seed-coat, *e* endosperm, *c* cotyledon, *hc* hypocotyl, *w* primary root, *w'* its secondary roots, *x* caruncle characteristic of the Euphorbiaceae.

FIG. 376. *Vicia Faba. A* a seed after removal of one of the cotyledons, the other *c* being retained; *w* extremity of the root, *kn* plumule, *s* seed-coat. *B* seed germinating; *s* seed-coat, *l* a lobe of the seed-coat torn away, *n* hilum, *st* stalk of a cotyledon, *k* curvature of the epicotyledonary portion of the axis, *i*, *hc* the very short hypocotyl, *h* the primary root, *ws* its tip, *Kn* bud axillary to one of the cotyledons.

appendage between them; this is most striking when the embryo attains a very considerable absolute size in a seed without endosperm and the cotyledons swell up into two thick fleshy bodies, as in *Aesculus, Castanea, Quercus* (Fig. 379), *Amygdalus, Vicia Faba, Phaseolus, Bertholletia excelsa* and many others; but in most cases the cotyledons are thin and resemble shortly stalked foliage-leaves of simple form, as in Cruciferae, Euphorbiaceae and *Tilia*, in which last the lamina has from three to five lobes; they often have their inner faces laid flat on one another (Figs. 375, 376), but are sometimes folded or wrinkled, as in *Theobroma* with thick cotyledons, *Acer*, the Convolvulaceae and others with thin ones; they are less often wound spirally round one another (convolute) (Fig. 374).

The axis of the embryo beneath the cotyledons is usually of an elongate conical shape, and in this form is termed the *radicle* in books of descriptive botany; but the

---

[1] Irmisch, Beitr. z. vergl. Morphol. d. Pflanzen, Halle, 1854, p. 12.
[2] Vergl. Untersuchungen, Stuttgart, 1875.

upper and usually the larger part of the fusiform body consists of the hypocotyledonary portion of the stem (*hypocotyl*), and it is only the lower, posterior, often very short terminal piece which is the rudiment of the primary root (Fig. 377); in the tissue of this latter the first rudiments of the secondary roots may sometimes be distinguished, as in *Cucurbita*, and according to Reinke in *Impatiens*.

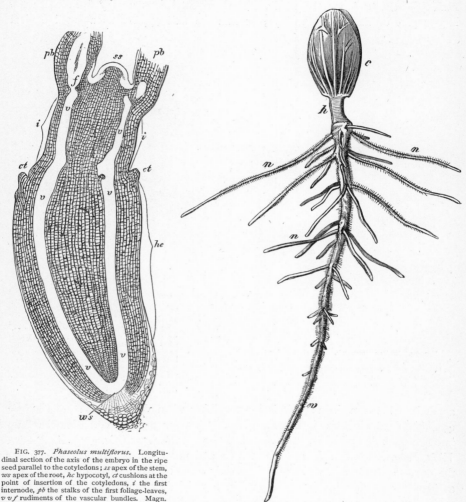

FIG. 377. *Phaseolus multiflorus*. Longitudinal section of the axis of the embryo in the ripe seed parallel to the cotyledons; *ss* apex of the stem, *ws* apex of the root, *hc* hypocotyl, *ct* cushions at the point of insertion of the cotyledons, *i* the first internode, *pb* the stalks of the first foliage-leaves, *v v f* rudiments of the vascular bundles. Magn. about 30 times.

FIG. 378. *Ricinus communis*. Young plant; *w* the primary root, *n* secondary roots, *h* hypocotyl, *c* cotyledons.

Germination.   After the seed-coat or, in dry indehiscent fruits, the pericarp has been ruptured by the swelling of the endosperm or the cotyledons, germination usually begins with the elongation of the hypocotyl and the consequent protrusion of the root from the seed; the root then begins to grow rapidly, and usually reaches a considerable length and forms secondary roots in acropetal succession, while the cotyledons and the plumule remain still in the seed (Figs. 375, 376, 377, 378).

Thick fleshy cotyledons usually remain in the seed during germination, and perish when all their food-material has been withdrawn from them, as in *Phaseolus multi-florus, Vicia Faba* (Fig. 376), and *Quercus* (Fig. 379); in this case the stalks of the cotyledons elongate so much, that the plumule between them is pushed out of the seed (Fig. 379) and then grows erect, so that the seed-coat with the cotyledons looks like a lateral appendage of the axis of the embryo. But usually the cotyledons, especially if

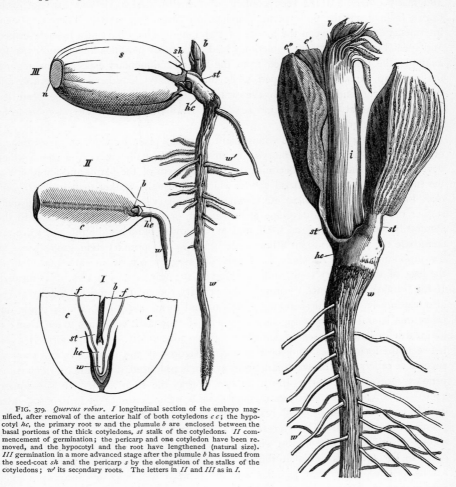

FIG. 379. *Quercus robur.* *I* longitudinal section of the embryo mag-nified, after removal of the anterior half of both cotyledons *c c*; the hypo-cotyl *hc*, the primary root *w* and the plumule *b* are enclosed between the basal portions of the thick cotyledons, *st* stalk of the cotyledons. *II* com-mencement of germination; the pericarp and one cotyledon have been re-moved, and the hypocotyl and the root have lengthened (natural size). *III* germination in a more advanced stage after the plumule *b* has issued from the seed-coat *sh* and the pericarp *s* by the elongation of the stalks of the cotyledons; *w'* its secondary roots. The letters in *II* and *III* as in *I*.

FIG. 380. Almond germinating; one of the cotyledons *c' c'* dividing; the letters as in figure 379; *i* the first internode very strongly developed.

they are thin, are destined to further development and form the first foliage-leaves of the plant; in order to liberate them and the plumule that lies between them from the seed, the hypocotyl lengthens considerably, forming thereby at first a curve convex upwards (Fig. 375), because the cotyledons are still detained in the seed while its lower end is fixed in the ground by the root; but ultimately a final elongation of its lower portion

[2] G g

draws the upper end with the cotyledons hanging from it out of the seed, and raises them above the ground; then the axis straightens itself and the cotyledons expand in the air, and the plumule now in an advanced state of development shoots up from between them. The cotyledons thus brought into the light usually increase rapidly and considerably in size and form the first green leaves of the plant, which are of simple form in *Cucurbita*, the Cruciferae, *Acer*, the Convolvulaceae, Euphorbiaceae and many others. If the seed contains endosperm, the cotyledons are not withdrawn from it, till the endosperm is exhausted (Figs. 375, 378). There are some intermediate forms between the modes of germination which have now been described, and special conditions of life sometimes lead to peculiar modifications; in *Trapa*, for example, the primary root, which from the first is rudimentary especially as regards the root-cap, remains undeveloped, while the hypocotyl lengthens considerably and turns its lower end upwards in the water at the bottom of which the seed has germinated, and at an early period sends out rows of numerous lateral roots to fix the plant in the ground.

The *increase in size* of the young plant may take place by vigorous development of the primary axis of the embryo; as this grows (usually erect), the shoot which developes from the plumule becomes the primary stem of the plant, and lengthens at the summit and produces lateral shoots which are usually weaker than itself (*Helianthus, Vicia, Populus, Impatiens,* etc.); when the primary stem is persistent, it usually sooner or later ceases to develope at its summit, or the lateral shoots nearest to the summit become as strong as itself, and as the lower branches die off and leave the stem bare the plant forms an arborescent head; or the primary stem grows erect as a sympodium (*Tilia, Ricinus*); or lateral shoots grow out at an early period from the base of the primary stem, and develope as strongly as it, and a shrub is formed. If the primary stem grows vigorously, the primary root of the embryo usually grows also vigorously in the descending direction, and forms a *tap-root*, which sends out numerous lateral roots in acropetal succession, so long as it continues to lengthen; if its growth in length ceases at some later time, adventitious roots are formed on it between the former ones, and these also grow vigorously and produce lateral roots of successive orders. In this way a large root-system is produced, the centre of which is the primary root of the embryo, and it lasts as long as the stem itself. By subsequent growth in thickness the primary stem as well as its branches assumes the form of a slender upright cone, the base of which rests on the base of the inverted cone formed by the primary root, which has also increased in thickness. While the mode of growth thus simply described prevails almost without exception in the Coniferae, many deviations occur in Dicotyledons similar to those which have been already noticed in Monocotyledons. The primary axis together with the primary root may die away soon after germination or at the end of the first period of vegetation, while the shoots axillary to the cotyledons or the higher leaves continue the life of the plant; for instance a strong lateral root is formed from the hypocotyl of *Dahlia variabilis* at the termination of the first vegetative period of the seedling plant, and then enlarges and becomes tuberous; the primary root-system and the epicotyledonary portion of the axis disappear, and there remains only the new root, the hypocotyl and the buds axillary to the cotyledons, to continue the vegetation. The arrangement is still more striking in *Ranunculus Ficaria*, where after the development of the primary root a tuberous lateral root enclosed in a coleorhiza is formed beneath the primary axis of the embryo, and persists with it, while the primary root and the first leaves perish. Among the numerous cases of this kind may be mentioned also *Physalis Alkekengi, Mentha arvensis, Bryonia alba, Polygonum amphibium* and *Lysimachia vulgaris* [1]. The formation of *bulbs* is not unknown in Dicotyledons, as in some species of *Oxalis*, though it does not occur so frequently as in Monocotyledons; *tubers* occur more frequently as swellings of underground branches, stolons or thick or slender rhizomes. The great majority of Dicotyledons are subterranean perennial plants, and send up periodically leafy and flowering shoots which die down at the close of each period of vegetation. In all such cases, if the primary root-system of the young plant perishes, new roots are repeatedly produced from portions of the stem; and the power which most Dicotyledons possess of forming roots from the stem when kept moist and in the dark permits their propagation from almost any branch or portion of a branch. Some, as *Hedera Helix*, climb by means of roots issuing constantly from the stem which is slender and needs support; others like *Fragaria* send out *runners* to a distance, the bud on which developes into a new plant, and the stem thus produced sends roots into the ground, and so on. The order of development of new roots from the stem is generally acropetal throughout the class, but they usually make their appearance at some distance behind the growing bud; in many Cactaceae however they may arise close to it.

The *branching*. In connection with the branching of Dicotyledons it is necessary to distinguish between radial and dorsiventral organs. In radial organs the normal monopodial branching is axillary; the lateral shoots arise in the angle formed by the median plane of the leaf and the internode above it; at least one lateral shoot is formed in the axil of each leaf on the vegetative stem, though many of these axillary buds remain latent. Other shoots are sometimes formed in a longitudinal row above the true original axillary shoot, as for instance above the axils of the foliage-leaves in *Aristolochia Sipho, Gleditschia* and *Lonicera*, above the axils of the cotyledons in *Juglans regia* and of the developed cotyledon in *Trapa*. In woody plants the axillary bud destined to live through the winter is often so grown round by the base of the leaf-stalk that it cannot be seen till after the fall of the leaf, as in the case in *Rhus typhinum, Virgilia lutea, Platanus*, etc.; these are termed *intrapetiolar buds*. Besides the ordinary axillary branching a few cases of lateral and monopodial but extra-axillary branching are known in Dicotyledons; to these belongs the formation of the tendrils of *Vitis* and *Ampelopsis*, which appear according to Nägeli and Schwendener beneath the growing point of the mother-shoot, opposite to and a little later than the youngest leaf; in *Asclepias syriaca* and some other plants a vegetative lateral shoot is formed beneath the terminal inflorescence between the insertions of the foliage-leaves, which themselves subtend axillary shoots.

In dorsiventral organs on the other hand the branching is usually extra-axillary [2]. Branched dorsiventral organs which are of very common occurrence in Thallophytes, Muscineae and Ferns are rare in the vegetative region of the Dicotyledons. The

---

[1] The above is taken from Irmisch's full accounts in his Beitr. z. Vgl. Morphol. d. Pflanzen, Halle, 1854 and 1856, in Bot. Zeit. 1861 and elsewhere.

[2] Goebel, Ueber d. Verzweigung dorsiventr. Sprosse (Arb. d. Bot. Inst. z. Würzburg, Bd. II, Heft I).

Utricularieae mentioned above (p. 446) are dorsiventral plants. The stem has a row of leaves on each of its lateral faces, and on its dorsal face lateral buds of various degrees of development, which are not therefore placed in the axils of leaves. Dorsiventral organs are less rare in the flowering region of the plant, in the inflorescence; they occur in some Urticaceae (see p. 410), which have the flowers only on the dorsal side of the axis of the inflorescence, and in the Boragineae, in which the inflorescences have leaves on their lateral faces, as in *Utricularia*, while a flower grows above each leaf on the dorsal face of the inflorescence, as in *Anchusa*.

The not infrequent absence of bracts in radial inflorescences must not be placed in the same category as the above cases of extra-axillary branching; in the latter there are large leaves near the extra-axillary lateral branches, in the former case, as in the Cruciferae and in the capitula of many Compositae, the formation of leaves on the branching axis which bears the flowers or the branches of the inflorescence is entirely suppressed, and there are no leaf-axils near which the branch can arise; yet they grow as if there were leaves actually there. It will be well to refer to what was said above (page 410), about this change in the conditions of the branching in passing from the vegetative to the floral region of the plant, and on the frequent displacement of the bracts upon their axillary shoot.

Adventitious shoots are of rare occurrence in Dicotyledons, as in Phanerogams generally; those are well known which are formed exogenously in the indentations on the margins of the leaves of *Bryophyllum calycinum*, and afterwards separate from the plant and are capable of a further development like gemmae; adventitious buds are sometimes found according to Peterhausen[1] in *Begonia coriacea* in the form of small bulbs on the surface of the peltate leaf, where the primary veins radiate. On the adventitious shoots on the leaves of *Utricularia* see Pringsheim[2]. Adventitious shoots are more common on roots, as in *Linaria vulgaris*, *Cirsium arvense*, *Populus tremula*, *Pyrus Malus* and many other plants according to Hofmeister. The shoots which spring from the bark of the stems of older trees are not necessarily adventitious, since the numerous dormant buds of woody plants may often be capable of development after having been long hidden out of sight.

The *leaves* of Dicotyledons display a greater variety of position and form than those of all other classes of plants put together. The usual whorl of two cotyledonary leaves in the seedling is either continued in decussate pairs, or passes into two rows of alternate leaves, or into whorls of several members, or into spiral arrangements with very various divergences. The more simple arrangements, especially that of decussate dimerous whorls, are usually constant in entire families; the more complicated are usually inconstant. Axillary shoots usually begin with a pair of opposite or alternate leaves, which stand right and left of the median plane of the subtending leaf.

It is simply impossible to give a sketch in a brief space of the forms even of foliage-leaves, not to speak of scale-leaves or cataphyllary leaves on the underground parts of stems and the scale-leaves which envelope peristent buds, or of bracts and

---

[1] Beitr. z. Entw. d. Brutknospen, Hameln, 1869, where various instances are discussed of axillary shoots in Dicotyledons which develope as deciduous gemmae, as in *Polygonum viviparum*, *Saxifraga granulata*, *Dentaria bulbifera*, *Ranunculus Ficaria*.

[2] Zur Morphol. d. Utricularien (Monatsber. d. k. Akad. d. Wiss. Berlin, Feb. 1869).

floral leaves; a few facts only can be mentioned here which are peculiar to or characteristic of the foliage-leaves of Dicotyledons. These are usually differentiated into
a slender stalk (*petiole*) and a flat blade (*lamina*) which is very often branched, that
is, lobed, pinnated, compound or divided; where the surface is not broken up in this
way, the tendency to branching is shown by indentations, teeth or notches at the
margin. The branching of the lamina is monopodial. The sheathing amplexicaul
base, such as occurs for instance in the Umbelliferae, is not common among the
Dicotyledons, and *stipules* occur more frequently in its place. Among special
peculiarities must be mentioned the not infrequent cohesion of opposite leaves into
a lamella which is pierced by the stem (*connate-perfoliate* leaves), as in *Lamium amplexi-
caule, Dipsacus fullonum,* some species of *Silphium, Lonicera Caprifolium,* and some
species of *Eucalyptus,* and the extension downwards of portions of the lamina on
the right and left of the insertion of the leaf forming wings on the stem (*decurrent*
leaves) in *Verbascum thapsiforme, Onopordon,* etc.; the not uncommon *peltate* leaf is
scarcely found in any other class in so marked a form as in *Tropaeolum, Victoria
regia* and some other Dicotyledons. The power possessed by the Dicotyledons to
develope their foliage-leaves into organs with a great variety of functions in accordance
with varied conditions of life is shown very strikingly in the frequent occurrence of
leaf-tendrils and *leaf-spines,* and still more in the formation of the *pitchers* of *Nepenthes,
Cephalotus* and *Sarracenia.*

The *venation* of all foliage leaves except the thick leaves of succulent plants is
distinguished by the numerous veins which project on the under surface, and by their
numerous curvilinear anastomoses formed by more slender vascular bundles running
through the mesophyll. The mid-rib, which divides the leaf usually into two symmetrical, but sometimes into two unsymmetrical portions, gives off lateral veins to the
right and left; and not unfrequently one, two or three stout veins start from the base
of the lamina right and left of the median line, and like it give off lateral veins. The
entire system of projecting veins in a foliage-leaf is a monopodial branch-system
developed in the same plane, the intervals between the branches being filled with a
green mesophyll, in which the anastomoses form a small-meshed network; still
slenderer bundles are usually formed inside the meshes and end blindly in the mesophyll. The projecting veins are generally wanting in the scale-like or membranous
cataphyllary leaves, in hypsophyllary leaves and in the leaves of the floral envelopes;
their venation is simpler and more like that of Monocotyledons.

It may be shown that the scales [1], which usually cover up the buds of woody
Dicotyledons during their resting period, are only forms of foliage-leaves arrested at
various stages in their development. Generally the rudiment of the lamina is only
slightly, while the lower part, the base of the leaf, is more strongly developed. That
they are only peculiar modifications of rudimentary foliage-leaves appears from the
fact, that the rudiments which normally become scales (bud-scales, etc.) may be made
by artificial means to develope into ordinary foliage-leaves.

The *flower* [2]. In the great majority of Dicotyledons the parts of the flower

---

[1] Goebel, Beitr. z. Morphol. u. Physiol. d. Blattes (Bot. Ztg. 1880). [See also note and reference
to Bower's investigations on p. 314.]

[2] 'The following floral diagrams are designed partly from my own observations and partly from
the statements of Payer and of Döll in his Flora d. Groszherzogthum Baden. The figures placed

are arranged in whorls, and the flowers are therefore *cyclic*; it is only in a comparatively small number of families, Ranunculaceae, Magnoliaceae, Calycanthaceae, Nymphaeaceae, Nelumboneae, that they are all or some of them arranged spirally (acyclic or hemicyclic).

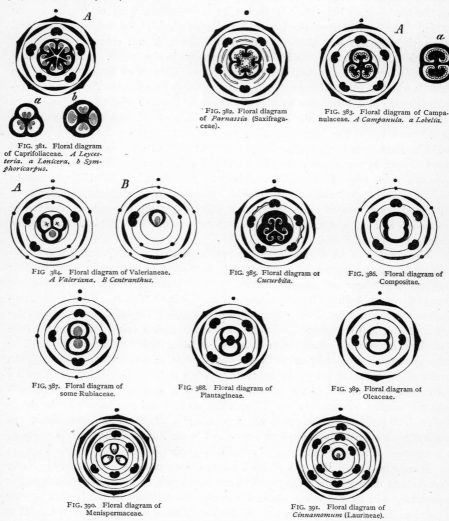

FIG. 381. Floral diagram of Caprifoliaceae. *A Leycesteria.* a *Lonicera.* b *Symphoricarpus.*

FIG. 382. Floral diagram of *Parnassia* (Saxifragaceae).

FIG. 383. Floral diagram of Campanulaceae. *A Campanula.* a *Lobelia.*

FIG 384. Floral diagram of Valerianeae. *A Valeriana. B Centranthus.*

FIG. 385. Floral diagram of *Cucurbita.*

FIG. 386. Floral diagram of Compositae.

FIG. 387. Floral diagram of some Rubiaceae.

FIG. 388. Floral diagram of Plantagineae.

FIG. 389. Floral diagram of Oleaceae.

FIG. 390. Floral diagram of Menispermaceae.

FIG. 391. Floral diagram of *Cinnamomum* (Laurineae).

The whorls of cyclic flowers are usually pentamerous, less frequently tetramerous, and both kinds are met with in the same groups of allied plants; trimerous and dimerous floral whorls or combinations of dimerous and tetramerous whorls are much less common than pentamerous whorls, and are usually characteristic of smaller groups in the natural system. Pentamerous or tetramerous flowers have usually

beneath the diagrams are intended to indicate the number and cohesion of the carpels and also the placentation of plants whose diagram is in other respects the same.' Sachs, IV. Ed.

four whorls, constituting calyx, corolla, androecium and gynaeceum, and any multiplication of the whorls is almost entirely confined to the androecium; in trimerous and dimerous flowers, the number of the whorls is much more variable, and two or more whorls may be devoted to one series of organs.

The corolla is not unfrequently wanting, and in that case the flower is said to be *apetalous*. If the calyx and corolla are both present, they almost always have the same number of parts (*Papaver* is an exception); but the number of their whorls varies; the calyx for instance may consist of two dimerous decussate whorls, the corolla of one whorl of four members, as in the Cruciferae. If the androecium and the perianth, whether consisting of calyx only or of calyx and corolla, are present in the same flower, they generally have the same number of parts, and the flowers are *isostemonous*, but there may often be more, seldom fewer stamens than the parts of the perianth, and then the flowers are *anisostemonous*[1]. In flowers with pentamerous and tetramerous whorls the number of the carpels is usually less than five or four; in those with dimerous or trimerous whorls or with the parts arranged in spirals there is often a larger number of carpels.

It will be seen from these few remarks that the conditions of number and position in the flowers of Dicotyledons are very various, and cannot, as in most Monocotyledons, be referred to a single type; even the attempt to assign different types to as many larger groups is attended with considerable uncertainty, for in many cases we do not possess the knowlege of development necessary for referring particular floral formulae to more general ones; moreover the excessive application of the spiral theory of phyllotaxis to cyclic flowers has hindered the true understanding of the latter, and raised doubts where without that theory there would have been none.

The formula *Sn Pn Stn* $(+n+..)$ *Cn* $(-m)$ may be given for a large majority of Dicotyledons; it is true for most pentamerous and truly tetramerous flowers and for octamerous flowers like *Michauxia*, so that $n = 5$ or 4 (or 8); in the androecium an indefinite number of (alternating) whorls is assumed *Stn* $(+n+..)$ in order to include the large number of flowers in which the androecium contains more than one whorl (Fig. 392); the symbol *Cn* $(-m)$ is meant to indicate that there are often less than 5 or 4 (or 8) carpels present, *m* meaning any value from o to *n*. In the larger part of the Gamopetalae and in other species

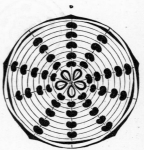

FIG. 392. Floral diagram of *Aquilegia* (Ranunculaceae)

also there are very often only two carpels, which are placed in the median line one posterior and one anterior; on the supposition that the gynaeceum has typically five alternating members and has only become dimerous by abortion, if one is median and anterior, the other must be obliquely posterior; a similar difficulty occurs sometimes in the trimerous and monomerous gynaeceum. It would require too much space to explain the reasons which determine many botanists to consider the formula given above as valid also for the gynaeceum of such flowers as these; we will only say that in the

---

[1] See what was said above on page 418 on diplostemonous and obdiplostemonous flowers.

very different families and orders which have usually less than five carpels, species and genera with the typical five carpels do occur.

The diagrams in Figs. 381–403 offer a selection of cases which, if no further attention is paid to the consideration just mentioned, will come under the general formula in its more simple expression $Sn \, Pn \, St \, n \, Cn \, (-m)$. That the vacant places marked with dots in the three outer whorls correspond to aborted members, in the sense already frequently explained, can scarcely be doubted after comparison with nearly allied forms, even in cases where those members are so absolutely wanting that no traces are to be seen of them even in early stages of the development of the flower; this remark applies also where the carpels fall short of the typical number. But there are other cases in which, as in *Rhus* (Fig. 393), certain members, in the case of *Rhus* two out of three carpels which show themselves, disappear in the course of further development, two developing only as style or stigma, and one alone is perfect. *Crozophora tinctoria* (Fig. 394) is particularly instructive on these

FIG. 393.   Floral diagram of *Rhus*
(Anacardiaceae).

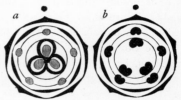

FIG. 394.   Floral diagram of *Crozophora*.   *a* female,
b male flower (Euphorbiaceae).

FIG. 395.   Floral diagram of Pentamerous flower of
Ericaceae and Epacrideae.

FIG. 396.   Floral diagram of *Aesculus*
(Hippocastaneae).

points; its flowers become unisexual because in the female flower the stamens develope as sterile staminodes, the first step to abortion, while in the male flowers the three carpels are replaced by three fertile stamens (Payer).

In the introduction to the Angiosperms attention was called to the interposition of a whorl of stamens between the members of an original whorl, and it was mentioned that in obdiplostemonous flowers according to some observers the epipetalous stamens are formed before the episepalous. Fig. 395 for example shows an obdiplostemonous flower. The shaded stamens are the epipetalous ones, and they stand further towards the outside than the episepalous ones. It is the same in most Gruinales, among which however the Balsamineae have only the typical five stamens; but the Lineae and the genus *Erodium* show five more rudimentary stamens interposed between these, while in *Peganum Harmala* and *Monsonia* the members of the interposed and more exterior whorl are double in number. The arrangement in the Æsculineae is of especial interest in this respect, because the interposed staminal whorl remains incomplete in some of its families (Acerineae, Hippocastaneae, Fig. 396), so that the sum total of the stamens is no multiple of the typical fundamental number, which in this case is five. Among pentamerous flowers the Lythrarieae, Crassulaceae and Papilionaceae, among tetramerous the Œnothereae may be mentioned as exemplifying the interposition of a complete staminal whorl.

One of the most remarkable deviations from the ordinary conditions is found in several families of the Dicotyledons, in which the single staminal whorl is *superposed*

FIG. 397. Floral diagram of Primulaceae.

FIG. 398. Floral diagram of *Vitis* (Ampelideae).

on the corolline whorl, as in Fig. 397, 398, and also in the Rhamneae, Celastrineae, the pentandrous Hypericineae, *Tilia* and many obdiplostemonous flowers; Pfeffer[1] discovered that the two superposed whorls in the Ampelideae are formed separately and in acropetal order, but that in the Primulaceae they appear as five protuberances, each of which forms a stamen and afterwards produces a petal on its outer side. In these cases there is no sufficient ground for the assumption that an alternating whorl has disappeared between the two superposed whorls; in the other cases however this assumption is justified or at least very probable. Thus in the series of Caryo-

FIG. 399. Floral diagram of *Scleranthus* (Illecebraceae).

FIG. 400. Floral diagram of *Phytolacca* (Phytolaccaceae).

FIG. 401. Floral diagram of *Celosia* (Amarantaceae).

phyllineae families, genera and species occur in which the corolla is wanting, and the stamens are superposed on the sepals; since in the same alliance there are plants with corollas, we may assume that where these are wanting, they are abortive[2]; the diagram of these plants is made more complicated by an evident tendency to a doubling of the stamens (Figs. 399, 400) and even of the carpels.

When there are more stamens in a flower than sepals or petals, this may be the result, as has been already pointed out, of an increase in the number of the staminal whorls, as is shown in Fig. 392, or by interposition of new stamens between those already formed, as in some Rosaceae (Fig. 404), or by an increase in the number of young stamens along with diminution in their size, as in *Potentilla* and *Rubus* (see p. 417), or by chorisis of the stamens, as shown in Fig. 399; these cases must

---

[1] Pfeffer, Zur Blüthenentwicklung d. Primulaceen u. Ampelideen in Pringsheim's Jahrb. VIII. p. 184.

[2] For another explanation see Eichler, Blüthendiagramme, II, p. 78.

be carefully distinguished from those in which the number of stamens is increased by the branching of the original stamens, a proceeding which occurs in various divisions of the Dicotyledons and is sometimes constant in entire families, as in the Dilleniaceae (Fig. 402) and Tiliaceae (Fig. 403), where each group of staminal symbols in the

FIG. 402. Floral diagram of *Candollea* (Dilleniaceae).

FIG. 403. Floral diagram of *Tilia americana* (Tiliaceae).

diagrams belongs to an original stamen ; here the number of the original stamens corresponds to that of the sepals and petals; but the former may be fewer, as in *Hypericum perforatum* with three bundles of stamens in a pentamerous flower, and then a multiplication of the staminal filaments is combined with a diminution of the typical number of the staminal leaves.

Branching is much rarer in the carpels than in the stamens. It is very distinctly shown in the Malvaceae where the typical number of the carpels is five, and they are often so developed, as in *Hibiscus*; but in many genera (*Malope, Malva, Althaea*, etc.) five rudiments of carpels are first formed in the shape of slight protuberances, each of which soon gives rise to a larger number of outgrowths lying side by side, and each of these produces a style and a one-seeded lobe of the peculiarly-formed gynaeceum[1].

These few remarks will be sufficient to show what variations are possible in the relations of number and position included under the formula $Sn\,Pn\,St\,n\,(+n+\,.\,.)\,Cn\,(-m)$, which, as has been already said, applies especially to flowers with pentamerous and true tetramerous whorls; with the latter may be placed flowers like *Michauxia* with octamerous whorls, and those with dimerous whorls, the Œnothereae especially, and among these *Epilobium* with the formula $S2 + 2P \times 4\,St4.4C4$, and *Circaea* with the formula $S2\,P2\,St2\,C2$; *Trapa* too with the formula $S2 + 2P \times 4\,St\,4\,C2$ should go with them. Though the calyx in *Epilobium* and *Trapa* is formed of two whorls, this apparent whorl of two decussate pairs of sepals is followed by the succeeding whorls exactly as if it were a true tetramerous whorl. But in other dimerous and tetramerous flowers there is a more considerable variation, inasmuch as two dimerous perianth-whorls developed like a tetramerous calyx are succeeded by a staminal whorl, which is superposed on this pseudo-whorl composed of two decussate pairs, as in *Urtica* and other Urticaceae and Proteaceae with the formula $S2 + 2St4\,C1$ (Fig. 282).

Among the dimerous and trimerous flowers of the orders Polycarpicae and Cruciflorae, where they are most perfectly developed, there is a tendency to devote more than one whorl to the formation of each of the series of organs, calyx, corolla,

---

[1] Payer, Organogénie, Taf. 6–8.

androecium and sometimes even the gynaeceum; this is expressed by the general formula, $Sp(+p+..) Pp(+p+..) Stp(+p+..) Cp(+p+..)$; e.g.

Fumariaceae: $S2 P2+2 St2+..C2$;

Berberideae:

$Epimedium \ S2+2P2+2St2+2C1$,

$Berberis \ S3+3P3+3St3+3C1$,

$Podophyllum \ S3 P3+3^2 St3^3+3 C1$;

Cruciferae $S2+2P \times 4St2+2^2C2(+2)$.

Many examples of this general formula are afforded by the family of the Menispermaceae, in which the whorls are sometimes trimerous, sometimes dimerous, sometimes even both dimerous and trimerous in the same flower, and in which almost any one of the series of organs may disappear by abortion[1].

There are other trimerous flowers besides those already mentioned which come under the general formula first proposed, $Sn Pn Stn(+n) Cn(-m)$, as *Rheum* with the formula $S3 P3 St3^2+3 C3$; but there are others again which seem to belong to a third-type, such as *Asarum* with the formula $S3 St3+6 C6$.

If the number of whorls in the androecium is considerably increased, it often happens that the number of members in the whorls is changed, and complicated alternations make their appearance; flowers of entirely different structure in other respects agree in this point, as is shown by the Papaveraceae on the one hand, and by the Cistineae and many Rosaceae (Fig. 404) on the other.

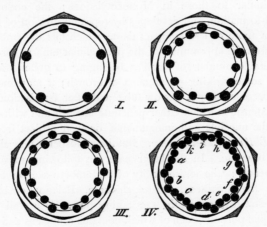

FIG. 404. Arrangement of the stamens in some Rosaceae. *I Agrimonia Eupatoria* and *Sibbaldia*. *II Agrimonia odorata*. *III* species of *Potentilla*. *IV Rubus Idaeus* (peculiar case), see p. 417.

In many Dicotyledons, as in Monocotyledons, the simplification of the flowers often goes so far that each consists only of an ovary with one or more stamens, or, when the flowers are unisexual, of a single ovary or of one or more stamens, the perianth being entirely wanting, as in the Piperaceae, or reduced to a cup-like structure, as in *Populus* and the female flower of the Cannabineae, or to hair-like scales between the sporophylls which represent different flowers, as in *Platanus*. Flowers of this kind are

---

[1] Payer, Organogénie, Taf. 45–49.—Eichler, Blüthendiagramme, II, p. 139, where the question hether the theory of abortion is applicable to this family is discussed at length.

usually very small, and generally closely crowded in inflorescences with many flowers, such as capitula, spikes and catkins. In some cases it may be a question whether we have to do with an inflorescence or with a single flower, as in the genus *Euphorbia*[1].

The development of the separate parts of the flower and the general form of the whole flower in its developed state in the Dicotyledons is so various, that scarcely any general statements can be made about them. Perigynous flowers are peculiar to Dicotyledons, as is also the hollowed axis of the inflorescence in the fig and in similar structures, as well as the cupule of some families, all of which are based on similar processes of growth.

The *ovules* show in the different divisions of the Dicotyledons all the varieties of structure which have been already mentioned in the introduction (p. 382); the nucellus, especially in the Gamopetalae, has often but one integument, which is then usually very thick before fertilisation; on the other hand the third integument, the aril, is much more common here than in the Monocotyledons; if there are two integuments, the outer one takes part in the formation of the micropyle, which is not the case in most Monocotyledons, and surrounds the entrance to it, the exostome. The ovules of some parasitic Dicotyledons are rudimentary; in many of the Balanophoreae they are reduced to a naked nucellus consisting of a few cells; in the Loranthaceae, where they spring from a free central placenta, they coalesce with the tissue of the floral axis in the inferior ovary.

The processes in the *embryo-sac*[2] of most Dicotyledons before and after fertilisation are similar to those in Monocotyledons; the endosperm is usually formed by free cell-formation, and developes by repeated division of the primary cells thus formed into a more or less compact tissue, which fills the embryo-sac either at an early period before the appearance of the pluricellular embryo, or some time after. In a very considerable number of families belonging to quite different groups the embryo-sac shows some striking phenomena of growth; it may lengthen out before fertilisation till it becomes only a narrow tube, and after fertilisation send out one or many vermiform extensions which either penetrate laterally and with destructive effect into the tissue of the nucellus and integuments, or even project free from the ovule as in *Pedicularis, Lathraea, Thesium*, etc. But the endosperm may also be formed by division of the embryo-sac. In the latter case the following variations have been observed by Hofmeister: 'the entire cavity of the embryo-sac serves as first cell of the endosperm in the Asarineae, Aristolochiaceae, Balanophoreae, Pyroleae, and Monotropeae, the first division of the sac taking place by a wall which separates it into two nearly equal portions, each of which contains a nucleus and produces at least two daughter-cells. In other cases the upper end of the embryo-sac constitutes the first cell of the endosperm, and appears immediately after the oosphere in it has been fertilised to be divided by a transverse wall into halves, the upper one of which is transformed into endosperm by a series of bipartitions, while no such cell-division takes place in the lower half in *Viscum, Thesium, Lathraea, Rhinanthus, Mazus*,

---

[1] The question which was for some time much debated, whether the 'cyathium' of *Euphorbia* should be regarded as an inflorescence or as a flower, must be considered to be decided in favour of the former view.

[2] Hofmeister in Jahrb. f. wiss. Bot. I, p. 185, and Abhandl. d. K. Sächs. Ges. d. Wiss. VI, p. 536. —Strasburger, Die Angiospermen u. d. Gymnospermen, and Ueber Zellbildung u. Zelltheilung.

Melampyrum and *Globularia.* The first cell of the endosperm fills the middle portion of the embryo-sac in *Veronica*, the Labiatae, *Nemophila*, *Pedicularis*, *Plantago*, *Campanula* and *Loasa*; it occupies the lower portion in *Loranthus*, *Acanthus*, *Catalpa*, *Hebenstreitia*, *Verbena* and *Vaccinium*.' In *Nymphaea*, *Nuphar* and *Ceratophyllum* the upper end of the embryo-sac is separated off from the rest of the cavity by a transverse wall soon after fertilisation, and the further formation of daughter-cells (endosperm) takes place only in that upper part which contained the egg-apparatus; but here the formation of endosperm so far differs from that in the plants enumerated above, that it commences with free cell-formation (Hofmeister).

By far the larger number of true parasites and saprophytes belong to the group of plants in which the endosperm is formed by division of the embryo-sac, with the exception of *Cuscuta* which produces it by free cell-formation.

Only slight traces of formation of endosperm are found in *Tropaeolum* and *Trapa*, according to Hofmeister.

The important points in the *formation of the embryo* in Dicotyledons have been already described in the introduction to the Angiosperms; it remains only to mention here that the seed in parasites destitute of chlorophyll and in saprophytes is 'ripe' before the embryo has passed beyond the condition of a roundish body of cellular tissue not yet differentiated externally, as in *Monotropa*, *Pyrola*, the Balanophoreae, Rafflesiaceae and *Orobanche*. There are some plants also which are not parasitic, in which the embryo is still but little developed by the time the seed is 'ripe' and is detached from the plant, and in which it is matured only after that time, as for example *Erigenia bulbosa*[1]. This recalls the circumstances described above in the case of *Gingko*.

The amount of variation in the degree of development of which the vegetative organs of Dicotyledons are capable may be illustrated here by the example of the Podostemaceae, a family of plants inhabiting tropical streams, the members of which often simulate the habit of Hepaticae. Fine plates of this highly interesting group are to be found in Tulasne's Monograph[2]; Cario[3] and especially Warming[4] have recently published researches into the history of development and the anatomy of some of the species. Warming found no stomata in those which he examined; the cells of *Tristicha* and other species contain peculiar concretions of silica. The roots of *Tristicha* have no root-cap; the species examined by Warming had the root-cap feebly developed and somewhat on one side; the roots are attached to the substratum by root-hairs and also by peculiar organs of adhesion which look like roots and are sometimes branched, but have no root-cap, are exogenous in origin and consist only of parenchyma; perhaps, as Warming suggests, they are roots modified in a peculiar manner. The leafy shoots are formed on the roots and in acropetal succession; they are endogenous in origin and their structure is dorsiventral. The leaves of *Tristicha hypnoides* are formed of one layer of cells and have no vascular bundle, and even in the stem the spiral vessels are destroyed as soon as they are formed. It is a remarkable fact, that the conditions here briefly mentioned are found also in many parasites or saprophytes; the endogenous origin of the leafy shoots in the

---

[1] Hegelmaier, Vgl. Unters. ii. Entw. dicotyler Keime, p. 144. Irmish gives a similar account of the seeds of *Ranunculus Ficaria* which are rarely matured.

[2] Tulasne, Monographia Podostemacearum (Archives du Muséum, VI, 1852).

[3] Anatomische Unters. d. *Tristicha hypnoides* (Bot. Ztg. 1881).

[4] Familien Podostemaceae, forste Afhandling: *Podostemon Ceratophyllum*, *Mniopsis Wedelliana*, *Mniopsis Glazioniana*. Vidensk. Selsk. Skr. 6. Rackke, with a summary in French, 1881.

roots occurs in *Monotropa Hypopitys*, and peculiar modifications of the roots like the organs of adhesion of the Podostemaceae occur in the parasitic Dicotyledons; hence we may conclude that in the Podostemaceae we have to do with retrogressively metamorphosed forms.

Histology[1]. As regards the histology of the Dicotyledons I confine myself here to some account of the behaviour of the vascular bundles and of secondary growth in thickness.

With the exception of a few water-plants of simple structure in which an axile vascular cylinder runs through the stem and is constantly developed at its apex as a cauline bundle, with which the bundles of the leaves which are of later formation afterwards become connected (*Hippuris, Aldrovanda, Ceratophyllum* and also *Trapa* partially), the general rule in Dicotyledons is that common bundles are first formed and their ascending limbs enter the stronger foliage-leaves usually in some numbers, where they run through the leaf-stalk and midrib beside[2] but usually separate from one another and give off bundles to form the venation in the lamina. The limbs which descend in the stem, the leaf-trace-bundles, generally pass downwards through several internodes, pushing in between the upper portions of older leaf-trace-bundles and sometimes dividing (Fig. 405), and ultimately laying themselves alongside the older bundles lower down and coalescing with them. In this process each bundle in the stem becomes twisted, as in *Iberis*, and always towards the same side, so that the bundles from leaves of different heights, which form a sympodium by their coalescence, ascend in a spiral line within the cortex; but they often run parallel to the axis of the stem, till they anastomose below with deeper lying bundles. The leaf-trace-bundles do not bend deeply inwards into the tissue of the stem but turn downwards and run parallel to one another and at the same distance everywhere from the surface of the stem, so that the layer in which they lie is concentric with it; this layer appears in the transverse section as a ring dividing the fundamental tissue into *pith* and *primary cortex*. The portions of the fundamental tissue which lie between the bundles appear in the transverse section as rays connecting the pith and the primary cortex, the *primary medullary rays*. If there is no secondary growth in thickness, no further change takes place; but usually even in annual stems (*Helianthus, Brassica,* etc.), and always in stems and twigs of more than one year and which become woody, growth in thickness begins after the elongation of the internodes. A layer of *cambium* forms in each bundle between the phloem which lies on the outside and the xylem which is nearer the axis of the stem, and these layers, which lie side by side in a ring and are at first separated by the medullary rays between the bundles, unite into a closed *cambium-ring* through the formation of *interfascicular* cambium by divisions in the intermediate cells of the medullary

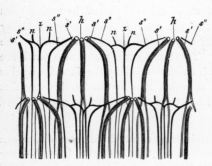

FIG. 405. *Sambucus Ebulus.* Leaf-trace bundles in two internodes; they lie in a cylinder which has been spread out in a plane; each internode bears two opposite leaves, and each leaf receives from the stem a middle bundle *h h* and two strong lateral bundles *s′ s′*; the descending bundles divide below and their limbs enter the intervals between the lower bundles. Besides these are slenderer bundles *s″ s″* united together by horizontal branches, from which bundles *nn* ascend into the stipules. After Hanstein.

---

[1] De Bary, Vergl. Anatomie.

[2] When several bundles enter a leaf-stalk, they are usually separated from one another by a considerable breadth of fundamental tissue; but sometimes, as in *Ficus Carica*, they are arranged in the transverse section of the leaf-stalk in a circle and form a closed hollow cylinder, which divides the stalk into pith and cortex. Isolated bundles also run through the medullary portion of the leaf-stalk of *Ficus*, as in the stems of some Dicotyledons.

rays, and the consequent bridging over of the intervals between the separate layers of the fascicular cambium (Fig 407). The cambium-ring thus formed produces layers of phloem on the outside and layers of xylem on the inside, and is itself constantly increasing in circumference ; all the tissue formed by the cambium-ring on the side of the cortex may be styled *secondary phloem*, all the xylem formed on the inside *secondary xylem*, in opposition to the primary phloem and the primary xylem of the leaf-trace-bundles which were in existence before the formation of the cambium-ring. While the wood produced by the cambium-ring forms a hollow cylinder, the xylem of the primary bundles projects like ridges into the pith, and often gives it the form of a star in the transverse section ; the whole of this protoxylem is included under the term *medullary sheath*, and we may in like manner with Nägeli designate as a *cortical sheath* the whole of the phloem of the primary bundles within the primary cortex. The medullary sheath and the cortical sheath, being masses of tissue that are in existence before the formation of the cambium-ring, grow in length with the elongation of the internodes, and therefore consist of elements usually of considerable length ; the medullary sheath has annular, spiral and reticulated vessels with long members intermixed with long wood-fibres, while the phloem-bundles of the cortical sheath, which have become separated further from one another by the increase in circumference of the stem, contain long bast-fibres, often much thickened but still flexible, with or without long cambiform cells and long-membered sieve-tubes. The elements of the secondary cortex and secondary wood which are formed from the cambium-ring are shorter ; in the latter there are no annular and spiral vessels, and instead of these we now find shortly-membered broader vessels with bordered pits, and round them wood-fibres with wood-parenchyma intermixed. The secondary phloem forms either repeated layers of thick-walled bast-fibres and masses of thin-walled partly parenchymatous phloem, or only the latter, or the two mixed up together in a great variety of ways. The primary cortex with the epidermis is ultimately superseded in most cases by formations of *periderm* and *bark*, though they sometimes keep pace with a considerable growth in

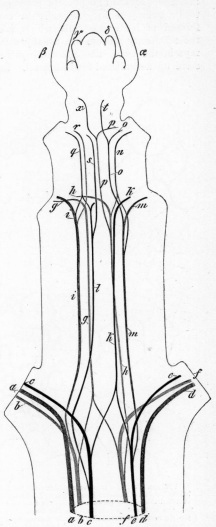

FIG. 406. *Clematis viticella.* Extremity of branch rendered transparent by removal of the outer surface and treatment with potash; the leaves decussate. The two youngest pairs are still without leaf-trace-bundles ; three bundles pass into each of the older leaves (which are removed). The leaf-trace is three-bundled. The central ones of these bundles (*a, d, g, k, x, t*) traverse one internode, split into two limbs in the next node and attach themselves by them to the lateral bundles of the pair of leaves belonging to that node (see e.g. *g* and *k*). The two lateral bundles also run through one internode, converge as they bend outwards at the next node, and attach themselves to the same lateral bundles to which the limbs of the middle bundles are united. After Nägeli.

thickness of the stem by increase in circumference combined with radial longitudinal divisions of their cells, as in *Viscum*, *Helianthus annuus*, etc. The
masses of xylem and phloem produced by the activity of the cambium-ring are seen
to be traversed longitudinally in radial direction by secondary medullary rays
formed of horizontal cells which are not always lignified in the wood, and in
the secondary phloem are usually soft and parenchymatous; they are called xylem-
rays in the wood, and phloem-rays in the phloem, and are adapted to receive and
store up assimilated food-material. In proportion as the cambium-ring increases, the

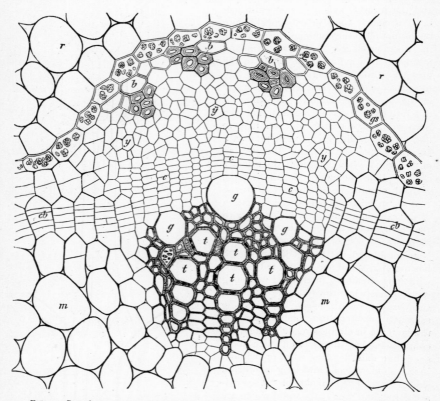

FIG. 407. Part of a transverse section from the fully developed hypocotyl of *Ricinus communis*. The vascular
bundle consists of phloem *b y* and xylem *t g*; between them is the cambium layer *c c*, which is continued into the fundamental tissue lying between the vascular bundles as interfascicular cambium *cb* formed by subsequent division of
large parenchymatous cells; *b b* are bast-fibres, *y y* phloem (sieve-tubes, parenchyma, etc), *t t* vessels with narrow
pits, *g g* vessels with broad pits, between them wood-parenchyma, *m* pith, *r* primary cortex.

number of these rays increases, and the later layers of wood are traversed by an ever-
increasing number of rays. The rays are thin plates formed by one or more layers
of cells thinning out like wedges above and below, and showing as radial ribbon-like
formations on the longitudinal section, the 'silver-grain' of the wood; the tangential
section shows how the vascular bundles and the elements as they run longitudinally
are curved outwards by the rays and form a network of long meshes, as may be
well seen in decaying cabbage-stalks, etc. The rays are formed, like the vascular
bundles, from the cambium-ring outwardly and inwardly, and as the latter increases in
circumference, it produces new rays between those already formed.
    Where the increase in the thickness of the stem ceases periodically and begins

again with the succeeding period of vegetation, as in our native woody plants, a layer of wood is formed in each period of vegetation accompanied usually by a layer of secondary phloem ; this woody layer is distinctly marked off from that of the previous and from that of the following year and is called the *annual ring*. The rings are generally clearly distinguishable by the naked eye, because the wood formed at the beginning of each period of vegetation, being of looser consistence and having a larger number of vessels especially in angiospermous trees, has a different appearance to the more compact wood of autumn. The cells of the spring wood are broader than those of the wood formed in autumn, and their radial diameter especially is greater ; the latter appear to be compressed from within outwards and broad in the tangential direction ; their lumen is smaller, and the area of wall is therefore greater on a similar transverse section, and consequently a given quantity of autumn wood is denser than the same quantity of wood formed in the spring[1]. While Dicotyledons differ widely from Monocotyledons they agree almost exactly with Gymnosperms in this mode of growth in thickness, only the latter have no shortly articulated vessels with small pits in the secondary wood ; in this point however *Ephedra* affords a transition to the Dicotyledons (Mohl) ; Dicotyledons also show a certain advance in organisation in the greater variety of forms in the cells of which the xylem and phloem are composed.

Very striking deviations from this normal structure are to be found in the Sapindaceae ; some species of the order are formed in the usual manner, but in others the transverse section of the stem shows in addition to the usual ring of wood a number of smaller closed rings of different sizes in the secondary phloem, each of which increases in thickness like the ordinary ring by means of a layer of cambium. Nägeli supposes the principal cause of this to be that the primary vascular bundles of the stem do not lie in a circle on the transverse section, but in groups more towards the outside or inside. When the interfascicular cambium is formed in the fundamental tissue, the isolated bundles are connected together according to their grouping on the transverse section into one closed ring in *Paullinia*, or into several in *Serjana*.

Many and various deviations from the normal structure of the stem[2] in different families are caused by the primary bundles not being arranged in a single ring ; they may even appear to be distributed without any order on the transverse section. 'These exceptions to the usual structure occur either in quite isolated species in genera and families in which the structure is normal, as in the Umbelliferae, or in a number of species of genera of typical construction, as *Begonia*, or they are characteristic of certain genera or smaller families, as Nymphaeaceae, Calycanthaceae, *Podophyllum*, *Diphylleja*, more rarely of large families, as the Piperaceae and Melastomaceae; in the latter there are exceptions to the grouping of the bundles which prevails in the majority of the allied forms.' These exceptions are due to the radial oblique direction of the leaf-trace-bundles or to the appearance of cauline bundles in addition to the common bundles disposed in the ring :—

a. Medullary bundles.

1. All the bundles are leaf-trace-bundles, some arranged after they have entered the stem in the typical ring and having a radially perpendicular course in it, others penetrating further into the stem and therefore appearing in the pith, and

---

[1] The cause of this difference, as Sachs formerly suggested in the first edition of the Lehrbuch and De Vries has ascertained by experiment, is the variation in the pressure exerted by the cortex on the cambium and the wood. This pressure is less in spring and is constantly increasing in autumn. See De Vries, Flora, 1872, No. 16.

[2] De Bary, Vergl. Anat. p. 258 ; the remarks are taken, partly literally, from De Bary's account.

either irregularly distributed there or arranged in rings. To this division belong most Cucurbitaceae, species of *Amarantus* and *Euxolus*, *Phytolacca dioica*, the Piperaceae, etc. The course of the bundles in the Piperaceae is very like that of the bundles in the Commelineae (see under the Monocotyledons).

2. All the bundles are leaf-trace-bundles, which after entering the stem become a network branching irregularly in every direction. To this division belong the Nymphaeaceae, Gunnereae, *Primula auricula* and its nearest allies.

3. The bundles are both leaf-trace-bundles and cauline bundles. The common bundles are disposed in the ring, the cauline are in the pith. To this division belong the Begoniaceae, Orobanchaceae, species of the genus *Mamillaria*, Melastomaceae, some Umbelliferae and Araliaceae.

b. Cortical bundles. These are of less frequent occurrence than those of the first group, and are partly leaf-trace-bundles which run for a certain distance outside the typical ring and afterwards bend into it, as in *Casuarina* and some Begoniaceae, partly distinct bundles belonging to leaf-traces composed of several bundles, which never enter the ring but form a system of cortical bundles connected with the ring only by anastomoses in the nodes, as in Calycanthaceae, many Melastomaceae, and other families.

Besides these different instances of abnormal arrangement of the vascular bundles, there are many cases also of anomalous formation of new tissue. Where the cambium is formed and disposed in the ordinary manner and has the normal persistent activity, an abnormal distribution of the tissue is sometimes found in the zone of the wood and bast. Thus the xylem in the stems of some lianes (Bignoniaceae, *Phytocrene*) appears to be deeply lobed, and the phloem reaches inwards into the indentations. The phloem in other woody plants has no sieve-tubes; these are found forming bundles with a soft parenchyma in the xylem, as in some species of *Strychnos.* But the formation and arrangement of the cambium, xylem and phloem are sometimes themselves abnormal :—

a. Besides the normal cambium-ring, a second sometimes appears concentric with it on the inner edge of the xylem, as in *Tecoma radicans.*

b. Instead of the one normal cambium-ring in the ring of bundles, several separate portions of cambium make their appearance beside each other round the primary vascular bundles and form partial cambium-rings distinct from the normal general ring, as in the Sapindaceae mentioned above and the Calycanthaceae.

c. Renewed thickening rings. Growth in thickness begins in the normal manner and then ceases, but is afterwards continued by a new cambium-zone formed in the parenchyma outside the first one. The process may be repeated and a number of nearly concentric zones be formed. This mode of proceeding, which has already been described in *Cycas* and *Gnetum* among the Gymnosperms, is found in Dicotyledons in the Menispermaceae and in the stem of *Avicennia*; in the latter cases all the zones of increase which succeed to the normal one are formed in the primary phloem. In the stems of some lianes (*Bauhinia*), in *Wistaria chinensis* and others, the new zones arise in the secondary phloem.

d. Extrafascicular cambium. The cambium-ring does not pass in the normal manner through the ring of primary vascular bundles, but lies quite outside it, as in the Chenopodiaceae, Amarantaceae, Nyctagineae, *Mesembryanthemum* and others.

e. Abnormal dilatation of the inner old parenchyma of the wood usually combined with the formation of new intercalary zones of xylem, phloem and cambium from secondary meristem. To this division belong especially certain lianes (*Bignonia*, *Caulotretus*, etc.) in which the wood is divided into separate portions by dilatation of the parenchyma ; also some fleshy roots, etc.

With respect to the structure of the vascular bundles of Dicotyledons it is to be observed that the arrangement of the xylem and phloem is usually *collateral*, the phloem lying on the outside towards the periphery, the xylem inside towards the pith. In the Cucurbitaceae, and some Solanaceae and Apocynaceae, phloem is also found on the inside, and this is especially developed in the Cucurbitaceae ; such vascular bundles are termed *bicollateral*.

The isolated bundles in the pith which are surrounded by the wood-cylinder sometimes show an abnormal arrangement of the phloem and xylem. Thus in *Aralia racemosa* according to Sanio, inside the outer circle which is constantly forming from a cambium-ring, there is an internal (endogenous) circle of closed bundles, in which the xylem is towards the periphery and the phloem towards the axis of the stem. The isolated bundles in the pith of *Phytolacca dioica* on the other hand according to Nägeli consist on the transverse section of a hollow cylinder of xylem, which entirely surrounds the phloem and is itself pierced by xylem-rays.

A layer of collenchyma beneath the epidermis of the internodes and leaf-stalks is very common in Dicotyledons.

The **classification** of Dicotyledons is now so far completed that the smaller groups known as families [1], which usually embrace nearly allied genera, are united into larger groups or orders, and few families still remain unplaced. The greater number of the orders may also be collected into more comprehensive groups evidently bound together by real affinity. Botanists however are not yet agreed as to how many of these cycles of affinity must be established, and what must be the primary divisions of the whole class in accordance with the requirements of a scientific classification. The arrangement of Dicotyledons by De Candolle and Endlicher [2] into three divisions, Apetalae, Gamopetalae and Choripetalae, is now pretty well given up in theory, though still often used in practice. A. Braun has placed the greater part of the Apetalae with the Choripetalae, and J. Hanstein has found room there for the remainder, so that the class has now only two sub-classes, Gamopetalae and Choripetalae. Eichler has also retained this arrangement in his syllabus, which will be followed in the present enumeration of the several groups with some slight alterations, as was done in the case of the Monocotyledons. The two primary groups of the Dicotyledons therefore are the Choripetalae with free separate petals, or without a corolla (formerly the Apetalae), and the Gamopetalae [3] with a tubular or bell-shaped corolla with free teeth at the margin.

A. CHORIPETALAE.

I. Juliflorae.

Very small inconspicuous flowers crowded in compact inflorescences, spikes, capitula, more rarely panicles, often of very peculiar form. Flowers naked or surrounded by a calyx-like perianth (not differentiated into calyx and corolla), usually diclinous, male and female often different ; leaves simple.

Order 1. AMENTACEAE : Flowers unisexual, in contracted panicles (false spikes), the female inflorescence with few flowers, surrounded with a cupule in Cupuliferae ; ovary inferior ; fruit one-seeded, dry indehiscent without endosperm. Trees with deciduous stipules.

Families : 1. Betuleae,   4. Salicineae,
           2. Cupuliferae,   5. Casuarineae.
           3. Juglandeae,

---

[1] [See note on p. 443.] The Traité général de Botanique descriptive et analytique par E. le Maout et J. Decaisne, Paris, 1876 (English Edition by Sir J. D. Hooker), is to be recommended for the study of the characters of the families. See also Eichler, Blüthendiagramme, I and II.

[2] Endlicher, Genera plantarum secundum ordines naturales disposita, Vindobonae, 1836–1840 ; and Enchiridion botanicum, Lipsiae-Viennae, 1841.

[3] Also recently and fitly termed Sympetalae (see Eichler, *loc. cit.*) ; the expression is apt, because the gamopetalous corolla is not the result of a cohesion of originally free parts, but is due to excessive growth of the zone of the floral axis in which rudiments of the petals are inserted. The term Gamopetalae may however be retained as a figurative expression.

Order 2. PIPERINEAE : Flowers very small, in compact spikes subtended by bracts, without a perianth ; the small embryo lies surrounded by endosperm in a depression of the copious perisperm. Herbs and shrubs, often with verticillate leaves.

Families : 1. Pipereae,   2. Saurureae,   3. Chloranthaceae.

Order 3. URTICINEAE : Perianth calyx-like, simple, trimerous to pentamerous, sometimes wanting ; stamens superposed on the perianth-leaves ; flowers hermaphrodite or unisexual and then the male and female dissimilar (Cannabineae), usually in crowded inflorescences, the female in spikes, umbels, capitula (Platanaceae) or sometimes panicles (Cannabineae), often developing into peculiar pseudocarps (*Morus, Ficus, Dorstenia, Artocarpus*) ; fruit usually unilocular, rarely bilocular, loculi with one, seldom two ovules ; usually with endosperm. Large shrubs or trees, leaves stalked usually with stipules.

Families : 1. Urticaceae,   2. Platanaceae,
                 Urticeae,   3. Cannabineae,
                 Moreae,   4. Ulmaceae (with Celtideae).
                 Artocarpeae,

II. Centrospermae [1] (Caryophyllineae).

Corolla usually wanting ; stamens fewer or usually more in number than the sepals, in the latter case often double the number (Amarantaceae, Phytolaccaceae, Portulaceae) ; ovary usually superior, unilocular, with one or more basilar often campylotropous ovules, rarely plurilocular with central placentation.

Families : 1. Polygonaceae,   7. Caryophylleae,
                 2. Nyctagineae,   *a.* Paronychieae,
                 3. Chenopodiaceae,   *b.* Scierantheae,
                 4. Amarantaceae,   *c.* Alsineae,
                 5. Phytolaccaceae,   *d.* Sileneae.
                 6. Portulaceae,

III. Aphanocyclae.

Flowers with parts arranged spirally, hemicyclic or cyclic, floral leaves usually free or coherent only in the gynaeceum, those of the perianth usually clearly distinguished into calyx and corolla ; the numbers of the parts in the four floral whorls very variable, stamens usually more than the leaves of the perianth ; carpels generally forming one, several or very many monomerous ovaries, in Schizandreae an unilocular, bilocular or plurilocular superior ovary; ovules occasionally springing from the inner surface of the carpels.

Order 1. POLYCARPICAE : Parts of the flower arranged spirally or in whorls ; whorls usually dimerous or trimerous, there being usually more than one whorl of each series of organs of the flower ; rarely with four pentamerous whorls (Dilleniaceae); gynaeceum of one, several or many monomerous ovaries; ovules one to many ; embryo small; endosperm none in Menispermaceae, copious or very large in Laurineae.

Families : 1. Ranunculaceae,   6. Calycanthaceae,
                 2. Dilleniaceae,   7. Berberideae,
                 3. Schizandreae,   8. Menispermaceae,
                 4. Anonaceae,   9. Laurineae,
                 5. Magnoliaceae,   10. Myristiceae.

Order 2. HYDROPELTIDINEAE : Water-plants with usually large lateral solitary flowers ; perianth-leaves and stamens varying in number, arranged spirally ; ovaries

---

[1] The name comes from the ventral or basilar position of the seeds and placenta.

several monomerous (Nelumboneae and Cabombeae), polymerous and plurilocular; embryo small, surrounded by scanty endosperm in a depression in the perisperm.

Families: 1. Nelumboneae,   2. Cabombeae,   3. Nymphaeaceae.

Order 3. RHOEADINAE (Cruciflorae): Perianth-whorls dimerous, in Cruciferae and Capparideae a tetramerous corolla placed diagonally; staminal whorls two or more, each dimerous or divisible by two; ovary superior bilocular, quadrilocular or plurilocular: seed with endosperm in Papaveraceae and Fumariaceae or without.

Families: 1. Papaveraceae,   3. Cruciferae,
2. Fumariaceae,   4. Capparideae.

Order 4. CISTIFLORAE: Flowers pentamerous with calyx and corolla; stamens usually more in number than the petals; ovary superior; seeds with endosperm or without in Resedaceae, Hypericineae, Elatineae, Tamariscineae, Ternstroemiaceae, Guttiferae, Ochnaceae.

Families:
1. Resedaceae,   9. Frankeniaceae,
2. Violarieae,   10. Elatineae,
3. Droseraceae,   11. Tamariscineae,
4. Sarraceniaceae,   12. Ternstroemiaceae (with Marcgraviaceae),
5. Nepenthaceae,   13. Guttiferae,
6. Cistineae,   14. Ochnaceae,
7. Bixineae,   15. Dipterocarpeae.
8. Hypericineae,

Order 5. COLUMNIFERAE: Flowers with calyx and corolla, stamens more numerous than the petals through branching, usually united into a column; ovary superior; seeds with endosperm.

Families: 1. Tiliaceae,   2. Sterculiaceae (with Büttnerieae),   3. Malvaceae.

IV. Eucyclae.

Flowers in whorls, with isostemonous, diplostemonous or obdiplostemonous androecium with hypogynous insertion; in the diplostemonous androecium the second whorl is sometimes incomplete, and then the number of the stamens is different from that of the corolla (Aesculineae), the isostemonous androecium sometimes superposed (Frangulineae); number of carpels equal to that of the sepals and petals or to both together; seeds usually without endosperm.

Order 1. GRUINALES: Flowers pentamerous with calyx and corolla, androecium obdiplostemonous or only with calycine stamens; ovary syncarpous, superior.

Families: 1. Geranieae,   4. Oxalideae,
2. Tropaeoleae,   5. Lineae,
3. Limnantheae,   6. Balsamineae.

Order 2. TEREBINTHINEAE: Flowers tetramerous or pentamerous with calyx and corolla, stamens usually twice as many as the sepals; ovary superior, with a disk between the stamens.

Families: 1. Rutaceae (with Diosmeae),   4. Simarubeae,
2. Zygophylleae,   5. Burseraceae,
3. Meliaceae (with Cedreleae),   6. Anacardiaceae (Terebinthaceae).

Order 3. ÆSCULINEAE: Flowers pentamerous with calyx and corolla; stamens by interposition of a second complete or incomplete whorl between the members of the first whorl twice as many as the sepals or fewer.

Families: 1. Sapindaceae,   4. Erythroxylaceae,
2. Acerineae,   5. Polygaleae,
3. Malpighiaceae,   6. Vochysiaceae.

Order 4. FRANGULINEAE: Flowers isostemonous and actinomorphous; stamens alternating with the petals (Celastreae, Ilicineae, etc.) or opposite them (Ampelideae, Rhamneae), very rarely with two staminal whorls.

Families : 1. Celastreae,　　　　　　5. Ilicineae,
　　　　　2. Olacineae,　　　　　　　6. Ampelideae,
　　　　　3. Hippocrateae,　　　　　7. Rhamneae.
　　　　　4. Pittosporeae,

V. Tricoccae.

Flowers with calyx and corolla or naked (Callitrichaceae) ; stamens one (Callitrichaceae) or more ; ovary of three carpels (Euphorbiaceae) or two (Callitrichaceae), superior ; seeds with endosperm. Monoecious.

Families : 1. Euphorbiaceae,　　　　3. Buxeae,
　　　　　2. Callitrichaceae,　　　　4. Empetreae.

VI. Calyciflorae.

Calyx, corolla and androecium with perigynous or epigynous insertion (except in Saxifragineae and Rosiflorae) ; the greater part of the families in this group have the perianth differentiated into calyx and corolla, but there are several exceptions ; flowers almost without exception cyclic (except in Cactaceae and in the androecium of Begoniaceae) ; androecium isostemonous, diplostemonous or obdiplostemonous (in the Rosaceae frequently more than two staminal whorls with the number of parts other than in calyx and corolla) ; carpels usually united, free in Crassulaceae, Rosaceae, etc.

Order 1. UMBELLIFLORAE : Ovary inferior, calyx often rudimentary, androecium isomerous with the corolla and alternating with it ; a nectariferous disk between the stamens and style.

Families : 1. Umbelliferae,　　　　2. Araliaceae,　　　　3. Cornaceae.

Order 2. SAXIFRAGINEAE : Calyx always developed, corolla often imperfectly developed or suppressed ; stamens usually in two whorls, with hypogynous (Francoeae, Ribesieae), perigynous or epigynous insertion ; carpels isomerous with the preceding whorls or reduced to two.

Families : 1. Saxifrageae (with Parnassieae),　　5. Escallonieae,
　　　　　2. Francoeae,　　　　　　　　　　　　6. Cunonieae,
　　　　　3. Hydrangeae,　　　　　　　　　　　7. Ribesieae (Grossularieae),
　　　　　4. Philadelpheae,　　　　　　　　　　8. Crassulaceae.

Order 3. OPUNTIEAE : Fleshy succulent plants usually without leaves ; sepals and petals many, usually arranged spirally and not sharply distinguished from one another ; anthers numerous ; ovary inferior.

Family : Cactaceae.

Order 4. PASSIFLORINEAE : Flowers usually regular, insertion of stamens epigynous or perigynous ; ovary of three carpels with parietal placentas, of more than one cell in Begoniaceae ; it is doubtful whether Datisceae and Begoniaceae belong to this order.

Families : 1. Samydaceae,　　　　4. Loaseae,
　　　　　2. Passifloraceae,　　　　5. Datisceae,
　　　　　3. Turneraceae,　　　　　6. Begoniaceae.

Order 5. MYRTIFLORAE : Flowers tetramerous regular ; anthers in two whorls or by branching very numerous as in Myrtaceae ; ovary syncarpous with complete dissepiments.

Families : 1. Onagrarieae,　　　　5. Lythrarieae,
　　　　　2. Haloragideae,　　　　6. Melastomaceae,
　　　　　3. Combretaceae,　　　　7. Myrtaceae.
　　　　　4. Rhizophoreae,

Order 6. THYMELINEAE: Flowers tetramerous; calyx petaloid (corolla almost always wanting); stamens in one or two whorls, perigynous: carpel solitary, free at the bottom of the torus, usually with one ovule. Woody plants.

Families: 1. Thymelaeaceae,   2. Elaeagnaceae,   3. Proteaceae.

Order 7. ROSIFLORAE: Flowers usually pentamerous (in *Rhodotypus* and some others tetramerous); stamens 5–30, carpels usually very numerous; insertion perigynous or epigynous, the perianth and stamens being placed on a torus which is sometimes tubular, sometimes expanded.

Family: Rosaceae,   *d.* Poterieae,
      a. Pomeae,   *e.* Spiraeeae,
      b. Roseae,   *f.* Pruneae,
      c. Dryadeae,   *g.* Chrysobalaneae.

Order 8. LEGUMINOSAE: Flowers zygomorphous (Papilionaceae, Caesalpineae), in Mimoseae usually regular; pentamerous with ten stamens (Papilionaceae, Caesalpinieae) with varying numbers in Mimoseae; carpel solitary, developing into a legume.

Families: 1. Papilionaceae,   2. Caesalpinieae,   3. Mimoseae.

B. GAMOPETALAE (Sympetalae).

I. *Isocarpae.* Carpels as many as sepals and petals (usually five, rarely more) uniting into an usually superior ovary; obdiplostemony is usual in Bicornes and Diospyrineae, diplostemony being often supposed to be typical in Primulineae, stamens superposed on the corolla in Primulineae in which the seeds are many on a projecting axial placenta in the unilocular ovary; ovary plurilocular and many-seeded in Bicornes.

Order 1. BICORNES.

Families: 1. Epacrideae,   4. Rhodoreae,
         2. Pyroleae,   5. Ericaceae,
         3. Monotropeae,   6. Vacciniaceae.

Order 2. PRIMULINEAE.

Families: 1. Plumbagineae,   2. Primulaceae,   3. Myrsineae.

Order 3. DIOSPYRINEAE.

Families: 1. Sapotaceae,   2. Ebenaceae (with Styraceae).

II. *Anisocarpae.* The typical number of whorls and members of whorls never increased (haplostemony); calyx or single stamens sometimes abortive; carpels usually only two (a posterior and anterior), sometimes three, forming one ovary.

Order 1. TUBIFLORAE.

Families: 1. Convolvulaceae (with Cuscuteae),   4. Boragineae (Asperifolieae),
         2. Polemoniaceae,   5. Solanaceae.
         3. Hydrophyllaceae,

Order 2. LABIATIFLORAE.

Families: 1. Labiatae,   6. Acanthaceae,
         2. Scrophularineae,   7. Selagineae (with Globularieae),
         3. Lentibularieae,   8. Verbenaceae,
         4. Gesneraceae (with Orobanchaceae), 9. Plantagineae.
         5. Bignoniaceae,

Order 3. CONTORTAE.

Families: 1. Oleaceae (with Jasmineae),   4. Apocynaceae,
         2. Gentianeae,   5. Asclepiadaceae.
         3. Loganiaceae (with Strychneae),

Order 4.   CAMPANULINEAE.

Families : 1. Campanulaceae,   4. Gardeniaceae,
           2. Lobeliaceae,   5. Cucurbitaceae.
           3. Stylidieae,

Order 5.   AGGREGATAE.

Families : 1. Rubiaceae,   4. Dipsaceae,
           2. Caprifoliaceae,   5. Compositae,
           3. Valerianeae,   6. Calycereae.

Families of unknown or doubtful affinity, chiefly parasitic (Podostemaceae and Ceratophyllaceae, water-plants).

           1. Aristolochiaceae,   5. Balanophoreae,
           2. Cytinaceae,   6. Podostemaceae,
           3. Santalaceae,   7. Ceratophyllaceae.
           4. Loranthaceae,

EXPLANATION OF TERMS.

Abjoint. To joint off or delimit by septa.

Abjunction of spores. Delimitation by septa of portions of a growing hypha as spores.

Abscise. To cut off or detach, by solution of a zone of connection.

Abscision of spores. Detachment of spores from the sporogenous structure by disappearance through disorganisation or otherwise of the connecting zone.

Abstriction of spores. (*a*) Delimitation of spores by the formation of septa at the extremity of a growing hypha. A form of **abjunction.** (*b*) Detachment of spores from the sporiferous structure. same as **abscision.**

Achene. Dry monospermous indehiscent fruit.

Acrocarpous. In Musci : forms are acrocarpous when archegonia (within which the sporocarp or 'Moss-fruit' is developed) are borne at the extremity of a primary leafy axis the growth of which is thereby arrested. Comp. **pleurocarpous.**

Acrogenous. (*a*) Produced at the summit. (*b*) Increasing by growth at the summit.

Acrogynous. In Jungermannieae : forms in which the growth of a shoot is terminated by the appearance of archegonia, formed in immediate proximity to the apical cell or from the apical cell itself, are termed by Leitgeb acrogynous. Comp. **anacrogynous.**

Acropetal. In the direction of the summit. Comp. **basipetal.**

Acroscopic. Looking towards the apex, i.e. on the side towards the apex. Comp. **basiscopic.**

Actinomorphous. Flowers divisible into similar halves in two or more vertical planes are termed by Braun actinomorphous. Same as **polysymmetrical.** Comp. **zygomorphous.**

Acyclic. A spiral flower in which the passage from one series of members to the succeeding series, as from calyx to corolla, does not coincide with a cycle of the phyllotaxis is termed by Braun acyclic. Comp. **hemicyclic.**

Adhesion. Union of dissimilar parts. Comp. **cohesion.**

Adventitious. Produced out of normal and regular order.

Aecidiospore. Spore formed in an aecidium.

Aecidium. In Uredineae : sporocarp consisting of a cup-shaped envelope (peridium) and a hymenium occupying the bottom of the cup from the basidia of which spores (aecidiospores) are serially and successively abjointed.

Aethalium. In Myxomycetes : compound sporiferous body formed by the coalescence of separate plasmodia. Same as one meaning of **syncarp.**

Aggregate fruit. Collection of separate carpels (fruits) produced from one flower i. e. the product of a polycarpellary apocarpous gynaeceum. Same as one meaning of **syncarp.**

Amentum. Deciduous spike. Same as **catkin.**

Ameristic. In Filices : prothallia are termed ameristic by Prantl which, in consequence of insufficient nourishment, are not fully developed and want the meristem tissue of the cushion from which archegonia are derived, and therefore have no archegonia, although they have numerous antheridia.

Amphigastria. In Hepaticae : small leaves on the ventral surface of the vegetative body.

Amphithecium. In Musci : peripheral layer of cells surrounding the endothecium at an early stage in the differentiation of the capsule.

Amplexicaul. Embracing a stem.

Amylogenesis. Formation of starch.

Amylum-body. Spherical or lenticular body in a chlorophyll-band or chlorophyll-plate, which is a centre of starch-formation.

Amylum-star. In Chara stelligera : tuber-like propagative body densely filled with reserve material consisting of an isolated subterranean node.

Anacrogynous. In Jungermannieae : forms in which archegonia do not rise either on or very near the apex of a shoot, which usually continues to grow after their formation are termed by Leitgeb anacrogynous. Comp. **acrogynous.**

Analogous. Having the same function.

Anatropous. An ovule is anatropous when the nucellus is straight, but its apex and therefore also the micropyle is turned through a half-circle towards the funiculus, which in its upper part extends along the whole length of the ovule united with the integument as the raphe. Same as **inverted.**

Androecium. Series of stamens (androphylls, male sporophylls) of a flower.

Androphore. Stalk supporting an androecium.

Androphyll. Stamen, a male sporophyll.

Androspore. In Oedogonieae : swarmspore giving rise to very small short-lived plants (dwarf-males) destined to produce spermatozoids.

Anemophilous. Pollinated by the agency of wind. Comp. **zoidiophilous, hydrophilous.**

Angiocarpous. In Ascomycetes and Basidiomycetes : forms in which the hymenium is disposed inside the tissue of the sporocarp are angiocarpous. Comp. **gymnocarpous.**

Anisostemonous. An androecium in which the stamens are not equal in number to the petals and to the sepals (or to the latter only in apetalous flowers) is anisostemonous. Comp. **isostemonous.**

Annulus. (*a*) In Musci : annular layer of epidermal cells surrounding the line of separation of the operculum from the capsule and thrown off as the operculum is detached. (*b*) In Filices : row of special cells running transversely obliquely or vertically in the wall of the sporangium ; the cells by contraction in drying cause the rupture of the capsule at right angles to the axile plane of the annulus. (*c*) In Equisetaceae: imperfectly developed foliar sheath below the sporangiferous spike.

Anodic half of leaf. The half turned in the direction in which the genetic spiral winds. Comp. **kathodic.**

Anterior. Of a flower or other lateral structure : the side turned away from the parent-axis is anterior. Comp. **posterior.**

Antero-posterior plane. Of a flower or other lateral structure : vertical plane bisecting the anterior and posterior sides and if prolonged passing through the centre of the parent-axis. Same as **median plane.**

Anthela. Cymose monopodial inflorescence in which lateral axes are formed in indefinite number on each axis that terminates in a flower ; the lateral shoots growing vigorously overtop the primary

axis and develope in such a manner that the entire inflorescence does not acquire any definite outline.

Anther. The pollen-sacs (microsporangia) borne upon the staminal leaf are collectively termed the anther.

Antheridium. Male sexual organ of various form and position, in most cases producing in its interior planogametes (spermatozoids). (*a*) In Rhodophyceae the 'antheridium' produces motionless gametes (spermatia). (*b*) In some Fungi the antheridium (formerly termed pollinodium) is the delimited extremity or other portion of a hyphal branch, and its contained protoplasm is conveyed within the antheridium to the receptive organ.

Anticlinal. Directed towards or cutting at right angles the circumference of a part. Comp. **periclinal.**

Antipetalous. Opposite to or superposed on, i. e. not alternating with a petal.

Antipodal cells. In Angiosperms : three cells at the base of the embryo-sac formed by division of the primary nucleus of the embryo-sac.

Antisepalous. Opposite to or superposed on, i. e. not alternating with a sepal.

Apetalous. Having no petals.

Apocarpous. Having two or more separate carpels. Comp. **syncarpous.**

Apogamy. Loss of sexual function ; when sexual organs though present are functionless, nevertheless the normal product of the sexual act is developed from the oosphere (ovum) or from the female sexual organ or from its vicinity. See **parthenogenesis.** Comp. **apospory.**

Apophysis. In Musci : enlargement of the seta beneath the capsule.

Apospory. Loss of sporogenous function ; when sporogenous organs though present are functionless, and the normal product of germination of the spore developes directly from the sporogenous organ or from its vicinity. Comp. **apogamy.**

Apothecium. In Ascomycetes : ascocarp in which the hymenium lies exposed when the asci are maturing. Same as **discocarp.**

Archegoniate. Having archegonia.

Archegonium. Female sexual organ with narrow upper portion (neck) pierced by a canal usually enclosing one or more cells (neck-canal-cells) and leading to a basal dilated portion (venter) containing one oosphere (ovum) and a smaller cell at the entrance of the neck-canal (ventral canal-cell). After fertilisation the embryo is developed within the venter.

Archesporium. In Archegoniatae : cell or group of cells from which spore-mother-cells are formed.

Archicarp. Literally commencements of

fructification and signifying the cell or group of cells fertilised by an act of conjugation. In this book restricted to a unicellular or pluricellular female sexual organ without a special receptive and transmitting apparatus, in which the protoplasm is not rounded off to form an oosphere, and which is stimulated by fertilisation to a process of growth resulting in a sporocarp ; seen in Ascomycetes. Same as **carpogonium** and **ascogonium.**

Aril. Any outgrowth of the funiculus or the coat of a seed.

Ascocarp. In Ascomycetes : sporocarp producing asci and ascospores ; its three kinds are apothecium or discocarp, perithecium or pyrenocarp, and cleistocarp.

Ascogonium (ascogone). In Ascomycetes : (*a*) same as **archicarp** ; (*b*) carpogenous portion of a procarp.

Ascospore. Spore formed in an ascus.

Ascus. A large cell usually the swollen extremity of a hyphal branch in the ascocarp of Ascomycetes within which spores (typically 8) are developed.

Asymmetrical flower. A flower not divisible in any vertical plane into similar halves. By English and French writers used to denote dissimilarity of the number of members in calyx, corolla and androecium. Comp. **symmetrical.**

Aulophyte. Plant living in the interior of another for the sake of shelter only, not parasitic. Same as '**Raumparasit.**'

Autoecious. In Fungi : forms which pass through all stages of their development on the same host are termed autoecious. Comp. **heteroecious.**

Auxospore. In Diatomaceae ; relatively large cell occurring in the course of a life-history, and the starting-point of a series of successive fissiparous divisions, the resulting daughter-cells being successively smaller until a minimum is reached, when an auxospore is again introduced in the life-cycle.

Axial. (*a*) Of the nature of an axis. (*b*) Belonging to an axis.

Axil. Angle formed on its upper side by the attachment of a lateral member.

Axile. In the axis of any structure.

Axillant. Subtending an axil.

Axillary. In or belonging to an axil.

Basal wall. In Archegoniatae : primary wall dividing the oospore into an anterior and a posterior half.

Basidiospore. Spore acrogenously abjointed upon a basidium.

Basidium. Mother-cell from which spores are acrogenously abjointed.

Basipetal. In the direction of the base. Comp. **acropetal.**

Basiscopic. Looking towards the apex, i. e. on the side towards the apex. Comp. **acroscopic.**

Berry. Fruit with seeds immersed in pulp.

Bicollateral vascular bundle. Vascular bundle with two groups of phloem lying upon opposite sides of the xylem. Comp. **collateral.**

Bisexual. Having both male and female organs : said of a flower it is the same as **hermaphrodite.**

Bostryx. Sympodial branching in which, from the homodromy of the phyllotaxis of the axes of limited growth that build up the system, the median plane of each successive axis is placed always upon the same side, i. e. always upon the right or always upon the left, of the median plane of the preceding axis, and thus the branches form a continuous spiral around the sympodium or false axis. Same as **helicoid cyme.**

Bracteole. Small leaflet upon an ultimate branch (pedicel) of an inflorescence.

Bract-scale. In Coniferae : scale of the cone above which lies the seminiferous scale.

Brood-bud. (*a*) In Lichens : same as **soredium.** (*b*) In Archegoniatae : same as **bulbil.**

Brood-cell. Propagative cell, naked or with a membrane, produced asexually and separating from the parent. Same as **gonidium.** It passes without demarcation into the **brood-gemma** and **bulbil.**

Brood-gemma. Pluricellular propagative body without differentiation into stem and leaf, produced asexually and separating from the parent. It passes without demarcation into the **brood-cell** on the one side, and into the **bulbil** on the other.

Bud-rudiment in Chara fragilis. Cell cut off from a proembryonic branch as the primordium of the young plant.

Bulbil. (*a*) In Chara : same as **amylum-star.** (*b*) In Archegoniatae : deciduous leaf-bud capable of propagating its kind ; also termed **bulblet.**

Bundle-sheath. Limiting layer of surrounding cellular tissue which forms a more or less complete sheath to a single vascular bundle, or marks off a whole bundle-ring from the cortical tissue. Same as **plerome-sheath.** It may be in the form of **endodermis** or of **starch-layer.**

Calycine. (*a*) Like or of the nature of a calyx. (*b*) Belonging to a calyx.

Calyculus. Same as **epicalyx.**

Calyptra. In Muscineae : venter of the archegonium increased in size with the development within it of the sporocarp; it is eventually ruptured and the upper portion is not infrequently carried up like a cap on the apex of the capsule as the seta elongates.

Calyx. Outermost series of leaves (sepals) in the flower forming the outer floral envelope.

Cambium. Meristematic zone from which new tissues are developed.

Campylotropous. An ovule, of which the nucellus with the integuments is bent upon itself so that its apex, and therefore also the micropyle, is brought close to the point of attachment of the funiculus, is termed campylotropous.

Canal cells of archegonium. See **archegonium.**

Cap. (*a*) In Basidiomycetes : same as **pileus.** (*b*) In Musci : same as **calyptra.**

Cap-cells. In Angiosperms : upper sister-cells of the embryo-sac (macrospore) in the ovule which are squeezed together as the embryo-sac developes and appear for a time as a cap upon its apex.

Capillitium. In Myxomycetes : sterile thread-like tubes or fibres often combined into a net within the spore-capsule, the function of which is to loosen the spore masses at the time of scattering of the spores.

Capitulum. (*a*) In Characeae : roundish cell borne upon each of the manubria in the antheridium. Same as **head-cell.** (*b*) In Phanerogams : simple racemose monopodial inflorescence in which the primary axis is contracted in the region of branching and the flowers are sessile. Same as **head.**

Capsule. General term for any box-like structure containing bodies which ultimately escape from it; thus sacs containing spores are capsules. It has the following special significations : (*a*) In Muscineae : upper part of the sporocarp in which the sporangium is contained. (*b*) In Phanerogams : dry dehiscent fruit.

Carinal canal. In Equisetum : air-canal on the inner side of the xylem and opposite a ridge on the stem-surface.

Carpel. Female sporophyll, a leaf of the gynaeceum of the flower.

Carpellary. (*a*) Like or of the nature of a carpel. (*b*) Belonging to a carpel.

Carpogenous cells. Cells of a carpogonium which after fertilisation grow out to form a sporocarp.

Carpogonium (carpogone). (*a*) Portion of a procarp consisting of carpogenous cells alone, or of these along with barren cells, excited by fertilisation to a process of growth resulting in formation of a sporocarp. (*b*) In Ascomycetes : same as **archicarp.**

Carpophore. In Fungi : used in this book in the sense of the German Fruchtträger to denote a structure that bears reproductive bodies (spores).

Carpospore. Spore formed in a sporocarp.

Caruncle. Localised outgrowth of seed-coat at apex of seed, a form of aril.

Caryopsis. Achene with pericarp adherent to the seed-coat.

Cataphyll. Scale-leaf below the foliage leaves on a shoot.

Cataphyllary leaf. Same as **cataphyll.**

Catkin. Same as **amentum.** In Cycadeae and Coniferae the male flower is erroneously designated 'catkin.'

Cauline bundle. Vascular bundle always remaining in the stem, growing acropetally with it, and having no direct connection with common bundles or having the latter attached laterally to them. Comp. **common bundle.**

Central cell of archegonium, Cell in the venter from which the oosphere (ovum) and the ventral canal-cell are formed.

Centrifugal. In the direction of the circumference or of the base.

Centripetal. In the direction of the centre or of the apex.

Chaff-scale. Same as **palea.**

Chalaza. Base of nucellus of ovule.

Choripetalous. Same as **polypetalous.**

Choriphyllous. Having separate leaves ; said of the series of members of the flower.

Chorisepalous. Same as **polysepalous.**

Chorisis. Development of two or more members where one only should be ; Either **collateral,** i.e. the plane (or planes) of separation of the members is anteroposterior ; or **parallel,** i. e. the plane (or planes) of separation of the members is lateral. Same as **dédoublement, duplication, doubling.**

Cicinus. Sympodial branching in which, from heterodromy of the phyllotaxis of the axes of limited growth that build up the system, the median plane of each successive axis is placed alternately right and left of the median plane of the preceding axis, and therefore the branches form a double row on one side of the sympodium or false axis. Same as **scorpioid cyme.**

Cilia. (*a*) Vibratile protoplasmic processes by which planogametes and other swarming cells move. (*b*) In Musci : teeth of the peristome.

Ciliated bodies in Characeae. Spherical protoplasmic bodies covered with fine rod-like projections in the rotating protoplasm.

Circinate. Rolled inwards from the tip in a coil.

Circulation of protoplasm. Streaming movement of protoplasm not only in a primordial utricle but also along threads passing from the utricle to a mass of protoplasm investing the cell-nucleus in the cavity of the cell. Comp. **rotation.**

Circumscissile. Cut transversely and circularly.

Cladode. Branch consisting of one internode counterfeiting a leaf. Same as **cladophyll.**

Cladophyll. Same as **cladode** and the better term.

Claw of petal. Petiole.

Cleistocarp. Ascocarp in which the asci and ascospores are formed inside a completely closed envelope from which the ascospores escape by its final rupture. In this book perithecium is used as equivalent to cleistocarp.

Cleistogamous. Flowers never expanding and systematically self-fertilised are cleistogamous.

Coenobium. Colony of independent organisms united by a common investment.

Cohesion. Union of similar parts. Comp. **adhesion.**

Coleorhiza. Sheath investing the radicle of some embryos through which roots burst in germination.

Collateral chorisis. See **chorisis.**

Collateral vascular bundle. Vascular bundle with a xylem and a phloem group lying side by side. Comp. **concentric.**

Columella. (*a*) In Myxomycetes: prolongation of its stalk into the interior of the spore capsule to which capillitium is attached. (*b*) In Muscineae: body of sterile tissue in the middle of the capsule around which the spore-sac is disposed. (*c*) In Hymenophylleae: prolongation of vein of leaf bearing a placenta.

Common bundle. Vascular bundle which runs for a certain distance in the stem and then enters a leaf and thus belongs in one part of its course to stem, in another to leaf. Comp. **cauline bundle.**

Concentric vascular bundle. Vascular bundle with the xylem group encircled by the phloem group or the phloem group encircled by the xylem group. Comp. **collateral.**

Conceptacle. In Fucaceae and Rhodophyceae: special cavities on the surface of the thallus in which sexual organs or spores are produced.

Conducting tissue. Loose cellular tissue filling the canal of the style.

Conidium. In Fungi: same as **gonidium.**

Conjugation. Union of two gametes to form a zygote.

Connate-perfoliate. Opposite leaves cohering by their bases around a stem are connate-perfoliate.

Connective. Portion of filament of stamen uniting two lobes of an anther.

Convolute. Rolled up inwards from one side.

Corolla. Second series of leaves (petals) of the flower forming the inner floral envelope.

Corolline. (*a*) Like or of the nature of a corolla. (*b*) Belonging to a corolla.

Corona. Whorl of ligules on petals either united or free.

Corpusculum. Central cell of archegonium in Coniferae.

Cortical sheath. In Dicotyledons and Gymnosperms: whole of the protophloem with intermediate portions of medullary rays marking off the bast from the cortex in a stem showing secondary thickening.

Cortina. In Hymenomycetes: velum partiale separating entirely from the stipe and hanging as a membranous curtain from the margin of the pileus.

Cotyledon. First leaf of embryo.

Craticular state. In Diatomaceae: resting condition in which a pair of new valves of different shape surrounds the protoplasm retracted from the old valves, the space between the old and new valves being filled with water.

Crest on seeds. Localised outgrowth of the seed-coat or funiculus, a form of aril.

Cross-fertilisation. Impregnation of the oosphere (ovum) in one flower by the male gamete from another. Also used in a wider sense to include cross-pollination and sometimes in sense of cross-pollination alone.

Cross-pollination. Dusting of the stigma of one flower with pollen from another.

Crown in Characeae. Rosette of five or ten cells at apex of nucule.

Crustaceous. In Lichens: a thallus forming a crust closely adherent to the substratum from which it cannot be separated without injury is termed crustaceous.

Cup. (*a*) In Ascomycetes: an apothecium. (*b*) In Gasteromycetes: basal portion of fructification. (*c*) In Phanerogams: same as **cupule.**

Cupule. Late outgrowth of floral axis (developing after fertilisation) below a flower or an inflorescence forming a more or less complete envelope for the fruit or fruits.

Cyclic. Flowers in which the foliar structures are arranged in whorls are termed by Braun cyclic. Comp. **spiral.** See also **eucyclic, acyclic, hemicyclic.**

Cyme. Monopodial branching in which lateral shoots grow more vigorously than and overtop their mother axis, the growth of which soon ceases.

Cymose. Of the nature of a cyme. Comp. **racemose.**

Cymose umbel. Cymose monopodial inflorescence in which three or more equally strong branches of limited growth arise in a whorl from the primary axis a short distance below its apex, and from each of them in turn arises a like whorl of branches and the process is repeated.

Cystidium. In Hymenomycetes: large unicellular spherical or ovoid body projecting beyond the basidia and paraphyses of the hymenium.

Cystocarp. In Rhodophyceae: same as **sporocarp.**

Decurrent. Running down into another structure.

Dédoublement. Same as **chorisis.**

Definite. (*a*) Of inflorescence: same as **cymose.** (*b*) Of stamens: not more than twenty in a flower. Comp. **indefinite.**

Dehiscent. Opening at one or more fixed points to allow contents to escape. Comp. **indehiscent.**

Dermal tissue. Tissue of the epidermis.

Dermatogen. Primordial meristematic epidermis of a growing point.

Diagonal plane. Of a flower: any vertical plane which is not antero-posterior or lateral.

Dialypetalous. Same as **polypetalous.**

Dialysepalous. Same as **polysepalous.**

Diaphragm. (*a*) In Characeae: constriction in the neck of nucule due to inward projections of the segments of the neck. (*b*) In Equisetum: transverse septum in the nodes of stem. (*c*) In Heterosporous Vascular Cryptogams: layer separating the prothallium from cavity of macrospore.

Dichasium. Cymose monopodial inflorescence in which a pair of opposite equally strong branches of limited growth arise from the primary axis a short distance below its apex, and from each of these in turn arises a pair of like branches, and the process is repeated. Same as **false dichotomy.**

Dichogamy. Asynchronous maturity of the two kinds of sporophyll in a hermaphrodite flower. Comp. **homogamy.**

Dichotomy. Forking in pairs, i.e. cessation of previous increase in length at an apex with continuation equally in two diverging directions. Comp. **monopodium.**

Diclinous. Same as unisexual. Comp. **monoclinous.**

Didynamous. An androecium of four stamens in two pairs, one pair being longer than the other, is termed didynamous.

Dimorphism. In flower: heterogony with two forms, one with anthers higher than stigma (short styled), the other with stigma higher than anthers (long styled).

Dioecious. Having male and female organs on different individuals. Comp. **monoecious.**

Diplostemonous. An androecium is diplostemonous when stamens are in two whorls, those of the outer whorl being opposite to the sepals and alternating with the petals (antisepalous or calycine), those of the inner whorl being opposite to the petals and alternating with the sepals (antipetalous or corolline). Comp. **obdiplostemonous.**

Discocarp. In Ascomycetes: same as **apothecium.**

Disk. Term of varying signification. In this book used in special sense of an outgrowth of torus between androecium and gynaeceum, usually nectariferous.

Dissepiment. Partition in a fruit.

Dorsiventral. Having a dorsal surface and a ventral surface. Comp. **radial.**

Doubling. Same as **chorisis.**

Drupe. Fleshy fruit with more or less indurated endocarp forming a single stone (putamen).

Duplication. Same as **chorisis.**

Dwarf-male. In Oedogonieae: a small short-lived plant of few cells developed from a zoospore (androspore) in the vicinity of the oogonium and producing spermatozoids.

Egg-apparatus. Oosphere (ovum) and the two synergidae at the top of embryo-sac of ovule.

Elaters. (*a*) In Hepaticae: sterile fusiform cells with spiral wall-thickening which loosen the spore-masses in the spore-capsule at the time of scattering of spores. (*b*) In Equisetaceae: four club-like very hygroscopic membranous bands attached at one point to a spore, formed by the splitting of an outer coat of the spore, and serving to keep the spores united in small groups as they leave the sporangium.

Embryo-sac. The macrospore in the nucellus of an ovule (macrosporangium).

Empirical diagram. Floral diagram representing the relative number and position of parts in any flower as they are found at once by examination of the flower.

Endocarp. Innermost layer of a pericarp.

Endochrome. In Diatomaceae: portions of the cell-contents coloured brown by diatomin.

Endodermis. Single layer of cells uninterruptedly connected laterally and with longitudinal undulation of the radial lateral walls, separating parenchymatous tissues from dissimilar systems of tissue and most commonly occurring as a bundle-sheath.

Endogenous. (*a*) Produced inside another body. (*b*) Increasing by growth on the inside.

Endogonidium. Gonidium formed within a receptacle (gonidangium).

Endophyte. Plant growing inside another plant and parasitic upon it or not parasitic. Comp. **epiphyte.**

Endosperm. (*a*) In Selaginella : tissue formed in the cavity of the macrospore below the prothallium. (*b*) In Gymnosperms : prothallium within the embryosac (macrospore); secondary endosperm may be formed as a nutritive tissue after the prothallium is absorbed. (*c*) In Angiosperms : tissue formed within the embryo-sac (macrospore) after fertilisation (commencing by division of the secondary nucleus) and serving for the nutrition of the embryo.

Endosporium. Innermost coat of a spore.

Endostome. Portion of micropyle of ovule bounded by the secundine.

Endothecium. (*a*) In Musci : central mass of four rows of cells surrounded by the amphithecium at an early stage of differentiation of the capsule. From it the archesporium is derived in most Musci. (*b*) In Phanerogams : all the layers of the wall of the mature anther within the exothecium.

Entomophilous. Pollinated by the agency of insects. See **zoidiophilous.**

Epibasal. In front of the basal wall ; said of the anterior half of a proembryo.

Epicalyx. Accessary calyx outside a true calyx. Same as **calyculus.**

Epicarp. Outermost layer of a pericarp.

Epicotyledonary. Above the cotyledons. Comp. **hypocotyledonary.**

Epidermis. Layer of cells, covered by and producing the cuticle, forming the outer surface of plants which are several layers of tissue thick except where replaced by cork.

Epigynous. Upon the top of the ovary. Comp. **hypogynous, perigynous.**

Epipetalous. Upon a petal.

Epiphragm. In Polytrichaceae : a layer of cells stretched over the mouth of the spore-capsule below the operculum.

Epiphyte. Plant growing upon the outside of, but not parasitic upon, another plant. Comp. **endophyte.**

Episepalous. Upon a sepal.

Episporium. (*a*) In Peronosporeae : same as **exosporium.** (*b*) In Heterosporous Filicineae : special envelope formed around the macrospore.

Eucyclic. A cyclic flower, in which each whorl has the same number of members and the members in successive whorls alternate, is termed by Braun eucyclic.

Eusporangiate. Having sporangia formed from a group of cells. Comp. **leptosporangiate.**

Excipulum. An outer envelope of apothecium formed by the thallus.

Exine (often written extine). Outermost coat (exosporium) of a pollen grain. Comp. **intine.**

Exogenous. (*a*) Produced on the outside. (*b*) Increasing by growth on the outside.

Exosporium. Outer (second) coat of a spore.

Exostome. Portion of micropyle of ovule, bounded by the primine.

Exothecium. Epidermis of anther.

Exstipulate. Having no stipules.

Extra-axillary. Beyond or out of an axil.

Extrorse. Anther with loculi turned towards the outer whorls of the flower is extrorse. Comp. **introrse.**

False axis. Same as **sympodium.**

False dichotomy. Same as **dichasium.**

False fruit. Same as **pseudocarp.** See **fruit.**

Fascicular tissue. Tissue of the vascular bundles.

Feeder. In Gnetaceae : outgrowth of the hypocotyl in some genera, serving as an organ of suction.

Fertilisation-tube. In Peronosporeae : tube put out by the antheridium which pierces the oogonium and is the channel through which gonoplasm passes from the antheridium to an oosphere.

Filament. Stalk-portion of a stamen.

Filiform-apparatus. Longitudinally striated upper end of each of the synergidae piercing and prolonged beyond the summit of an embryo-sac.

Flagellum. (*a*) In Schizophyta : whiplike process serving as a motile organ. (*b*) In Jungermannieae : whip-like branches with small or rudimentary leaves formed endogenously on the ventral surface of a stem.

Floral leaf. Leaf of the flower.

Foliaceous. (*a*) Leaf-like. In Lichens : forms are termed foliaceous in which a leaf-like thallus forms flat often crisped expansions, which can be removed in their entirety from the substratum on which they have grown, being attached to them only in places by rhizines. (*b*) Bearing leaves.

Foliar gap. In Filices : a mesh in the vascular bundle-cylinder from the margin of which vascular bundles pass into a leaf.

Foliose. Bearing leaves.

Follicle. Monocarpellary unilocular capsule dehiscing by one suture.

Foot. Development from hypobasal portion of proembryo, serving as organ of attachment and suction.

Fovea. In Isoetes : depression on upper surface of leaf-sheath in which the sporangium is formed.

Foveola. In Isoetes : small depression above the fovea in the leaf, from out of which the ligule springs.

Fovilla. Contents of the pollen-grain.

Frondescence. Same as **phyllody**.

Frondose. Same as **thalloid**.

Fructification. In Cryptogams : any sporogenous structure or collection of sporogenous structures. In a limited sense is the result of a sexual act but in this book is used in its widest sense.

Fruit. In Phanerogams : in limited sense, is a pericarp containing seeds, i.e. an ovary which has developed and become changed physiologically by the effects of fertilisation and which contains ripe seeds : in a wider sense, is all those parts whether of the flower itself or in its vicinity which exhibit a striking change after fertilisation and form a distinct whole separate from the rest of the plant. The term **pseudocarp** is applied to a fruit consisting of other parts besides the pericarp and seeds.

Fruticose. Shrub-like. In Lichens : forms are termed fruticose in which the thallus is attached to the substratum at one point only and by a narrow base, from which it grows upwards with a branching shrub-like habit.

Fundamental spiral. Same as **genetic spiral**.

Fundamental tissue. Tissue not belonging to the dermal or to the fascicular system of tissues.

Funiculus (funicule, funicle). Stalk of ovule.

Funnel. In Heterosporous Filicineae : space below the thick outer coats of the macrospore into which the apical papilla projects.

Gamete. Sexual protoplasmic body, naked or invested with a membrane, motile (zoogamete or planogamete) or non-motile, which on conjugation with another gamete of like or unlike outward form gives rise to a body termed zygote.

Gamopetalous. Having cohering petals. Same as **monopetalous, sympetalous**. Comp. **polypetalous**.

Gamophyllous. Having cohering leaves ; said of the flower.

Gamosepalous. Having cohering sepals. Same as **monosepalous, synsepalous**. Comp. **polysepalous**.

Genetic spiral. Spiral line passing through the point of insertion of all equivalent lateral members on an axis, in order of age from older to younger. Called also **generating spiral, fundamental spiral**.

Germ-nucleus. Nucleus resulting from coalescence of a sperm-nucleus (male pronucleus) with the nucleus of an oosphere or ovum (female pronucleus).

Germ-tube. Tube of the endosporium put out in germination from a spore.

Germinal vesicle. Oosphere (ovum) in embryo-sac of ovule.

Girdle. In Diatomaceae : overlapping edges of the valves.

Glans. Inferior achene with indurated pericarp. Same as **nut**.

Gleba. In Gasteromycetes : chambered hymenophorous portion in the 'fructification.'

Globule. In Characeae : antheridium.

Glochidium. In Heterosporous Filicineae : barbed hair-like structure on the massulae, serving to anchor them to a macrospore.

Glumaceous. (*a*) Belonging to glumes. (*b*) Of the consistence of glumes.

Glume. In Gramineae : chaffy leaf at base of simple inflorescence or of each branch of compound inflorescence.

Gonidangium. Receptacle within which gonidia are produced.

Gonidial layer. In Lichens : layer of algal cells in a heteromerous thallus.

Gonidiophore. Single hypha or compound body of hyphae on or in which gonidia are formed.

Gonidium. Same as **brood-cell**. In Lichens : algal cell of thallus.

Gonophore. Stalk supporting female and male organs.

Gonoplasm. In Peronosporeae : portion of protoplasm of antheridium which passes through fetilisation-tube and coalesces with oosphere. Comp. **periplasm**.

Growth-form. A vegetative structure marked by some easily recognised feature of growth characterising individuals or stages in the life cycles of types which have no necessary genetic affinity. Thus tree, shrub, sprout-fungus are growth-forms.

Gymnocarpous. In Fungi : forms with the hymenium exposed when the spores are maturing are gymnocarpous. Comp. **angiocarpous**.

Gymnostomous. In Musci : forms in which the capsule has no peristome are gymnostomous.

Gynaeceum. Series of carpels (female sporophylls) in a flower.

Gynobasic. A style adhering by its base to a prolongation upwards of the torus between carpels is gynobasic.

Gynophore. Stalk supporting a female organ.

Gynostemium. Compound structure formed by the adhesion of androecium to gynaeceum.

Handle. In Characeae : same as **manubrium.**

Haustorium. Special organ of attachment and suction.

Head. In Phanerogams : same as **capitulum.**

Head-cell. In Characeae. Same as **capitulum.**

Helicoid cyme. Same as **bostryx.**

Hemicyclic. A spiral flower in which the passage from one series of members to the succeeding series, as from calyx to corolla, coincides with a cycle of the phyllotaxis, is termed by Braun hemicyclic. Comp. **acyclic.** Sachs applies the term also to flowers which are in part spiral and in part cyclic.

Hermaphrodite. Of the flower : same as **bisexual.**

Hesperidium. Superior polycarpellary syncarpous plurilocular berry with spongy rind and pulp formed in numerous hairs on inner surface of back and sides of the carpels.

Heterocyst. In Nostocaceae : cell interposed at intervals on the filaments, differently coloured, larger and with more watery contents than the other cells and with no capacity for further development.

Heterodromy of spirals. Difference in direction of the genetic spiral in branch and parent axis. Comp. **homodromy.**

Heteroecious. In Fungi : forms which pass through different stages of development on different hosts are termed heteroecious. Same as **metoecious.** Comp. **autoecious.**

Heterogony. Different relationships of a definite character in respect of height of anthers and stigma in hermaphodite flowers in individuals of same species. Same as **heterostyly.** Comp. **homogony.**

Heteromerous. In Lichens : a thallus with stratified tissue owing to algal cells forming a gonidial layer and dividing the hyphal tissue into an outer and an inner stratum is termed heteromerous. Comp. **homoiomerous.**

Heterosporous. Having more than one kind of asexually produced spore. In Vascular Cryptogams : having macrospores (female spores) and microspores (male spores). Comp. **homosporous.**

Heterostyly. Same as **heterogony.**

Hilum. Scar on seed-coat left by separation of seed from its attachment either to funiculus or placenta ; it marks the base of the seed. The term is extended to the ovule and denotes the point in it which will become the hilum in the seed.

Homodromy of spirals. Uniformity in direction of the genetic spiral in branch and parent axis. Comp. **heterodromy.**

Homogamy. Synchronous maturity of the two kinds of sporophyll in a hermaphrodite flower. Comp. **dichogamy.**

Homogony. Uniform relationship in respect of height of anthers and stigma in hermaphrodite flowers in individuals of same species. Same as **homostyly.** Comp. **heterogony.**

Homoiomerous. In Lichens : a thallus with algal cells and hyphae distributed uniformly and in about equal proportion is termed homoiomerous. Comp. **heteromerous.**

Homologous. Having the same position and development.

Homosporous. Having asexually produced spores of only one kind. Comp. **heterosporous.**

Homostyly. Same as **homogony.**

Hormogonium. In Nostocaceae : row of roundish cells from which new coenobia are formed.

Hydrophilous. Pollinated by agency of water. Comp. **anemophilous, zoidiophilous.**

Hymenial gonidia. In Lichens : algal cells in the sporocarp.

Hymenium. In Fungi : stratum or aggregation of spore-mother-cells on a sporocarp or other sporiferous body.

Hymenophore. In Fungi : part bearing hymenium.

Hypha. The element of a thallus in Fungi ; a cylindric thread-like branched body consisting of a membrane enclosing protoplasm, developing by apical growth, and usually becoming transversely septate as it developes.

Hypobasal. Behind the basal wall ; said of the posterior half of a proembryo. Comp. **epibasal.**

Hypocotyl. Stem of an embryo below the cotyledons.

Hypocotyledonary. Below the cotyledons. Comp. **epicotyledonary.**

Hypodermal. Beneath the epidermis.

Hypogynous. On the torus below the ovary. Comp. **epigynous, perigynous.**

Hypophloeodic. Living in the periderm ; said of some Lichens.

Hypophysis. In Angiosperms : cell from which the primary root and root-cap of the embryo are derived.

Hypothallus. In crustaceous Lichens : marginal out-growth of hyphae, often strand-like, from the thallus.

Hypothecium. Layer of hyphal tissue immediately beneath an hymenium. Same as **subhymenial layer.**

Hypsophyll. Bract.

Hypsophyllary leaf. Same as hypsophyll.

Indefinite. (*a*) Of inflorescence : same as **racemose monopodial.** (*b*) Of stamens : more than twenty in androecium. Comp. **definite.**

Indehiscent. Not opening at one or more fixed points to allow contents to escape. Comp. **dehiscent.**

Indusium. Outgrowth of a leaf covering or surrounding one or more sporangia.

Inferior ovary. Ovary from the summit of which the floral leaves spring is termed inferior. Comp. **superior ovary.**

Inflorescence. (*a*) Mode of branching of floral axis. (*b*) Branched floral axis.

Innovation. In Muscineae : new shoot which becomes independent by dying off behind of parent shoot.

Integument of ovule. Envelope to the nucellus.

Interfascicular cambium. Portion of a cambial ring between the primary vascular bundles.

Interposition. In flower : development of new members in a whorl between those already formed.

Intine. Innermost coat (endosporium) of a pollen grain. Comp. **exine.**

Intrapetiolar. Inclosed by the expanded base of a petiole.

Introrse. Anther with loculi turned towards the centre of the flower is introrse. Comp. **extrorse.**

Involucel. Rosette of leaves surrounding an ultimate branching of a compound involucrate inflorescence.

Involucrate. Having an involucre.

Involucre. (*a*) In Anthoceroteae : tissue of the thallus grown up around and overarching the embryo and subsequently pierced by the elongating sporogonium. (*b*) In Phanerogams : rosette of leaves surrounding the base of an inflorescence.

Irregular. Of flower : (*a*) a flower not divisible into similar halves in any plane is termed irregular. Same as **asymmetrical.** (*b*) A flower divisible into similar halves in only one plane is termed irregular. Same as **zygomorphous.** By English and French writers the term is used to signify inequality in form and size in members of the calyx or of the corolla or of both. Comp. **regular.**

Isogamous. Conjugation in which the two coalescing gametes are of similar form is isogamous. Comp. **oogamous.**

Isostemonous. An androecium in which the stamens are equal in number to the petals and to the sepals (or to the latter only in apetalous flowers) is isostemonous. Comp. **anisostemonous.**

Kathodic half of leaf. The half turned away from the direction in which the genetic spiral winds. Comp. **anodic.**

Labellum. In Orchideae : enlarged and irregularly shaped posterior member of inner perianth whorl become anterior by torsion of ovary through half-circle.

Labium. In Isoetes : lip-like lower margin of foveola on the leaf.

Lamella. In Hymenomycetes : vertical plate on the under surface of the pileus upon which the hymenium is extended.

Lamina. Blade of leaf.

Lateral plane. Of a flower or other lateral structure : vertical plane at right angles to the antero-posterior plane.

Leaf-trace. Whole of common bundles in a stem belonging to any one leaf, which represent within the stem the anatomically demonstrable trace of the leaf.

Legume. Monocarpellary unilocular capsular fruit opening in dehiscence along two lines.

Leptosporangiate. Having sporangia formed from a single cell.

Lid-cells of archegonium. Terminal cells of neck closing for a time canal of neck. Same as **stigmatic cells.**

Ligule. Appendage on anterior surface of a leaf at point where lamina joins petiole or sheath. See **corona.**

Limb of petal. Lamina.

Loculicidal. Dehiscence of a fruit along median dorsal line of carpel is loculicidal.

Lodicule. In Gramineae : small delicate expansive scale inserted anteriorly on torus outside base of stamens.

Lomentum. Legume become plurilocular by formation of spurious dissepiments.

Macropodous. An embryo with enlarged hypocotyl forming the greater part of its mass is macropodous.

Macrosporangium. Sporangium containing macrospores. Comp. **microsporangium.**

Macrospore. Large asexually produced spore compared with others belonging to same species. Comp. **microspore.**

Macrozoospore. Large zoospore compared with others belonging to same species. Comp. **microzoospore.**

Marginal ovule. Ovule borne on margin of a carpel.

Massula. (*a*) In Heterosporous Filicineae : portion of hardened frothy mucilage enclosing group of microspores. (*b*) In Phanerogams : group of cohering pollen-grains produced by one primary mother-cell.

Median plane. Of flower or other lateral structure : same as **anteroposterior plane.**

Median wall. In Archegoniatae : wall in a plane at right angles to the basal wall dividing proembryo into lateral halves.

Medullary ray. Radiating vertical band of parenchyma in a stem ; is of two kinds ; (*a*) primary : extending from pith to cortex ; (*b*) secondary : of all degrees of less extent than primary.

Medullary sheath. Protoxylem and tissue in zone with it immediately surrounding the pith in a stem with secondary thickening.

Mericarp. Portion of a fruit separating as a distinct fruit.

Meristem. Actively dividing cell tissue.

Mesocarp. Middle layer of a pericarp.

Mesophyll. Parenchymatous tissue between the epidermal layers of a flat leaf-lamina.

Metoecious. Same as **heteroecious.**

Micropyle. Canal bounded by the integument of the ovule leading to the apex of the nucellus.

Microsporangium. Sporangium containing microspores. Comp. **macrosporangium.**

Microspore. Small asexually produced spore compared with others belonging to same species. Comp. **macrospore.**

Microzoospore. Small zoospore compared with others belonging to same species. Comp. **macrozoospore.**

Monocarpellary. Composed of one carpel. Comp. **polycarpellary.**

Monocarpic. A plant producing fruit only once and then dying off after fruiting is termed monocarpic. Comp. **polycarpic.**

Monocarpous. A flower in which the gynaeceum forms only one ovary whether simple or compound is monocarpous. Comp. **polycarpous.**

Monoclinous. Of flower : same as **hermaphrodite.**

Monoecious. Having male and female organs on the same individual ; in Phanerogams the flowers are unisexual. Comp. **dioecious.**

Monomerous. An ovary formed of one carpel only is monomerous. Same as **monocarpellary.** Comp. **polymerous.**

Monopetalous. Same as **gamopetalous.**

Monopodium. An axis of growth which continues to grow at the apex in the direction of previous growth, while lateral structures of like kind are produced beneath it in acropetal succession. Comp. **dichotomy.**

Monosepalous. Same as **gamosepalous.**

Monospermous. Having one seed. Comp. **polyspermous.**

Monosymmetrical. Same as **zygomorphous.**

Mucilage slit. In Anthoceroteae : slit on the under surface of thallus with no special guard-cells and leading like a stoma into an intercellular space filled with mucilage (mucilage-cavity).

Mycelium. Vegetative hyphae of Fungi spreading in or on the substratum. Same as **spawn.**

Nectary. Any organ secreting nectar.

Neutral zone. In Characeae : the line, marked on the external stationary layer of the protoplasm utricle of a cell by the absence of chlorophyll-corpuscles, where the ascending and descending portions of rotating protoplasm flow alongside one another in opposite directions. Called also **indifferent line.**

Nucellus. Body of the ovule (macrosporangium) containing the embryo-sac (macrospore).

Nucleus of the oosphere. Nucleus in oosphere (female pronucleus) with which a sperm-nucleus (male pronucleus) coalesces to form a germ-nucleus.

Nucule. In Chara : female sexual organ.

Nut. Same as **glans.**

Nutlet. Loosely used term for a small monospermous dry indehiscent fruit whether formed as an independent achene or as a mericarp of a schizocarp.

Obdiplostemonous. An androecium is obdiplostemonous when the stamens are arranged in two whorls, those of the outer whorl alternating with the sepals and being therefore opposite to the petals (antipetalous or corolline stamens), those of the inner whorl alternating with the petals and being opposite to the sepals (antisepalous or calycine stamens). Comp. **diplostemonous.**

Oogamous. Conjugation in which the two coalescing gametes are of dissimilar form is oogamous. Comp. **isogamous.**

Oogonium. Female sexual organ usually a more or less spherical sac without the differentiation into neck and venter of archegonium, and containing one or more oospheres (ova). The oospore does not divide to form a proembryo within the cavity of the oogonium on the parent plant.

Oophore. In Archegoniatae : same as **oophyte.**

Oophyte. In Archegoniatae : segment or stage of life cycle of a plant that bears sexual organs. Same as **oophore.** Comp. **sporophyte.**

Oosphere (egg, ovum). Naked nucleated spherical or ovoid mass of protoplasm which, after the sperm-nucleus has coalesced with its nucleus, developes the oospore.

Oospore. Immediate product of fertilisation in oosphere.

Operculum. In Musci : lid of capsule.

Opposite. In a flower : same as **superposed.**

Orthotropous. An ovule of which the nucellus is straight and appears as a prolongation, in the same straight line, of the funiculus is orthotropous. Same as **straight.**

Ovary. That part in a flower which contains the ovules.

Ovule. In Phanerogams: macrosporangium consisting of a body or nucellus with or without one or two integuments (primine and secundine) and containing one macrospore, the embryo-sac.

Palea. (*a*) In Filices : a flat outgrowth of the epidermis composed of one or several layers of cells and attached at one side, i.e. a scale-hair attached laterally. Same as **chaff-scale** and **ramentum.** (*b*) In Gramineae : an inner bract subtending one flower.

Panicle. A twice or more branched racemose monopodial inflorescence with the primary branches at least elongated.

Pappus. In Compositae : tuft or circle of hairs or scales developed at the summit of the inferior achene.

Parallel chorisis. See **chorisis.**

Paraphyses. Sterile unicellular or pluricellular filaments or narrow plates accompanying sporogenous or sexual organs ;— in Fungi : with asci or basidia in hymenium ; in Muscineae : with antheridia and archegonia ; in Filices : with sporangia in a sorus.

Parasite. An organism living on or in and at the expense of another organism (host).

Parthenogenesis. Form of apogamy in which the oosphere (ovum) developes into the normal product of fertilisation without a preceding sexual act.

Pedicel. Stalk of a flower as an ultimate branch of inflorescence.

Peduncle. Stalk of a flower.

Peltate. A leaf is peltate when the lamina is expanded at right angles to the petiole in such a way that the petiole is attached to the lower surface.

Penicillate. Having the form of a pencil of hairs. Used in this book erroneously as equivalent to feathery.

Pentacyclic. A flower with five whorls of members is pentacyclic.

Pentamerous. A flower in which calyx, corolla and androecium have each five (or a multiple of five) members is pentamerous.

Perianth. Floral envelope composed of calyx and corolla or of calyx alone.

Periblem. Meristematic zone lying between the plerome and dermatogen in a growing point. Same as **primary cortex.**

Pericarp. Wall of an ovary developed into fruit.

Perichaetium. In Muscineae : envelope of leaves surrounding a group of antheridia and archegonia or of archegonia alone.

Periclinal. Running in the same direction with the circumference of a part. Comp. **anticlinal.**

Periderm. The cork-cambium and its products. This is the sense in which De Bary uses the term and is an extension of its original signification.

Peridiola. In Gasteromycetes : nests of tissue within the ' fructification ' inside which the hymenium is formed.

Peridium. In Angiocarpous Fungi : outer envelope forming a complete investment of the ' fructification.'

Perigonium. In Musci : envelope of leaves surrounding a group of antheridia.

Perigynium. In Hepaticæ : special envelope of the archegonia.

Perigynous. Inserted on a cup of the torus around an ovary. Comp. **hypogynous, epigynous.**

Periplasm. In Peronosporeae : protoplasm in the oogonium and the antheridium which does not share in the conjugation. Comp. **gonoplasm.**

Perisperm. Tissue filled with nutrient material in the seed derived from the nucellus and therefore outside the embryo-sac. Comp. **endosperm.**

Peristome. In Musci : series of teeth round mouth of open capsule.

Perithecium. Cup-shaped ascocarp with the margin incurved so as to form a narrow mouthed cavity. Same as **pyrenocarp** ; used also in this book in sense of **cleistocarp.**

Perizonium. In Diatomaceae : thin non-silicious membrane of a young auxospore.

Petal. Leaf of corolla.

Petaloid. Like a petal.

Petiole. Stalk of leaf.

Phloem. Region of a vascular bundle or of an axis with secondary thickening which contains sieve-tubes. Comp. **xylem.**

Phylloclade. Branch resembling a leaf. Same as **cladode** and **cladophyll,** but these latter are properly restricted to branches of one internode.

Phyllody. Substitution of a foliage leaf for the normal organ. Same as **phyllomorphy** and **frondescence.**

Phyllomorphy. Same as **phyllody.**

Phyllopodium. A leaf regarded morphologically as an axis which may be branched or unbranched.

Pileus. In Hymenomycetes : cap-like summit of a 'fructification' bearing the hymenium.

Pitcher. A tubular expansion backwards of a portion of a leaf-lamina forming a trap for the capture of insects which are digested by the agency of a pepsin ferment secreted within the pitcher.

Placenta. In vascular Cryptogams and Phanerogams : the tissue from which sporangia arise.

Placentation. Disposition of the placenta.

Planogamete. Motile gamete. Same as zoogamete.

Plasmodium. In Myxomycetes : body of naked multinucleated protoplasm exhibiting amoeboid movements.

Plerome. Axile meristematic portion of a growing point surrounded by the periblem.

Plerome sheath. Same as **bundle sheath.**

Pleurocarpous. In Musci : forms are pleurocarpous when archegonia (within which the sporocarp or 'Moss-fruit' is developed) are borne at the extremity of a leafy axis of the second or third order and the growth of the primary axis is thus unlimited. Comp. **acrocarpous.**

Plumule. Primary leaf-bud of an embryo.

Pluricellular. Composed of two or more cells.

Plurilocular. Having two or more loculi.

Polar-nucleus. The fourth nucleus in each group at the two extremities of the embryo-sac which move towards the middle of the embryo-sac and there coalesce to form the secondary nucleus of the embryo-sac.

Pollen-chamber. In Cycads : cavity at apex of ovule beneath the integuments in which the pollen-grains (microspores) lie after pollination.

Pollen-grain. Microspore in Phanerogams.

Pollen-sac. Microsporangium in Phanerogams.

Pollination. Dusting of receptive surface of female organ with pollen-grains.

Pollinium. Body composed of all the pollen-grains of an anther-loculus.

Pollinodium. In Ascomycetes : term for male sexual organ which either directly or by means of an outgrowth conjugates with the female sexual organ.

Polycarpellary. Composed of two or more carpels free or united. Comp. **monocarpellary.**

Polycarpic. A plant producing fruit more than once in course of its life is polycarpic. Comp. **monocarpic.**

Polycarpous. A flower in which the gynaeceum forms two or more distinct ovaries is polycarpous. Comp. **monocarpous.**

Polyembryony. In Phanerogams : production of more than one embryo within an ovule.

Polygamous. Having hermaphrodite and unisexual flowers on the same or on different individuals of a species.

Polyhedra. In Hydrodictyon : special angular cells with horn-like processes formed by the swarm-cells produced in the zygospore and within each of which a new coenobium is developed.

Polymerous. An ovary formed of two or more carpels united together is polymerous. Comp. **monomerous.**

Polypetalous. Having free petals. Same as **choripetalous.** Comp. **gamopetalous.**

Polysepalous. Having free sepals. Same as **chorisepalous.** Comp. **gamosepalous.**

Polyspermous. Having two or more seeds. Comp. **monospermous.**

Polysymmetrical. Same as **actinomorphous.**

Pore-capsule. Capsule dehiscing by pores.

Posterior. Of flower or other lateral member : side next the parent axis is posterior. Camp. **anterior.**

Primary cortex. Same as **periblem.**

Primary tapetal cell or layer. In Eusporangiatae : the cell or layer from which by division the tapetum is derived. It is formed by bipartition of a cell or layer of periblem, the other product being the archesporium.

Primine. Outer integument of an ovule when two are present.

Primordial utricle. Layer of protoplasm lining the inner surface of the wall of a vacuolated cell.

Primordium. First beginning of any structure.

Procarp. In Rhodophyceae and Ascomycetes : a unicellular or pluricellular female sexual organ consisting of a receptive apparatus, trichogyne, (and in the most complex forms of a transmitting apparatus, trichophore,) and of a portion, carpogonium, in which the protoplasm is not rounded off to form an oosphere and which is excited by fertilisation to a process of growth resulting in a sporocarp.

Proembryo. (*a*) In Characeae : product of development and division of oospore upon which the characeous plant developes as a lateral bud. (*b*) In Archegoniatae : product of development and division of oospore before differentiation of embryo.

Proembryonic branch. In Chara : propagative body with structure of proembryo springing from a node of the stem.

Progamous cell. Cell formed in the pollen-grain which has the sperm-nucleus.

Prolification of flower. Production of terminal and lateral leaf-buds in the flower.

Promycelium. In Uredineae and Ustilagineae : a short and short-lived tubular product of germination of a spore, which abjoints a small number of spores (sporidia) unlike the mother-spore and then dies off.

Pronucleus. Nucleus of a conjugating gamete which on coalescing with another pronucleus forms the germ-nucleus.

Protandry. Maturity of the androecium before the gynaeceum in a hermaphrodite flower ; a form of dichogamy. Comp. **protogyny.**

Prothallium. In Vascular Cryptogams and Angiosperms : a thalloid oophyte or its homologue.

Protogyny. Maturity of the gynaeceum before the androecium in a hermaphrodite flower ; a form of dichogamy. Comp. **protandry.**

Protomeristem. Primary meristem, i. e. meristem forming the first foundation of a member.

Protonema. In Muscineae : pluricellular confervoid or plate-like structure upon which the conspicuous plant bearing sexual organs is developed as a lateral or a terminal shoot.

Protophloem. First formed elements of phloem in a vascular bundle.

Protoxylem. First formed elements of xylem in a vascular bundle.

Pseudaxis. Same as **sympodium.**

Pseudocarp. See **fruit.**

Pseudopodium. In Musci : elongated extremity of a branch of the oophyte in the form of a stalk supporting a sporogonium or bearing gemmae.

Pullulation. Mode of cell multiplication in which a cell forms a small protuberance, this enlarges to the size of the mother cell, becomes cut off from it by the formation of a dividing wall at the narrow point of junction, and finally separates from it entirely. Same as **sprouting.**

Pulvinus. Enlargement of petiole at its point of insertion.

Putamen. Indurated endocarp in a drupe.

Pycnidium. In Ascomycetes : special receptacle in which spores (gonidia) termed stylospores (also pycnospores and pycnogonidia) are abjointed from sterigmata.

Pyrenocarp. Same as **perithecium.**

Pyxidium. Capsule with circumscissile dehiscence.

Raceme. Simple racemose monopodial inflorescence with primary axis elongated in region of branching and flowers pedicellate.

Racemose. A monopodial branching is racemose when the mother-axis continues to elongate and produce daughter-axes by none of which is it overtopped.

Radial. A member developing uniformly on all sides around its longitudinal axis is radial. Comp. **dorsiventral.**

Radicle. Portion of embryo below cotyledons consisting of hypocotyl and primary root.

Ramentum. See **palea.**

Raphe. Portion of funiculus in anatropous ovule extending along whole length of ovule and adherent to the integument.

Raumparasit. Same as **aulophyte.**

Receptacle. Term of varying, signification. In this book used to denote :— (*a*) in Marchantieae : special outgrowth of thallus bearing sexual organs ; (*b*) in Filices : placenta.

Receptive spot. Hyaline spot in an oosphere at which the male gamete enters.

Regular. Of flower: same as **actinomorphous.** By English and French writers the term is used with reference to the flower to denote equality in size and form in the members of calyx and corolla.

Rejuvenescence. Transformation of whole of protoplasm of a previously existing cell into a cell of a different character.

Replum. Frame of a siliqua formed by united margins of the two carpels and across which the spurious dissepiment is stretched.

Resting cell. Isolated cell which has passed into a quiescent or dormant state.

Resting spore. See **resting cell.**

Rhachis. A primary or main axis.

Rhizine. Same as **rhizoid.**

Rhizoid. Filamentous structure analogous with a root found on compound thalli of all kinds and on the stems of Muscineae.

Rhizome. Dorsiventral creeping or subterranean stem sending up annually aerial shoots from the extremity of its branches.

Rod-fructification. In Basidiomycetes : special simple gonidiophores.

Rotation of protoplasm. Streaming movement of protoplasm following the contour of a cell i. e. in the primordial utricle, as in cells of Characeae.

Ruminate endosperm. Endosperm mottled on section ; due to unfolding of a dark inner layer of the seed-coat into the lighter coloured endosperm.

Samara. Winged achene or winged mericarp of a schizocarp.

Saprophyte. Plant living on decaying organic matter.

Sarcocarp. Fleshy mesocarp.

Schizocarp. Pericarp splitting into two or more one-seeded indehiscent portions (mericarps). Same as **split-fruit**.

Sclerotium. In Fungi : tuber-like pluricellular body, filled with nutrient material, which becomes detached when mature from the mycelium producing it, and after remaining dormant for a time puts out shoots which develope into 'fructification.' In Myxomycetes the sclerotium is formed out of a plasmodium and after its period of rest developes again a plasmodium.

Scolecite. Tulasne's term for the vermiform archicarp in Ascobolus pulcherrimus.

Scorpioid cyme. Same as **cicinnus**.

Scutellum. In Gramineae : shield-like expansion of hypocotyl which acts as an organ of suction through which the embryo absorbs the nutrient substance of the endosperm.

Scutiform leaf. In Salviniaceae : the cotyledon.

Secundine. Integument of an ovule immediately surrounding the nucellus.

Seed-coat. Integument of the seed derived from ovular structures.

Seminiferous scale. In Coniferae : scale above the bract-scale upon which the ovules are placed and the seed is ultimately borne.

Sepal. Leaf of calyx.

Sepaloid. Like a sepal.

Septicidal. Dehiscence through the dissepiments and the ventral sutures of the carpels in a syncarpous fruit is septicidal.

Septifragal. Dehiscence of a syncarpous fruit is septifragal when the whole or a part of each dissepiment remains attached to a central column whilst the valves are detached.

Seta. In Musci : stalk of capsule in sporogonium.

Shield. In Characeae : one of eight flat cells constituting the wall of the globule.

Siliqua. Bicarpellary capsule with parietal placentas and bilocular through the formation of a spurious dissepiment stretched across between the united margins of the carpels which form the replum.

Soredial branch. Branch produced by the development of a soredium into a new thallus while still on the mother thallus.

Soredium. In Lichens : single algal cell or group of algal cells wrapt in hyphal tissue which when set free from the thallus is able at once to grow into a new thallus. Same as **brood-bud**.

Sorus. In Filices : group of sporangia arising together from a placenta.

Spadix. Fleshy spike.

Spathe. Sheath-like leaf enveloping an inflorescence belonging to its own axis.

Spawn. Same as mycelium.

Spermatium. A male non-motile gamete conjugating with the trichogyne of a procarp. In Rhodophyceae produced in or on variously formed structures, usually termed antheridia. In Fungi formed by abjunction on sterigmata in cup-like organs termed spermogonia. The male sexual function of all spermatia in Fungi has not been demonstrated.

Spermatocyte. Mother-cell of a spermatozoid.

Spermatozoid. Male ciliated motile gamete, produced within an antheridium.

Sperm-nucleus. Nucleus of a male gamete (male pronucleus) which coalesces with nucleus of oosphere (female pronucleus) to form a germ-nucleus.

Spermogonium. Cup-shaped receptacle in which spermatia are abjointed on sterigmata.

Spike. (*a*) In Equisetaceae : aggregation of sporophylls at apex of a shoot. (*b*) In Phanerogams : simple racemose monopodial inflorescence with primary axis elongated in region of branching and flowers sessile.

Spiral flower. Flower in which the members are arranged in spiral series.

Split-fruit. Same as **schizocarp**.

Sporangiophore. In Equisetaceae : a sporophyll.

Sporangium. A sac producing spores endogenously.

Spore. Any single cell that becomes free and is capable of developing directly into a new individual.

Sporidium. Spore abjointed on a promycelium.

Sporiferous. Bearing spores.

Sporocarp. A pluricellular body developed as the product of a sexual act serving essentially for the formation of spores and ceasing to exist after having once with comparative rapidity formed a number of spores ; the fructification developed from an archicarp or procarp in Fungi and Rhodophyceae is a sporocarp, the sporogonium in Muscineae is a sporocarp. The term is also used for the capsule-like structure formed by the indusium enclosing the sporangia in Heterosporous Filicinae.

Sporocyte. Mother-cell of a spore.

Sporogenous. Producing spores.

Sporogonium. The sporocarp in Muscineae. The whole product of the sexual act remaining attached to, but not in organic connection with, the plant bearing the sexual organs (oophyte), and forming the ' Moss-fruit.'

Sporophore. In Archegoniatae: same as sporophyte.

Sporophyll. Leaf bearing spores.

Sporophyte. In Archegoniatae: the spore-bearing stage or segment in a life cycle. Same as **sporophore.** Comp. **oophyte.**

Sprout-chain. Chain of cells formed by pullulation (sprouting).

Sprouting. Same as **pullulation.**

Spur. In Coniferae: contracted lateral shoot bearing at its summit a few foliage leaves in a tuft.

Spurious dissepiment. Partition in a fruit which cannot be regarded as formed by the primary infolding of the margins of a carpel or growth upwards of torus.

Squama fructifera. Same as **semini-ferous scale.**

Stalk. In Musci: same as **seta.**

Stamen. Male sporophyll in a flower.

Staminode. Sterile or arrested stamen.

Starch-layer. Form of bundle-sheath consisting of a single layer of cells closely connected laterally without undulation of the radial lateral walls and filled with small grains of starch.

Sterigma. In Fungi: stalk from which a spore or spermatium is abjointed.

Stichidium. In Rhodophyceae: special branch of thallus with imbedded tetra-gonidia.

Stigma. Receptive surface of style.

Stigmatic cells of archegonia. Same as lid cells.

Stilogonidium. In Fungi: gonidium abjointed from the end of a sterigma on a gonidiophore.

Stipe. In Basidiomycetes: stalk of the pileus.

Stipulate. Having stipules.

Stipule. (*a*) In Characeae: short or long unicellular tubes on the inner and outer side of a 'leaf.' (*b*) In Archegoniatae: appendage at the point of insertion of a leaf, either wholly attached to the leaf or to the stem, or to both.

Stolon. (*a*) In Musci: shoot running along or beneath the ground and eventually rising into the air and producing fully leaved shoots. (*b*) In Phanerogams: slender prostrate rooting branch.

Stoma. Apparatus lying between the cells of the epidermis consisting of a pair of cells (guard cells) between the opposed concave sides of which lies a slit extending through the whole height of epidermis and forming an open communication between the surrounding medium and an intercellular space on the inside of the epidermis.

Stroma. In Ascomycetes: variously shaped body of tissue on which sporocarps are borne.

Strophiole. Localised outgrowth of the funiculus or of the seed-coat at the base of a seed, a form of aril.

Style. The upper (usually narrowed) portion of a carpel enclosing one or more canals often filled with conducting tissue and upon which the stigma is found.

Stylospore. Spore (gonidium) abjointed from a sterigma in a pycnidium.

Subhymenial layer. Same as **hypothe-cium.**

Superior ovary. An ovary is superior when none of the leaves of the flower are inserted upon it but all arise upon the torus below it. Comp. **inferior.**

Superposed. A member placed vertically over another in a flower is said to be superposed upon it. Same as **opposite.**

Suspensor. In Selaginelleae and Phanerogams: thread of cells at the extremity of which is situated the developing embryo.

Suture. (*a*) A line of union. (*b*) A line of opening.

Swarm-cell. Naked protoplasmic body moving by means of cilia.

Symbiosis. The living together of dissimilar organisms.

Symmetrical. Of flower: divisible into halves each of which appears to be the exact reflection of the other. By English and French writers the term is used to signify similarity of the number of members in the calyx, the corolla and the androecium. Comp. **asymmetrical.**

Sympetalous. Same as **gamopetalous.**

Sympodium. An axis made up of the bases of a number of successive axes arising as branches in succession one from the other. Comp. **false axis, pseudaxis.**

Syncarp. A term with more than one signification. In this book used in sense of **aethalium,** and also of **aggregate fruit.**

Syncarpous. Composed of two or more united carpels. Comp. **apocarpous.**

Synergidae. Two cells situated at the apex of the embryo-sac and forming with the oosphere the egg-apparatus.

Synsepalous. Same as **gamosepalous.**

Tapetal cell. Cell of a tapetum.

Tapetum. Cell or layer of cells immediately outside an archesporium which becomes disorganised and absorbed as the spores develope and mature.

Tap-root. Primary root growing vigorously downward and giving off lateral roots in acropetal succession.

Teeth. General term for any short pointed marginal lobe. In Musci: applied to the delicate processes, formed of portions of cell-membrane, surrounding the mouth of the capsule after removal of the operculum.

Teleutospore. In Uredineae: gonidium formed by abjunction on, but not separating from, a sterigma, and on germination producing a promycelium.

Tetracyclic. A flower with four whorls of members is tetracyclic.

Tetradynamous. An androecium in which there are four long and two short stamens is tetradynamous.

Tetragonidium. In Rhodophyceae: one of the gonidia formed by division into four parts of a mother-cell.

Tetramerous. A flower in which calyx, corolla, and androecium have each four (or a multiple of four) members, is tetramerous.

Thalloid. Hepaticae in which the vegetative body is not a leafy stem are termed thalloid.

Thallus. A vegetative body without differentiation into stem and leaf.

Theca. Used in the same general sense as capsule. In this book applied especially to the capsule in Musci.

Theoretical diagram. A floral diagram, not representing what may be found at once by examination of a flower, but containing indications of circumstances suggested by purely theoretical considerations.

Torus. Portion of floral axis on which the leaves of a flower are inserted.

Trabecula. In Ligulatae: sterile row or plate of cells with intercellular spaces crossing the cavity of a sporangium.

Trama. In Hymenomycetes: hyphal tissue in middle of lamella on pileus.

Transversal wall. In Archegoniatae: wall cutting the basal wall and the median wall in a proembryo at right angles, and separating an upper from a lower half.

Trichogyne. Thread-like receptive portion of a procarp.

Trichophore. In Rhodophyceae: row of cells of procarp bearing the trichogyne.

Trimorphism. In flower: heterogony with three forms, the long-styled, the mid-styled, and the short-styled flower. See **dimorphism.**

Tryma. Inferior drupe in which the mesocarp and epicarp separate from the hard endocarp as in Juglans.

Tuber. Thickened underground branch, globular or ovoid in form without a coating of scale leaves and bearing leaf buds.

Typical diagram. When comparison of a number of empirically different diagrams yields the same theoretical diagram, this is termed a type or typical diagram.

Umbel. Simple racemose monopodial inflorescence with primary axis contracted in the region of branching and flowers pedicellate.

Umbellule. An ultimate umbel in a compound umbel.

Uniaxial. When the primary stem of a plant does not branch and ends in a flower, the plant is uniaxial.

Unilocular. Having one cavity or loculus.

Uniparous cyme. Cymose branching in which only one member is produced at each branching.

Unisexual. Having only one kind of sexual organ.

Uredospore. In Uredineae: gonidium formed by acrogenous abjunction on a sterigma from which it separates when mature, and on germination produces a mycelium bearing uredospores and teleutospores.

Urn. In Musci: same as **theca** and **capsule.**

Vaginula. In Musci: apex of the stem which sheaths round the embedded foot of the sporogonium.

Vallecular canal. In Equisetaceae: intercellular canal in the cortical parenchyma and opposite a groove on the surface of the stem.

Valve. (*a*) In Diatomaceae: each half of the silicified membrane is a valve. (*b*) In Phanerogams: a portion which is separated off or raised like a valve in dehiscence of anthers and fruits.

Velum. In Isoetes: out-grown membranous margin of the fovea of leaf covering over the sporangium; is also termed **indusium.**

Velum partiale. In Hymenomycetes: a veil of varying texture stretching across from the stipe to the margin of the pileus and covering the hymenium.

Velum universale. In Hymenomycetes: a membrane or wrapper enclosing the whole developing 'fructification.' Same as **volva.**

Venter. Expanded basal portion of archegonium in which oosphere is formed.

Ventral canal-cell. Small cell in archegonium cut off from mother-cell of oosphere below the entrance of neck.

Versatile. Swinging freely on a support.

Volva. Same as **velum universale.**

Wendungszellen. In Characeae: disc-shaped group of hyaline cells or single cell at base of oosphere.

Wrapper. Same as **volva.**

Xylem. Region of a vascular bundle or of an axis with secondary thickening which contains tracheae. Comp. **phloem.**

Zoidiophilous. Pollinated by the agency of animals. See **entomophilous.** Comp. **anemophilous, hydrophilous.**

Zoogamete. Same as **planogamete.**

Zoogloea. Colony of Schizomycetes immersed in a gelatinous substance formed by the walls of their cells.

Zoogonidium. Motile gonidium.

Zoosporangium. Sporangium producing zoospores or zoogametes.

Zoospore. A motile spore. Applied frequently to a planogamete.

Zygomorphous. Flowers divisible into similar halves in only one plane are termed by Braun zygomorphous. Sachs extends the term to cases where bisection into similar halves is possible in two planes at right angles to one another, the halves of one section being different from the halves of the other. Same as **monosymmetrical.** Comp. **actinomorphous.**

Zygospore. Spore formed by conjugation of two similar gametes.

Zygote. General term for the product of the coalescence of two gametes.

Zygozoospore. A motile zygospore.

INDEX.

[2]

THE END.

S

(15)

62 474A P-70